13/9

D1436232

15/9

# AFRICAN DISCOVERY

# MARGERY PERHAM
and
## J. SIMMONS

# AFRICAN DISCOVERY

*an anthology of exploration*

# FABER AND FABER
London

*First published in November Mcmxlii*
*by Faber and Faber Limited*
*24 Russell Square London W.C.1*
*Printed in Great Britain by*
*Latimer Trend & Co Ltd Plymouth*
*All Rights Reserved*

*The typography and binding*
*of this book conform to*
*the authorized economy standards*

# PREFACE

This is an anthology from the works of the British explorers of Africa, covering the period from 1769 to 1873. Its scope and purpose are more fully outlined in the Introduction but a brief preface is necessary in order to explain its plan.

Our extracts have been taken from the books of eleven travellers they are arranged in the order in which the writers first arrived in Africa. The career of Livingstone extends over such a long period that we have found it necessary to divide our extracts from his books into two parts: Section IV relates to his first journey, Section IX (in which he is bracketed with Stanley) to his last. The short introductions which precede the extracts and are printed in italics contain brief details of the travellers' careers and are designed to fit the chosen passages into the perspective of their lives and work.

We have closely followed the spelling and punctuation of the originals, altering them only when it seemed essential to do so for the sake of clearness. We have reproduced the travellers' own spelling of proper names (except in the matter of accents, which have been omitted throughout): where the modern version is so different as to be unrecognizable, we have added it in square brackets; in our commentary and on the maps we have generally used the modern forms. Omissions of short passages have been denoted by dots in the text, of several pages by a line of dots: a blank space indicates that there is a space in the original. All but a few of the travellers' footnotes have been left out: the unsigned notes are our own.

The purpose of the maps in the text is to indicate the main outline of the travellers' journeys and the position of the principal places menti oned. They must be regarded merely as sketch-maps, since in or der to make them clearer certain minor journeys and deviations have been omitted, and it is impossible in some cases to determine the exact position of places which no longer exist to-day. The general map at the end of the book is designed to bring the smaller maps into relation with each other and with the continent as a whole, and to illustrate the Introduction.

# PREFACE

For permission to include the illustrations from Livingstone's *Last Journals* and our extracts from Stanley's *How I Found Livingstone* we are indebted to Messrs. John Murray and Messrs. Sampson Low, Marston & Co. Ltd., respectively.

M.P.
J.S.

*Oxford*
*18th August 1942*

# CONTENTS

7

# CONTENTS

8

# ILLUSTRATIONS

# MAPS

# INTRODUCTION

## I. PURPOSE AND CHARACTER OF THE ANTHOLOGY

### by Margery Perham

The motives which move people to produce anthologies seem, in the main, to be creditable. If I may judge by myself, and if I judge myself rightly, these motives are intellectual altruism or, at the least, literary gregariousness, while the writer who turns editor must impose some temporary restraint upon his egotism. For many years my work has led me to study the records of African travel and often I have almost exclaimed aloud at the interest or dramatic character of certain passages, and have wished to go out of my study, book in hand, to find someone with whom to share my appreciation. As such action was not always convenient nor certain of immediate success, the alternative plan of making an anthology of African travel began to take shape. It changed from shape into substance only when I met Mr. Simmons, and found in him not merely a fellow enthusiast but a colleague in African studies, ready to share with me equally in the labour and in the love—not to speak of the laughter—which were bound up with the task.

The first question the would-be reader of an anthology must ask of the compilers is 'Upon what thread have you strung your jewels?' We used only one criterion for these selections, and it is perhaps too bare and subjective to satisfy our more serious questioners, that of 'readability'. We have simply picked out some of the passages which struck us most, and it still remains, therefore, for our readers and ourselves to put the further very justifiable 'Why?'

To this second question many answers can be given and those of our readers may be as good as, or better than, our own. Sometimes the reason for choice seems to have been sheer literary merit; sometimes the intrinsic interest of the subject; sometimes the dramatic character of the episode; sometimes the revelation of human character. The wares we wish to advertise, the writings of the great travellers, are so rich both in abundance and variety that no one

13

kind of sample would have done them justice. There is material for all tastes and types of readers, from those sensationalists whom the purveyors of the mysterious drums and sorceries of 'Darkest Africa' have so long exploited to those whose perceptions are trained to distil the subtlest flavours of irony, comedy or pathos even from these forthright records. For those who like a good story, a tour, recorded day by day, makes a natural plot, and the 'on and on-ness' which gives its flavour to the most sober walking or motoring tour in England, reaches its supreme expression in journeys launched into savage and utterly unknown lands. As for the naturalists—but here I will quote from our first explorer, Bruce, to whose advice we have attended in this matter: 'With regard to the Natural History, however numerous and respectable they may be who have dedicated themselves to this study, they bear but a very small proportion to those who for amusement or instruction, seek the miscellaneous and general occurrences of life that ordinarily compose a series of travels.' It is 'unpleasant to have a very rapid, well-told narrative . . . interrupted by the appearance of a nettle or a daffodil'. Thus, although the Natural History of Africa, in its impressive, pervasive, and frequently dynamic character, is fully treated in the explorers' records, it is not proportionately represented in these selections. Adventures with dangerous animals, which make up the bulk of these accounts, seem to raise the legitimate self-dramatization of the traveller to a distasteful point, as our extract from Baker on this theme—in significant contrast to the other from Livingstone—may illustrate. I hope our readers will agree that for our generation the killing or wounding of large animals satiates as quickly in the relation as I know that it can in actuality.

While there are subjects for all tastes, there is one idea which must dominate, directly or indirectly, a collection of this kind. It is that contained in our title, that which goaded the travellers from the waxing domestic and material comforts of nineteenth-century England into the wilderness—the hunger for discovery.

These discoverers seem to be almost like a separate species of man, or men set apart by some strange mental condition. They illustrate human purposefulness in such extreme and naked fashion as to take on a symbolic meaning. This reaches, perhaps, its highest expression in Mungo Park and David Livingstone, and in the latter it is welded with a spiritual passion that has set him among the very great. It induced also at times a ruthlessness and intolerance directed not only towards the explorers' own suffering bodies but—notably in Livingstone, upon his Zambesi expedition, and in Park upon his second journey—towards their European companions. The physical and mental miseries that Africa at her worst can inflict upon the civilized stranger are illustrated in this volume sufficiently to make marvels of the decision of these men to endure such things a second and a third time, and to endow with something sacramental the refusal of Livingstone to accept the escape which Stanley came to offer him. It is no accident that of the ten explorers represented in this book, half failed to reach the age of forty and half died in Africa.

These men may have been self-selected for their task by reason of their own discipline and energy, but their achievements must be seen also as a response to the ideas of their time. In the section immediately following Mr. Simmons has placed their work in the sequence, and upon the map, of African discovery, and it is only in this setting that they can be fully understood. At this period there was great honour for geographical discovery, and it was to this spur that their spirits answered, though for most, honour was certainly not synonymous with honours. Livingstone, above all, gave the word his own special meaning. These men were necessarily of strongly marked character and behind the record of travel lies another story of personal sacrifice, generosities, and, unfortunately, of jealousies, which in the case of Speke and Burton may have reached—for the truth is not wholly clear—to the height of tragedy.

The explorers were put to two hard tests of human nature, that of facing danger, loneliness and barbarism and that of recording— generally without possibility of challenge—their own conduct in this ordeal. These journals will reveal more than any of the writers intended: different facets of character will strike the reader according to his own angle of vision and, according to his own standards, he will judge how well or how badly these men represented their century, their nation, and their religion. It is an interesting exercise to see how far these first intruders from a capitalist world into an innocent continent can be made to fit into their proper place in modern pictures of imperialism, whether these are painted in tones of gold or red.

So much of the men. What of the background, physical and human, against which they could so justifiably dramatize themselves? In their journals the continent plays such an active and,

15

indeed, violent part as to fill something like a distinct role in the drama, certainly that of the villain. Africa is allowed at times her beauties, but the general impression given by the explorers is one of caprice, of treachery, of violent extremes, and of hostility to men, which, combined with the allure which held them, has suggested the ready analogy of the dark slave, ravished, beautiful but untameable. She was still at the height of her power against these first intruders, and the passages in this book are sufficient to show how strongly she guarded to the last the secret of the great waters in her rivers and lakes, which had been hidden from the civilized world for the thousands of years of its history.

The contemporaries for whom the explorers wrote were probably more interested in the character of the continent than of its peoples. That order is reversed to-day and to many the most interesting subject upon which their evidence can be sought is that of the state of African society when untouched by direct contact with the civilized world. These extracts have not been made with any considered reference to this large question, and it would be unwise to draw general conclusions from this selection in a sphere where further reading would give the richest results. Yet even these extracts raise some problems and provoke some interpretation.

I found, myself, that the first and most important effect of the travellers' books was one of revaluation. At school and subsequently, I had absorbed the idea that pre-European Africa was a place of complete and anarchic savagery. I do not know how this impression was received, but it was probably an accumulation from many sources. Now, as a student of these matters, I have come across many opinions expressed by administrators, missionaries and colonists in Africa, both living and dead, which repeat this view. 'South Africa,' wrote a Colonial Secretary of the last century, 'beyond the reach of the White man is one scene of violence and rapine.' This view still lingers, in spite of the revelations of the anthropologists, and it has important results. It helps to fix an uncritical and generalized attitude of superiority towards Africans and it acts not only as a justification of European annexation and government, for which a less gloomy view of the old Africa might suffice, but as an excuse for the less defensible activities of imperialism. How often have I heard it said in answer to some criticism of European policy or conduct, 'Well, after all, think what Africa was before the white man came!' Well, what *was* Africa? How far do our travellers help us here? It would take a volume analysing the evidence of their many volumes, to give the full answer this question deserves. But even in the following pages we get some indications.

We should distinguish two spheres of Africa into which our travellers penetrated. To the north lay regions reached by the tide of world civilization, if only in a shallow and half stagnant fringe, or from which it had long ago ebbed to leave isolated pools. In the Western Sudan Islam was professed, and the Sahara caravan routes linked this region, however thinly, to the great Moslem world and drew at second hand upon the products of Europe. This semi-civilization had radiated its influences to some of the hostile pagan peoples to the south. These had also been injected from the sea with such economic and cultural forces from Europe as slave-ships could carry. To the east, Somaliland and Harar, for all their savagery and stagnation, were part of Islam, that comity of peoples in which Burton had qualified himself to masquerade and which was so much more widely fraternal than anything Christendom achieved. Cut off by these marcher-lands of the Prophet, on her fortress of mountains, stood Abyssinia, the outpost of another great world religion, where Europe and Asia had fused with Africa. Here Bruce found churches, courts and kings, literacy and fire-arms, a sense of nationalism, and an ancient Christian history.

Further south, and down to the missionary outposts of the Cape, was the great central block of Africa shut off, for geographical reasons to be given in the next section, from the civilized world. Here, in lands sealed at once from the culture and the fanaticism of the two world-religions, the travellers had to deal with scores of separate tribes with all their variety of customs, languages, and organization. They were, or had been until a few years before, as utterly cut off from contact with the outside world as was possible for people who had, after all, lived for thousands of years on the same continent as the ancient Egyptians, and had received wave upon wave of migration from the north-east. The penetration of Arab slave-traders inland from the coast only just preceded the explorations of the Europeans and these it at once stimulated and, in parts, facilitated. Sometimes, indeed, as with Livingstone in Manyuema, and with Baker in Unyoro, the arrival was simultaneous.

This distinction between the two spheres of Africa must be given, but it must not be carried too far. Savagery still survived in the semi-civilized parts while elements of civilization, as these pages will bear witness, were not unknown in the more isolated regions. And almost everywhere, even though most of these travellers were too much part of their self-confident day and generation to emphasize this, there was, upon its own primitive level, a fully functioning society which met all the main needs of man.

This point deserves a moment's thought. The peoples the explorers found were narrow in their tribal boundaries; they were desperately poor in their equipment for living and therefore helpless in their dependence upon a very cruel and moody nature. But nowhere did savagery spell anarchy. The element of 'degree' lauded by Shakespeare's Ulysses, without which 'each thing meets in mere oppugnancy' was almost everywhere visible in:

'The primogenity and due of birth,
Prerogative of age, crowns, sceptres, laurels . . .'

Everywhere, kings, chiefs, or headmen were found even if it was only to obstruct these astonishing strangers. Everywhere markets were in operation from the famous caravan-hub of Kano, to the emporium of the kingless Manyuema, guarded by the rigid sanctuary of the 'market-peace' which it took the intruding Arabs to shatter. Trade was indeed almost everywhere encountered, with tracks, tolls, ferries, simple manufactures and, often, close and admirable cultivation. These peoples—again on the level of their poverty—shared nearly all the joys of the civilized: singing and dancing and drinking; the display of dress and martial splendour; the indulgence of oratory and, to a much lesser extent, the self-expression of the manual arts.

That the explorers seldom drew these conclusions from what they observed may be due to two reasons. The first is that the original pattern of African society they saw was, over large areas, broken or marred by the Asiatic or internal African slave-trade. From Bruce to Livingstone, from Senegal to Zanzibar, we see how this other—and older—trade reproduced the coastal traffic of the Europeans in the heart of Africa and prolonged the evil to our own day. Full allowance for this must be made in trying to form any view of pre-European Africa, especially as it was the character of the trade to corrupt the stronger tribes as well as to destroy the weaker and to radiate like a quick infection far away from the narrow routes trodden by the merchants themselves. It is thus at times a society almost in dissolution, or at least deeply wounded by its first contact with an outer world more cruel than itself, that we are being shown.

The word 'cruelty' calls to mind the need for another caution, and one that is not easy to phrase without causing misunderstanding. It is probable that Anglo-Saxon—and with it perhaps, Scandinavian—society in the last century and a half has, in spite of certain inconsistencies, reached the highest standards of humanity towards human beings and animals that the world has known. As man successively exalts each virtue to priority, so its opposite vice sinks into a proportionate depth of opprobrium. The emotions to some extent react automatically to the current moral habit, and when they are called into action, a sense of historical perspective is rarely summoned to regulate them. Acts of cruelty therefore powerfully command both the feelings and the attentions of our travellers as they do of their readers; the result is in all probability a distorted picture of African society. Thus Speke's Uganda will probably be best remembered for the sudden and apparently meaningless murders by its king—it was the shocking fantasy of the Queen of Hearts' 'Off with his head!' in grim fact—and the state of his kingdom will be only half seen. Yet that kingdom, with its high degree of organization, its graded ranks of officers, its roads and large buildings, was an astonishing phenomenon in the heart of equatorial Africa. The price paid for this order was the divine right to do wrong of the representative of the ancient dynasty which had been its centre and symbol, and his victims themselves seemed prepared to pay the price. It was only with the increase of European influences and the coming of rival missionaries that the Uganda polity collapsed, and the first British Commissioner, Sir Harry Johnston, charged to restore artificially through foreign power the native order that had been lost, himself declared that the Baganda might well look back on their life under Mtesa and his predecessors as one of ideal happiness.

This question of cruelty is raised again in a most interesting form by Bruce who makes us believe at once in the charm, sensibility and —by English standards—utter inhumanity of the King of Abyssinia, his friend. Yet this throne, held to-day by the Emperor Hailé Selassie, was, for all its eclipse in Bruce's day, the nucleus round which a relatively civilized kingdom had been built up and maintained in a region of backward and divided tribes.

We must ask where this argument is taking us. It is not to the conclusion that we should dilute our hatred of cruelty or cease to

19

rejoice that Speke and Bruce and, above all, Livingstone, found its crude African expression intolerable. It need not even lead us to the vain regret that African society came under European control. But if we can remember that cruelty may not be the deepest defect of men and nations, and that in its grossest embodiment it went hand in hand with the civilization of our Elizabethans and was strong even in some of the greatest of them, we may take a more favourable view of the past of Africans, and therefore—which is even more important—of their future. It is also worth remembering that the inhumanity witnessed by the travellers was committed by men to whom, in the given situation, no other behaviour could ever have been suggested by any external agency to their minds. Yet—and this is surely the real mystery—there could be collected from these writers almost as much evidence of the natural goodness as of the natural sinfulness of man.

This brings us to consider the treatment dealt out by Africans to these first white intruders into their tropical sanctuary. Looking at the matter from the point of view of the large number of small separate societies in a state of hostility, or, at best, of armed neutrality towards their neighbours, and with no civic obligations outside their own small group, it seems at first sight almost culpable negligence on their part that only two of these ten Europeans were killed. The strangers often came to a tribe straight from the head-quarters of its bitterest enemies. They were generally unable to give any intelligible reason for their presence. (It was characteristic common sense on the part of the later Mary Kingsley to travel as a merchant, a profession some of our explorers proudly renounced.) Their behaviour was generally unaccountable and often menacing and improper. They made sinister attempts to reach places that were profitless or forbidden. They were possessed of novel and exciting possessions which were a standing temptation to robbery, and, finally, they had powers and weapons that made them a mystery and a danger. Yet these men, utterly dependent and sometimes destitute, were allowed to pass chief after chief and tribe after tribe at the cost here of some restraint upon their impatient purposes and there of a persecution for presents nearly always stopping short of the violence which was well within the power of these chiefs. They were, on the contrary, not infrequently assisted at the cost of their hosts.

There is sadness in the reflection that Africans were allowed at this first moment of their contact with Europeans to show qualities that have since been crushed with the establishment of our absolute domination. The equal friendship in sport and arms formed by Bruce with the young bloods of the Abyssinian court; the hospitality of Rumanika; the discreet generosity of Mansong—what counterparts could they have to-day, as between Africans and Europeans? The Galla wept for Burton, and, in perhaps one of the most poignant biographical passages in our literature, the derelict and utterly insignificant Park was cherished by an unknown African woman. Finally, there was that great act of unconstrained courage and devotion by which the bones of the one explorer who may be said to have lived and died for Africans rather than for Africa, were carried for a thousand miles through every danger by his negro servants. But to-day Africans are subjected to our beneficence as well as to our power. How long will it be before they, who are now asked only to serve and to accept, will be able to turn to us again that side of their nature which gives?

There remain some few excuses and explanations to be made.

We must first defend ourselves from the charge of insularity. This is not difficult. Among the great foreign explorers not many were in action in this period between the last great days of the Portuguese and the first efforts of the most famous Germans and Frenchmen. The discovery of the source of the Nile, and the opening up of the vast regions of Central Africa were mainly the work of British travellers. Even had it not been so, it would have been small justice to a foreign explorer, in an anthology in which the style, and sometimes the literary merit, of the writer are inseparable from his other qualifications, to present him in the medium of translation.

We must also point out that we had to choose between, on the one side, a book so loaded with editorial matter that many of the readers we wished to reach would have flinched away from its very appearance, and, on the other, one offering the bare minimum of explanation required to make our extracts intelligible. It was difficult to fix upon any half-way point between these courses. We chose the second and the brevity of the introductions often obliged us to deal summarily with geographical or personal questions that are still open to dispute, and to make omissions and unqualified generalizations. Again, there is hardly a page which could not have carried notes explaining the exact meaning of native or other terms used, 'placing' some minor character, or putting some event into relation with earlier incidents. Where the lack of this information did not seem to destroy the general sense of the narrative, we assumed our readers would prefer not to have their attention distracted by annotation. The manner in which we have interspersed our commentary with the extracts has been governed by our desire to present them as a continuous story, in which the incidents can be seen against the background of the explorers' lives and travels.

We can only justify this treatment by our main object in making this anthology. This brings me back to the point from which I began this introduction. Our hope, of course, is that having taken this ground-bait you will be lured into following up the explorers into their own volumes. These are the precious calf-bound productions of the eighteenth and early nineteenth century with their characteristic lettering and magnificent wood-engravings, and the Victorian books, which, less elegant in their workmanship and cruder in the appeal of their illustrations to our sense of adventure, are yet racy of their period. The enjoyment of these books does not depend upon any previous knowledge of Africa and its geography. In the course of my work I have myself followed these explorers west to Kano; east to Berbera; south to the Victoria Falls, and along the Nile from its birth in the great Lakes to its Egyptian delta; yet I do not think this has added much to my appreciation of their writings. My own impressions may, indeed, have slightly blurred their pictures. Their continent has changed so quickly, if not in appearance—though bridges span the Ripon and Victoria Falls and carry railways over the Niger and the junction of the Niles—at least in its whole atmosphere. The peace of Europe, the huge framework of her state systems, embrace those little warring, lusty communities in a wide, firm grip. Yet, in the books from which we have made this anthology, the old Africa, with its open challenge to the science, courage and compassion of the nineteenth century, comes to life again.

## II. THE CONTINENT AND
## THE EXPLORERS

### by J. Simmons

Any survey of the exploration of Africa must begin by discussing the physical features of the continent; for all penetration from the outside has been governed, or at least conditioned, by them.

The coast of Africa is extremely uninviting. Vast stretches of it hardly afford even a sheltering roadstead, and, except on the north, good natural harbours are very rare. Nearly half of it is backed by desert or semi-desert; much of the rest by thick forest, difficult or impossible to penetrate. Few of the rivers are navigable: either their course is impeded by cataracts, or their mouths are blocked by bars, or they run out into the sea through a maze of creeks, bordered by jungle. Access to the interior by water is therefore difficult. By land, until the coming of mechanical transport, it was little easier; for the presence of the tsetse-fly made it impossible to use horses or cattle of any kind over large areas of Africa: the interior could only be reached on foot, using human porterage. The climate of the continent, except at its northern and southern extremities, has always been unpleasant to Europeans, and until the modern treatment of tropical diseases had been evolved it was often fatal to them.

In the face of these obstacles, it is not surprising that the 'opening-up' of Africa has only been achieved in recent times. Yet it has been attempted, sometimes with an astonishing measure of success, for at least three thousand years—for much more, if we include here the racial migrations into the continent from the north-east.

The story of the exploration of Africa by Europeans divides itself naturally into five phases.[1] The first of these includes the dis-

[1] It must be remembered that Africa was not explored only by Europeans. During the Middle Ages the continent was far better known to the Arabs, who maintained caravan routes across the Sahara from the north coast to Timbuktu: Ibn Battuta, the most famous of Arab travellers, wrote a full account of this area in the fourteenth century. But, like all the other information about Africa acquired by the Arabs, it remained unknown outside the Moslem world and had little influence on the course of later exploration.

coveries made by Egyptian, Greek and Roman pioneers along three main routes, the east and west coasts and the valley of the Nile. Their knowledge of the shores of Africa extended down to Cape Delgado and Sierra Leone; while they knew something of the White Nile as far up as the *sudd* and the great swamp which begins in about latitude 9° N. The mystery of its source fascinated geographers in ancient, as it has in modern, times. This is not surprising: it was the longest river known to Europeans before the discovery of the New World; it had nourished the ancient civilization of Egypt; it flowed in great volume through a thousand miles of desert without receiving a single tributary; the way to its source was barred by tropical swamp and fabulous peoples. In the second period, stretching from the fifteenth century to the seventeenth, explorers from Western Europe, led by the Portuguese, completed the outline of the coasts of Africa; and some information was gained about the interior, notably by the Jesuit missionaries in Abyssinia and Angola. The third period, the 'classical age' of African discovery, starts with Bruce's journey in 1768 and ends with the death of Livingstone 105 years later. The fourth may be called the period of political exploration: it comprises roughly the last quarter of the nineteenth century, beginning with Stanley's journey down the Congo in 1874 and ending with the Partition of Africa between the European Powers. The fifth phase is that of detailed scientific exploration, a necessary prelude to the full political and economic development of the country. We are still in this stage to-day.

It is with the third of these periods that this book is concerned. When it opened, very little of the interior of the continent had been visited by Europeans and less still had been at all carefully described: nor was the coast fully known—it was not adequately charted until the great survey of Captain Owen in 1821–5. The journey of JAMES BRUCE,[1] which may be said to begin the new phase, was no great event in the history of geography: he did not visit any place of importance which had not been reached by earlier travellers. The significance of his work lies rather in the purpose for which he undertook it and in the manner of its presentation. The very title of his book, *Travels to discover the source of the Nile*, indicates his modern attitude of mind. Bruce was the first great scientific explorer of Africa; the first to go out there neither for

[1] The names of explorers represented in this book are printed in capital letters.

trade, nor for war, nor to hoist a flag, nor for the glory of God, but from curiosity—to find out *the truth* about the source of the Nile. That he did not discover the whole truth, that what he did find (the source of the Blue Nile) had been found 150 years earlier by one of those Portuguese Jesuits he wrongly despised—none of this mattered: he collected a great deal of valuable detail about the country he visited, which he published in a sober, yet delightfully readable form, and he stimulated the interest of the civilized world in Africa, just as Cook had aroused it in the Pacific.

That interest had previously been confined almost entirely to the West India proprietors, who looked to Africa for the slave labour on which their plantations depended. While Bruce was still in Abyssinia, the attack on the slave trade had opened in England. The subject had been forced into notice by Lord Mansfield's judgment in the Somerset case in 1772: this was the match that eventually set ablaze the whole train laid with such care by the Abolitionists—Granville Sharp, Zachary Macaulay, Clarkson, above all Wilberforce. Inevitably, the stir this case aroused had the effect of increasing public interest in Africa; and there were other causes, too, which helped to bring it into prominence in these years—the strategic importance of the West Coast in the naval war of 1778–83, the capture of Goree from the French and its subsequent return to them at the peace.[1]

Such were some of the reasons for the growth of interest in Africa in the late eighteenth century. A symptom of it was the founding in 1788 of the African Association, a dining-club presided over by Sir Joseph Banks, the most famous English scientist of his day. The Association's attention was directed not to the Nile but to another major geographical problem, the problem of the Niger. This was even more perplexing than the ancient riddle of the source of the Nile: for the Niger was not yet known as a river, it was only a name; no one knew where it rose, or where it ended—whether in the sea or in some great lake; no one even knew in what direction it flowed. Was it perhaps the Upper Nile? Or were the Senegal and the Gambia (on which French and British traders had long been established) its mouths? The African Association set itself to solve these questions.

---

[1] Goree is an island at the entrance to the bay on which stands the modern port of Dakar. Its importance in eighteenth-century naval strategy was somewhat similar to that of Dakar to-day: it should not be forgotten that they are virtually one and the same.

Its first attempts were unfortunate. Four travellers—Ledyard, Lucas, Hornemann, Houghton—were sent out one after another under its auspices, but all of them were unsuccessful and three died in Africa. The Association's fifth choice was MUNGO PARK, who did reach the Niger, established the fact that it flowed eastward, and brought home the natives' account of its geography. It still remained to find where the river rose, to trace its course, and to discover its mouth. Many lives were lost in attempting to settle these questions. Park himself made a second journey, this time at the expense of Government: he sailed down the Niger for more than half its length, but was killed near Bussa early in 1806. Expeditions were planned to start from Egypt, from the Bight of Benin, from Morocco; Tuckey was sent up the Congo in 1816, on the chance that it and the Niger might prove to be one. All these attempts miscarried: but they were not fruitless, for each failure bred a new effort, and—more important than the solution of any mere geographical conundrum—intelligent people began to take a deeper interest in Africa than they ever had before.

In 1822 came another step forward, when Laing succeeded in determining the position of the Niger sources: the lower course of the river had yet to be traced, and its mouth to be found. Next year another expedition set forth on this quest: it was better organized and in its results more valuable than any which had been sent out since the death of Park. Its three white members were Dixon Denham, HUGH CLAPPERTON, and Walter Oudney. Starting from Tripoli, they crossed the Sahara and discovered Lake Chad: Clapperton visited Kano and Sokoto, Denham found the River Shari. Timbuktu, that fabulous city, was reached by Laing in 1825 and by the astonishing young Frenchman René Caillié, who spent some time there and described it fully, two years later. The *réclame* of these feats penetrated even the torpor of an English university of that day. The subject set for the Chancellor's Gold Medal for English verse at Cambridge in 1829 was 'Timbuctoo': the prize was won by an undergraduate of Trinity, Alfred Tennyson.

If these last journeys contributed little to solving the Niger problem, they added much useful information about the Southern Sahara and revealed its highly organized Moslem civilization. They had another result, too, which commended them to a great body of Englishmen who were not particularly interested in geography, but who did care about Africa warmly and for the most part sincerely—the evangelical anti-slavery party. To them, and to the British Government, which on this question thought with them, the opening-up of the interior seemed to offer a new line of attack on the slave trade, a possibility of cutting off its supply at the source. As always, the intelligent Abolitionists urged, quite rightly, that it was useless to try and destroy it unless 'legitimate commerce' took its place: and it was to open up trade relations with Sultan Bello of Sokoto (who was the dominant power in the Western Sudan) that Clapperton was sent out by Government on his second journey. With him went his servant RICHARD LANDER. He reached his objective, this time by way of the Bight of Benin, but found that Bello, who on his previous visit had welcomed him kindly, was not interested in the treaty, and he died without managing to conclude it. His papers were brought back to England by Lander, who was under that old, recognizable spell which African travellers have so often felt, the imperative urge to return there. At once he agreed to go out and resume the search for the mouth of the Niger—again under the orders, and at the expense, of the British Government. He took his brother with him: they started inland from Badagri, reached the Niger at Bussa, and thence, with comparative ease though not without some excitements, sailed down to the sea. They came out in November 1830 by way of those 'Oil Rivers' which had long been known to Europeans as a market for palm-oil and slaves.

With the publication of the Landers' account of their travels in 1832 the last great question as to the course of the Niger was settled, and the geographers were for the moment satisfied. But not the Abolitionists or the traders: for them this was the beginning, not the end, of the story. The book came out at an opportune moment (perhaps that was why John Murray was willing to pay 1,000 guineas for it); for Africa was in the news: the great attack on slavery was brewing. In the next year, just after Wilberforce's death, the Emancipation Act was passed, which declared slavery illegal in the British colonies. This did something to right a crying and ancient wrong; but the more far-seeing of the Abolitionists— and notably their leader Thomas Fowell Buxton—realized that it did not fulfil all their objects (just as the more intelligent Reformers had understood that the Act of 1832 did not of itself end all Parliamentary injustices and abuses). Buxton and his friends at once proclaimed that the attack, so successfully carried through in England, must be pursued relentlessly against the Powers which countenanced slavery and the slave trade; and that at the same time another attempt must be made to stop up the sources of supply in the heart of Africa. Here they joined hands with the merchants, who hoped to recoup the losses they had suffered through the abolition of slavery in the West Indies, and the consequent decline in the sugar production of the islands, by finding new crops to exploit and new markets for their goods, and who turned naturally enough to Africa.

Soon after Lander returned to England he was approached by Macgregor Laird, a Liverpool shipowner, with an invitation to accompany a new expedition to the Niger for the purpose of promoting trade. He accepted, and the party set off in July 1832. Their equipment was elaborate, including two steamships; but the venture proved unlucky. Lander himself was killed in a skirmish with some natives in the delta, and of the other 47 Europeans who went out, 38 died (mostly from disease) before the expedition returned in 1834. Seven years later another expedition was dispatched, this time by Government, strongly supported by the Abolitionists, Exeter Hall, and the Prince Consort: it was on a much larger scale, and it was similarly disastrous. The official account of it, published in 1848, was scornfully reviewed by Dickens, who exposed the follies—he almost called them crimes—committed by the ill-informed philanthropists who backed it. He returned to the charge in a lighter vein when he created the immortal Mrs. Jellyby, with her settlement of Borrioboola-Gha on the Niger, in *Bleak House*.

Such criticisms did not deflect the British Government from its purpose of opening up the interior of Africa by whatever means and whatever route might prove practicable. Success was close at hand: the 'fifties were to prove the most fruitful decade in the history of the European penetration of the continent.

In 1849 another expedition was sent out to explore the Southern Sahara and to make contact with its Moslem states. James Richardson was chosen to lead it: with him went two Germans, Heinrich Barth and Adolf Overweg. They crossed the desert from Tripoli. Richardson died in 1851, Overweg in 1852, but Barth went on: in his wanderings, which lasted five and a half years, he discovered the Upper Benue, visited Katsina, Sokoto and Timbuktu, and eventually returned over the Sahara, reaching England in September 1855. Barth's journey is one of the greatest feats in the history of African travel, and the huge book in which he described it one of the masterpieces of the subject. For the moment, however, his discoveries were not followed up.

But they had already had one indirect result of great significance. When Barth was lost in the interior a search-party was sent to look for him, not across the Sahara but up the Niger. It was to have been commanded by John Beecroft, British Consul for the Bights of Benin and Biafra;[1] but he died before starting, and his place was taken by W. B. BAIKIE. The search for Barth was unsuccessful, but in other respects the expedition was a triumph. It showed that steamships could be taken up the Niger, and a considerable distance up the Benue. More important still, it proved that by the constant use of quinine Europeans could avoid that fever which had decimated the previous expeditions: not one man died of disease on the whole trip.

Meanwhile, a journey of a very different character from any of those we have previously considered was in progress further south. In 1841, the year of that disastrous Niger expedition which had aroused the sarcasm of Dickens, DAVID LIVINGSTONE arrived in South Africa. For eight years he worked as a missionary in Bechuanaland. Then, in 1849, actuated not so much by geographical curiosity as by the desire to see what fields for missionary enterprise lay further north, he crossed the Kalahari and discovered Lake Ngami. Here he heard that the country which lay beyond was populous and watered by many rivers—very different from the barren land he had been living in and the desert he had just crossed. Into this region, which held out such wonderful promises, he determined to advance as quickly as he could; and in 1852 he began the great journey which was to take him first to the Atlantic and then across the continent to the Indian Ocean. This is not the place to describe that journey or the two which followed it: an outline of them will be found in the sections dealing with Livingstone below. Here we are only concerned with their results.

In the first place they drew attention to what may be called East Central Africa—the valley of the Zambesi and the country northwards up to Lake Tanganyika: this huge area had previously been quite unknown, except in a very limited degree to the Portuguese. Livingstone showed that much of it was thickly populated and fertile, that it had great economic potentialities—but that it was devastated by the slave trade.

This was not the West Coast trade, which was now nearing its

[1] The establishment of this post in 1849 is evidence of the increasing interest which was now being taken in this region by the British Government, urged on by the Liverpool merchants.

end (it received its death-blows in the early 'sixties), but another, of which little had been heard before, having its centre at Zanzibar and supplying the slave markets of Arabia and the Persian Gulf. It was carried on by Arabs and the mixed Arab-African Swahili, who were financed in many cases by Indian merchants living at Zanzibar and on the coast opposite. The slave-traders were at this time making their way ever further and further into the interior in search of their victims. But not all the slaves they acquired were seized by themselves: they bought many of them from native chiefs who, greedy for the goods the traders offered them (especially the guns and cloth), raided their neighbours; and the consequence was those wars which were ravaging the country when Livingstone and Stanley saw it. There was nothing new in this: in West Africa slave-raiding had gone on, unchecked, for centuries. But that was at last being ended, on the initiative of Britain: and Livingstone now demanded that the East Coast trade should be stopped too. The means he proposed for suppressing it were similar to those which had been advocated by Buxton and his party in the 'forties: a naval squadron for seizing the slave-ships, combined with the opening-up of the interior by means of Christianity and commerce (a union which offers an obvious target for cynics, but which was in fact neither hypocritical nor ineffective). The Zambesi expedition of 1858, which Livingstone took out to put these principles into practice, bears some resemblance to the Niger expedition of 1841. But though they were alike in their lack of complete success, Livingstone's gained a great deal of valuable information and, in spite of all its shortcomings, justified the money spent on it, where the Niger expedition had been a complete disaster. Nor was this surprising: for he had practical knowledge of the country he was to operate in and of the conditions of work there, while the organizers of the earlier expedition had little but zeal, excellent intentions, and the accounts given by previous travellers, to go upon.

Livingstone was not the only explorer to direct attention to East Africa at this time. While he was still on his great journey across the continent, RICHARD BURTON made his *début* as an African traveller much further north, with a dangerous expedition across Somaliland to the unknown city of Harar. He set off again on a more momentous journey two months before Livingstone reached England. Accompanied by J. H. SPEKE, he travelled inland from the coast opposite Zanzibar: after a march of seven and a half months they reached Lake Tanganyika. This was the first of the three great Central African lakes to be discovered: six months afterwards, on 30th July 1858, Speke caught his first glimpse of Victoria Nyanza, the greatest of them; a little over a year later Livingstone found the third, Nyasa.

Speke at once made up his mind, by intuition well founded on probability and the reports of Arab traders, that the Victoria Nyanza was much more than a mere lake: that it was the source of the Nile; that he had solved the question which, as he himself wrote, had been 'the first geographical desideratum of many thousand years to ascertain, and the ambition of the first monarchs of the world to unravel'.

Inevitably, his claims were doubted; and as soon as he came home he began to make arrangements for another expedition to prove them. This he succeeded in doing by his great journey, with J. A. Grant, from Zanzibar to Gondokoro on the Nile. It is true that, even after the publication of his splendid account of it, his achievement was still questioned (notably by his former companion Burton, who was now his bitter enemy), on the grounds that he had not himself traced the whole of the upper course of the river; but this omission was soon repaired by SAMUEL BAKER and H. M. STANLEY, and all but a few irreconcilable critics were satisfied.

The 'fifties, then, saw an immense development in the knowledge of Africa, through the labours of Barth, Baikie, Livingstone, Burton and Speke: they also saw a new political interest in the continent on the part of the European Powers. It was at this time that Britain took the first small step which led eventually to the establishment of Nigeria—to-day the greatest of all the Crown Colonies: in 1851 she declared a virtual protectorate over Lagos (made absolute ten years later),solely in order to facilitate the suppression of the slave trade. The foundations of the huge French West African empire were also laid in these years by Faidherbe, who became Governor of Senegal in 1854.

The 'scramble' for East Africa began later and went on more slowly. The first sign of it was, paradoxically, the Anglo-French Declaration of 1862, binding both Powers to respect the Sultan of Zanzibar's independence. The Declaration was followed by a steady growth of British influence at Zanzibar, which eventually, in 1890, developed into a full protectorate. This influence made itself decisively felt in 1873, when the Sultan agreed to prohibit his subjects from exporting slaves overseas. That meant in effect the end of the

Arab slave trade from Africa: it was a complete victory for Livingstone.

But he was not alive to see it. In March 1866 he had started out from Zanzibar on his third and last journey. For nearly six years the outside world had no certain news of him. Then, in the spring of 1872, H. M. Stanley arrived in England and announced that he had 'found' Livingstone. He had gone on his quest as a journalist, sent by his paper the *New York Herald*. (How many other explorers besides Livingstone have had a 'news value' which could have made this worth while?) With great efficiency, backed—as on all his African journeys—by ample funds, Stanley performed his mission, reached Livingstone at Ujiji, supplied his wants, and sent up porters from the coast to aid him. Thus reinforced (when Stanley found him his condition was poor indeed), Livingstone determined to finish off his work, the examination of the country south of Lake Tanganyika, and to return home as quickly as possible. But, weakened by disease, even his constitution was unequal to this final demand upon it, and near Lake Bangweolo he died—five weeks before the treaty which virtually ended the East African slave trade was concluded.

Stanley was a man of very different type from Livingstone. But he came back deeply impressed—there can be no doubt of it—by 'the Doctor's' character; and when he heard the news of his death, in February 1874, he determined that he would himself carry on what he conceived to be Livingstone's work. This he did, in his own way, by his second journey in 1874-7, which solved most of the problems that preoccupied Livingstone in his last years: he secured final confirmation of Speke's theory of the source of the Nile and he proved that the Lualaba was one with the Congo, which he followed down to the sea at Boma. The last of the four great African rivers had at length been traced.

But this immense journey had a much wider importance too. It led directly to the Partition of Africa. Stanley was alive to the political significance of the work he had done, and he pressed Britain to take control of the Congo basin and to open it up by a road and railway from the sea to the point at which the river becomes navigable (now known as Stanley Pool). Here he failed; but he was successful in another quarter: King Leopold II of the Belgians entered readily enough into his plans. The result was the founding of the International African Association (its name is, surely unconsciously, reminiscent of Banks's club of 1788): this led in its turn to the establishment of the Congo Free State and the 'scramble' for tropical Africa which began in 1884.

Stanley's second journey was in fact, in its results if not its original intention, the first of the new political expeditions ('imperialist', if you will). In its execution, too, it offers a strong contrast to most of those which are described in this book. Its brutal attitude to hostile or puzzled African chiefs, its lavish equipment, its huge array of porters, the ruthless discipline under which they were kept, would have amazed, and often horrified, Lander or Livingstone or Speke. Yet in a sense they were only the logical conclusion of the work of the earlier travellers: it was inevitable that when once the physical obstacles to the exploration of Africa were overcome and a need for her products developed, Europe should intervene in full strength to exploit the country those travellers had revealed.

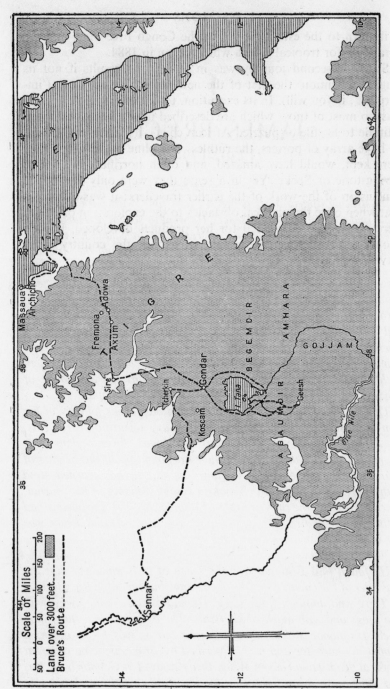

1. THE TRAVELS OF BRUCE IN ABYSSINIA, 1769–72

# I

# JAMES BRUCE
## 1730–1794

Bruce was a Scotchman of good position and education, and of
striking appearance, being six foot four, with dark red hair,
and a commanding presence. He went to school at Harrow and
afterwards studied law. During a residence in Spain he took up
Arabic, and having learned something of Ethiopia and the Amharic
language, he conceived a great longing to discover the source of the
Nile. During the 'sixties he lived and travelled in Mediterranean
countries. He distinguished himself as Consul at Algiers at a dangerous time and went on to travel, study and draw antiquities in
Italy, Barbary, Libya, Syria and Crete. In 1768 he was in Egypt
where, by acting as a doctor to some of the ruling personalities, he
gained from them valuable letters of recommendation to Moslem
authorities on the Red Sea, with others from the Patriarch of
Alexandria to the Christian Smyrna Greeks in Ethiopia.

Thus provided, he made an arduous and dangerous journey at his
own expense, travelling, equipped with heavy scientific instruments,
by Aswan, Cosseir and Jiddah to Massaua. After a dangerous
interlude at Massaua, he scaled the escarpment up to the heights of
Tigre—the language of which country he had already learned—and
with many adventures, which make exciting reading in his journal,
reached Gondar, the then capital of Ethiopia, in 1770. Europeans had
before this visited the country only at rare intervals and Bruce was
one of only two or three Europeans known to have entered during the
eighteenth century.

He found that Ethiopia was the scene of civil wars and that the
real ruler of the country was the aged, cruel, but very able Ras Michael
of Tigre who dominates his story. He had already made away with
two kings and with many of his rivals. The existing king, the young
Tecla Haimanot, was now in his power but he was by no means a
puppet in character and he is described by Bruce as being of great
physical beauty and charm. When Bruce arrived at Gondar both Ras
and King were away fighting a leading Galla chieftain, Fasil. He

35

*was able, however, to win the favour of one of the leading nobles,*
*Ayto Aylo, of the Queen Mother (the Iteghe) and of Ras Michael's*
*young, spirited, and beautiful wife, Ozoro Esther, by curing the lat-*
*ter's son, Confu, and others of their household at Koscam, from*
*smallpox, and stemming the plague by measures of hygiene. He at*
*once provoked the jealousy and suspicion of some of the clergy,*
*whose attempts at a miraculous cure had failed, and especially of*
*Abba Salama, who as the Acab Saat, was the third head—the Abuna*
*was the first—of the Ethiopian Church and religious guardian of the*
*palace.*

*The first extract opens at the point where, upon the return of the*
*King and the old Ras from their expedition, Bruce is ushered into the*
*formidable presence of the latter.*

## 1. RECEPTION AT GONDAR

We went in and saw the old man sitting upon a sofa; his white hair
was dressed in many short curls. He appeared to be thoughtful, but not
displeased; his face was lean, his eyes quick and vivid, but seemed to be
a little sore from exposure to the weather. He seemed to be about six
feet high, though his lameness made it difficult to guess with accuracy.
His air was perfectly free from constraint, what the French call *dégagée*.
In face and person he was liker my learned and worthy friend the Count
de Buffon, than any two men I ever saw in the world. They must have
been bad physiognomists that did not discern his capacity and understanding by his very countenance. Every look conveyed a sentiment
with it: he seemed to have no occasion for other language, and indeed
he spoke little. I offered, as usual, to kiss the ground before him; and
of this he seemed to take little notice, stretching his hand and shaking
mine upon rising.

I sat down with Aylo, three or four of the judges, Petros, Heikel the
queen's chamberlain, and an Azage from the king's house, who whispered something in his ear, and went out; which interruption prevented
me from speaking as I was prepared to do, or give him my present,
which a man held behind me. He began gravely, 'Yagoube, I think that
is your name, hear what I say to you, and mark what I recommend to
you. You are a man, I am told, who make it your business to wander
in the fields in search after trees and grass in solitary places, and to sit
up all night alone looking at the stars of the heavens. Other countries
are not like this, though this was never so bad as it is now. These
wretches here are enemies to strangers; if they saw you alone in your

own parlour, their first thought would be how to murder you; though they knew they were to get nothing by it, they would murder you for mere mischief.'—'The devil is strong in them,' says a voice from a corner of the room, which appeared to be that of a priest. 'Therefore,' says the Ras, 'after a long conversation with your friend Aylo, whose advice I hear you happily take, as indeed we all do, I have thought that situation best which leaves you at liberty to follow your own designs, at the same time that it puts your person in safety; that you will not be troubled with monks about their religious matters, or in danger from these rascals that may seek to murder you for money.'

'What are the monks?' says the same voice from the corner; 'the monks will never meddle with such a man as this.'—'Therefore the king,' continued the Ras, without taking any notice of the interruption, 'has appointed you Baalomaal,[1] and to command the Koccob horse, which I thought to have given to Francis, an old soldier of mine; but he is poor, and we will provide for him better, for these appointments have honour, but little profit.' 'Sir,' says Francis, who was in presence, but behind, 'it is in much more honourable hands than either mine or the Armenian's, or any other white man's, since the days of Hatze Menas, and so I told the king to-day.' 'Very well, Francis,' says the Ras; 'it becomes a soldier to speak the truth, whether it makes for or against himself. Go then to the king, and kiss the ground upon your appointment. I see you have already learned this ceremony of ours; Aylo and Heikel are very proper persons to go with you. The king expressed his surprise to me last night he had not seen you; and there too is Tecla Mariam, the king's secretary, who came with your appointment from the palace to-day.' The man in the corner, that I took for a priest, was this Tecla Mariam, a scribe. Out of the king's presence men of this order cover their heads, as do the priests, which was the reason of my mistake.

I then gave him a present, which he scarce looked at, as a number of people were pressing in at the door from curiosity or business. Among them I discerned Abba Salama. Everybody then went out but myself, and these people were rushing in behind me, and had divided me from my company. The Ras, however, seeing me standing alone, cried, 'Shut the door;' and asked me, in a low tone of voice, 'Have you anything private to say?' 'I see you are busy, Sir,' said I, 'but I will speak to Ozoro Esther.' His anxious countenance brightened up in a moment. 'That is true,' says he, 'Yagoube; it will require a long day to settle that account with you. Will the boy live?' 'The life of man is in the hand of God,' said I, 'but I should hope the worst is over;' upon which he called to one of his servants, 'Carry Yagoube to Ozoro Esther.'

[1] Literally 'keeper of the goods, or effects'. It is a post resembling that of our lords of the bed-chamber. The Koccob horse are the cavalry in the guards. (*Bruce's note.*)

It is needless for me to take up the reader's time with anything but what illustrates my travels; he may therefore guess the conversation that flowed from a grateful heart on that occasion. I ordered her child to be brought to her every forenoon, upon condition she returned him soon after mid-day. I then took a speedy leave of Ozoro Esther, the reason of which I told her when she was following me to the door. She said, 'When shall I lay my hands upon that idiot Aylo? The Ras would have done anything; he had appointed you Palambaras, but, upon conversing with Aylo he had changed his mind. He says it will create envy and take up your time. What signifies their envy? Do not they envy Ras Michael? And where can you pass your time better than at court, with a command under the king?' I said, 'all is for the best; Aylo did well; all is for the best.' I then left her unconvinced, and saying, 'I will not forgive this to Ayto Aylo these seven years.'

Aylo and Heikel had gone on to the palace, wondering, as did the whole company, what could be my private conference with Michael, which, after playing abundantly with their curiosity, I explained to them next day.

I went afterwards to the king's palace, and met Aylo and Heikel at the door of the presence chamber. Tecla Mariam walked before us to the foot of the throne; after which I advanced and prostrated myself upon the ground. 'I have brought you a servant,' says he to the king, 'from so distant a country, that if you ever let him escape, we shall never be able to follow him, or know where to seek him.' This was said facetiously by an old familiar servant; but the king made no reply, as far as we could guess, for his mouth was covered, nor did he shew any alteration of countenance. Five people were standing on each side of the throne, all young men, three on his left, and two on his right. One of these, the son of Tecla Mariam, (afterwards my great friend) who stood uppermost on the left hand, came up, and taking hold of me by the hand, placed me immediately above him; when seeing I had no knife in my girdle, he pulled out his own and gave it to me. Upon being placed, I again kissed the ground.

The king was in an alcove; the rest went out of sight from where the throne was, and sat down. The usual questions now began about Jerusalem and the holy places—where my country was? which it was impossible to describe, as they knew the situation of no country but their own —why I came so far?—whether the moon and the stars, but especially the moon was the same in my country as in theirs?—and a great many such idle and tiresome questions. I had several times offered to take my present from the man who held it, that I might offer it to his Majesty and go away; but the king always made a sign to put it off, till, being tired to death with standing, I leaned against the wall. Aylo was fast asleep, and Ayto Heikel and the Greeks cursing their master in their heart for spoiling the good supper that Anthule his treasurer had prepared for us. This, as we afterwards found out, the king very well knew, and resolved to try our patience to the utmost. At last, Ayto Aylo stole away to bed, and everybody else after him, except those who had accompanied me, who were ready to die with thirst, and drop down with weariness. It was agreed by those that were out of sight, to send Tecla Mariam to whisper in the king's ear, that I had not been well, which he did, but no notice was taken of it. It was now past ten o'clock and he shewed no inclination to go to bed.

Hitherto, while there were strangers in the room, he had spoken to us by an officer called Kal Hatze, *the voice or word of the king*; but now, when there were nine or ten of us, his menial servants only, present, he uncovered his face and mouth, and spoke himself. Sometimes it was about Jerusalem, sometimes about horses, at other times about shooting; again about the Indies; how far I could look into the heavens with my telescopes: and all these were deliberately and circumstantially repeated, if they were not pointedly answered. I was absolutely in despair, and scarcely able to speak a word, inwardly mourning the hardness of my lot in this my first preferment, and sincerely praying it might be my last promotion in this court. At last all the Greeks began to be impatient and got out of the corner of the room behind the alcove and stood immediately before the throne. The king seemed to be astonished at seeing them and told them he thought they had all been at home long ago. They said, however, they would not go without me; which the king said could not be, for one of the duties of my employment was to be charged with the door of his bed-chamber that night.

I think I could almost have killed him in that instant. At last Ayto Heikel, taking courage, came forward to him, pretending a message from the queen, and whispered him something in the ear, probably that the Ras would take it ill. He then laughed, said he thought we had supped, and dismissed us.

We went all to Anthule's house to supper in violent rage, such anger as is usual with hungry men. We brought with us from the palace three of my brother Baalomaals, and one who had stood to make up the number, though he was not in office; his name was Guebra Mascal; he was a Sister's son of the Ras, and commanded one-third of the troops of Tigre, which carried fire-arms, that is about 2000 men. He was reputed the best officer of that kind that the Ras had, and was a man about 30 years of age, short, square, and well made, with a very unpromising countenance; flat nose, wide mouth, of a very yellow complexion, and much pitted with the smallpox; he had a most uncommon presumption upon the merit of past services, and had the greatest opinion of his own knowledge in the use of fire-arms, to which he did not scruple to say Ras Michael owed all his victories. Indeed it was to the good opinion that the Ras had of him as a soldier that he owed his being suffered to continue at Gondar; for he was suspected to have been familiar with one of his uncle's wives in Tigre, by whom it was thought he had a child; at least the Ras put away his wife, and never owned the child to be his.

This man supped with us that night, and thence began one of the most serious affairs I ever had in Abyssinia. Guebra Mascal, as usual, vaunted incessantly his skill in fire-arms, the wonderful gun that he had, and feats he had done with it. Petros said, laughing, to him, 'You have a genius for shooting, but you have had no opportunity to learn. Now Yagoube is come, he will teach you something worth talking of.' They had all drank abundantly, and Guebra Mascal had uttered words that I thought were in contempt of me. 'I believe,' replied I, peevishly enough, 'Guebra Mascal, I should suspect from your discourse, you neither knew men nor guns; every gun of mine in the hands of my servants shall kill twice as far as yours; for my own, it is not worth my while to put a ball in it. When I compare with you, the end of a tallow-candle in my gun shall do more execution than an iron ball in the best of yours, with all the skill and experience you pretend to.'

He said I was a Frank, and a liar, and, upon my immediately rising up, he gave me a kick with his foot. I was quite blind with passion, seized him by the throat and threw him on the ground, stout as he was. The Abyssinians know nothing either of wrestling or boxing. He drew his knife as he was falling, attempting to cut me in the face; but his arm not being at freedom, all he could do was to give me a very trifling stab, or wound, near the crown of the head, so that the blood trickled down over my face. I had tript him up, but till then had never struck him. I now wrested the knife from him with a full intention to kill him; but Providence directed better. Instead of the point, I struck so violently with the handle upon his face as to leave scars, which would be distinguished even among the deep marks of the small-pox. An adventure so new, and so unexpected, presently overcame the effects of wine. It was too late to disturb any body either in the palace or at the house of the Ras. A hundred opinions were immediately started; some were for sending us up to the king, as we were actually in the precincts of the palace, where lifting a hand is death. Ayto Heikel advised that I should go, late as it was to Koscam, and Petros, that I should repair immediately to the house of Ayto Aylo, while the Baalomaals were for taking me to sleep in the palace. Anthule, in whose house I was, and who was therefore most shocked at the outrage, wished me to stay in his house, where I was, from a supposition that I was seriously wounded, which all of them, seeing the blood fall over my eyes, seemed to think was the case; and he, in the morning, at the king's rising, was to state the matter as it happened. All these advices appeared good when they were proposed;

for my part, I thought they only tended to make bad worse, and bore the appearance of guilt, of which I was not conscious.

I now determined to go home, and to bed in my own house. With that intention, I washed my face and wound with vinegar, and found the blood to be already staunched. I then wrapt myself up in my cloak and returned home without accident, and went to bed. But this would neither satisfy Ayto Heikel nor Petros, who went to the house of Ayto Aylo, then past midnight, so that early in the morning when scarce light, I saw him come into my chamber. Guebra Mascal had fled to the house of Kefla Yasous his relation; and the first news we heard in the morning after Ayto Aylo arrived, were, that Guebra Mascal was in irons at the Ras's house.

Every person that came afterward brought up some new account; the whole people present had been examined and had given, without variation, the true particulars of my forbearance, and his insolent behaviour. Every body trembled for some violent resolution the Ras was to take on my first complaint. The town was full of Tigre soldiers, and nobody saw clearer than I did, however favourable a turn this had taken for me in the beginning, it might be my destruction in the end.

I asked Ayto Aylo his opinion. He seemed at a loss to give it to me; but said, in an uncertain tone of voice, he could wish that I would not complain of Guebra Mascal while I was angry, or while the Ras was so inveterate against him, till some of his friends had spoken, and appeased, at least, his first resentment. I answered, 'That I was of a contrary opinion, and that no time was to be lost: remember the letter of Mahomet Gibberti; remember his confidence yesterday of my being safe where he was; remember the influence of Ozoro Esther, and do not let us lose a moment.' 'What,' says Aylo to me in great surprise, 'are you mad? Would you have him cut to pieces in the midst of 20,000 of his countrymen? Would you be dimmenia, that is, guilty of the blood of all the province of Tigre, through which you must go in your way home?' 'Just the contrary,' said I; 'nobody has so great a right over the Ras's anger as I have, being the person injured; and, as you and I can get access to Ozoro Esther when we please, let us go immediately thither, and stop the progress of this affair while it is not yet generally known. People that talk of my being wounded expect to see me, I suppose, without a leg or an arm. When they see me so early riding in the street, all will pass for a story as it should do. Would you wish to pardon him entirely?'—'That goes against my heart, too,' says Aylo; 'he is a bad man.'—'My good friend,' said I, 'be in this guided by me; I know we both think the same thing. If he is a bad man, he was a bad man before I knew him. You know what you told me yourself of the Ras's jealousy of him. What if he was to revenge his own wrongs, under pretence of giving me satisfaction for mine? Come, lose no time, get upon your mule, go with me to Ozoro Esther, I will answer for the consequences.'

We arrived there; the Ras was not sitting in judgment; he had drank hard the night before, on occasion of Powussen's marriage, and was not in bed when the story of the fray reached him. We found Ozoro Esther in a violent anger and agitation, which was much alleviated by my laughing. On her asking me about my wound, which had been represented to her as dangerous, 'I am afraid,' said I 'poor Guebra Mascal is worse wounded than I.' 'Is he wounded too?' says she; 'I hope it is in his heart.' 'Indeed,' replied I, 'Madam, there are no wounds on either side. He was very drunk, and I gave him several blows upon the face as he deserved, and he has already got all the chastisement he ought to have; it was all a piece of folly.' 'Prodigious!' says she, 'is this so?' 'It is so,' says Aylo, 'and you shall hear it all by-and-by; only let us stop the propagation of this foolish story.'

The Ras in the instant sent for us. He was naked, sitting on a stool, and a slave swathing up his lame leg with a broad belt or bandage. I asked him, calmly and pleasantly, if I could be of any service to him? He looked at me with a grin, the most ghastly I ever saw, as half displeased. 'What,' says he, 'are you all mad? Aylo, what is the matter between him and that miscreant Guebra Mascal?'—'Why,' said I, 'I am come to tell you that myself; why do you ask Ayto Aylo? Guebra Mascal got drunk, was insolent, and struck me. I was sober and beat him, as you will see by his face; and I have not come to you to say I am sorry that I lifted my hand against your nephew; but he was in the wrong, and drunk; and I thought it was better to chastise him on the spot, than trust him to you, who perhaps might take the affair to heart; for we all know your justice, and that being your relation is no excuse when you judge between man and man.' 'I order you, Aylo,' says Michael, 'as you esteem my friendship to tell me the truth, really as it was, and without disguise or concealment.'

Aylo began accordingly to relate the whole history, when a servant called me out to Ozoro Esther. I found with her another nephew of the Ras, a much better man, called Welleta Selasse, who came from Kefla Yasous, and Guebra Mascal himself, desiring I would forgive and intercede for him, for it was a drunken quarrel without malice. Ozoro Esther had told him part. 'Come in with me,' said I, 'and you shall see I never will leave the Ras till he forgive him.' 'Let him punish him,' says Welleta Selasse; 'he is a bad man, but don't let the Ras either kill or maim him.' 'Come,' said I, 'let us go to the Ras, and he shall neither kill, maim, nor punish him if I can help it. It is my first request; if he refuses me, I will return to Jidda; come and hear.'

Aylo had urged the thing home to the Ras in the proper light—that of my safety. 'You are a wise man,' says Michael, now perfectly cool, as soon as he saw me and Welleta Selasse. 'It is a man like you that goes far in safety, which is the end we all aim at. I feel the affront offered you more than you do, but will not have the punishment attributed to you; this affair shall turn to your honour and security, and in that light only I can pass over his insolence.—Welleta Selasse' says he, falling into a violent passion in an instant, 'what sort of behaviour is this my men have adopted with strangers; and my stranger, too, and in the king's palace, and the king's servant? What! am I dead? or become incapable of governing longer?' Welleta Selasse bowed, but was afraid to speak, and indeed the Ras looked like a fiend.

'Come,' says the Ras, 'let me see your head.' I shewed him where the blood was already hardened, and said it was a very slight cut. 'A cut,' continued Michael, 'over that part, with one of our knives, is mortal.' 'You see, Sir,' said I, 'I have not even clipt the hair about the wound; it is nothing. Now give me your promise you will set Guebra Mascal at liberty; and not only that, but you are not to reproach him with the affair further than that he was drunk, not a crime in this country.' 'No, truly,' says he, 'it is not, but that is, because it is very rare that people fight with knives when they are drunk. I scarce ever heard of it, even in the camp.' 'I fancy,' said I, endeavouring to give a light turn to the conversation, 'they have not often wherewithal to get drunk in your camp.' 'Not this last year,' says he, laughing, 'there were no houses in the country.' 'But let me only merit,' said I, 'Welleta Selasse's friendship, by making him the messenger of good news to Guebra Mascal, that he is at liberty, and you have forgiven him.' 'At liberty!' says he, 'where is he?' 'In your house,' said I, 'somewhere, in irons.' 'That is Esther's intelligence,' continued the Ras; 'these women tell you all their secrets, but when I remember your behaviour to them, I do not wonder at it; and that consideration likewise obliges me to grant what you ask. Go, Welleta Selasse, and free that dog from his collar, and direct him to go to Welleta Michael, who will give him his orders to levy the meery in Woggora; let him not see my face till he returns.'

Ozoro Esther gave us breakfast, to which several of the Greeks came. After which I went to Koscam, where I heard a thousand curses upon Guebra Mascal. The whole affair was now made up, and the king was acquainted with the issue of it. I stood in my place, where he shewed me very great marks of favour; he was grave, however, and sorrowful, as if mortified with what had happened. The king ordered me to stay and dine at the palace, and he would send me my dinner. I there saw the sons of Kasmati Eshte, Aylo and Engedan, and two Welleta Selasses; one the son of Tecla Mariam, the other the son of a great nobleman in Gojam, all young men, with whom I lived ever after in perfect familiarity and friendship. The two last were my brethren Baalomaal, or gentleman of the king's bed-chamber.

They all seemed to have taken my cause to heart more than I wished them to do, for fear it should be productive of some new quarrel. For my own part, I never was so dejected in my life. The troublesome prospect before me presented itself day and night. . . .

I began, however, to look upon every thing now as full of difficulty and danger; and from this constant fretting and despondency, I found my health much impaired, and that I was upon the point of becoming seriously ill. There was one thing that contributed in some measure to dissipate these melancholy thoughts, which was, that all Gondar was in one scene of festivity. Ozoro Ayabdar, daughter of the late Welled Hawaryat, by Ozoro Altash, Ozoro Esther's sister, and the Iteghe's youngest daughter, consequently grand-daughter to Michael, was married to Powussen, now governor of Begemder. The King gave her large districts of land in that province, and Ras Michael a large portion of gold, muskets, cattle and horses. All the town, that wished to be well looked upon by either party, brought something considerable as a present. The Ras, Ozoro Esther, and Ozoro Altash, entertained all Gondar. A vast number of cattle was slaughtered every day, and the whole town looked like one great market; the common people, in every street, appearing loaded with pieces of raw beef, while drink circulated in the same proportion. The Ras insisted upon my dining with him every day, when he was sure to give me a headache with the quantity of mead, or hydromel, he forced me to swallow, a liquor that never agreed with me from the first day to the last.

After dinner we slipt away to parties of ladies, where anarchy prevailed as completely as at the house of the Ras. All the married women ate, drank and smoaked, like the men; and it is impossible to convey to the reader any idea of this bacchanalian scene in terms of common decency. I found it necessary to quit this riot for a short time, and get leave to breathe the fresh air of the country, at such a distance as that, once a day, or once in two days, I might be at the palace, and avoid the constant succession of those violent scenes of debauchery, of which no European can form any idea, and which it was impossible to escape, even at Koscam.

Although the king's favour, the protection of the Ras, and my obliging, attentive and lowly behaviour to every body, had made me as popular as I could wish at Gondar, and among the Tigrans fully as much as those of Amhara, yet it was easy to perceive, that the cause of my quarrel with Guebra Mascal was not yet forgot.

One day, when I was standing by the king in the palace, he asked, in discourse, 'Whether I, too, was not drunk in the quarrel with Guebra Mascal, before we came to blows?' and, upon my saying that I was perfectly sober, both before and after, because Anthule's red wine was finished, and I never willingly drank hydromel, or mead, he asked me with a degree of keenness, 'Did you then soberly say to Guebra Mascal, that an end of a tallow candle, in a gun in your hand, would do more execution than an iron bullet in his?'—'Certainly, Sir, I did so.'—'And why did you say this?' says the king dryly enough, and in a manner I had not before observed. 'Because,' replied I, 'it was truth, and a proper reproof to a vain man, who, whatever eminence he might have obtained in a country like this, has not knowledge enough to entitle him to the trust of cleaning a gun in mine.' 'O, ho!' continued the king; 'as for his knowledge, I am not speaking of that, but about his gun. You will not persuade me, that, with a tallow candle, you can kill a man or a horse?'— 'Pardon me, Sir,' said I, bowing very respectfully, 'I will attempt to persuade you of nothing but what you please to be convinced of: Guebra Mascal is my equal, no more; you are my master, and, while I am at your court, under your protection, you are in place of my sovereign; it would be great presumption in me to argue with you, or lead to a conversation against an opinion that you profess you are already fixed in.'—'No, no,' says he, with an air of great kindness, 'by no means; I was only afraid you would expose yourself before bad people; what you say to me is nothing.'—'And what I say to you, Sir, has always been as scrupulously true, as if I had been speaking to the king, my native sovereign and master. Whether I can kill a man with a candle, or not, is an experiment that should not be made. Tell me, however, what I shall do before you, that you may deem an equivalent? Will piercing the table, upon which your dinner is served (it was of sycamore, about three quarters of an inch thick), at the length of this room, be deemed a sufficient proof of what I advance?'

'Ah, Yagoube, Yagoube,' says the king, 'take care what you say. That is indeed more than Guebra Mascal will do at that distance; but take great care; you don't know these people; they will lie themselves all day; nay, their whole life is one lie; but of you they expect better, or would be glad to find worse; take care.' Ayto Engedan, who was then present, said, 'I am sure if Yagoube says he can do it, he will do it, but how, I don't know. Can you shoot through my shield with a tallow candle?'—'To you, Ayto Engedan,' said I, 'I can speak freely; I could shoot through your shield if it was the strongest in the army, and kill the strongest man in the army that held it before him. When will you see this tried?'—'Why now,' says the king; 'there is *nobody here*.'—'The sooner the better,' said I; 'I would not wish to remain for a moment longer under so disagreeable an imputation as that of lying, an infamous one in *my* country, whatever it may be in this. Let me send for my gun; the king will look out at the window.'—'*Nobody*,' says he, 'knows any thing of it; *nobody will come*.'

The king appeared to be very anxious, and I saw plainly, incredulous. The gun was brought; Engedan's shield was produced, which was of a strong buffalo's hide. I said to him, 'This is a weak one, give me one stronger.' He shook his head, and said, 'Ah, Yagoube, you'll find it strong enough; Engedan's shield is known to be no toy.' Tecla Mariam brought such a shield, and the Billetana Gueta Tecla another, both of which were most excellent in their kind. I loaded the gun before them, first with powder, then upon it slid down one half of what we call a farthing candle; and, having beat off the handles of three shields, I put them close in contact with each other, and set them all three against a post.

'Now, Engedan,' said I, 'when you please say—Fire! but mind you have taken leave of your good shield for ever.' The word was given and the gun fired. It struck the three shields, neither in the most difficult nor the easiest part for perforation, something less than half-way between the rim and the boss. The candle went through the three shields with such violence, that it dashed itself to a thousand pieces against a stone wall behind it. I turned to Engedan, saying very lowly, gravely, and without exultation or triumph, on the contrary with absolute indifference, 'Did not I tell you your shield was naught?' A great shout of applause followed from about a thousand people that were gathered together. The three shields were carried to the king, who exclaimed in great transport, 'I did not believe it before I saw it, and I can scarcely believe it now I have seen it! Where is Guebra Mascal's confidence now? But what do either he or we know? We know nothing.' I thought he looked abashed.

'Ayto Engedan,' said I, 'we must have a touch at that table. It was said, the piercing that was more than Guebra Mascal could do. We have one half of the candle left still; it is the thinnest, weakest half, and I shall put the wick foremost, because the cotton is softest.' The table being now properly placed, to Engedan's utmost astonishment, the candle, with the wick foremost, went through the table, as the other had gone through the three shields. 'By St. Michael!' says Engedan, 'Yagoube, hereafter say to me you can raise my father Eshte from the grave, and I will believe you.' Some priests who were there, though surprised at first, seemed afterwards to treat it rather lightly, because they thought it below their dignity to be surprised at any thing. They said it was done by writing (mucktoub), by which they meant magic. Every body embraced that opinion, as an evident and rational one, and so the wonder with them ceased. But it was not so with the king: it made the most favourable and lasting impression upon his mind; nor did I ever after see, in his countenance, any marks either of doubt or diffidence, but always, on the contrary, the most decisive proofs of friendship, confidence, and attention, and the most implicit belief of every thing I advanced upon any subject from my own knowledge.

The experiment was twice tried afterwards, in presence of Ras Michael. But he would not risk his good shields, and always produced the table, saying 'Engedan and these foolish boys were rightly served; they thought Yagoube was a liar like themselves, and they lost their shields, but I believed him, and gave him my table for curiosity only, and so I saved mine.'

*Travels to discover the source of the Nile,*
2nd edition, vol. IV, pp. 413–32

*After many adventures and campaigns with the Ras and the King, during which he developed his friendship with Ozoro Esther, Bruce at last obtained permission to attempt the accomplishment of his one great object, the discovery of the source of the Nile. This was, of course, the Blue Nile, as the extent of the White Nile was then unknown. The King actually endowed him with the lordship of Gheesh, where the springs rose. He was unable to approach the place, however, except by favour of Fasil, the Galla chief who dominated the region. In spite of intrigues against the expedition by Abba Salama, Bruce won Fasil over by his feats of horsemanship and the chief gave him his own horse to drive before him, saddled and bridled, as a surety of his favour and protection. To reach Gheesh Bruce had to go through the country of the wild Agow people and he was therefore provided with an Agow, Woldo, as his guide and seven Galla chiefs. Strates, one of the Greeks resident in Ethiopia, also accompanied him. The narrative opens when the party came within sight of their goal.*

## 2. FINDING THE SOURCE OF THE BLUE NILE

At three quarters after one we arrived at the top of the mountain, whence we had a distinct view of all the remaining territory of Sacala, the mountain of Geesh, and church of St Michael Gheesh, about a mile and a half distant from St Michael Sacala, where we then were. We saw, immediately below us, the Nile itself, strangely diminished in size, and now only a brook that had scarcely water to turn a mill. I could not satiate myself with the sight, revolving in my mind all those classical prophecies that had given the Nile up to perpetual obscurity and concealment. . . .

I was awakened out of this delightful reverie by an alarm that we had lost Woldo our guide. Though I long had expected something from his behaviour, I did not think, for his own sake, it could be his intention to

47

leave us. The servants could not agree when they last saw him: Strates and Aylo's servant were in the wood shooting, and we found by the gun that they were not far from us; I was therefore in hopes that Woldo, though not at all fond of fire-arms, might be in their company; but it was with great dissatisfaction I saw them appear without him. They said, that, about an hour before, they had seen some extraordinary large, rough apes, or monkeys, several of which were walking upright, and all without tails; that they had gone after them through the wood till they could scarce get out again; but they did not remember to have seen Woldo at parting. Various conjectures immediately followed; some thought he had resolved to betray and rob us; some conceived it was an instruction of Fasil's to him, in order to our being treacherously murdered; some again supposed he was slain by the wild beasts, especially those apes or baboons, whose voracity, size and fierce appearance were exceedingly magnified, especially by Strates, who had not the least doubt, if Woldo met them, but that he would be so entirely devoured, that we might seek in vain without discovering even a fragment of him. For my part, I began to think that he had been really ill when he first complained, and that the sickness might have overcome him upon the road; and this, too, was the opinion of Ayto Aylo's servant, who said, however, with a significant look, that he could not be far off; we therefore sent him, and one of the men that drove the mules, back to seek after him; and they had not gone but a few hundred yards when they found him coming, but so decrepid, and so very ill, that he said he could go no farther than the church, where he was positively resolved to take up his abode that night. I felt his pulse, examined every part about him, and saw, I thought evidently, that nothing ailed him. Without losing my temper, however, I told him firmly, that I perceived he was an impostor, that he should consider that I was a physician, as he knew I cured his master's first friend, Welleta Yasous; that the feeling of his hand told me as plain as his tongue could have done, that nothing ailed him; that it told me likewise that he had in heart some prank to play, which would turn out very much to his disadvantage. He seemed dismayed after this, said little, and only desired us to halt for a few minutes, and he should be better; 'for,' says he, 'it requires strength in us all to pass another great hill before we arrive at Geesh.'

'Look you,' said I, 'lying is to no purpose; I know where Geesh is as well as you do, and that we have no more mountains or bad places to pass through; therefore, if you choose to stay behind, you may; but tomorrow I shall inform Welleta Yasous at Bure of your behaviour.' I said this with the most determined air possible, and left them, walking as hard as I could down to the ford of the Nile. Woldo remained above with the servants, who were loading their mules; he seemed to be perfectly cured of his lameness, and was in close conversation with Ayto

Aylo's servant for about ten minutes, which I did not choose to interrupt, as I saw that man was already in possession of part of Woldo's
secret. This being over they all came down to me, as I was sketching a
branch of a yellow rose-tree, a number of which hang over the ford.

The whole company passed without disturbing me; and Woldo, seeming to walk as fast as ever, ascended a gentle rising hill, near the top of
which is St. Michael Geesh. The Nile here is not four yards over, and
above four inches deep where we crossed; it was indeed become a very
trifling brook, but ran swiftly over a bottom of small stones, with hard
black rock appearing amongst them: it is at this place very easy to pass,
and very limpid, but, a little lower, full of inconsiderable falls; the
ground rises gently from the river to the southward, full of small hills
and eminences, which you ascend and descend almost imperceptibly.
The whole company had halted on the north side of St. Michael's
church, and there I reached them, without affecting any hurry.

It was about four o'clock in the afternoon, but the day had been very
hot for some hours, and they were sitting in the shade of a grove of
magnificent cedars, intermixed with some very large and beautiful cusso
trees, all in flower; the men were lying on the grass, and the beasts fed,
with their burdens on their backs in most luxuriant herbage. I called for
my herbary, to lay the rose-branch I had in my hand smoothly, that it
might dry without spoiling the shape; having only drawn its general
form, the pistil and stamina, the finer parts of which (though very
necessary in classing the plant) crumble and fall off, or take different
forms in drying, and therefore should always be secured by drawing
while green. I just said indifferently to Woldo in passing, that I was glad
to see him recovered; that he would presently be well, and should fear
nothing. He then got up, and desired to speak with me alone, taking
Aylo's servant along with him. 'Now,' said I, very calmly, 'I know by
your face you are going to tell me a lie. I do swear to you solemnly, you
never, by that means, will obtain anything from me, no not so much as
a good word; truth and good behaviour will get you everything; what
appears a great matter in your sight, is not perhaps of such value in
mine: but nothing except the truth and good behaviour will answer to
you; now I know for a certainty you are no more sick than I am.' 'Sir,'
said he, with a very confident look, 'you are right; I did counterfeit; I
neither have been, nor am I at present, any way out of order; but I
thought it best to tell you so, not to be obliged to discover another
reason, that has much more weight with me, why I cannot go to Geesh,
and much less show myself at the sources of the Nile, which I confess
are not much beyond it, though I declare to you there is still a *hill*
between you and those sources.' 'And pray,' said I calmly, 'what is this
mighty reason? have you had a dream, or a vision in that trance you fell
into when you lagged behind, below the church of St Michael Sacala?'

'No,' says he, 'it is neither trance, nor dream, nor devil either; I wish it were no worse; but you know as well as I, that my master Fasil defeated the Agows at the battle of Banja. I was there with my master, and killed several men, among whom some were of the Agows of this village Geesh; and you know the usage of this country; when a man, in these circumstances, falls into their hands, his blood must pay for their blood.'

I burst into a violent fit of laughter which very much disconcerted him. 'There,' said I, 'did not I say to you it was a lie you was going to tell me? do not think I disbelieve or dispute with you the vanity of having killed men; many men were slain at that battle; somebody must, and you may have been the person who slew them; but do you think that I can believe that Fasil, so deep in that account of blood, could rule the Agows in the manner he does, if he could not put a servant of his in safety among them, twenty miles from his residence? do you think I can believe this?' 'Come, come,' said Aylo's servant to Woldo, 'did you not hear the truth and good behaviour will get you everything you ask? Sir,' continues he, 'I see this affair vexes you, and what this foolish man wants will neither make you richer nor poorer; he has taken a great fancy for that crimson silk-sash which you wear about your middle. I told him to stay till you sent back to Gondar, but he says he is to go no farther than to the house of Shalaka Welled Amlac in Maitsha, and does not return to Gondar; I told him to stay till you had put your mind at ease, by seeing the fountains of the Nile which you were so anxious about. He said, after that had happened, he was sure you would not give it him, for you seemed to think little of the cataract at Goutto, and of all the rivers and churches which he had shown you; except the head of the Nile shall be finer than all these, when, in reality, it will be just like another river, you will then be dissatisfied, and not give him the sash.'

I thought there was something very natural in these suspicions of Woldo; besides, he said he was certain that, if ever the sash came into the sight of Welled Amlac, by some means or other he would get it into his hands. This rational discourse had pacified me a little; the sash was a handsome one; but it must have been fine indeed to have stood for a minute between me and the accomplishment of my wishes. I laid my hand then upon the pistols that stuck in my girdle, and drew them out to give them to one of my suite, when Woldo, who apprehended it was for another purpose, ran some paces back, and hid himself behind Aylo's servant. We were all diverted at this fright, but none so much as Strates, who thought himself revenged for the alarm he had given him, by falling hrough the roof of the house at Goutto. After having taken off my sash, 'Here is your sash, Woldo,' said I, 'but mark what I have said, and now most seriously repeat to you, truth and good behaviour will get anything from me; but if, in the course of this journey, you play one trick more, though ever so trifling I will bring such a vengeance upon your head, that you shall not be able to find a place to hide it in, when not the sash only will be taken from you, but your skin also will follow it: remember what happened to the Seis at Bamba.'

He took the sash, but seemed terrified at the threat, and began to make apologies. 'Come, come,' said I, 'we understand each other; no more words; it is now late; lose no more time, but carry me to Geesh, and the head of the Nile, directly, without preamble, and show me the hill that separates me from it.' He then carried me round to the south side of the church, out of the grove of trees that surrounded it. 'This is the hill,' says he, looking archly, 'that, when you was on the other side of it, was between you and the fountains of the Nile; there is no other. Look at that hillock of green sod in the middle of that watery spot; it is in that the two fountains of the Nile are to be found: Geesh is on the face of the rock where yon green trees are. If you go the length of the fountains, pull off your shoes, as you did the other day, for these people are all Pagans, worse than those that were at the ford; and they believe in nothing that you believe, but only in this river, to which they pray every day, as if it were God; but this perhaps you may do likewise.' Half undressed as I was by loss of my sash, and throwing my shoes off, I ran down the hill, towards the little island of green sods, which was about two hundred yards distant; the whole side of the hill was thick grown over with flowers, the large bulbous roots of which appearing above the surface of the ground, and their skins coming off on treading upon them, occasioned me two very severe falls before I reached the brink of the marsh; I after this came to the island of green turf, which was in form of an altar, apparently the work of art, and I stood in rapture over the principal fountain which rises in the middle of it.

It is easier to guess than to describe the situation of my mind at that moment—standing in that spot which had baffled the genius, industry and inquiry of both ancients and moderns, for the course of near three thousand years. Kings had attempted this discovery at the head of armies and each expedition was distinguished from the last, only by the difference of the numbers which had perished, and agreed alone in the disappointment which had uniformly and without exception, followed them all. Fame, riches and honour, had been held out for a series of ages to every individual of those myriads these princes commanded, without having produced one man capable of gratifying the curiosity of his sovereign, or wiping off this stain upon the enterprise and abilities of mankind, or adding this desideratum for the encouragement of geography. Though a mere private Briton, I triumphed here, in my own mind, over kings and their armies; and every comparison was leading nearer and nearer to presumption, when the place itself where I stood, the object of my vain-glory, suggested what depressed my short-lived triumph. I was but a few minutes arrived at the sources of the Nile, through numberless dangers and sufferings, the least of which would have overwhelmed me, but for the continual goodness and protection of Providence; I was, however, but then half through my journey, and all those dangers which I had already passed, awaited me again on my return. I found a despondency gaining ground fast upon me, and blasting the crown of laurels I had too rashly woven for myself. I resolved, therefore, to divert, till I could, on more solid reflection, overcome its progress.

I saw Strates expecting me on the side of the hill. 'Strates,' said I, 'faithful squire! come and triumph with your Don Quixote, at the island Barataria, where we have most wisely and fortunately brought ourselves! come and triumph with me over all the kings of the earth, all their armies, all their philosophers, and all their heroes!' 'Sir,' says Strates, 'I do not understand a word of what you say, and as little what you mean: you very well know I am no scholar. But you had much better leave that bog; come into the house and look after Woldo; I fear he has something further to seek than your sash, for he has been talking with the old devil-worshipper ever since we arrived.' 'Did they speak secretly together,' said I. 'Yes, sir, they did, I assure you.' 'And in whispers, Strates!' 'Every syllable; but for that,' replied he, 'they need not have been at the pains; they understand one another I suppose, and the devil, their master, understands them both; but as for me, I comprehend their discourse no more than if it was Greek, as they say. Greek!' says he, 'I am an ass; I should know well enough what they said if they spoke Greek.' 'Come,' said I, 'take a draught of this excellent water, and drink with me a health to his majesty King George III and a long line of princes.' I had in my hand a large cup made of cocoanut shell, which I procured in Arabia, and which was brim-full. He drank to the king speedily and cheerfully, with the addition of, 'Confusion to his enemies,' and tossed up his cap with a loud huzza. 'Now, friend,' said I, 'here is to a more humble, but still a sacred name, here is to— Maria!' He asked if that was the Virgin Mary? I answered, 'In faith, I believe so, Strates.' He did not speak, but only gave a humph of disapprobation.

The day had been very hot, and the altercation I had with Woldo had occasioned me to speak so much, that my thirst, without any help from curiosity, led me to these frequent libations at this long-sought-for spring, the most ancient of all altars. 'Strates,' said I, 'here is to our happy return. Come, friend, you are yet two toasts behind me; can you ever be satiated with this excellent water?' 'Look you, sir,' says he very gravely, 'as for King George, I drank to him with all my heart, to his children, to his brothers and sisters, God bless them all! Amen;—but as for the Virgin Mary, as I am no Papist, I beg to be excused from drinking healths which my church does not drink. As for our happy return, God knows, there is no one wishes it more sincerely than I do, for I have been long weary of this beggarly country. But you must forgive me if I refuse to drink any more water. They say these savages pray over that hole every morning to the devil, and I am afraid I feel his horns in my belly already, from the great draught of that hellish water I drank first.' It was, indeed, as cold water as ever I tasted. 'Come, come,' said I, 'don't be peevish, I have but one toast more to drink.' 'Peevish or not peevish,' replied Strates, 'a drop of it never again shall cross my throat: there is no humour in this, no joke, show us something pleasant as you used to do; but there is no jest in meddling with devil-worshippers, witchcraft, and inchantments to bring some disease upon one's self here, so far from home in the fields. No, no; as many toasts in wine as you please, or better in brandy, but no more water for Strates. I am sure I have done myself harm already with these follies—God forgive me!' 'Then,' said I, 'I will drink it alone, and you are henceforward unworthy of the name of Greek; you do not even deserve that of a Christian.' Holding the full cup then to my head 'Here is to Catharine, empress of all the Russias, and success to her heroes at Paros; and hear my prediction from this altar to-day; Ages shall not pass, before this ground, whereon I now stand, shall become a flourishing part of her dominions.'

He leaped on this a yard from the ground. 'If the old gentleman has whispered you this,' says he, 'out of the well, he has not kept you long waiting; tell truth and shame the devil, is indeed the proverb, but truth is truth, wherever it comes from, give me the cup; I will drink that health though I should die.' He then held out both his hands. 'Strates,' said I, 'be in no such haste; remember the water is inchanted by devil-worshippers: there is no jesting with these, and you are far from home, and in the fields, you may catch some disease, especially if you drink the Virgin Mary; God forgive you. Remember the horn the first draught produced; they may with this come entirely through and through.' 'The cup, the cup,' says he 'and fill it full; I defy the devil and trust in St. George and the dragon. Here is to Catharine, empress of all the Russias; confusion to her enemies, and damnation to all at Paros.' 'Well, friend,' said I 'you was long in resolving, but you have done it at last to some purpose; I am sure I did not drink damnation to all at Paros.' 'Ah!' says he, 'but I did and will do it again—Damnation to all at Paros, and Cyprus, and Rhodes, Crete, and Mytilene into the bargain: Here it goes with all my heart. Amen, so be it.' 'And who do you think,' said I, 'are at Paros?' 'Pray, who should be there,' says he, 'but Turks and devils, the worst race of monsters and oppressors in the Levant. I have been at Paros myself; was you ever there?' 'Whether I was ever there or not, is no matter,' said I; 'the empress's fleet, and an army of Russians, are now possibly there; and here you, without provocation, have drank damnation to the Russian fleet and army, who have come so far from home, and are at this moment sword in hand, to restore you to your liberty, and the free exercise of your religion; did not I tell you, you was no Greek, and scarcely deserved the name of Christian?' 'No, no sir,' cries Strates, 'for God's sake do not say so; I would rather die. I did not understand you about Paros; there was no malice in my heart against the Russians. God will bless them and my folly can do them no harm— Huzza! Catharine and victory!' whilst he tossed his cap into the air.

A number of the Agows had appeared upon the hill, just before the valley, in silent wonder what Strates and I were doing at the altar. Two or three only had come down to the edge of the swamp, had seen the grimaces and action of Strates, and heard him huzza; on which they had asked Woldo, as he entered into the village, what was the meaning of all this? Woldo told them, that the man was out of his senses, and had been bit by a mad dog; which reconciled them immediately to us. They, moreover, said he would be infallibly cured by the Nile; but the custom, after meeting with such a misfortune, was to drink the water in the morning fasting. I was very well pleased both with this turn Woldo gave the action, and the remedy we stumbled upon by mere accident which discovered a connection, believed to subsist at this day, between this river and its ancient governor the dog star.

. . . . . .

The night of the 4th, that very night of my arrival, melancholy reflections upon my present state, the doubtfulness of my return in safety, were I permitted to make the attempt, and the fears that even this would be refused, according to the rule observed in Abyssinia with all travellers who have once entered the kingdom; the consciousness of the pain that I was then occasioning to many worthy individuals, expecting daily that information concerning my situation which it was not in my power to give them; some other thoughts, perhaps, still nearer the heart than those, crowded upon my mind, and forbade all approach of sleep.

I was at that very moment, in possession of what had, for many years, been the principal object of my ambition and wishes: indifference, which, from the usual infirmity of human nature, follows, at least for a time, complete enjoyment, had taken place of it. The marsh, and the fountains, upon comparison with the rise of many of our rivers, became now a trifling object in my sight. I remember that magnificent scene in my own native country, where the Tweed, Clyde, and Annan rise, in one hill; three rivers, as I now thought, not inferior to the Nile in beauty, preferable to it in the cultivation of those countries through which they flow; superior, vastly superior to it in the virtues and qualities of the inhabitants, and in the beauty of its flocks crowding its pastures in peace, without fear of violence from man or beast. I had seen the rise of the Rhine and Rhone, and the more magnificent sources of the Saone;

I began, in my sorrow, to treat the inquiry about the source of the Nile as a violent effort of a distempered fancy:—

> What's Hecuba to him, or he to Hecuba,
> That he should weep for her?—

Grief or despondency, now rolling upon me like a torrent; relaxed, not refreshed, by unquiet and imperfect sleep, I started from my bed in the utmost agony; I went to the door of my tent; everything was still; the Nile at whose head I stood, was not capable either to promote or to interrupt my slumbers, but the coolness and serenity of the night braced my nerves, and chased away those phantoms that, while in bed, had oppressed and tormented me.

It was true, that numerous dangers, hardships, and sorrows, had beset me through this half of my excursion; but it was still as true that another Guide, more powerful than my own courage, health or understanding, if any of these can be called man's own, had uniformly protected me in all that tedious half; I found my confidence not abated, that still the same Guide was able to conduct me to my now wished for home: I immediately resumed my former fortitude considering the Nile indeed as no more than rising from springs, as all other rivers do, but widely different in this, that it was the palm for three thousand years held out to all the nations in the world as a *detur dignissimo*, which, in my cool hours, I had thought was worth the attempting at the risk of my life, which I had long resolved to lose, or lay this discovery, a trophy in which I could have no competitor, for the honour of my country, at the feet of my sovereign, whose servant I was.

> *Travels to discover the source of the Nile,*
> 2nd edition, vol. v, pp. 262–74, 309–11

*Bruce returned from this expedition to join the king as he was marching upon Gondar, intent to revenge himself upon those who had supported an attempt to oust Ras Michael and to set up a rival king.*

# 3. PUNISHMENT FOR REBELLION

As for me, the king's behaviour shewed me plainly all was not right, and an accident in the way confirmed it. He had desired me to ride before him, and shew him the horse I had got from Fasil, which was then in great beauty and order, and which I had kept purposely for him. It happened that, crossing the deep bed of a brook, a plant of the kantuffa hung across it. I had upon my shoulders a white goat-skin, of which it did not take hold; but the king, who was dressed in the habit of peace, his long hair floating all around his face, wrapt up in his mantle, or thin cotton cloak, so that nothing but his eyes could be seen, was paying more attention to the horse than to the branch of kantuffa beside him; it took the first hold of his hair, and the fold of the cloak that covered his head, then spread itself over his whole shoulder in such a manner, that, notwithstanding all the help that could be given him, and that I had, at first seeing it, cut the principal bough asunder with my knife, no remedy remained but he must throw off the upper garment, and appear in the under one, or waistcoat, with his head and face bare before all the spectators.

This is accounted great disgrace to a king, who always appears covered in public. However, he did not seem to be ruffled, nor was there any thing particular in his countenance more than before, but with great composure, and in rather a low voice, he called twice, 'Who is the Shum of this district?' Unhappily he was not far off. A thin old man of sixty, and his son about thirty, came trotting, as their custom is, naked to their girdle, and stood before the king, who was, by this time, quite cloathed again. What had struck the old man's fancy, I know not, but he passed my horse laughing, and seemingly wonderfully content with himself. I could not help considering him as a type of mankind in general, never more confident and careless than when on the brink of destruction. The king asked if he was Shum of that place? He answered in the affirmative, and added, which was not asked of him, that the other was his son.

There is always near the king, when he marches, an officer called Kanitz Kitzera, the executioner of the camp; he has upon the tore of his saddle a quantity of thongs made of bull hide, rolled up very artificially; this is called the tarade. The king made a sign with his head, and another with his hand, without speaking; and two loops of the tarade were instantly thrown round the Shum and his son's neck, and they were both hoisted upon the same tree, the tarade cut and the end made fast to a branch. They were both left hanging, but I thought so aukwardly, that they would not die for some minutes, and might surely have been saved had any one dared to cut them down; but fear had fallen upon every person who had not attended the king to Tigre.

This cruel beginning seemed to me an omen that violent resolutions had been taken, the execution of which was immediately to follow; for though the king had certainly a delight in the shedding of human blood in the field, yet till that time I never saw him order an execution by the hands of the hangman; on the contrary, I have often seen him shudder and express disgust, lowly and in half words, at such executions ordered every day by Ras Michael. In this instance he seemed to have lost that feeling; and rode on, sometimes conversing about Fasil's horse, or other indifferent subjects, to those who were around him, without once reflecting upon the horrid execution he had then so recently occasioned.

In the evening of the 23d, when encamped upon Mogetch, came Sanuda, the person who had made Socinios King, and who had been Ras under him; he was received with great marks of favour, in reward of the treacherous part he had acted. He brought with him prisoners, Guebra Denghel, the Ras's son-in-law, one of the best and most amiable men in Abyssinia, but who had unfortunately embraced the wrong side of the question; and with him Sebaat Laab and Kefla Mariam, both men of great families in Tigre. These were, one after the other, thrown violently on their faces before the king. I was exceedingly distressed for Guebra Denghel; he prayed the king, with the greatest earnestness, to order him to be put to death before the door of his tent, and not delivered to his cruel father-in-law. To this the king made no answer nor did he shew any signs of pity, but waved his hand, as a sign to carry them to Ras Michael, where they were put in custody and loaded with irons.

About two hours later came Ayto Aylo, son of Kasmati Eshte, whom the king had named governor of Begemder; he brought with him Chremation, brother to Socinios, and Abba Salama the Acab Saat, who had excommunicated his father, and been instrumental in his murder by Fasil. I had a great curiosity to see how they would treat the Acab Saat; for my head was full of what I had read in the European books, of exemption that churchmen had in this country from the jurisdiction of the civil power.

Aylo had made his legs to be tied under the mule's belly, his hands behind his back, and a rope made fast to them, which a man held in his hand on one side, while another led the halter of the mule on the other, both of them with lances in their hands. Chremation had his hands bound, but his legs were not tied, nor was there any rope made fast to his hands by which he was held. While they were untying Abba Salama, I went into the presence-chamber, and stood behind the king's chair. Very soon after, Aylo's men brought in their prisoners, and, as is usual, threw them down violently with their faces to the ground; their hands being bound behind them, they had a very rude fall upon their faces.

The Acab Saat rose in a violent passion; he struggled to get loose his hands, that he might be free to use the act of denouncing excommunication, which is by lifting the right hand, and extending the fore-finger; finding that impossible, he cried out, 'Unloose my hands, or you are all excommunicated.' It was with difficulty he could be prevailed upon to hear the king, who with great composure, or rather indifference said to him, 'You are the first ecclesiastical officer in my household, you are the third in the whole kingdom; but I have not yet learned you ever had power to curse your sovereign, or exhort his subjects to murder him.

You are to be tried for this crime by the judges to-morrow, so prepare to shew in your defence, upon what precepts of Christ, or his apostles, or upon what part of the general councils, you found your title to do this.'

'Let my hands be unloosed,' cried Salama violently; 'I am a priest, a servant of God; and they have power, says David, to put kings in chains, and nobles in irons. And did not Samuel hew king Agag to pieces before the Lord? I excommunicate you, Tecla Haimanout.' And he was going on, when Tecla Mariam, son of the king's secretary, a young man, struck the Acab Saat so violently on the face, that it made his mouth gush out with blood, saying, at the same time, 'What! suffer this in the king's presence?' Upon which both Chremation and the Acab Saat were hurried out of the tent without being suffered to say more; indeed the blow seemed to have so much disconcerted Abba Salama, that it deprived him for a time of the power of speaking.

In Abyssinia it is death to strike, or lift the hand to strike, before the king; but in this case the provocation was so great, so sudden, and unexpected, and the youth's worth and the insolence of the offender so apparent to every body, that a slight reproof was ordered to be given to Tecla Mariam (by his father only); but he lost no favour for what he had done, either with the King, Michael, or the people. . . .

There was at Gondar a sort of mummers, being a mixture of buffoons and ballad-singers, and posture-masters. These people, upon all public occasions, run about the streets; and on private ones, such as marriages, come to the court-yards before the houses, where they dance, and sing songs of their own composing in honour of the day, and perform all sorts of antics; many a time, on his return from the field with victory, they had met Ras Michael, and received his bounty for singing his praises, and welcoming him upon his return home. The day the Abuna excommunicated the king, this set of vagrants made part of the solemnity; they abused, ridiculed and traduced Michael in lampoons and scurrilous rhymes, calling him crooked, lame, old, and impotent, and several other opprobrious names, which did not affect him nearly so much as the ridicule of his person: upon many occasions after, they repeated this, and particularly in a song they ridiculed the horse of Sire, who had run away at the battle of Limjour, where Michael cried out, 'Send these horse to the mill.' It happened that these wretches, men and women, to the number of about thirty and upwards, were then, with very different songs, celebrating Ras Michael's return to Gondar. The King and Ras, after the proclamation, had just turned to the right to Aylo Meidan, below the palace, a large field where the troops exercise. Confu and the king's household troops were before, and about 200 of the Sire horse were behind; on a signal made by the Ras, these horse turned short and fell upon the singers, and cut them all to pieces. In less than two minutes they were all laid dead upon the field, excepting one young man, who, mortally wounded, had just strength enough to arrive within twenty yards of the king's horse, and there fell dead without speaking a word.

All the people present, most of them veteran soldiers, and consequently inured to blood, appeared shocked and disgusted at this wanton piece of cruelty. For my part, a kind of faintishness, or feebleness, had taken possession of my heart, ever since the execution of the two men on our march, about the kantuffa; and this second act of cruelty occasioned such a horror, joined with an absence of mind, that I found myself unable to give an immediate answer, though the king had spoken twice to me.

It was about nine o'clock in the morning when we entered Gondar; every person we met on the street wore the countenance of a condemned malefactor; the Ras went immediately to the palace with the king, who retired, as usual, to a kind of cage or lattice-window, where he always sits unseen when in council. We were then in the council-chamber, and four of the judges seated; none of the governors of provinces were present but Ras Michael, and Kasmati Tesfos of Sire. Abba Salama was brought to the foot of the table without irons, at perfect liberty. The accuser for the king (it is a post in this country in no great estimation) began the charge against him with great force and eloquence. He stated, one by one, the crimes committed by him at different periods; the sum of which amounted to prove Salama to be the greatest monster upon earth; among these were various kinds of murder, especially by poison; incest, with every degree collateral and descendant. He concluded this black, horrid list, with the charge of high treason, or cursing the king, and absolving his subjects from their allegiance, which he stated as the greatest crime human nature was capable of, as involving in its consequences, all sorts of other crimes. Abba Salama, though he seemed under very great impatience, did not often interrupt him, further than, 'You lie,' and, 'It is a lie,' which he repeated at every new charge. His accuser had not said one word of the murder of Joas, but passed it over without the smallest allusion to it.

In this, however, Abba Salama did not follow his example. Being desired to answer in his own defence, he entered upon it with great dignity, and an air of superiority, very different from his behaviour in the king's tent the day before: he laughed, and made extremely light of the charges on the article of women, which he neither confessed nor denied; but said these might be crimes among the Franks (looking at me) or other Christians, but not the Christians of that country, who lived under a double dispensation, the law of Moses and the law of Christ; he said the Abyssinians were *Beni Israel*, as indeed they call themselves, that is, children of Israel; and that, in every age, the patriarchs had acted as he did, and were not less beloved of God. He went roundly into the murder of Joas, and of his two brothers, Adigo and Aylo, on the mountain of Wechne, and charged Michael directly with it, as also with the poisoning the late Hatze Hannes, father of the present king.

The Ras seemed to avoid hearing, sometimes by speaking to people standing behind him, sometimes by reading a paper; in particular, he asked me, standing directly behind his chair, in a low voice, 'What is the punishment in your country for such a crime?' It was his custom to speak to me in his own language of Tigre, and one of his greatest pastimes to laugh at my faulty expression. He spoke this to me in Amharic, so I knew he wanted my answer should be understood: I therefore said, in the same low tone of voice he had spoke to me, 'High treason is punished with death in all the countries I have ever known.'— This I owed to Abba Salama, and it was not long before I had my return.

Abba Salama next went into the murder of Kasmati Eshte, which he confessed he was the promoter of. He said the Iteghe, with her brothers and Ayto Aylo, had all turned Franks, so had Gusho of Amhara; and that, in order to make the country Catholic, they had sent for priests, who lived with them in confidence, as that Frank did, pointing to me: that it was against the law of the country that I should be suffered here; that I was accursed, and should be stoned as an enemy to the Virgin Mary. There the Ras interrupted him, by saying, 'Confine yourself to your own defence; clear yourself first, and then accuse any one you please: it is the king's intention to put the law in execution against all offenders, and it is only as believing you the greatest, that he has begun with you.'

This calmness of the Ras seemed to disconcert the Acab Saat; he lost all method; he warned the Ras, that it was owing to his excommunicating Kasmati Eshte that room was made for him to come to Gondar, without that event, this king would never have been upon the throne; so that he had still done them as much good by his excommunications as he had done them harm. He told the Ras, and the judges, that they were all doubly under a curse, if they offered either to pull out his eyes, or cut out his tongue; and prayed them, bursting into tears, not so much as to think of either, if it was only for old fellowship, or friendship, which had long subsisted between them.

There is an officer, named Kal Hatze, who stands always upon steps at the side of the lattice-window, where there is a hole covered in the inside with a curtain of green taffeta; behind this curtain the king sits, and through this hole he sends what he has to say to the Board, who rise, and receive the messenger standing. He had not interfered till now, when the officer said, addressing himself to Abba Salama, 'The king requires of you to answer directly, why you persuaded the Abuna to excommunicate him? The Abuna is a slave of the Turks, and has no

king; you are born under a monarchy; why did you, who are his inferior
in office, take upon you to advise him at all? or why, after having presumed to advise him, did you advise him wrong, and abuse his ignorance
in these matters?' This question, which was a home one, made him lose
all his temper; he cursed the Abuna, called him Mahometan, Pagan,
Frank, and Infidel; and was going on in this wild manner, when Tecla
Haimanout, the eldest of the judges, got up, and addressing himself to
the Ras, 'It is no part of my duty to hear all this railing; he has not so
much as offered one fact material to his exculpation.'

The king's secretary sent up to the window the substance of his defence, the criminal was carried at some distance to the other end of the
room, and the judges deliberated whilst the king was reading. Very few
words were said among the rest; the Ras was all the time speaking to
other people. After he had ended this, he called upon the youngest judge
to give his opinion; and he gave it, 'He is guilty, and should die;' the
same said all the officers, and after them the judges; and the same said
Kasmati Tesfos after them. When it came to Ras Michael to give his
vote, he affected moderation; he said, 'That he was accused for being
his enemy and accomplice; in either case, it is not fair that he should
judge him.' No superior officer being present, the last voice remained
with the king, who sent Kal Hatze to the Board with his sentence; 'He
is guilty, and *shall* die *the death.—*The hangman *shall* hang him upon
a tree *to-day.'* The unfortunate Acab Saat was immediately hurried
away by the guards to the place of execution, which is a large tree before
the king's gate; where uttering, to the very last moment, curses against
the King, the Ras, and the Abuna, he suffered the death he very richly
deserved, being hanged in the very vestments in which he used to sit
before the king, without one ornament of his civil or sacerdotal pre-
eminence having been taken from him before the execution. In going to
the tree, he said he had 400 cows, which he bequeathed to some priests
to say prayers for his soul; but the Ras ordered them to be brought to
Gondar, and distributed among his soldiers.

I have entered into a longer detail of this trial, at the whole of which
I assisted, the rather that I might ask this question of those that maintain
the absolute independence of the Abyssinian priesthood, 'Whether, if
the many instances already mentioned have not had the effect, this one
does not fully convince them, that all ecclesiastical persons are subject
to the secular power in Abyssinia, as much as they are in Britain, or any
European state whatever?'

Chremation, Socinios's brother, was next called; he seemed half dead
with fear; he only denied having any concern in his brother being elected
king. He said he had no post, and in this he spoke the truth, but confessed that he had been sent by Abba Salama to bring the Itchegue and
the Abuna [administrative and spiritual heads of the Church] to meet

him the day of excommunication at Dippabye. It was further unluckily proved against him, that he was present with his brother at plundering the houses in the night-time when the man was killed; and upon this he was sentenced to be immediately hanged. The court then broke up, and went to breakfast. All this had passed in less than two hours; it was not quite eleven o'clock when all was over; but Ras Michael had sworn he would not taste bread till Abba Salama was hanged; and on such occasions he never broke his word.

Immediately after this last execution, the kettle-drums beat at the palace-gate, and the crier made this proclamation, 'That all lands and villages, which are now, or have been given to the Abuna by the king, shall revert to the king's own use, and be subject to the government, or the Cantiba of Dembea, or such officers as the king shall afterwards appoint in the provinces where they are situated.'

I went home, and my house being but a few yards from the palace, I passed the two unfortunate people hanging upon the same branch; and, full of the cruelty of the scene I had witnessed, which I knew was but a preamble to much more, I determined firmly, at all events, to quit this country.

The next morning came on the trial of the unfortunate Guebra Denghel, Sebaat Laab, and Kefla Mariam; the Ras claimed his right of trying these three at his own house, as they were all three subjects of his government of Tigre. Guebra Denghel bore his hard fortune with great unconcern, declaring, that his only reason of taking up arms against the king was, that he saw no other way of preventing Michael's tyranny and monstrous thirst of money and of power: that the Ras was really king, had subverted the constitution, annihilated all difference of rank and persons, and transferred the efficient parts of government into the hands of his own creatures. He wished the king might know this was his only motive for rebellion, and that, unless it had been to make this declaration, he would not have opened his mouth before so partial and unjust a judge as he considered Michael to be.

But Welleta Selasse, his daughter, hearing the danger her father was in, broke suddenly out of Ozoro Esther's apartment, which was contiguous; and coming into the council-room at the instant her father was condemned to die, threw herself at the Ras's feet with every mark and expression of the most extreme sorrow. I cannot, indeed, repeat what her expressions were, as I was not present, and I thank God that I was not; I believe they are ineffable by any mouth but her own; but they were perfectly unsuccessful. The old tyrant threatened her with immediate death, spurned her away with his foot, and in her hearing ordered her father to be immediately hanged. Welleta Selasse, in a fit, or faint, which resembled death, fell speechless to the ground. The father, forgetful of his own situation, flew to his daughter's assistance, and they were both dragged out at separate doors, the one to death, the other to after-sufferings, greater than death itself.

Fortune seemed to have taken delight, from very early life, constantly to traverse the greatness and happiness of this young lady. She was first destined to be married to Joas, and the affair was nearly concluded, when the fatal discovery, made at the battle of Azazo, that the king had sent his household troops privately to fight for Fasil against Michael, prevented her marriage, and occasioned his death. She was then destined to old Hatze Hannes, Tecla Haimanout's father: Michael, who found him incapable of being a king, judged him as incapable of being a husband to a woman of the youth and charms of Welleta Selasse, and therefore deprived him at once of his life, crown, and bride. She was now not seventeen, and it was designed she should be married to the present king; Providence put a stop to a union that was not agreeable to either party. She died some time after this, before the battle of Serbraxos; being strongly pressed to gratify the brutal inclinations of the Ras, her grandfather, whom when she could not resist or avoid, she took poison: others said it was given her by Ozoro Esther from jealousy; but this was certainly without foundation. I saw her in her last moments, but too late to give her any assistance; and she had told her women-servants and slaves, that she had taken arsenic, having no other way to avoid committing so monstrous a crime as incest with the murderer of her father.

The rage, that the intercession of the daughter for her father Guebra Denghel had put the Ras into, was seen in the severity of the sentence he passed upon the other two criminals; Kefla Mariam's eyes were pulled out, Sebaat Laab's eye-lids were cut off by the roots, and both of them were exposed in the market-place to the burning sun, without any covering whatever. Sebaat Laab died of a fever in a few days; Kefla Mariam lived, if not to see, at least to hear, that he was revenged, after the battle of Serbraxos, by the disgrace and captivity of Michael.

I will spare myself the disagreeable task of shocking my readers with any further account of these horried cruelties; enough has been said to give an idea of the character of these times and people. Blood continued to be spilt as water, day after day, till the Epiphany; priests, lay-men, young men and old, noble and vile, daily found their end by the knife or the cord. Fifty-seven people died publicly by the hand of the executioner in the course of a very few days; many disappeared, and were either murdered privately, or sent to prisons, no one knew where.

The bodies of those killed by the sword were hewn to pieces and scattered about the streets, being denied burial. I was miserable, and almost driven to despair, at seeing my hunting dogs, twice let loose by the carelessness of my servants, bringing into the court-yard the head and arms of slaughtered men, and which I could no way prevent but by the destruction of the dogs themselves; the quantity of carrion, and the stench of it, brought down the hyænas in hundreds from the neighbouring mountains; and, as few people in Gondar go out after it is dark, they enjoyed the streets by themselves, and seemed ready to dispute the possession of the city with the inhabitants. Often when I went home late from the palace, and it was this time the king chose chiefly for conversation, though I had but to pass the corner of the market-place before the palace, had lanthorns with me, and was surrounded with armed men, I heard them grunting by two's and three's so near me as to be afraid they would take some opportunity of seizing me by the leg; a pistol would have frightened them, and made them speedily run, and I constantly carried two loaded at my girdle; but the discharging a pistol in the night would have alarmed every one that heard it in the town, and it was not now the time to add any thing to people's fears. I at last scarce ever went out, and nothing occupied my thoughts but how to escape from this bloody country by the way of Sennaar, and how I could best exert my power and influence over Yasine at Ras el Feel to pave my way, by assisting me to pass the desert into Atbara.

The king missing me some days at the palace, and hearing I had not been at Ras Michael's, began to inquire who had been with me. Ayto Confu soon found Yasine, who informed him of the whole matter; upon this I was sent for to the palace, where I found the king, without any body but menial servants. He immediately remarked that I looked very ill; which, indeed, I felt to be the case, as I had scarcely ate or slept since I saw him last, or even for some days before. He asked me, in a condoling tone, 'What ailed me? that, besides looking sick, I seemed as if something had ruffled me, and put me out of humour.' I told him that what he observed was true: that, coming across the market-place, I had seen Za Mariam, the Ras's door-keeper, with three men bound, one of whom he fell a-hacking to pieces in my presence. Upon seeing me running across the place, stopping my nose, he called me to stay till he should come and dispatch the other two, for he wanted to speak to me, as if he had been engaged about ordinary business: that the soldiers, in consideration of his haste, immediately fell upon the other two, whose cries were still remaining in my ears: that the hyænas at night would scarcely let me pass in the streets when I returned from the palace; and the dogs fled into my house to eat pieces of human carcases at leisure.

Although his intention was to look grave, I saw it was all he could do to stifle a laugh at grievances he thought very little of. 'The men you saw with Za Mariam just now,' says he, 'are rebels, sent by Kefla Yasous for examples: he has forced a junction with Tecla and Welleta Michael in Samen, and a road is now open through Woggora, and plenty established in Gondar. The men you saw suffer were those that cut off the provisions from coming into the city; they have occasioned the death of many poor people; as for the hyæna, he never meddles with living people, he seeks carrion, and will soon clear the streets of those incumbrances that so much offend you; people say that they are the Falasha of the mountains, who take that shape of the hyæna, and come down into the town to eat Christian flesh in the night.' 'If they depend upon Christian flesh, and eat no other,' said I, 'perhaps the hyænas of Gondar will be the worst fed of any in the world.' 'True,' says he, bursting out into a loud laughter, 'that may be; few of those that die by the knife anywhere are Christians, or have any religion at all; why then should you mind what they suffer?' 'Sir,' said I, 'that is not my sentiment; if you was to order a dog to be tortured to death before me every morning, I could not bear it. The carcases of Abba Salama, Guebra Denghel, and the rest, are still hanging where they were upon the tree; you smell the stench of them at the palace-gate, and will soon, I apprehend, in the palace itself. This cannot be pleasant, and I do assure you it must be very pernicious to your health, if there was nothing else in it. At the battle of Fagitta, though you had no intention to retreat, yet you went half a day backward, to higher ground, and purer air, to avoid the stench of the field; but here in the city you heap up carrion about your houses, where is your continual residence.'

'The Ras has given orders,' says he, gravely, 'to remove all the dead bodies before the Epiphany, when we go down to keep that festival, and wash away all this pollution in the clear-running water of the Kahha: but, tell me, Yagoube, is it really possible that you can take such things as these so much to heart? You are a brave man; we all know you are, and have seen it: we have all blamed you, stranger as you are in this country, for the little care you take of yourself; and yet about these things you are as much affected as the most cowardly woman, girl, or child could be.' 'Sir,' said I, 'I do not know if I am brave or not; but if to see men tortured, or murdered, or to live among dead bodies without concern, be courage, I have it not, nor desire to have it: war is the profession of noble minds; it is a glorious one; it is the science and occupation of kings; and many wise and many humane men have dedicated their whole life to the study of it in every country; it softens men's manners, by obliging them to society, to assist, befriend, and even save one another, though at their own risk and danger. A barbarian of that profession should be pointed at. Observe Ayto Engedan (who came at that very instant into the room); there is a young man,' said I, 'who, with the bravery, has also the humanity and gentleness of my countrymen that are soldiers.'

Engedan fell on his face before the king, as is usual, while the king went on seriously—'War you want; do you, Yagoube? war you shall have; it is not far distant, and Engedan is come to tell us how near.' They went then into a considerable conversation about Gusho, Powussen, and the preparations they were making, and where they were; with which I shall not trouble the reader, as I shall have an occasion to speak of the particulars afterwards as they arise. 'I want Confu,' says the king; 'I want him to send his men of Ras el Feel to Sennaar, and to the Baharnagash, to get horses and some coats of mail. And what do you think of sending Yagoube there? he knows their manners and their language, and has friends there to whom he is intending to escape, without so much as asking my leave.' 'Pardon me, sir,' said I; 'if I have ever entertained that thought, it is proof sufficient of the extreme necessity I am under to go.' 'Sir,' says Engedan, 'I have rode in the Koccob horse; I will do so again, if Yagoube commands them, and will stay with us till we try the horse of Begemder. I have eight or ten coats of mail, which I will give your majesty: they belonged to my father Eshte, and I took them lately from that thief Abou Barea, with whom they were left at my father's death: but I will tell your majesty, I had rather fight naked, without a coat of mail, than that you should send Yagoube to Sennaar, to purchase them from thence, for he will never return.'

Ras Michael was now announced, and we made haste to get away. 'I would have Confu, Engedan, and you, come here to-morrow night,' says the king, 'as soon as it is dark; and do not you, Yagoube, for your life, speak one word of Sennaar, till you know my will upon it.' He said this in the sternest manner, and with all the dignity and majesty of a king.

We passed the Ras in the ante-chamber, attended by a great many people. We endeavoured to slide by him in the crowd, but he noticed us, and brought us before him. We both kissed his hands, and he kept hold of one of mine, while he asked Engedan, 'Is Fasil at Ibaba?' to which he was answered, 'Yes.' 'Who is with him?' says the Ras. 'Damot, Agow, and Maitsha,' answered Engedan. 'Was you there?' says the Ras. 'No,' answered Engedan; 'I am at Tshemera, with few men.' He then turned to me, and said, 'My son is ill; Ozoro Esther has just sent to me, and complains you visit her now no more. Go see the boy, and don't neglect Ozoro Esther; she is one of your best friends.'

> *Travels to discover the source of the Nile,*
> 2nd edition, vol. VI, pp. 12–31

*The final extract from Bruce deals with an event at court shortly before his departure and throws light upon another aspect of Ethiopian character.*

# 4. A NASTY SOVEREIGN

Another interview, which happened at the Kahha, was much more extraordinary in itself, though of much less importance to the state. Guangoul, chief of the Galla of Angot, that is, of the eastern Galla, came to pay his respects to the king and Ras Michael: he had with him about 500 foot and 40 horse: he brought with him a number of large horns for carrying the king's wine, and some other such trifles. He was a little, thin, cross-made man, of no apparent strength or swiftness, as far as could be conjectured; his legs and thighs being thin and small for his body, and his head large; he was of a yellow, unwholesome colour, not black nor brown; he had long hair plaited and interwoven with the bowels of oxen, and so knotted and twisted together as to render it impossible to distinguish the hair from the bowels, which hung down in long strings, part before his breast and part behind his shoulder, the most extraordinary ringlets I had ever seen. He had likewise a wreath of guts hung about his neck, and several rounds of the same about his middle, which served as a girdle, below which was a short cotton cloth dipt in butter, and all his body was wet, and running down with the same; he seemed to be about fifty years of age, with a confident and insolent superiority painted in his face. In his country it seems, when he appears in state, the beast he rides upon is a cow. He was then in full dress and ceremony, and mounted upon one, not of the largest sort, but which had monstrous horns. He had no saddle on his cow. He had short drawers, that did not reach the middle of his thighs; his knees, feet, legs, and all his body were bare. He had a shield of a single hide, warped by the heat in several directions, and much in the shape of a high-crowned, large, straw-hat, with which the fashionable women in our own country sometimes disguise themselves. He carried a short lance in his right hand, with an ill-made iron head, and a shaft that seemed to be of thorn-tree, but altogether without ornament, which is seldom the case with the arms of barbarians. Whether it was necessary for the poizing himself upon the sharp ridge of the beast's back, or whether it was meant as graceful riding, I do not know, being quite unskilled in cowmanship; but he leaned exceedingly backwards, pushing his belly forwards, and holding his left arm and shield stretched out on one side of him, and his right arm and lance in the same way on the other, like wings.

The king was seated on his ivory chair, to receive him, almost in the middle of his tent; the day was very hot and an insufferable stench of carrion soon made every one in the tent sensible of the approach of this nasty sovereign, even before they saw him. The king, when he perceived him coming, was so struck with the whole figure and appearance, that he could not contain himself from an immoderate fit of laughter, which finding it impossible to stifle, he rose from his chair, and ran as hard as he could into another apartment behind the throne.

The savage got from his cow at the door of the tent with all his tripes about him; and, while we were admiring him as a monster, seeing the king's seat empty, he took it for his own, and down he sat upon the crimson silk cushion, with the butter running from every part of him. A general cry of astonishment was made by every person in the tent: he started up I believe without divining the cause, and before he had time to recollect himself, they fell all upon him, and with pushes and blows drove this greasy chieftain to the door of the tent, staring with wild amazement not knowing what was next to happen. It is high treason, and punishable by immediate death, to sit down upon the king's chair. Poor Guangoul owed his life to his ignorance. The king had beheld the scene through the curtain; if he laughed heartily at the beginning, he laughed ten times more at the catastrophe; he came out laughing, and unable to speak. The cushion was lifted and thrown away, and a yellow Indian shawl spread on the ivory stool; and ever after, when it was placed, and the king not there, the stool was turned on its face upon the carpet to prevent such like accidents. . . .

After the king returned to the palace, great diversion was made at Guangoul's appearance, in so much that Ozoro Esther, who hated the very name of Galla, and of this race in particular, insisted upon seeing a representation of it. Doho, accordingly, a dwarf belonging to Ras Michael, very ugly, with a monstrous big head, but very sharp and clever, and capable of acting his part, was brought to represent the person of Guangoul: a burnt stick and a bad shield were provided: but the difficulty remained, how to persuade Doho, the dwarf, to put on the raw guts about his neck and waist, and, above all, to plait them in the hair, which he absolutely refused, both from religious and cleanly motives; as for the butter, it was no objection, as all the Abyssinians anoint themselves with it daily, after bathing. Here we were very near at a stand, all the ladies having in vain supplicated him to suffer for their sakes a temporary pollution, with promises that oceans of rose and scented water should be poured upon him afterwards, to restore his former sweetness. Doho was a man who constantly spent his time in reading scripture, the acts of the councils, the works of St. John Chrysostom, and other such books as they have among them. He remained inflexible: at last I suggested that several hanks of cotton, dyed blue, red, and yellow, should be got from the weavers in the Mahometan town; and these oiled, greased, and knotted properly, and twisted among the hair, well anointed with butter, would give a pretty accurate resemblance of what we saw in the king's tent. All hands were immediately set to work; the cotton was provided; Ozoro Esther's servants and slaves decked Doho to the life. I spotted his face with stibium, and others anointed him with butter: an old milk-cow was found, contrary to my experience, that suffered a rider without much impatience, and in came Guangoul into a great hall in Ozoro Esther's apartment.

Never was any thing better personated, or better received; the whole hall resounded with one cry of laughter; Doho encouraged by this, and the perfect indifference and steadiness of his cow, began to act his part with great humour and confidence: he was born in the neighbourhood of these very Galla, knew their manners, and spoke their language perfectly. Amha Yasous, Confu, Aylo, brother to Engedan, with some servants of the king, acted the part that we did in the tent the day of the audience, that is, stood on each side of the king's chair: the cow was brought into the middle of the room, and Guangoul descended with his lance and shield in great state; a cushion was not spared, nor did Doho spare the cushion: the butter shewed very distinctly where he had been sitting: we all fell upon him and belaboured him heartily, and chased him to the door. His speedy retreat was not counterfeited. Ozoro Altash, Esther's sister, and a number of the ladies were present. Ozoro Esther declared she would send for the Ras, he having been in great good humour since the arrival of Amha Yasous. I had not seen him since the recovery of his son, and happened to be at the door next him; he took me by the hand and said, 'Welleta Hawaryat (that was the name of his son) is well, you are very kind.'

Michael was esteemed the best orator in his country, and spoke his own language, Tigréan, with the utmost purity and elegance; yet in common conversation he was very sententious, two or three words at a time, but never obscure; this he had contracted by a long practice of commanding armies, where he saw as instantly and clearly, as he spoke shortly and distinctly. He bowed very civilly to the ladies, and pointed to me to sit down on the seat by him. Amha Yasous was standing before him; I hastened to sit down on the carpet at his feet, and he seemed to recollect himself, and place Amha Yasous beside him: it was easy to perceive by his look, that he gave me credit for my behaviour. When they were all seated, 'Well,' says he, in great good humour, 'what now, what is the matter? what can I do for you, Yagoube? are the women in your country as idle and foolish as these? has Ozoro Esther chosen a wife for you? she shall give you your dinner: I will give her a portion; and, as you are a horseman, the king, with Amha Yasous's leave,' said he, bowing, 'shall give you the command of the Shoa horse; I have seen them; the men, I think, are almost as white as yourself.' Amha Yasous bowed in return, and said, 'Sir, if the king bestows them so worthily, I promise to bring another thousand, as good as these, to join them after the rains, before next Epiphany.'—'And I,' says Ozoro Esther, 'for my part, I have long had a wife for him. But this is not the present business; we know your time is precious; Guangoul is without, and desires an audience of you.'—'Poh!' says the Ras, 'Guangoul is gone to Gusho, at Minziro, and there is like to be a pretty story: here are accounts from Tigre, that he has committed great barbarities in his journey, laid waste some villages, killed the people, for not furnishing him with provisions: here in Belessen he also burnt a church and a village belonging to the Iteghe, and killed many poor people; I do not know what he means; I hope they will keep him where he is, and not send him home again through Tigre.'

A communication of this kind, very uncommon from the Ras, occasioned a serious appearance in the whole company; but he had no sooner done with speaking, than in comes Doho upon his cow; neither man nor woman that had yet seen him ever laughed so heartily as the old Ras; he humoured the thing entirely; welcomed Doho in Galla language, and saw the whole farce, finished by his flight to the door, with the utmost good humour.

*Travels to discover the source of the Nile,*
2nd edition, vol. VI, pp. 43–9

*Shortly after this the civil wars broke out with renewed fierceness. After pitched battles, in which Bruce took part, Ras Michael's enemies, the lords of rival provinces, took him prisoner and the king passed under their control. Bruce at last obtained permission to leave the country, after living there for three years. Taking a valuable collection of Amharic documents, he went out westwards towards the Atbara and Sennar, breaking his journey to stay with Ozoro Esther, now in semi-exile at Tcherkin. Meeting her there with her son and some of his other friends was, he says, 'one of the happiest moments of my life'. Here he was enthusiastically received and enjoyed some exciting hunting of buffalo, elephant and rhinoceros, of which last animal there is a pleasing illustration in his book. His journey back to Egypt was slow and dangerous; he was detained by the king of Sennar, and he had finally to cross the great desert between Shendi and Aswan.*

*Upon his return to England in 1774 he received no other official recognition than an interview with King George III. There was widespread refusal to believe many of his stories, especially his account of the eating of raw flesh. Much mortified, he returned to Kinnaird, his estate in Scotland, now enriched by the discovery of coal. It was twelve years before he could be persuaded to write up his travels, which were published with magnificent illustrations in five volumes in 1790. He met his death in 1794 through falling downstairs in the haste with which he ran to the staircase to show a lady to her carriage.*

RHINOCEROS
From Bruce's *Travels*

# II

# MUNGO PARK
## 1771–1806

M ungo Park was born near Selkirk, the son of a farmer.
Having qualified as a doctor at Edinburgh University, he
entered the East India Company's service as a ship's surgeon. In 1792-3 he made the voyage to Sumatra and back as
medical officer on the Worcester. On his return he was invited by
the African Association (see p. 25) to undertake a journey in search
of the Niger: he accepted the offer at once and sailed from Portsmouth in May 1795, arriving at Pisania on the Gambia in July.
After a five months' stay here he set out for the interior accompanied
by one negro servant, Johnson, a boy, two asses, and an unlucky
horse. He was robbed of his goods by extortionate negro kings,
and—much worse—captured and held prisoner for nearly three
months by a Moorish chief named Ali at his camp at Benowm.
(Park uses the term 'Moors' indiscriminately for all non-negro
Moslems, except the partly Moslem Fulani, whom he calls 'Foulahs'.) This detention he always spoke of with horror: 'never did any
period of my life', he wrote, 'pass away so heavily; from sunrise to
sunset was I obliged to suffer with an unruffled countenance, the
insults of the rudest savages on earth'. He escaped from it on 27th
June, but he was only able to travel slowly on account of the condition of his horse, 'which the Moors had reduced to a perfect
Rosinante'.

## 5. ESCAPE FROM THE MOORS

On the afternoon of the 1st of July, as I was tending my horse in the
fields, Ali's chief slave and four Moors arrived at Queira, and took up
their lodging at the Dooty's [headman's] house. My interpreter, Johnson, who suspected the nature of this visit, sent two boys to overhear
their conversation; from which he learnt that they were sent to convey
me back to Bubaker. The same evening, two of the Moors came privately
to look at my horse, and one of them proposed taking it to the Dooty's

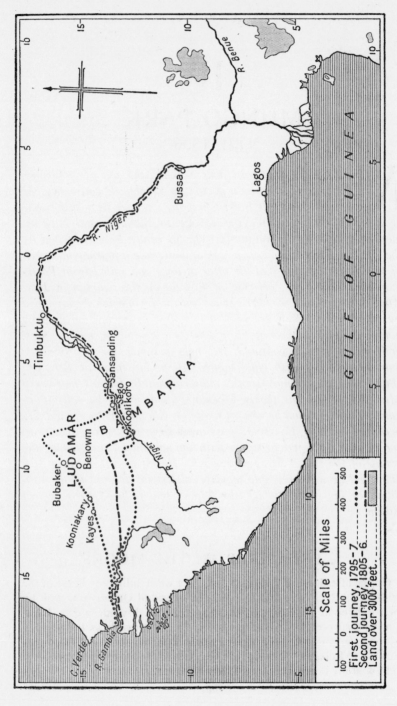

2. THE TRAVELS OF PARK, 1795–7 and 1805–6

hut, but the other observed that such a precaution was unnecessary, as I could never escape upon such an animal. They then inquired where I slept, and returned to their companions.

All this was like a stroke of thunder to me, for I dreaded nothing so much as confinement again among the Moors; from whose barbarity I had nothing but death to expect. I therefore determined to set off immediately for Bambarra; a measure which I thought offered almost the only chance of saving my life, and gaining the object of my mission. I communicated the design to Johnson, who, altho' he applauded my resolution, was so far from shewing any inclination to accompany me, that he solemnly protested, he would rather forfeit his wages than go any farther. He told me that Daman had agreed to give him half the price of a slave for his service, to assist in conducting a coffle [caravan] of slaves to Gambia, and that he was determined to embrace the opportunity of returning to his wife and family.

Having no hopes therefore of persuading him to accompany me, I resolved to proceed by myself. About midnight I got my clothes in readiness, which consisted of two shirts, two pair of trowsers, two pocket handkerchiefs, an upper and under waistcoat, a hat, and a pair of half boots; these, with a cloak, constituted my whole wardrobe. And I had not one single bead, nor any other article of value in my possession, to purchase victuals for myself, or corn for my horse.

About daybreak, Johnson, who had been listening to the Moors all night, came and whispered to me that they were asleep. The awful crisis was now arrived, when I was again either to taste the blessing of freedom, or languish out my days in captivity. A cold sweat moistened my forehead, as I thought on the dreadful alternative, and reflected that, one way or the other, my fate must be decided in the course of the ensuing day. But to deliberate was to lose the only chance of escaping. So, taking up my bundle, I stepped gently over the Negroes, who were sleeping in the open air, and having mounted my horse, I bade Johnson farewell, desiring him to take particular care of the papers I had entrusted him with, and inform my friends in Gambia that he had left me in good health, on my way to Bambarra.

I proceeded with great caution; surveying each bush, and frequently listening and looking behind me for the Moorish horsemen, until I was about a mile from the town, when I was surprised to find myself in the neighbourhood of a Korree [watering-place for cattle], belonging to the Moors. The shepherds followed me for about a mile, hooting and throwing stones after me; and when I was out of their reach, and had begun to indulge the pleasing hopes of escaping, I was again greatly alarmed to hear somebody holla behind me; and looking back, I saw three Moors on horseback, coming after me at full speed; hooping and brandishing their double-barrelled guns. I knew it was in vain, to think of escaping, and therefore turned back and met them: when two of them caught hold of my bridle, one on each side, and the third, presenting his musket told me I must go back to Ali. When the human mind has for some time been fluctuating between hope and despair, tortured with anxiety, and hurried from one extreme to another, it affords a sort of gloomy relief to know the worst that can possibly happen: such was my situation. An indifference about life, and all its enjoyments, had completely benumbed my faculties, and I rode back with the Moors with apparent unconcern. But a change took place much sooner than I had any reason to expect. In passing through some thick bushes, one of the Moors ordered me to untie my bundle, and shew them the contents. Having examined the different articles, they found nothing worth taking except my cloak, which they considered as a very valuable acquisition, and one of them pulling it from me, wrapped it about himself. This cloak had been of great use to me; it served to cover me from the rains in the day, and to protect me from the musketoes in the night; I therefore earnestly begged him to return it, and followed him some little way to obtain it; but without paying any attention to my request, he and one of his companions rode off with their prize. When I attempted to follow them, the third, who had remained with me, struck my horse over the head, and presenting his musket, told me I should proceed no further. I now perceived that these men had not been sent by any authority to apprehend me, but had pursued me solely in the view to rob and plunder me. Turning my horse's head therefore once more towards the east, and observing the Moor follow the track of his confederates, I congratulated myself on having escaped with my life, though in great distress, from such a horde of barbarians.

I was no sooner out of sight of the Moor, than I struck into the woods, to prevent being pursued, and kept pushing on, with all possible speed, until I found myself near some high rocks, which I remembered to have seen in my former route from Queira to Deena; and directing my course a little to the northward, I fortunately fell in with the path.

It is impossible to describe the joy that arose in my mind, when I looked around and concluded that I was out of danger. I felt like one recovered from sickness; I breathed freer; I found unusual lightness in my limbs; even the Desert looked pleasant; and I dreaded nothing so much as falling in with some wandering parties of Moors, who might convey me back to the land of thieves and murderers, from which I had just escaped.

I soon became sensible, however, that my situation was very deplorable; for I had no means of procuring food, nor prospect of finding water. About ten o'clock, perceiving a herd of goats feeding close to the road, I took a circuitous route to avoid being seen and continued

MUNGO PARK
From Park's *Travels*

travelling through the Wilderness, directing my course, by compass, nearly east-south-east, in order to reach, as soon as possible, some town or village of the kingdom of Bambarra.

A little after noon, when the burning heat of the sun was reflected with double violence from the hot sand, and the distant ridges of the hills, seen through the ascending vapour, seemed to wave and fluctuate like the unsettled sea, I became faint with thirst, and climbed a tree in hopes of seeing distant smoke, or some other appearance of a human habitation; but in vain: nothing appeared all around but thick under-wood, and hillocks of white sand.

About four o'clock, I came suddenly upon a large herd of goats, and pulling my horse into a bush, I watched to observe if the keepers were Moors or Negroes. In a little time I perceived two Moorish boys, and with some difficulty persuaded them to approach me. They informed me that the herd belonged to Ali, and that they were going to Deena, where the water was more plentiful, and where they intended to stay, until the rain had filled the pools in the Desert. They shewed me their empty water-skins, and told me that they had seen no water in the woods. This account afforded me but little consolation; however, it was in vain to repine, and I pushed on as fast as possible, in hopes of reaching some watering-place in the course of the night. My thirst was by this time become insufferable; my mouth was parched and inflamed; a sudden dimness would frequently come over my eyes, with other symptoms of fainting; and my horse being very much fatigued, I began seriously to apprehend that I should perish of thirst. To relieve the burning pain in my mouth and throat, I chewed the leaves of different shrubs, but found them all bitter, and of no service to me.

A little before sunset, having reached the top of a gentle rising, I climbed a high tree, from the topmost branches of which I cast a melancholy look over the barren Wilderness, but without discovering the most distant trace of a human dwelling. The same dismal uniformity of shrubs and sand every where presented itself, and the horizon was as level and uninterrupted as that of the sea.

Descending from the tree, I found my horse devouring the stubble and brushwood with great avidity; and as I was now too faint to attempt walking, and my horse too much fatigued to carry me, I thought it but an act of humanity, and perhaps the last I should ever have it in my power to perform, to take off his bridle and let him shift for himself; in doing which I was suddenly affected with sickness and giddiness; and falling upon the sand, felt as if the hour of death was fast approaching. 'Here then, thought I, after a short but ineffectual struggle, terminate all my hopes of being useful in my day and generation: here must the short span of my life come to an end.'—I cast (as I believed) a last look on the surrounding scene, and whilst I reflected on the awful change that was about to take place, this world with its enjoyments seemed to vanish from my recollection. Nature, however, at length resumed its functions; and on recovering my senses, I found myself stretched upon the sand, with the bridle still in my hand, and the sun just sinking behind the trees. I now summoned all my resolution, and determined to make another effort to prolong my existence. And as the evening was somewhat cool, I resolved to travel as far as my limbs would carry me, in hopes of reaching (my only resource) a watering-place. With this view, I put the bridle on my horse, and driving him before me, went slowly along for about an hour, when I perceived some lightning from the north-east; a most delightful sight; for it promised rain. The darkness and lightning increased very rapidly; and in less than an hour I heard the wind roaring among the bushes. I had already opened my mouth to receive the refreshing drops which I expected; but I was instantly covered with a cloud of sand, driven with such force by the wind as to give a very disagreeable sensation to my face and arms; and I was obliged to mount my horse, and stop under a bush, to prevent being suffocated. The sand continued to fly in amazing quantities for near an hour, after which I again set forward, and travelled with difficulty, until ten o'clock. About this time I was agreeably surprised by some very vivid flashes of lightning, followed by a few heavy drops of rain. In a little time the sand ceased to fly, and I alighted, and spread out all my clean clothes to collect the rain, which at length I saw would certainly fall. For more than an hour it rained plentifully, and I quenched my thirst by wringing and sucking my clothes.

There being no moon, it was remarkably dark, so that I was obliged to lead my horse, and direct my way by the compass, which the lightning enabled me to observe. In this manner I travelled, with tolerable expedition, until past midnight; when, the lightning becoming more distant, I was under the necessity of groping along, to the no small danger of my hands and eyes. About two o'clock my horse started at something, and looking round, I was not a little surprised to see a light at a short distance among the trees, and supposing it to be a town, I groped along the sand in hopes of finding corn-stalks, cotton, or other appearances of cultivation, but found none. As I approached, I perceived a number of other lights in different places, and began to suspect that I had fallen upon a party of Moors. However, in my present situation, I was resolved to see who they were, if I could do it with safety. I accordingly led my horse cautiously towards the light, and heard by the lowing of the cattle, and the clamorous tongues of the herdsmen, that it was a watering-place, and most likely belonged to the Moors. Delightful as the sound of the human voice was to me, I resolved once more to strike into the woods, and rather run the risk of perishing of hunger, than trust myself again in their hands; but being still thirsty, and dreading the approach of the burning day, I thought it prudent to search for the wells, which I expected to find at no great distance. In this pursuit, I inadvertently approached so near to one of the tents, as to be perceived by a woman, who immediately screamed out. Two people came running to her assistance from some of the neighbouring tents, and passed so very near to me, that I thought I was discovered; and hastened again into the woods.

About a mile from this place, I heard a loud and confused noise somewhere to the right of my course, and in a short time was happy to find it was the croaking of frogs, which was heavenly music to my ears. I followed the sound, and at daybreak arrived at some shallow muddy pools, so full of frogs, that it was difficult to discern the water. The noise they made frightened my horse, and I was obliged to keep them quiet, by beating the water with a branch until he had drank. Having here quenched my thirst, I ascended a tree, and the morning being calm, I soon perceived the smoke of the watering-place which I had passed in the night; and observed another pillar of smoke east-south-east, distant 12 or 14 miles. Towards this I directed my route, and reached the cultivated ground a little before eleven o'clock; where seeing a number of Negroes at work planting corn, I inquired the name of the town; and was informed that it was a Foulah village, belonging to Ali, called Shrilla. I had now some doubts about entering it; but my horse being very much fatigued, and the day growing hot, not to mention the pangs of hunger which began to assail me, I resolved to venture; and accordingly rode up to the Dooty's house, where I was unfortunately denied admittance, and could not obtain even a handful of corn, either for myself or horse. Turning from this inhospitable door, I rode slowly out of the town, and perceiving some low scattered huts without the walls, I directed my route towards them; knowing that in Africa, as well as in Europe, hospitality does not always prefer the highest dwellings. At the door of one of these huts, an old, motherly-looking woman sat, spinning cotton; I made signs to her that I was hungry, and inquired if she had any victuals with her in the hut. She immediately laid down her distaff, and desired me, in Arabic, to come in. When I had seated myself upon the floor, she set before me a dish of kouskous [boiled corn], that had been left the preceding night, of which I made a tolerable meal; and in return for this kindness, I gave her one of my pocket-handkerchiefs; begging at the same time, a little corn for my horse, which she readily brought me.

Overcome with joy at so unexpected a deliverance, I lifted up my eyes to heaven, and whilst my heart swelled with gratitude, I returned thanks to that gracious and bountiful Being, whose power had supported me under so many dangers, and had now spread for me a table in the Wilderness.

*Travels in the interior districts of Africa*,
1st edition, pp. 171–81

*After this providential deliverance Park continued his journey to the south-east. On 11th July he joined a party of Kaartans, who were fleeing from the tyranny of the Moors. He knew that he was getting near the Niger, and that he would strike it at the great market-town of Segou, for which he was now making.*

## 6. DISCOVERY OF THE NIGER

July 18th. We continued our journey; but, owing to a light supper the preceding night, we felt ourselves rather hungry this morning, and endeavoured to procure some corn at a village; but without success. The towns were now more numerous, and the land that is not employed in cultivation affords excellent pasturage for large herds of cattle; but, owing to the great concourse of people daily going to and returning from Sego, the inhabitants are less hospitable to strangers.

My horse becoming weaker and weaker every day, was now of very little service to me: I was obliged to drive him before me for the greater part of the day; and did not reach Geosorro until eight o'clock in the evening. I found my companions wrangling with the Dooty, who had absolutely refused to give or sell them any provisions; and as none of us had tasted victuals for the last twenty-four hours, we were by no means disposed to fast another day, if we could help it. But finding our entreaties without effect, and being very much fatigued, I fell asleep, from which I was awakened, about midnight, with the joyful information '*kinne-nata*' (the victuals is come). This made the remainder of the night pass away pleasantly; and at daybreak, July 19th, we resumed our journey, proposing to stop at a village called Doolinkeaboo, for the night following. My fellow-travellers, having better horses than myself, soon left me; and I was walking barefoot, driving my horse, when I was met by a coffle of slaves, about seventy in number, coming from Sego. They were tied together by their necks with thongs of a bullock's hide, twisted like a rope; seven slaves upon a thong; and a man with a musket between every seven. Many of the slaves were ill conditioned, and a great number of them women. In the rear came Sidi Mahomed's servant, whom I remembered to have seen at the camp of Benowm: he presently knew me, and told me that these slaves were going to Morocco, by the way of Ludamar, and the Great Desert.

In the afternoon, as I approached Doolinkeaboo, I met about twenty Moors on horseback, the owners of the slaves I had seen in the morning; they were well armed with muskets, and were very inquisitive concerning me, but not so rude as their countrymen generally are. From them I learned that Sidi Mahomed was not at Sego, but had gone to Cancaba for gold-dust.

78

When I arrived at Doolinkeaboo, I was informed that my fellow-travellers had gone on; but my horse was so much fatigued that I could not possibly proceed after them. The Dooty of the town, at my request, gave me a draught of water, which is generally looked upon as an earnest of greater hospitality; and I had no doubt of making up for the toils of the day, by a good supper and a sound sleep: unfortunately, I had neither one nor the other. The night was rainy and tempestuous, and the Dooty limited his hospitality to the draught of water.

July 20th. In the morning, I endeavoured, both by entreaties and threats, to procure some victuals from the Dooty, but in vain. I even begged some corn from one of his female slaves, as she was washing it at the well, and had the mortification to be refused. However, when the Dooty was gone to the fields, his wife sent me a handful of meal, which I mixed with water, and drank for breakfast. About eight o'clock, I departed from Doolinkeaboo, and at noon stopped a few minutes at a large Korree; where I had some milk given me by the Foulahs. And hearing that two Negroes were going from thence to Sego, I was happy to have their company, and we set out immediately. About four o'clock, we stopped at a small village, where one of the Negroes met with an acquaintance, who invited us to a sort of public entertainment, which was conducted with more than common propriety. A dish, made of sour milk and meal, called *Sinkatoo*, and beer made from their corn, was distributed with great liberality; and the women were admitted into the society; a circumstance I had never before observed in Africa. There was no compulsion; every one was at liberty to drink as he pleased: they nodded to each other when about to drink, and on setting down the calabash, commonly said *berka* (thank you). Both men and women appeared to be somewhat intoxicated, but they were far from being quarrelsome.

Departing from thence, we passed several large villages, where I was constantly taken for a Moor, and became the subject of much merriment to the Bambarrans; who, seeing me drive my horse before me, laughed heartily at my appearance.—He has been at Mecca, says one; you may see that by his clothes: another asked me if my horse was sick; a third wished to purchase it, &c.; so that I believe the very slaves were ashamed to be seen in my company. Just before it was dark, we took up our lodging for the night at a small village, where I procured some victuals for myself, and some corn for my horse, at the moderate price of a button; and was told that I should see the Niger (which the Negroes call Joliba, or *the great water*), early the next day. The lions are here very numerous; the gates are shut a little after sunset, and nobody allowed to go out. The thoughts of seeing the Niger in the morning, and the troublesome buzzing of musketoes, prevented me from shutting my eyes during the night; and I had saddled my horse, and was in readiness before daylight: but, on account of the wild beasts, we were obliged to wait until the people were stirring, and the gates opened. This happened to be a market-day at Sego, and the roads were every where filled with people, carrying different articles to sell. We passed four large villages, and at eight o'clock saw the smoke over Sego.

As we approached the town, I was fortunate enough to overtake the fugitive Kaartans, to whose kindness I had been so much indebted in my journey through Bambarra. They readily agreed to introduce me to the king; and we rode together through some marshy ground, where, as I was anxiously looking around for the river, one of them called out, *geo affilli*, (see the water); and looking forwards, I saw with infinite pleasure the great object of my mission; the long sought for, majestic Niger, glittering to the morning sun, as broad as the Thames at Westminster, and flowing slowly to the *eastward*. I hastened to the brink, and, having drank of the water, lifted up my fervent thanks in prayer, to the Great Ruler of all things, for having thus far crowned my endeavours with success.

The circumstance of the Niger's flowing towards the east, and its collateral points, did not, however, excite my surprise; for although I had left Europe in great hesitation on this subject, and rather believed that it ran in the contrary direction, I had made such frequent inquiries during my progress, concerning this river; and received from Negroes of different nations, such clear and decisive assurances that its general course was *towards the rising sun*, as scarce left any doubt on my mind; and more especially as I knew that Major Houghton had collected similar information, in the same manner.

Sego, the capital of Bambarra, at which I had now arrived, consists, properly speaking, of four distinct towns; two on the northern bank of the Niger, called Sego Korro and Sego Boo; and two on the southern bank, called Sego Soo Korro and Sego See Korro. They are all surrounded with high mud-walls; the houses are built of clay, of a square form, with flat roofs; some of them have two stories, and many of them are whitewashed. Besides these buildings, Moorish mosques are seen in every quarter; and the streets, though narrow, are broad enough for every useful purpose, in a country where wheel carriages are entirely unknown. From the best inquiries I could make, I have reason to believe that Sego contains altogether about thirty thousand inhabitants. The King of Bambarra constantly resides at Sego See Korro; he employs a great many slaves in conveying people over the river, and the money they receive (though the fare is only ten Kowrie shells for each individual) furnishes a considerable revenue to the king, in the course of a year. The canoes are of a singular construction, each of them being formed of the trunks of two large trees, rendered concave, and joined together, not side by side, but end ways; the junction being exactly across the middle

PARK ON HIS JOURNEY
From Park's *Travels*

of the canoe: they are therefore very long and disproportionably narrow, and have neither decks nor masts; they are, however, very roomy; for I observed in one of them four horses, and several people, crossing over the river. When we arrived at this ferry, we found a great number waiting for a passage, they looked at me with silent wonder, and I distinguished, with concern, many Moors among them. There were three different places of embarkation, and the ferrymen were very diligent and expeditious; but, from the crowd of people, I could not immediately obtain a passage; and sat down upon the bank of the river, to wait for a more favourable opportunity. The view of this extensive city; the numerous canoes upon the river; the crowded population, and the cultivated state of the surrounding country, formed altogether a prospect of civilization and magnificence, which I little expected to find in the bosom of Africa.

I waited more than two hours, without having an opportunity of crossing the river; during which time the people who had crossed, carried information to Mansong the King, that a white man was waiting for a passage, and was coming to see him. He immediately sent over one of his chief men, who informed me that the king could not possibly see me, until he knew what had brought me into his country; and that I must not presume to cross the river without the king's permission. He therefore advised me to lodge at a distant village, to which he pointed, for the night; and said that in the morning he would give me further instructions how to conduct myself. This was very discouraging. However, as there was no remedy, I set off for the village; where I found, to my great mortification, that no person would admit me into his house. I was regarded with astonishment and fear, and was obliged to sit all day without victuals, in the shade of a tree; and the night threatened to be very uncomfortable, for the wind rose, and there was great appearance of a heavy rain; and the wild beasts are so very numerous in the neighbourhood, that I should have been under the necessity of climbing up the tree, and resting amongst the branches. About sunset, however, as I was preparing to pass the night in this manner, and had turned my horse loose, that he might graze at liberty, a woman, returning from the labours of the field, stopped to observe me, and perceiving that I was weary and dejected, inquired into my situation, which I briefly explained to her; whereupon, with looks of great compassion, she took up my saddle and bridle, and told me to follow her. Having conducted me into her hut, she lighted up a lamp, spread a mat on the floor, and told me I might remain there for the night. Finding that I was very hungry, she said she would procure me something to eat. She accordingly went out, and returned in a short time with a very fine fish; which, having caused to be half broiled upon some embers, she gave me for supper. The rites of hospitality being thus performed towards a stranger in distress, my worthy benefactress (pointing to the mat, and telling me I might sleep there without apprehension) called to the female part of her family, who had stood gazing on me all the while in fixed astonishment, to resume their task of spinning cotton; in which they continued to employ themselves great part of the night. They lightened their labour by songs, one of which was composed extempore; for I was myself the subject of it. It was sung by one of the young women, the rest joining in a sort of chorus. The air was sweet and plaintive, and the words, literally translated, were these.—'The winds roared, and the rains fell.—The poor white man, faint and weary, came and sat under our tree.—He has no mother to bring him milk; no wife to grind his corn. *Chorus*: Let us pity the white man; no mother has he, &c. &c.' Trifling as this recital may appear to the reader, to a person in my situation the circumstance was affecting in the highest degree. I was oppressed by such unexpected kindness; and sleep fled from my eyes. In the morning I presented my compassionate landlady with two of the four brass buttons which remained on my waistcoat; the only recompence I could make her.

July 21st. I continued in the village all this day, in conversation with the natives, who came in crowds to see me; but was rather uneasy towards evening, to find that no message had arrived from the king; the more so, as the people began to whisper, that Mansong had received some very unfavourable accounts of me, from the Moors and Slatees [black slave-merchants] residing at Sego; who it seems were exceedingly suspicious concerning the motives of my journey. I learnt that many consultations had been held with the king, concerning my reception and disposal; and some of the villagers frankly told me, that I had many enemies, and must expect no favour.

July 22nd. About eleven o'clock, a messenger arrived from the king; but he gave me very little satisfaction. He inquired particularly if I had brought any present; and seemed much disappointed when he was told that I had been robbed of every thing by the Moors. When I proposed to go along with him, he told me to stop until the afternoon, when the king would send for me.

July 23rd. In the afternoon, another messenger arrived from Mansong, with a bag in his hands. He told me, it was the king's pleasure that I should depart forthwith from the vicinage of Sego; but that Mansong, wishing to relieve a white man in distress, had sent me five thousand Kowries,[1] to enable me to purchase provisions in the course of my

[1] Mention has already been made of these little shells, ... which pass current as money, in many parts of the East-Indies, as well as Africa. In Bambarra, and the adjacent countries, where the necessaries of life are very cheap, one hundred of them would commonly purchase a day's provisions for myself, and corn for my horse. I reckoned about two hundred and fifty Kowries, equal to one shilling. (*Park's note.*)

journey: the messenger added, that if my intentions were really to proceed to Jenne, he had orders to accompany me as a guide to Sansanding. I was at first puzzled to account for this behaviour of the king; but, from the conversation I had with the guide, I had afterwards reason to believe, that Mansong would willingly have admitted me into his presence at Sego; but was apprehensive he might not be able to protect me, against the blind and inveterate malice of the Moorish inhabitants. His conduct, therefore, was at once prudent and liberal. The circumstances under which I made my appearance at Sego, were undoubtedly such as might create in the mind of the king, a well warranted suspicion that I wished to conceal the true object of my journey. He argued, probably, as my guide argued; who, when he was told that I had come from a great distance, and through many dangers, to behold the Joliba river, naturally inquired if there were no rivers in my own country, and whether one river was not like another. Notwithstanding this, and in spite of the jealous machinations of the Moors, this benevolent prince thought it sufficient that a white man was found in his dominions, in a condition of extreme wretchedness; and that no other plea was necessary to entitle the sufferer to his bounty.

*Travels*, 1st edition, pp. 191–200

*Leaving Segou, Park rode along the banks of the Niger for six days, until he reached the town of Silla. Here he reluctantly decided that he must turn back. The supply of money which Mansong had so generously given him was beginning to run out; the country beyond was in the hands of fanatical Moslems: it was clearly hopeless to think of travelling further down the river. Accordingly, on 30th July he began his return journey. All went comparatively well with him until 25th August, when he was attacked by robbers and plundered of everything he possessed except a shirt, a pair of trousers, and—most fortunately —his hat, the crown of which held his memoranda. On 19th September he fell seriously ill at Kamalia, where he was treated with the greatest kindness by a negro slave-dealer named Karfa Taura. He remained at Kamalia for exactly seven months and then set off with Karfa for Pisania, which he reached on 10th June 1797: on 22nd December he arrived at Falmouth.*

*His welcome in England was warm, but not effusive. He set to work to write an account of his journey, which appeared as* Travels in the interior districts of Africa *in 1799: it had a considerable success, reaching a fourth edition in 1800. Meanwhile Park had*

*retired to his own country, and in 1801 he set up in practice as a
doctor at Peebles. He became a friend of his neighbour Walter Scott,
who wrote a moving account of his last meeting with him. He was
never at ease at home: he longed to return and finish the work he had
begun; and when the Colonial Secretary offered him the chance of
doing so in 1804, he eagerly accepted it.*

*Park's second expedition was a grander affair than his first. He
sailed from Portsmouth on 30th January 1805, taking with him his
brother-in-law Alexander Anderson and a schoolfellow, George Scott.
At Goree they picked up Lieutenant Martyn, thirty volunteer soldiers, four carpenters and two sailors. With this large company of
white men Park set out from the Gambia in May: when he reached
the Niger at Bamako on 19th August all but ten of his companions
were dead of disease. But he refused to turn back or to slacken his
pace: he was determined to sail down the river to its mouth. On 27th
September he reached Sansanding: here he remained for two months,
during the course of which Anderson died. From Sansanding he wrote
the last of his letters to his wife which have survived.*

# 7. LAST LETTER TO HIS WIFE

*Sansanding, 19th November, 1805*

It grieves me to the heart to write any thing that may give you uneasiness; but such is the will of him who *doeth all things well!* Your
brother Alexander, my dear friend, is no more! He died of the fever at
Sansanding, on the morning of the 28th of October; for particulars I
must refer you to your father.

I am afraid that, impressed with a woman's fears and the anxieties of
a wife, you may be led to consider my situation as a great deal worse
than it really is. It is true, my dear friends, Mr. Anderson and George
Scott, have both bid adieu to the things of this world; and the greater
part of the soldiers have died on the march during the rainy season; but
you may believe me, I am in good health. The rains are completely over,
and the healthy season has commenced, so that there is no danger of
sickness: and I have still a sufficient force to protect me from any insult
in sailing down the river, to the sea.

We have already embarked all our things, and shall sail the moment
I have finished this letter. I do not intend to stop or land any where, till
we reach the coast; which I suppose will be some time in the end of
January. We shall then embark in the first vessel for England. If we have

to go round by the West Indies, the voyage will occupy three months longer; so that we expect to be in England on the 1st of May. The reason of our delay since we left the coast was the rainy season, which came on us during the journey; and almost all the soldiers became affected with the fever.

I think it not unlikely but I shall be in England before you receive this.—You may be sure that I feel happy at turning my face towards home. We this morning have done with all intercourse with the natives; and the sails are now hoisting for our departure for the coast.

*Journal of a mission to the interior of Africa in the year 1805*, 2nd edition, pp. 81–2

*On the same day Park left Sansanding, with the four Europeans who were still alive, three slaves and a guide. From this time onwards all certain knowledge of him ceases; but it seems that he and all his white companions were drowned in the Niger when their boat sank after a fight with the inhabitants of Bussa.*

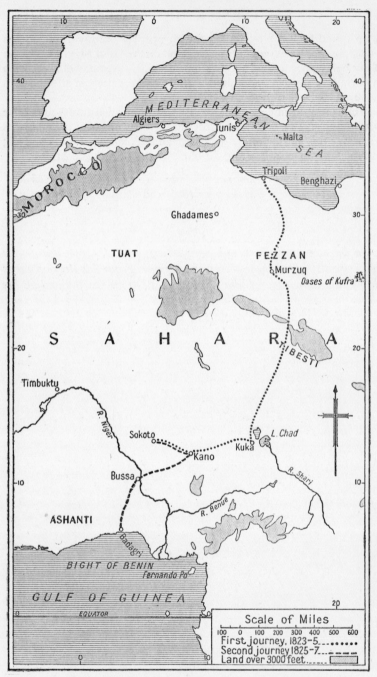

3. THE TRAVELS OF CLAPPERTON, 1822–7

# III

## HUGH CLAPPERTON
### 1788–1827

## and

## RICHARD LEMON LANDER
### 1804–1834

*C*lapperton, like Park, was a Lowland Scot, the son of a surgeon at Annan. After a meagre education he went to sea, first as a cabin-boy on a merchant ship and then in the navy (he was a victim of the press-gang). From 1808 to 1813 he served on the East India station: at the capture of Mauritius in 1810 he got first into the breach and himself hauled down the French flag. In 1814 he joined the British squadron on the Great Lakes of Canada: there he became romantically involved with the Hurons, and is said to have thought of marrying a Red Indian princess. In 1817 he came home on half-pay.

Three years later he met Dr. Walter Oudney, who had been invited by the British Government to undertake a mission into the interior of Africa: Clapperton volunteered to accompany him, and his offer was accepted. With them was associated Major Dixon Denham. They left Tripoli early in 1822 and made their way across the desert to Lake Chad, which they were the first Europeans to see. Here they separated, Denham going south-eastwards and finding the River Shari, Clapperton and Oudney making for the Niger through the Hausa states to the west in the company of a merchant of Fezzan named Mohamoud el Wordee. Oudney died at Murmur in January 1824, but Clapperton pushed on to Kano.

Kano was—it is still—the mercantile centre of the whole country between Lake Chad and the Niger, and at least as important as Timbuktu. Its name must continually have been mentioned to Clapperton during his journey as that of a great market, for it was the goal of the Arab caravans which travelled across the desert from Tripoli. After hearing so much of the great city for so long, it was almost *inevitable that the reality should fall short of his expectation; but, as we shall see, his initial disappointment soon gave place to a deep interest in the market, which is very much the same to-day as when Clapperton wrote. There is another and fuller description of Kano written thirty years later, in Barth's* Travels and discoveries in North and Central Africa *(1857-8), vol. ii, pp. 97–147.*

# 8. CLAPPERTON'S ARRIVAL AT KANO

Jan. 20.—By El Wordee's advice, I prepared myself this morning for entering Kano, which was now at hand. Arrayed in naval uniform, I made myself as smart as circumstances would permit. For three miles to the north of Duakee, the country was open and well cultivated. It then became thickly covered with underwood, until we ascended a rising ground, whence we had a view of two little mounts within the walls of Kano. The soil here is a tough clay mixed with gravel, the stones of which appear to be clay iron-stone. The country was now clear of wood, except here and there a few large shady trees, resorted to as usual by the women of the country selling refreshments. The villages were numerous, and the road was thronged with people of all descriptions.

At eleven o'clock we entered Kano, the great emporium of the kingdom of Haussa, but I had no sooner passed the gates, than I felt grievously disappointed; for from the flourishing description of it given by the Arabs, I expected to see a city of surprising grandeur: I found, on the contrary, the houses nearly a quarter of a mile from the walls, and in many parts scattered into detached groups, between large stagnant pools of water. I might have spared all the pains I had taken with my toilet; for not an individual turned his head round to gaze at me, but all, intent on their own business, allowed me to pass by without notice or remark.

I went with El Wordee directly to the house of Hadje Hat Salah, to whom I had a letter of recommendation from the sheikh of Bornou. We found Hat Salah sitting under a rude porch in front of his house amid a party of Arabs, Tuaricks,[1] and people of the town. When El Wordee presented me, and told him of the sheikh's letter of recommendation, he bade me welcome, and desired me to sit down by his side. After exchanging many compliments, I inquired for the house he had hired for me, as El Wordee had sent a messenger on horseback the day before, to inform him of my approach, and to request him to have a house ready for my reception. Hat Salah now sent one of his slaves to conduct us to the house.

[1] I.e. Tuareg, known as 'the People of the Veil', a group of Hamitic tribes inhabiting the Eastern Sahara.

HUGH CLAPPERTON
From Clapperton's *Journal of a Second Expedition*

We had to retrace our steps more than half a mile through the market-place, which is bordered to the east and west by an extensive swamp covered with reeds and water, and frequented by wild ducks, cranes, and a filthy kind of vulture. The last is extremely useful, and by picking up offal serves as a sort of town scavenger. The house provided for me was situated at the south end of the morass, the pestilential exhalations of which, and of the pools of standing water, were increased by the sewers of the houses all opening into the street. I was fatigued and sick, and lay down on a mat that the owner of the house spread for me. I was immediately visited by all the Arab merchants who had been my fellow travellers from Kouka, and were not prevented by sickness from coming to see me. They were more like ghosts than men, as almost all strangers were at this time, suffering from intermittent fever. My house had six chambers above, extremely dark, and five rooms below, with a dismal looking entrance or lobby, a back court, draw-well and other conveniences. Little holes or windows admitted a glimmering light into the apartments. Nevertheless this was here thought a handsome mansion.

Feb. 1. 1824.—After breakfast I accompanied Hat Salah, the sheikh's agent, to the sansan [encampment], which, since it became a town, is also called Fanisoe, and presented the governor with one of the watches. He was highly pleased with it, and requested me to teach Hat Salah the use of it, that he might give lessons to the wan-bey [chief minister], who would in turn instruct him. I also showed him the sheikh's letter to his master Bello.[1] He read it, and told me I should be sent forward to Sackatoo[2] without delay in a kafila [caravan] which was then assembling.

On my return I met two governors with troops repairing to the sansan. They had each about five hundred horse and foot. The foot were armed with bows and arrows. The quiver is slung over the left shoulder, together with a small, highly ornamented leathern pouch for little necessaries, and a canteen of dried grass, so compactly plaited, that it is used for holding water. The bow unstrung is sometimes carried in the hand as a walking stick. Many carried on the head a little triangular bag, filled with bruised Guinea corn. Others wore a little conical grass cap, with a tuft of feathers. The rest of their dress consists solely of a tanned skin, strung with coarse shells, or fringed with tassels, girt round the loins, and a pair of sandals of very simple workmanship.

The cavalry were armed with shields, swords, and spears, and otherwise more sumptuously accoutred. The spear is about six feet long, the wooden shaft slender, and the point of iron. The swords are broad,

[1] The Sultan of Sokoto, who was also suzerain of the surrounding Emirates, including Kano.

[2] The accepted modern spelling of the name is 'Sokoto', but it is still pronounced, as some of the early travellers wrote it, 'Sockatoo'.

straight, and long, but require no particular description, as, by a vicissitude somewhat singular, they are in fact the very blades formerly wielded by the knights of Malta. These swords are sent from Malta to Benghazee, in the state of Tripoli, where they are exchanged for bullocks. They are afterwards carried across the desert to Bornou, thence to Haussa, and at last remounted at Kano, for the use of the inhabitants of almost all central Africa. The shields, covered with the hides of tame or wild animals, are generally plain and round. There is, however, a remarkable variety, not uncommon, of an oval shape, somewhat broader below than above, with an edging of blue cloth, forming six little lappets, one above, one below, and two on each side. In the centre of the shield there is a stripe of scarlet cloth fastened by the same studs that clinch the iron handle, and around it is scored a perfect Maltese cross. This kind of shield is borne by horsemen only; but it is found of the same shape and figure, equally among Tibboes [Tiber], Tuaricks, Felatahs,[1] and Bornouese. A cross of the same form, moulded in a sort of low relief, is not an unfrequent ornament on the clay plaster of their huts. Crosses of other forms also are sometimes cut in the doors of their houses. Several camels, loaded with quilted cotton armour, both for men and horses, were in attendance. One of the governor's slaves wore a quilted helmet of red cloth, very unwieldy, not unlike a bucket in shape, only scooped out in front for the face, and terminating on the crown in a large tin funnel, full of ostrich feathers. He was also clad in a red quilted corslet of the same cumbrous materials. The other articles of this armour are trunk hose for the rider, and a head piece, poitrel, and hausing, all quilted and arrow proof, for the horse. Armour, however, is hardly ever worn, except in actual combat, and then it must very much impede the quickness of their military evolutions. The saddles have high peaks before and behind. The stirrup irons are in the shape of a fireshovel, turned up at the sides, and so sharp as to render spurs superfluous. This body of heavy horse protects the advance and retreat of the army, the bowmen being drawn up in the rear, and shooting from between the horsemen as occasion offers.

Feb. 10.—Kano is the capital of a province of the same name, and one of the principal towns of the kingdom of Soudan, and is situate in 12° 0′ 19″ north latitude by observation, and 9° 20′ east longitude by dead reckoning, carried on from a lunar observation at Kouka in Bornou.

Kano may contain from 30,000 to 40,000 resident inhabitants, of whom more than one half are slaves. This estimate of the population is of course conjectural, and must be received with due allowance, although I have studiously underrated my rough calculations on the subject. This

[1] I.e. the Fulani, who are to-day the ruling class in Northern Nigeria, though much mixed with the Hausa.

90

From a Sketch by Major Denham.     LANCERS OF THE SULTAN OF BEGHARMI.     Engraved by E. Finden.

Published Feb. 1826, by John Murray, London.

## HORSEMAN OF THE WESTERN SUDAN
From the *Narrative* of Denham, Clapperton and Oudney

number is exclusive of strangers who come here in crowds during the dry months from all parts of Africa, from the Mediterranean and the Mountains of the Moon, and from Sennar and Ashantee.

The city is rendered very unhealthy by a large morass, which almost divides it into two parts, besides many pools of stagnant water, made by digging clay for building houses. The house gutters also open into the street, and frequently occasion an abominable stench. On the north side of the city are two remarkable mounts, each about 200 feet in height, lying nearly east and west from one another, and a trifling distance apart. They are formed of argillaceous iron-stone, mixed with pebbles, and a rather soft kind of marl. The city is of an irregular oval shape, about fifteen miles in circumference, and surrounded by a clay wall thirty feet high, with a dry ditch along the inside, and another on the outside. There are fifteen gates, including one lately built up. The gates are of wood, covered with sheet iron, and are regularly opened and shut at sunrise and sunset. A platform inside, with two guard-houses below it, serves to defend each entrance. Not more than one fourth of the ground within the walls is occupied by houses: the vacant space is laid out in fields and gardens. The large morass, nearly intersecting the city from east to west, and crossed by a small neck of land, on which the market is held, is overflowed in the rainy season. The water of the city being considered unwholesome, women are constantly employed hawking water about the streets, from the favourite springs in the neighbourhood. The houses are built of clay, and are mostly of a square form, in the Moorish fashion, with a central room, the roof of which is supported by the trunks of palm trees, where visitors and strangers are received. The apartments of the ground floor open into this hall of audience, and are generally used as store-rooms. A staircase leads to an open gallery overlooking the hall, and serving as a passage to the chambers of the second story, which are lighted with small windows. In a back courtyard there is a well and other conveniences. Within the enclosure in which the house stands, there are also a few round huts of clay, roofed with the stalks of Indian corn, and thatched with long grass. These are usually very neat and clean, and of a much larger size than those of Bornou. The governor's residence covers a large space, and resembles a walled village. It even contains a mosque, and several towers three or four stories high, with windows in the European style, but without glass or frame-work. It is necessary to pass through two of these towers in order to gain the suite of inner apartments occupied by the governor.

The soug, or market, is well supplied with every necessary and luxury in request among the people of the interior. It is held, as I have mentioned, on a neck of land between two swamps; and as this site is covered with water during the rainy season, the holding it here is consequently limited to the dry months, when it is numerously frequented as well by strangers as inhabitants: indeed, there is no market in Africa so well regulated. The sheikh of the soug lets the stalls at so much a month, and the rent forms a part of the revenues of the governor. The sheikh of the soug also fixes the prices of all wares, for which he is entitled to a small commission, at the rate of fifty whydah or cowries, on every sale amounting to four dollars or 8,000 cowries, according to the standard exchange between silver money and this shell currency. There is another custom regulated with equal certainty and in universal practice: the seller returns to the buyer a stated part of the price, by way of blessing, as they term it, or of luck-penny, according to our less devout phraseology. This is a discount of two per cent. on the purchase money; but, if the bargain is made in a hired house, it is the landlord who receives the luck-penny. I may here notice the great convenience of the cowrie, which no forgery can imitate; and which, by the dexterity of the natives in reckoning the largest sums, forms a ready medium of exchange in all transactions, from the lowest to the highest. Particular quarters are appropriated to distinct articles; the smaller wares being set out in booths in the middle, and cattle and bulky commodities being exposed to sale in the outskirts of the market-place: wood, dried grass, bean straw for provender, beans, Guinea corn, Indian corn, wheat, &c. are in one quarter; goats, sheep, asses, bullocks, horses, and camels, in another; earthenware and indigo in a third; vegetables and fruit of all descriptions, such as yams, sweet potatoes, water and musk melons, pappaw fruit, limes, cashew nuts, plums, mangoes, shaddocks, dates, &c. in a fourth, and so on. Wheaten flour is baked into bread of three different kinds; one like muffins, another like our twists, and the third a light puffy cake, with honey and melted butter poured over it. Rice is also made into little cakes. Beef and mutton are killed daily. Camel flesh is occasionally to be had, but is often meagre; the animal being commonly killed, as an Irish grazier might say, to save its life: it is esteemed a great delicacy, however, by the Arabs, when the carcass is fat. The native butchers are fully as knowing as our own, for they make a few slashes to show the fat, blow up meat, and sometimes even stick a little sheep's wool on a leg of goat's flesh, to make it pass with the ignorant for mutton. When a fat bull is brought to market to be killed, its horns are died red with henna; drummers attend, a mob soon collects, the news of the animal's size and fatness soon spreads, and all run to buy. The colouring of the horns is effected by applying the green leaves of the henna tree, bruised into a kind of poultice. Near the shambles there is a number of cook-shops in the open air; each consisting merely of a wood fire, stuck round with wooden skewers, on which small bits of fat and lean meat, alternately mixed, and scarcely larger than a pennypiece each, are roasting. Every thing looks very clean and comfortable; and a woman does the honours of the table, with a mat dish-cover placed on her knees, from which she serves

her guests, who are squatted around her. Ground gussub water is re-
tailed at hand, to those who can afford this beverage at their repast: the
price, at most, does not exceed twenty cowries, or about two farthings
and 4/10 of a farthing, English money, estimating the dollar at five
shillings. Those who have houses eat at home; women never resort to
cook-shops, and even at home eat apart from men.

The interior of the market is filled with stalls of bamboo, laid out in
regular streets; where the more costly wares are sold, and articles of
dress, and other little matters of use or ornament made and repaired.
Bands of musicians parade up and down to attract purchasers to particular booths. Here are displayed coarse writing paper, of French
manufacture, brought from Barbary; scissors and knives, of native
workmanship; crude antimony and tin, both the produce of the country;
unwrought silk of a red colour, which they make into belts and slings, or
weave in stripes into the finest cotton tobes; armlets and bracelets of
brass; beads of glass, coral, and amber; finger rings of pewter, and a few
silver trinkets, but none of gold; tobes, turkadees, and turban shawls;
coarse woollen cloths of all colours; coarse calico; Moorish dresses; the
cast off gaudy garbs of the Mamelukes of Barbary; pieces of Egyptian
linen, checked or striped with gold; sword blades from Malta, &c. &c.
The market is crowded from sunrise to sunset every day, not excepting
their Sabbath, which is kept on Friday. The merchants understand the
benefits of monopoly as well as any people in the world; they take good
care never to overstock the market, and if any thing falls in price, it is
immediately withdrawn for a few days.—The market is regulated with
the greatest fairness, and the regulations are strictly and impartially
enforced. If a tobe or turkadee, purchased here, is carried to Bornou or
any other distant place, without being opened, and is there discovered
to be of inferior quality, it is immediately sent back, as a matter of course,
the name of the *dylala*, or broker, being written inside every parcel. In
this case the *dylala* must find out the seller, who, by the laws of Kano, is
forthwith obliged to refund the purchase money.

The slave market is held in two long sheds, one for males, the other
for females, where they are seated in rows, and carefully decked out for
the exhibition; the owner, or one of his trusty slaves, sitting near them.
Young or old, plump or withered, beautiful or ugly, are sold without
distinction; but, in other respects, the buyer inspects them with the
utmost attention, and somewhat in the same manner as a volunteer sea-
man is examined by a surgeon on entering the navy: he looks at the
tongue, teeth, eyes, and limbs, and endeavours to detect rupture by a
forced cough. If they are afterwards found to be faulty or unsound, or
even without any specific objection, they may be returned within three
days. When taken home, they are stripped of their finery, which is sent
back to their former owner. Slavery is here so common, or the mind of

slaves is so constituted, that they always appeared much happier than their masters; the women, especially, singing with the greatest glee all the time they are at work. People become slaves by birth or by capture in war. The Felatahs frequently manumit slaves at the death of their master, or on the occasion of some religious festival. The letter of manumission must be signed before the cadi [a Moslem judge], and attested by two witnesses; and the mark of a cross is used by the illiterate among them, just as with us. The male slaves are employed in the various trades of building, working in iron, weaving, making shoes or clothes, and in traffic; the female slaves in spinning, baking, and selling water in the streets. Of the various people who frequent Kano, the *Nyffuans* [people of Nupe] are most celebrated for their industry; as soon as they arrive, they go to market and buy cotton for their women to spin, who, if not employed in this way, make *billam* for sale, which is a kind of flummery made of flour and tamarinds. The very slaves of this people are in great request, being invariably excellent tradesmen; and when once obtained, are never sold again out of the country.

I bought, for three Spanish dollars, an English green cotton umbrella, an article I little expected to meet with, yet by no means uncommon: my Moorish servants, in their figurative language, were wont to give it the name of 'the cloud'. I found, on inquiry, that these umbrellas are brought from the shores of the Mediterranean, by the way of Ghadamis.

> Denham, Clapperton and Oudney, *Narrative of travels and discoveries in Northern and Central Africa*, 1st edition, Clapperton's narrative, pp. 39–55

*While he was at Kano, Clapperton saw a boxing match, of which he gives a lively account.*

## 9. BOXING MATCH AT KANO

Having heard a great deal of the boxers of Haussa, I was anxious to witness their performance. Accordingly I sent one of my servants last night to offer 2000 whydah for a pugilistic exhibition in the morning. As the death of one of the combatants is almost certain before the battle is over, I expressly prohibited all fighting in earnest; for it would have been disgraceful, both to myself and my country, to hire men to kill one another for the gratification of idle curiosity. About half an hour after the massi dubu[1] were gone, the boxers arrived, attended by two drums,

[1] Some jugglers who had performed before Clapperton in the morning.

MUSICIANS OF THE WESTERN SUDAN
From the *Narrative* of Denham, Clapperton and Oudney

and the whole body of butchers, who here compose 'the fancy.' A ring was soon formed, by the master of the ceremonies throwing dust on the spectators to make them stand back. The drummers entered the ring, and began to drum lustily. One of the boxers followed, quite naked, except a skin round the middle. He placed himself in an attitude as if to oppose an antagonist, and wrought his muscles into action, seemingly to find out that every sinew was in full force for the approaching combat; then coming from time to time to the side of the ring, and presenting his right arm to the bystanders, he said, 'I am a hyena;' 'I am a lion;' 'I am able to kill all that oppose me.' The spectators, to whom he presented himself, laid their hands on his shoulder, repeating, 'The blessing of God be upon thee;' 'Thou art a hyena;' 'Thou art a lion.' He then abandoned the ring to another, who showed off in the same manner. The right hand and arm of the pugilists were now bound with narrow country cloth, beginning with a fold round the middle finger, when, the hand being first clinched with the thumb between the fore and mid fingers, the cloth was passed in many turns round the fist, the wrist, and the fore arm. After about twenty had separately gone through their attitudes of defiance, and appeals to the bystanders, they were next brought forward by pairs. If they happened to be friends, they laid their left breasts together twice, and exclaimed, 'We are lions;' 'We are friends.' One then left the ring, and another was brought forward. If the two did not recognise one another as friends, the set-to immediately commenced. On taking their stations, the two pugilists first stood at some distance parrying with the left hand open, and, whenever opportunity offered, striking with the right. They generally aimed at the pit of the stomach, and under the ribs. Whenever they closed, one seized the other's head under his arm, and beat it with his fist, at the same time striking with his knee between his antagonist's thighs. In this position, with the head *in chancery*, they are said sometimes to attempt to gouge or scoop out one of the eyes. When they break loose, they never fail to give a swinging blow with the heel under the ribs, or sometimes under the left ear. It is these blows which are so often fatal. The combatants were repeatedly separated by my orders, as they were beginning to lose their temper. When this spectacle was heard of, girls left their pitchers at the wells, the market people threw down their baskets, and all ran to see the fight. The whole square before my house was crowded to excess. After six pairs had gone through several rounds, I ordered them, to their great satisfaction, the promised reward, and the multitude quietly dispersed.

Denham, Clapperton and Oudney, *Narrative of travels and discoveries in Northern and Central Africa*, 1st edition, Clapperton's narrative, pp. 57–9

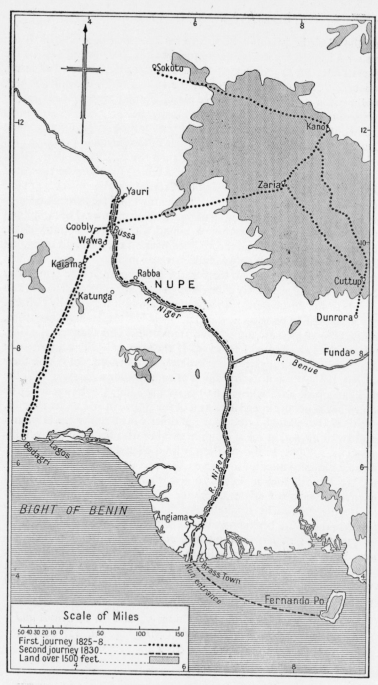

4. THE TRAVELS OF LANDER, 1825-34

*Leaving Kano, Clapperton went on to Sokoto. Sultan Bello received him kindly but refused to let him pursue his journey to the Niger, although in fact the river lies only 150 miles away. So he was obliged to return eastwards: he met Denham at Kuka, and together they went back to Tripoli. They reached England on 1st June 1825.*

*Clapperton was immediately invited by the Secretary for War and the Colonies, Lord Bathurst (who was a good friend to the cause of African exploration), to lead another expedition into the interior, by a different route, northwards from the Bight of Benin, and to open up relations with Bello, who wished to conclude a treaty with England. Before the year was out Clapperton arrived at Badagri with four English companions, one of whom was his twenty-one year old servant Richard Lander.*

# RICHARD LEMON LANDER
## 1804–1834

*Lander was a Cornishman, born at Truro (where his father kept an inn) in 1804. His education had been a little better than Clapperton's, but it had come to an end when he was thirteen. Since then he had led a roving life as a servant with various masters, visiting the West Indies, several parts of Europe, and South Africa. Soon after his return from the last of these journeys he offered his services to Clapperton, which were accepted. It is clear that he was romantically fired with the idea of African exploration: 'there was a charm in the very sound of Africa,' he afterwards wrote, 'that always made my heart flutter on hearing it mentioned'.*

*Almost as soon as they left the coast on this journey inland two of their English companions died, while the third had determined to follow another route through Dahomey, so that Clapperton and Lander had to travel on by themselves. They made first for Bussa, the town on the Niger at which Park was supposed to have met his death. Their journey was easy and not unduly slow until they reached Wawa, where they were delayed by the following adventures from 21st March to 5th April.*

## 10. THE WIDOW ZUMA

Whilst we remained in the city of Wow Wow, we were visited almost every day by a widow lady, of Arab extraction, named *Zuma* (*Honey* in

English), between thirty and forty years of age, who, if one might be allowed to judge from the remaining charms which were still visible in her countenance, had been really beautiful in her younger years. This individual was vastly rich, being the acknowledged mistress of a thousand slaves; and from her excessive plumpness, and extraordinary size, was the exact counterpart of our bulky friend Ebo, the fat eunuch of Katunga. Zuma's affection for my master and myself was unbounded, and as it led to an adventure perhaps never equalled in novelty by any incident that has occurred to Europeans in the bosom of Africa, I hope I may be forgiven in attempting to trace its causes and effects, without which my narrative would be incomplete; for they are so intimately connected with each other, that it would be impossible to disunite them.

In order to give a clearer idea of the story, it will be necessary to remark, that Zuma was married in early life to one of the principal inhabitants of Wow Wow; but her spouse dying shortly after she had given birth to a son, she was left immensely rich, and lived in almost regal splendour in the native town of her deceased husband. Nature had endowed Zuma with an active, restless, and ambitious mind; insomuch that not long after she had become a widow, and before the regular term of mourning had expired, her weeds were thrown aside, and she aspired to the government of Wow Wow, by attempting to depose her sovereign. But Mohammed, although an imbecile and superstitious prince, could

'Bear, like a Turk, no rival near his throne!'

and was roused into action at the threatening aspect his too powerful subject had assumed. Instantly arming his vassals, he made a sudden and unexpected attack on the slaves of the rebellious lady, who for want of an efficient leader were put completely to the rout, though without bloodshed, and Zuma herself taken prisoner. Whether it was owing to the profound veneration in which that elegant lady's charms were held by the monarch, to the natural mildness of his disposition, or to the fear of stirring up the people against him, I could not learn; but certain it is that Zuma was pardoned, and set at liberty, after a confinement of only one or two days; and though she had repeated her treasonable attempt several times, even up to the period of our visiting the city, the same amiable forbearance had been extended to her.

It was the misfortune of the far-famed Zuma to fancy herself, for no reason in the world, to be extremely fair, and although she had certainly passed the 'Age of the Passions,' she took it into her head to fall desperately in love with me, whose complexion, she affirmed, rivalled her own in whiteness! The frequency of her visitations to our house nourished the tender feeling, which was encouraged by Captain Clapperton, who relished a joke with all his heart, and did his utmost to inflame the lady's passion, by passing a thousand unmeaning compliments on the regularity of my features, and the handsomeness of my person. 'See what beautiful eyes he has,' observed the Captain; 'if you were to search from Badagry to Wow Wow, you would not find such eyes.' For my own part I was but a novice in the art of courtship, and imagining it to be altogether in jest, took little pains to spoil the fun by shrinking from it. Besides, Zuma had behaved remarkably well to us in sending, repeatedly, presents of provisions, together with every luxury with which she was acquainted, and I was rather glad than otherwise to have her for our guest,

——'For the heart must
Leap kindly back to kindness;'

and neither of us wished to offend a lady of her consequence by being morose and unsociable in manners, or by repelling her advances with ridicule and contempt.

For an hour together the widow would gaze intently on me, while the most amorous glances shot from her large, full, and certainly beautiful eyes, which confused and disconcerted me not a little, even though I was surrounded by strangers and in the heart of Africa; for I had been a wanderer from my childhood, and had had but few opportunities of mingling in the delightful company of the gentler sex in my own country, and consequently was excessively bashful on coming in contact with ladies, whether in the country of the Hottentots, or the birth-place of the widow Zuma.

As for my master, he was sensibly delighted with these interviews, and with his arms folded on his breast, while thick volumes of tobacco-smoke rolled from his pipe, he with the most impenetrable gravity enjoyed the scene, and looked as happy and as much at home as if he had been seated by his friends in his native Scotland. After the widow's departure, it was his usual custom, tapping me on the shoulder, to ask how I felt my heart, and observe what a boast I could make, on our return to England, of so magnificent a conquest.

All this I took in good part for some days; but things beginning, at length, to wear a more serious aspect than I had at first anticipated, I was resolved to bring this whimsical courtship to a conclusion as speedily as possible. I was the more inclined to do so, because I did not wish to wound the feelings of even a *black* lady (for black she most certainly was, although not quite so deep a sable as the aborigines), by trifling with them; nor did I forget the exclamation of the frog in the fable:—'It may be sport to you, but it is death to us!'

Independently of the delicate state of my health, which incapacitated me from carrying on so curious an amour with the spirit and gallantry it required, I was positively afraid that, from the warmth and energy of Zuma's embraces, I should actually be pressed to death between her monstrous arms! I was but a youth, and my short residence in the country had certainly impaired a constitution originally robust and vigorous; by reason of which I was sadly apprehensive that one of her Brobdingnagian hugs would send me into the other world with very little ceremony. These reflexions I had seriously revolved in my mind; and on her next visit I candidly told the widow by signs, words, and gestures, that I could not love her; but she either did not or would not understand me. I remarked that I should never choose a *black* wife: she pointed to her face, and said she was a *white* woman. I then observed that it would be impossible for me to exist in her country, the heat being insupportable. Her reply was disinterested and tender:—'Then I will quit it, and follow you to whichever part of the world you may be inclined to lead me to.' Thus beset on all sides, I hardly knew what to say next; but after a short pause, summing up all my resolution, I gave my greasy inamorata a flat refusal to see her again in the light of a lover, as it was out of her power to awaken in my breast a corresponding sensation to that which reigned in her own! and saying this I instantly left the apartment; whilst Zuma, poor lady,

> ——'Rais'd a sigh so piteous and profound,
> As it did seem to shatter all her bulk,
> And end her being!'

I was surprised, however, to find that my cruelty had produced no visible effect on the widow, and that her *heart* was big in proportion to the largeness of her *body*; for I discovered that she could love *two* individuals at the same time with as much ardour and sincerity as *one* only. Seeing all hopes of success effectually shut out on my side, she had the good sense to discontinue her solicitations (although she continued her kindness), and looked as tenderly on me as ever; and applied herself strenuously to be on a more affectionate and friendly footing with Captain Clapperton, whose favourable notice she strove to attract by all the fascinating allurements she was mistress of; and actually went so far as to bribe Pasko, our Houssa interpreter, in order that he might use his *powerful* influence to bring the matter between my master and herself to an amicable adjustment. The old libertine accepted the present with rapture, which made the third or fourth spouse he had had since leaving Badagry, but he was prudent enough to retain his counsel within his own bosom.

A white husband and happiness were synonymous terms with the gentle and delicate Zuma, and she grasped at even the shadow of it with an eagerness and determination that caused her to overstep the boundaries of that amiable modesty which is so pleasing and peculiar a characteristic of her sex, whereby she did more towards injuring her own cause than coyness or reserve would have done. The Captain carried on the innocent game for some time, for we were greatly in want of something to enliven us; and so romantic an adventure as this, in such a place, and under such circumstances, caused us very many hours of diversion, and was an amusing subject of conversation even up to the period of my master's last illness at Soccatoo.

Poor widow Zuma! I almost fancy I see her now, waddling into our house, a moving world of flesh, 'puffing and blowing like a blacksmith's bellows,' and the very pink and essence of African fashion. Her hair used to be carefully dyed with indigo, and of a rich and vivid blue; her feet and hands stained with hennah and an extract of the goora-nut, produced alternate streaks of red and yellow; and her teeth were also tinged with a delicate crimson stain. In the adornment of her person, likewise, the buxom widow evinced considerable taste. Her bared neck and bosom were ornamented with coral and gold beads, which, contrasted with the dingy colour of her skin, occasioned a truly captivating effect! while a dress of striped silk, hanging in graceful folds from the waist to the ancles, set off her *fairy form* to the best possible advantage! Thus beautified, the accomplished Zuma used to sit cross-legged on our mat, and chewing the goora-nut, or a little tobacco-snuff, she was without exception the most ravishing object that came across our path in all our wanderings!

One day she invited my master to visit her at her own house, where she took the opportunity of displaying to him her wealth and grandeur, the number of her slaves, and her princely domestic establishment, all of which the tempter assured him he should share with her if he would consent to be her husband. No encouragement whatever was given to the lady; but when Capt. Clapperton left the town for Boussa a short time afterwards, Madam Zuma, dressed in her gaudiest attire, followed when he had got about six miles on his journey, having called before she set out to see me. On this occasion she wore a mantle of silk and gold, and loose trowsers of scarlet silk, with red morocco boots; her blue head was enveloped in the ample folds of a white turban, and she rode astride on the back of a noble horse, which came prancing before the door of our hut, decorated with a number of brass plates and bells, as well as a profusion of charms or amulets enclosed in green, red, and yellow leather. Her saddle-cloth was of scarlet, and the appearance of both widow and horse was singularly imposing. In her train were many spearmen on horseback, and bowmen on foot, with a band of musicians furnished with drums, fiddles, guitars, and flutes, who continued playing till their mistress was fairly out of the town. The widow briefly told me of her intention to accompany Capt. Clapperton to Kano, &c. &c. which éclaircissement startled me for an instant; but, putting on my most serious look, I wished her a pleasant journey, and hoped I should overtake her myself in a day or two. Zuma then took her leave, and the whole cavalcade was quickly out of sight.

I was absolutely longing to learn the issue of this strange elopement of Zuma's; and was engaged in making preparations previously to my departure for Coulfo, in Nyffe [Nupe], when a message from the king forbidding my departure from Wow Wow, diverted me from my intention, and overturned all my plans. I had an interview with the irritated Mohammed the same day, and another on the following one; but my efforts to induce him to change his resolution were abortive. He turned a deaf ear to all my eloquence, and would not suffer me to quit the town for any consideration; 'For,' said the king, 'your countryman has eloped with the captious Zuma, who will raise up enemies, and make war upon me, if she be not speedily checked; and the better way to accomplish this is to detain you here with the baggage, which will bring back the "great white man," and the widow will not be able to remain behind long after.'

In order to secure me the more effectually, our house was guarded by a dozen soldiers, who had received strict injunctions not to let me escape on any account. I contrived, however, to elude the vigilance of my keepers, and, taking with me a boy only twelve years of age, who had assisted me in making my escape, I hastily mounted my Yariba pony, and was on the road to Boussa in an instant.

At sunset I crossed the Menai, a branch of the Quorra [Niger], leading to the island; and after landing shortly entered the city. As soon as I was recognized as one of the strangers, a good house was immediately prepared for my reception, and I was presently honored with a visit from the king and queen, who informed me that my master had left Boussa, and that, if I were to travel all night, it would be impossible to overtake him before the next morning; they would therefore insist upon my remaining and sleeping in the city. My royal visitors staid with me a considerable time, and the queen gave directions about my supper, and even assisted to prepare it with her own hands.

A multitude of the usual questions were put to me by their majesties, which, on account of my almost total ignorance of the language in which they were uttered, I was not very well qualified to answer; but, notwithstanding this inconvenience, we succeeded in making ourselves pretty well understood; and from the excessive kindness, and watchful anxiety to anticipate my wants, it was evident that I was a great favourite with them.

The queen had certainly not much of the widow Zuma about her, either in appearance or manners; being delicate in person, and possessing a native delicacy and gracefulness of mien that could not fail to please. The features of the royal couple bore a closer resemblance to the European than the negro cast, and might be styled handsome, even in England; besides which an ineffable sweetness shone upon the countenance of Medaki, the queen, and there was an agreeableness in the innocent freedom of her deportment that captivated me at first sight. A tear of pity trembled in the expressive eye of Medaki, when, observing my emaciated looks, and surveying me from head to foot, she enquired if I had a mother in my own country; and when I answered that I had not, she said, 'Poor white man! then who have you at home to talk about you, and make fetishes for your preservation whilst you remain away?' I was certainly not prepared to meet with such extraordinary kindness at Boussa; and it shows the great revolution that has taken place in the opinions of the people since Mr. Park's appearance in the interior.

I had been extremely unwell before leaving Wow Wow; and my rapid journey on the back of a lean horse, without saddle or bridle, had no-wise improved my health; fatigue also had rendered me so sleepy that after supper I could with difficulty keep my eyes open, and my answers to the queries of the royal pair were given at random. It was in vain that I bit my tongue and lips, and used every other means I could devise in order to arouse myself from the stupid state I was in; the inclination to slumber overcame them all, and at last I fell fast asleep. On awakening in the night I found myself alone, with a solitary lamp burning in my apartment; and was informed, an hour or two afterwards that their majesties, as soon as they saw me fairly insensible, had left me in the care of two slaves, and returned to their own abode, after expressly desiring them to make no noise that might awaken me. Next morning I went to the king to apologize for my unintentional breach of etiquette; and shaking hands with the royal couple, who wished me every happiness, I returned to Wow Wow (whither I had learnt Captain Clapperton had also gone back), in company of two armed men, who had been furnished as a protection against highway robbers, with which the road was declared to be infested. On my arrival in the city, I found that my master had entered it but a few minutes before, but had not seen the fat widow during his absence.

A short time only had elapsed before we resolved to go to the king; and being ushered into an apartment, found the important personage yawning from the effects of his afternoon's nap. The Captain was the fittest person in the world to deal with the African rulers. The first thing he did was to shake hands affectionately and heartily with the sullen Mohammed, covering his face at the same time with smiles and looks of joy on seeing him again; but the king accepted the compliment with just so good a grace as a growling mastiff would receive the caresses of a person against whom he bears a grudge; neither willing to bite the hand that pats its big head, nor wishing to be altogether on a friendly footing with its suspected friend. 'What pleasure it gives me to see you again,' said my master; 'I have not beheld so handsome a face as yours since leaving the city. I suppose you did not think it safe to send my baggage after me; and am therefore come to fetch it myself. I have seen the king of Boussa, who, with the Medaki, gave so very favorable an account of you, that really I am filled with admiration for your talents and virtues; and am sure there cannot be your equal in the whole country.' All this the great man listened to with a deal of attention, and one could perceive plainly enough that the sternness of his features gradually gave place to a softer and kindlier expression; indeed, from the commencement of the above well-timed encomium, a smile overspread his sable countenance which promised the most flattering results. His majesty then, with the utmost dignity, detailed his reasons for the line of conduct he had been obliged to adopt, in consequence of his belief that the Captain and the rebellious Zuma had entered into a conspiracy to usurp his authority; that when their treasonable object should be accomplished, he would be put out of the way, in order that my master might take the reins of government into his own hands. He added that the widow had been guilty of similar unlawful practices before, but had failed in her attempts; and that notwithstanding the lenity with which she had been treated, her thoughts were perpetually employed in devising means for the execution of her ambitious designs; and she had moreover threatened him unceasingly with raising an army to overcome and destroy him. As this was spoken with an air of great solemnity, and towards the latter part of it with emotion, which was plainly evinced by his tears, my master thought proper to disclaim, with correspondent energy and seriousness, the imputations on his own character, by professing himself a total stranger to the widow's movements from the time of his departure from Wow Wow; and as for deposing so powerful a prince as Mohammed, and taking Zuma to wife, such things were altogether beyond his ambition; and he ridiculed the very idea of it. He therefore hoped that the king would no longer refuse his permission for the party under his (Captain Clapperton's) command, to go on immediately, as he had bargained with the chief of the Houssa caravan to convey the goods to Kano, and he was impatiently waiting his arrival at the ferry. The old gentleman, however, was not quite so easily prevailed upon as we had anticipated; and in all probability was smitten with the widow's charms himself; for he declared with firmness, that until the absent lady returned, both my master and myself must abandon all thoughts of proceeding on our journey, or of again leaving Wow Wow. Further cajolery, we knew, would have been superfluous, so we were obliged to make a virtue of necessity, and wait patiently the re-appearance of our affectionate friend, the amiable Zuma. To our infinite joy that circumstance took place on the 5th of April, the day after our conference with the prince; the widow had not been able to meet with the object of her tender solicitude, and hearing that he had re-visited Wow Wow, agreeably to the prediction of Mohammed, returned to that town in much the same order as she had quitted it about a week before, without discovering the slightest symptoms either of disappointment of the ill-success of her jaunt, or fear for having so egregiously offended her sovereign.

Like most of her sex, however, Zuma knew perfectly well how to adapt her conduct to circumstances, and was, moreover, complete mistress of the art of dissimulation and deceit; for no sooner had she entered her own habitation, than her splendid habiliments were instantly thrown aside, and a dress of common country cloth substituted in their stead. Thus meanly attired, she paid her respects to Mohammed in our presence, and saluted him by falling on her knees, with her elbows to the earth, while, supporting her head on the palms of her hands, she shed a whole river of tears. Surely

> 'Heav'n gave to woman the peculiar grace,
> To spin, to weep, and cully human race.'

The great man looked sternly on her at first; but whose heart could be proof against *so much* loveliness in distress, and in that humiliating posture? Anger forsook his brow, as the prince of Wow Wow requested the repentant woman to rise; and simply upbraiding her for disregarding his authority and threatening to subvert his government, he shook hands, and desired her to go her way, but be more cautious of offending him in future. The widow accordingly left the house, and shaking the dust from her feet in token of bravado, cast a 'longing, lingering look behind;'—and we saw no more of the generous, the affectionate, but above all the enormous widow Zuma!

This singular adventure, though it caused us to laugh heartily, had been of a much more serious nature than we could have foreseen, and had given us much unnecessary trouble, as well as occasioned some days' delay; but when it was thus satisfactorily terminated, we resolved to be more guarded in encouraging, even in jest, the advances of the African belles, as our lives might thereby be endangered, by exciting the prejudices of the people against us. The widow being returned, and having promised to abide in peace, his majesty of Wow Wow offered no further impediment to our departure, and we quitted his capital on the following day.

*Records of Captain Clapperton's last expedition,*
vol. I, pp. 150–171

*After leaving Wawa they crossed the Niger by a ferry below Bussa and made their way north-eastwards to Kano, where they arrived on 20th July. Both the travellers suffered continually from fever on the way, and at Kano Lander had a bad attack of dysentery. Clapperton had decided to go on to Sokoto by himself in order to see Bello. He travelled light, intending to return to Kano to pick up Lander and the heavy baggage and then to explore the country to the east. But on his way he learnt that Bello was away from Sokoto at the time, engaged in a campaign against Bornu. He did not reach the Sultan's camp until 15th October, when he found him completely preoccupied with the war and little interested in entering into relations with so remote and shadowy a Power as England. But Clapperton had set his heart on securing the treaty: his failure to do so preyed on his mind; and when Lander, who had meanwhile determined to follow his master from Kano, arrived on 23rd December, he found him dispirited and ill. Together they continued in the neighbourhood of Sokoto, dancing attendance on Bello. The way in which they kept up their spirits during this time is well illustrated at the beginning of the next extract.*

## 11. THE DEATH OF CLAPPERTON

Before retiring to rest of an evening, cigars we had brought from England with us were generally produced; and we inhaled their grateful fragrance oftentimes for an hour or two. This was the only luxury left us; our tea and sugar had been consumed long before, and we fared in every respect like the Falatahs [Fulani] themselves. Squatted on mats in our huts, we spent the lingering hours in reading aloud, or chatting of our respective homes, and reciting village anecdotes; and it is really incredible to believe to what a ridiculous consequence the most trivial incident in the world was magnified in these our solitary conversations; and how often we laughed at jests which had been laughed at a thousand times before. But this can only be felt in an equal degree by persons similarly circumstanced with ourselves; every other avenue to enjoyment had been effectually blocked up; nor could we derive any pleasure from the society of the treacherous Arab or interested Falatah.

Sometimes, although neither of us was gifted with a voice of much power or compass, we attempted to sing a few English or Scotch tunes; and sometimes I played others on my bugle-horn. How often have the pleasing strains of 'Sweet, sweet Home,' resounded through the melancholy streets of Soccatoo? How often have its inhabitants listened with breathless attention to the music of the white-faced strangers? and observed to each other, as they went away, 'Surely those Christians are sending a blessing to their country and friends!' Any thing that reminded my master of his native Scotland was always heard with interest and emotion. The little poem, 'My native Highland home,' I have sung scores of times to him, as he has sat with his arms folded on his breast opposite to me in our dwelling; and notwithstanding his masculine understanding, and boasted strength of nerve, the Captain used to be somewhat moved on listening to the lines:

'Then gang wi' me to Scotland dear,
    We ne'er again will roam;
And with thy smile, so bonny, cheer
    My native Highland home!

For blithsome is the breath of day,
    And sweet's the bonny broom,
And pure the dimpling rills that play
    Around my Highland home.'

Thus our lonely evenings were spent; and when the time, the place, and the thousand other circumstances, are considered, the puerility of our amusements may surely be pardoned us. Such entertainments could not fail of awakening melancholy but pleasing associations within us; and to picture to our imaginations when in the bosom of Africa, and surrounded by wretches who sought our destruction, our own free and happy country, its heathy hills and flowery fields, and contrast them with the withering aspect of existing scenes, afforded us many an hour of delight and sorrow, gladness and gloom—although filling us with hopes that proved delusive, and expectations that we found, by fatal experience, to be in the highest degree visionary;—for, like the beautiful apple said to grow on the borders of the Red Sea, our hopes wore a fair and promising outside, but produced only bitter ashes.

For two months our manner of living and occupation were nearly unvaried. The Sheikh of Bornou had entered Houssa, during this period, with a multitude of men, and was reported to have laid siege to Kano, after the fall of which city he was to march to Soccatoo. This news terrified the inhabitants of the latter place to so great a degree, that every individual of consequence in it fled to the more secure and remote town of Magaria; and we were obliged to follow their example; but, events not turning out agreeably to anticipation, we returned to Soccatoo a week or fortnight afterwards.

On the 12th of March all thoughts of further enjoyment ceased, through the sudden illness of my dear kind master, who was attacked with dysentery on that day. He had been almost insensibly declining for a week or two previously, but without the slightest symptoms of this frightful malady. From the moment he was first taken ill, Captain Clapperton perspired freely, large drops of sweat continually rolling over every part of his body, which weakened him exceedingly; and, being unable to obtain any one, even of our own servants, to assist, I was obliged to wash the clothes, kindle and keep in the fire, and prepare the victuals with my own hands. Owing to the intense heat, my master was frequently fanned for hours together: indeed, all my leisure moments were devoted to this tedious occupation; and I have often held the fan till, from excessive weakness, it has fallen from my grasp.

Finding that, from increasing debility, I was unable to pay that unremitting attention to the numerous wants of the invalid which his melancholy state so peculiarly demanded, I sent to mallam Mudey on the 15th, entreating him to lend me a female slave to perform the operation of fanning. On her arrival the girl began her work with alacrity and cheerfulness; but soon becoming weary of her task, ran away, and never returned to our hut. I was therefore obliged to resume it myself; and, regardless of personal inconvenience and fatigue, strained every nerve, in order to alleviate, as much as possible, the sufferings occasioned by this painful disorder. My master daily grew weaker, and suffered severely from the intolerable heat of the atmosphere, the thermometer being, in the coolest place, 107 at twelve at noon, and 109 at three in the afternoon.

At his own suggestion I made a couch for him outside our dwelling, in the shade, and placed a mat for myself by its side. For five successive days I took him in my arms from his bed to the couch outside, and back again at sunset, after which he was too much debilitated to encounter even so trifling an exertion. He expressed a wish to write once, and but once, during his illness, but before paper and ink could be handed to him, he had fallen back on his bed, completely exhausted by his ineffectual attempt to sit up.

Fancying by certain suspicious symptoms, that my sick master had inadvertently taken poison, I asked him one day whether he thought that in any of his visits to the Arabs or Tuaricks in the city, any venomous ingredient had been secretly put into the camel's milk they had given him to drink, of which he was particularly fond. He replied, 'No, my dear boy, no such thing has been done, I assure you. Do you remember,' he continued, 'that when on a shooting expedition in Magaria, in the early part of February, after walking the whole of the day, exposed to the scorching rays of the sun, I was fatigued, and for some time lay under the branches of a tree? The soil on that occasion was soft and wet, and from that hour to the present I have not been free from cold. This has brought on my present disorder, from which, I believe, I shall never recover.'

For twenty days the Captain remained in a low and distressed state, and during that period was gradually but perceptibly declining; his body, from being strong and vigorous, having become exceedingly weak and emaciated, and, indeed, little better than a skeleton. There could not be a more truly pitiable object in the universe than was my poor dear master, at this time. His days were sorrowfully and ignobly wasting in vexatious indolence; he himself languishing under the influence of a dreadful disease, in a barbarous region, far, very far removed from his tenderest connections, and beloved country; the hope of life quenched in his bosom; the great undertaking, on which his whole soul was bent, unaccomplished; the active powers of his mind consumed away; and his body so torn and racked with pain, that he could move neither head, hand, nor foot without suppressed groans of anguish; while the fire and energy that used to kindle in his eye had passed away, and given place to a glossy appearance—a dull saddening expression of approaching dissolution.

In those dismal moments, Capt. Clapperton derived considerable consolation from the exercise of religious duties; and, being unable himself to hold a book in his hand, I used to read aloud to him daily and hourly some portions of the Sacred Scriptures. At times a gleam of hope, which the impressive and appropriate language of the Psalmist is so admirably calculated to excite, would pierce the thick curtain of melancholy that enveloped us; but, like the sun smiling through the dense clouds of a winter's day, it shone but faintly; and left us in a state of gloomier darkness than before.

Abderachman, an Arab from Fezzan, intruded himself one day into our hut, and wished to read some Mohammedan prayers to my master, but was instantly desired to leave the apartment, with a request that he would never enter it again. This individual was the only stranger that visited him during his sickness.

The Captain's sleep was uniformly short and disturbed, and troubled with frightful dreams, in which he often reproached the Arabs with emphasis and bitterness; but being myself almost a stranger to the language (Arabic) I could not distinctly understand the tenor of his remarks.

The unceasing agitation of mind, and exertion of body, which I had myself undergone in my unremitting duties, (never having in a single instance slept out of my clothes,) weakened me greatly; and a fever having come on me not long before my master's death, hung upon me for fifteen days, and brought me to the very verge of the grave. Almost at the commencement of this illness, there being no other person to assist me in the manner I could wish, I obtained permission to take Pasko again into our service. As soon as he entered the hut, the repentant old man fell upon his knees before the couch of his sick master, and intreated so piteously to be forgiven for the offences of which he had been guilty, that he was desired to rise, with a promise to overlook all that had passed, if his after-conduct should correspond with his apparent penitence.

By this means, the washing and all the drudgery were taken from my shoulders, which enabled me to devote my whole time and attention to my affectionate master's person; and, indeed, all my energies were required to bear me up under the pressure that almost bowed me to the dust. I fanned the invalid nearly the whole of the day, and this seemed to cool the burning heat of his body, of which he repeatedly complained. Almost the whole of his conversation reverted to his country and friends, although I never heard him regret his having left them; and he was patient and resigned to the last, a murmur of disappointment never escaping his lips.

On the first of April the patient became considerably worse; and, although evidently in want of repose, the virulence of his complaint prevented him from enjoying any refreshing slumbers. On the 9th, Maddie, a native of Bornou whom my master had retained in his service, brought him about twelve ounces of green bark, from the [shea] butter-tree, recommended to him by an Arab in the city; and assured us that it would produce the most beneficial effects. Notwithstanding all my remonstrances, a decoction of it was ordered to be prepared immediately, the too-confiding invalid remarking that no one would injure him. Accordingly, Maddie himself boiled two basons full, the whole of which stuff was swallowed in less than an hour.

On the following day he was greatly altered for the worse, as I had foretold he would be, and expressed regret for not having followed my advice. About twelve o'clock at noon, calling me to his bed-side, he said,

'Richard! I shall shortly be no more; I feel myself dying.' Almost choked with grief, I replied,

'God forbid! my dear master; you will live many years to come.'

'Do not be so much affected, my dear boy, I intreat you,' rejoined he; 'you distress me by your emotion; it is the will of the Almighty; and therefore cannot be helped. Take care of my journal and papers after my decease; and when you arrive in London, go immediately to my agents, and send for my uncle, who will accompany you to the Colonial office, and see you deposit them with the Secretary. After my body is laid in the earth, apply to Bello, and borrow money to purchase camels and provisions for crossing the desert to Fezzan in the train of the Arab merchants. On your arrival at Mourzouk, should your money be expended, send a messenger to Mr. Warrington, our Consul for Tripoli, and wait till he returns with a remittance. On your reaching the latter place, that gentleman will further advance you what money you may require, and send you to England the first opportunity. Do not lumber yourself with my books, but leave them behind, as well as my barometer and sticks, and indeed every heavy or cumbersome article you can conveniently part with; you may give them to mallam Mudey, who will preserve them. Remark whatever towns or villages you may pass through, and put on paper any thing remarkable that the chiefs of the different places may say to you.'

I said, as well as my agitation would permit me, 'If it be the will of God to take you, Sir, you may confidently rely, as far as circumstances will permit me, on my faithfully performing all that you have desired; but I hope and believe that the Almighty will yet spare you to see your home and country again.'

'I thought at one time,' continued he, 'that that would be the case, but I dare not entertain such hopes now; death is on me, and I shall not be long for this world; God's will be done.' He then took my hand betwixt his, and looking me full in the face, while a tear glistened in his eye, said in a tremulous, melancholy tone:

'My dear Richard, if you had not been with me I should have died long ago. I can only thank you with my latest breath for your devotedness and attachment to me; and if I could live to return to England with you, you should be placed beyond the reach of want; the Almighty, however, will reward you.'

This pathetic conversation, which occupied almost two hours, greatly exhausted my master, and he fainted several times whilst speaking. The same evening he fell into a slumber, from which he awoke in much perturbation, and said that he had heard with peculiar distinctness the tolling of an English funeral bell; but I entreated him to be composed, observing that sick people frequently fancy things which in reality can have no existence. He shook his head, but said nothing.

About six o'clock on the morning of the 11th April, on my asking him how he did, my master replied in a cheerful tone, that he felt much better; and requested to be shaved. He had not sufficient strength to lift his head from the pillow; and after finishing one side of the face I was obliged myself to turn his head in order to get at the other. As soon as he was shaved, he desired me to fetch him a looking-glass which hung on the opposite side of the hut; and on seeing the reflection of his face in it, observed that he looked quite as ill in Bornou on his former journey, and that as he had borne his disorder for so long a time, there was some possibility of his yet recovering. On the following day he still fancied himself to be convalescent, in which belief I myself agreed, as he was enabled to partake of a little hashed guinea fowl in the course of the afternoon, which he had not done before during the whole of his confinement, having derived his sole sustenance from a little fowl soup and milk and water.

These flattering anticipations, however, speedily vanished, for on the morning of the 13th, being awake, I was greatly alarmed on hearing a peculiar rattling noise issuing from my master's throat, and his breathing at the same time was loud and difficult. At that moment, on his calling out 'Richard!' in a low, hurried, and singular tone, I was instantly at his side, and was astonished beyond measure on beholding him sitting upright in his bed (not having been able for a long time previously to move a limb), and staring wildly around. Observing him ineffectually struggling to raise himself on his feet, I clasped him in my

111

arms, and whilst I thus held him, could feel his heart palpitating violently. His throes became every moment less vehement, and at last they entirely ceased, insomuch that thinking he had fallen into a slumber, or was overpowered by faintings I placed his head gently on my left shoulder, gazing for an instant on his pale and altered features; some indistinct expressions quivered on his lips, and whilst he vainly strove to give them utterance, his heart ceased to vibrate, and his eyes closed for ever!

I held the lifeless body in my arms for a short period, overwhelmed with grief; nor could I bring myself to believe that the soul which had animated it with being, a few moments before, had actually quitted it.

I then unclasped my arms, and held the hand of my dear master in mine; but it was cold and dead, and instead of returning the warmth with which I used to press it, imparted some of its own unearthly chillness to my frame, and fell heavily from my grasp. O God! what was my distress in that agonizing moment? Shedding floods of tears, I flung myself along the bed of death, and prayed that Heaven would in mercy take my life!

The violence of my grief having subsided, Pasko and Mudey, whom my exclamations had brought into the apartment, fetched me water, with which I washed the corpse, and with their assistance, carried it outside the hut, laid it on a clean mat, and wrapped it in a sheet and blanket. After leaving it in this state nearly two hours, I put a large neat mat over the whole, and sent a messenger to make Bello acquainted with the mournful event, as well as to obtain his permission to have the body buried after the manner of my own country; and also to learn in what particular place the Sultan would wish to have it interred. The man soon returned with a favourable answer to the former part of my request, and about twelve o'clock on the morning of the same day, a person came into the hut, accompanied by four slaves, to dig the grave; and wished me to follow him with the corpse. Accordingly, saddling my camel, the body was placed on the animal's back, and throwing a British flag over it, I requested the men to proceed. Having passed through the dismal streets of Soccatoo, we travelled almost unobservedly, at a solemn pace, and halted near Jungavie, a small village, built on a rising ground about five miles south-east of the city. The body was then taken from the camel's back, and placed in a shed, whilst the slaves were employed in digging the grave. Their task being speedily accomplished, the corpse was borne to the brink of the pit, and I planted the flag close to it; then, uncovering my head, and opening a prayer-book, amidst showers of tears, I read the impressive funeral service of the Church of England over the remains of my valued master—the English flag waving slowly over them at the same moment. Not a single soul listened to this peculiarly distressing ceremony; for the slaves were quarrelling with each other the whole of the time it lasted.

This being done, the flag was taken away, and the body slowly lowered into the earth; and I wept bitterly as I gazed, for a last time, on all that remained of my intrepid and beloved master. The grave was quickly closed, and I returned to the village, about thirty yards to the eastward of it, and giving the most respectable inhabitants of both sexes a few trifling presents, entreated them to let no one disturb the ashes of the dead; and also offered them a sum of money to erect a shed over the spot, which having accepted, they promised to do.

Thus perished, and thus was buried, Captain Hugh Clapperton in the prime of life, and in the strength and vigour of his manhood. No one could be better qualified than he by a fearless, indomitable spirit, and utter contempt of danger and death, to undertake and carry into execution an enterprise of so great importance and difficulty, as the one with which he was entrusted. He had studied the African character in all its phases—in its moral, social, and external form; and like Alcibiades accommodated himself with equal ease to good as well [as] to bad fortune—to prosperity, as well as to adversity. He was never highly elated at the prospect of accomplishing his darling wishes—the great object of his ambition—nor deeply depressed when environed by danger, care, disappointment, and bodily suffering, which hanging heavily upon him forbade him to indulge in hopeful anticipations. The negro loved him, because he admired the simplicity of his manners, and mingled with pleasure in his favourite dance; the Arab hated him, because he was overawed by his commanding appearance, and because the keen penetrating glance of the British Captain detected his guilty thoughts, and made him quail with apprehension and fear.

Captain Clapperton's stature was tall; his disposition was warm and benevolent; his temper mild, even, and cheerful; while his ingenuous, manly countenance pourtrayed the generous emotions that reigned in his breast. In fine, he united the figure and determination of a man, with the gentleness and simplicity of a child; and, if I mistake not, he will live in the memory of many thousands of Africans, until they cease to breathe, as something more than mortal; nor have I the least doubt that the period of his visiting their country will be regarded by some as a new era, from which all events of consequence, that affect them, will hereafter be dated.

The grave was dug on a naked piece of ground, with no remarkable object near it to invite attention;—no mournful cypress or yew weeps over the lonely spot—no sculptured marble shines above all that remains of heroic enterprize and daring adventure! But the sleeper needs no funereal emblem to perpetuate his name and actions, having erected for himself a nobler and far more imperishable mausoleum in the breasts of his countrymen and the civilized world, than all the artists in the universe could rear over his ashes.

Returning, after the funeral, disconsolate and oppressed, to my solitary habitation, I leaned my head on my hands, and could not help being deeply affected with my lonesome and dangerous situation. A hundred and fifteen days' journey from the sea-coast; surrounded by a selfish and barbarous race of strangers;—my only friend and protector and last hope, mouldering in his grave, and myself suffering dreadfully from fever: I felt as if I stood alone in the world, and wished, ardently wished, I had been enjoying the same deep, undisturbed, cold sleep as my master, and in the same grave. All the trying evils I had encountered —all the afflictions I had endured—all the bereavements I had experienced, never affected me half so much as the bitter reflections of that distressing period. After a sleepless night, I went alone to the grave, and found that nothing had been done to it, nor did there seem to be the least inclination on the part of the inhabitants of the village to redeem their pledge. Knowing it would be useless to remonstrate with such wretches, I hired two slaves in Soccatoo the next day, who went to work immediately, and the shed over the grave was finished on the 15th.

*Records of Captain Clapperton's last expedition,*
vol. II, pp. 63–81

*Lander's business was now to return to England with his master's papers. As we have seen, Clapperton advised him to travel back across the Sahara, following the route he had himself taken in 1822–4. But Lander saw a rich prize in view in another direction. Why should he not make for Funda, which he had often heard spoken of at Sokoto as a town on the Niger, and thence trace the course of the river down to its mouth?[1] Having made up his mind to do this, he travelled back to Kano and then struck out southwards. But when he reached Dunrora, twelve days' journey from Funda, he was overtaken by some horsemen of the King of Zaria who peremptorily ordered him to accompany them back to their master. With this demand he had of course to comply. He was thus compelled to give up for the time being his hopes of solving the Niger question, and made his way back to Badagri by the same route he had taken with Clapperton on the outward journey. He reached Portsmouth on 30th April 1828.*

[1] In fact, as he subsequently discovered, Funda was on the Benue, three days' march from its junction with the Niger. It was destroyed by the Fulani in 1853.

114

*After delivering up his master's papers, he set to work to write a short account of his adventures, which was published in 1829 with Clapperton's Narrative of a second expedition into the interior of Africa. The following year there appeared his more finished version of the whole story, Records of Captain Clapperton's last expedition.*

*Lander must have been a man of very striking personality, for though he was only twenty-five years old, and a servant at that, he prevailed upon Lord Bathurst to send him out again to Africa for the purpose of tracing the Niger from Bussa to its mouth, and he obtained leave to take with him his younger brother John. They left England on 9th January 1830 and Badagri on 31st March. Following the old route, they reached Kaiama on 28th May. Here, on 2nd June, they saw a horse race in celebration of a Moslem festival known as 'Bebun Salah', or 'Great Prayer Day'.*

# 12. HORSE RACE AT KAIAMA

In the afternoon, all the inhabitants of the town, and many from the little villages in its neighbourhood, assembled to witness the horse-racing, which takes place always on the anniversary of the 'Bebun Salah,' and to which every one had been looking forward with impatience. Previous to its commencement, the king, with his principal attendants, rode slowly round the town, more for the purpose of receiving the admiration and plaudits of his people than to observe where distress more particularly prevailed, which was his avowed intention. A hint from the chief induced us to attend the course with our pistols, to salute him as he rode by; and as we felt a strong inclination to witness the amusements of the day, we were there rather sooner than was necessary, which afforded us, however, a fairer opportunity of observing the various groups of people which were flocking to the scene of amusement.

The race-course was bounded on the north by low granite hills; on the south by a forest; and on the east and west by tall shady trees, among which were habitations of the people. Under the shadow of these magnificent trees the spectators were assembled, and testified their happiness by their noisy mirth and animated gestures. When we arrived, the king had not made his appearance on the course; but his absence was fully compensated by the pleasure we derived from watching the anxious and animated countenances of the multitude, and in passing our opinions on the taste of the women in the choice and adjustment of their fanciful and many-coloured dresses. The chief's wives and younger children sat near us in a group by themselves; and were distinguished from their companions by their superior dress. Manchester cloths of inferior quality, but of the most showy patterns, and dresses made of common English bed-furniture, were fastened round the waist of several sooty maidens, who, for the sake of fluttering a short hour in the gaze of their country-men, had sacrificed in clothes the earnings of a twelvemonth's labour. All the women had ornamented their necks with strings of beads, and their wrists with bracelets of various patterns, some made of glass beads, some of brass, others of copper; and some again of a mixture of both metals: their ancles also were adorned with different sorts of rings, of neat workmanship.

The distant sound of drums gave notice of the king's approach, and every eye was immediately directed to the quarter from whence he was expected. The cavalcade shortly appeared, and four horsemen first drew up in front of the chief's house, which was near the centre of the course, and close to the spot where his wives and children and ourselves were sitting. Several men bearing on their heads an immense quantity of arrows in huge quivers of leopard's skin came next, followed by two persons who, by their extraordinary antics and gestures, we concluded to be buffoons. These two last were employed in throwing sticks into the air as they went on, and adroitly catching them in falling, besides per-forming many whimsical and ridiculous feats. Behind these, and im-mediately preceding the king, a group of little boys, nearly naked, came dancing merrily along, flourishing cows' tails over their heads in all directions. The king rode onwards, followed by a number of fine-looking men, on handsome steeds; and the motley cavalcade all drew up in front of his house, where they awaited his further orders without dismounting. This we thought was the proper time to give the first salute, so we accordingly fired three rounds; and our example was immediately fol-lowed by two soldiers, with muskets which were made at least a century and a half ago.

Preparations in the mean time had been going on for the race, and the horses with their riders made their appearance. The men were dressed in caps and loose tobes and trowsers of every colour; boots of red morocco leather, and turbans of white and blue cotton. The horses were gaily caparisoned; strings of little brass bells covered their heads; their breasts were ornamented with bright red cloth and tassels of silk and cotton; a large quilted pad of neat embroidered patchwork was placed under the saddle of each; and little charms, inclosed in red and yellow cloth, were attached to the bridle with bits of tinsel. The Arab saddle and stirrup were in common use; and the whole group presented an imposing appearance.

The signal for starting was made, and the impatient animals sprung forward and set off at a full gallop. The riders brandished their spears, the little boys flourished their cows' tails, the buffoons performed their antics, muskets were discharged, and the chief himself, mounted on the finest horse on the ground, watched the progress of the race, while tears of delight were starting from his eyes. The sun shone gloriously on the tobes of green, white, yellow, blue, and crimson, as they fluttered in the breeze; and with the fanciful caps, the glittering spears, the jingling of the horses' bells, the animated looks and warlike bearing of their riders, presented one of the most extraordinary and pleasing sights that we have ever witnessed. The race was well contested, and terminated only by the horses being fatigued and out of breath; but though every one was emulous to outstrip his companion, honour and fame were the only reward of the competitors.

A few naked boys, on ponies without saddles, then rode over the course, after which the second and last heat commenced. This was not by any means so good as the first, owing to the greater anxiety which the horsemen evinced to display their skill in the use of the spear and the management of their animals. The king maintained his seat on horseback during these amusements, without even once dismounting to converse with his wives and children who were sitting on the ground on each side of him. His dress was showy rather than rich, consisting of a red cap, enveloped in the large folds of a white muslin turban; two under tobes of blue and scarlet cloth, and an outer one of white muslin, red trowsers, and boots of scarlet and yellow leather. His horse seemed distressed by the weight of his rider, and the various ornaments and trappings with which his head, breast, and body, were bedecked. The chief's eldest and youngest sons were near his women and other children, mounted on two noble looking horses. The eldest of these youths was about eleven years of age. The youngest being not more than three, was held on the back of his animal by a male attendant, as he was unable to sit upright in the saddle without this assistance. The child's dress was ill suited to his age. He wore on his head a tight cap of Manchester cotton, but it overhung the upper part of his face, and together with its ends, which flapped over each cheek, hid nearly the whole of his countenance from view; his tobe and trowsers were made exactly in the same fashion as those of a man, and two large belts of blue cotton, which crossed each other, confined the tobe to his body. The little legs of the child were swallowed up in clumsy yellow boots, big enough for his father; and though he was rather pretty, his whimsical dress gave him altogether so odd an appearance, that he might have been taken for any thing but what he really was. A few of the women on the ground by the side of the king wore large white dresses, which covered their persons like a winding-sheet. Young virgins, according to custom, appeared in a state of nudity; many of them had wild flowers stuck behind their ears, and strings of beads, &c, round their loins; but want of clothing did not seem to damp their pleasure in the entertainment for they appeared to enter into it with as much zest as any of their companions. Of the different coloured tobes worn by the men, none looked so well as those of a deep crimson colour on some of the horsemen; but the clean white tobes of the Mohammedan priests, of whom not less than a hundred were present on the occasion, were extremely neat and becoming. The sport terminated without the slightest accident, and the king's dismounting was a signal for the people to disperse.

*Journal of an expedition to explore the course and termination of the Niger*, 1st edition, vol. I, pp. 240–6

*Three days later they left Kaiama, and passing through Wawa, where Richard Lander renewed acquaintance with the Widow Zuma, they arrived at Bussa on 17th June. Bussa remained their headquarters, from which they made visits to Yauri and Wawa, until 20th September. The king and queen behaved as kindly to them as they had to Richard Lander and Clapperton in 1826. While they were there, another Moslem festival occurred, during which the king made a remarkable speech.*

## 13. THE KING OF BUSSA

*Wednesday, September* 1st.—Day was drawing to a close, and evening fast approaching, when the king came out of his residence to show himself to his people. He was attended by a number of his head men, with whom he perambulated the town; and afterwards proceeded outside the gates to offer up a short prayer with them to the gods of his religion, for he is still a pagan, as all his fathers were, though he employs Mahomedan priests to pray for his welfare, and intercede with their prophet in his behalf, agreeably to their form of worship. Several musicians were in attendance with drums, fifes, and long Arab trumpets of brass; these men preceded their sovereign, and played lustily on their instruments all the while he was returning to his house. He shortly came out again, and rode slowly up the race-course, attended by people of both sexes, most uncouthly dressed, singing and dancing before him, and followed by a party of well-dressed men mounted on mettlesome horses, and equipped as if for war. On our saluting him, the monarch stopped and sent us a goora-nut, which, on such an occasion as this, is considered as a mark of great condescension, and a sign of peculiar favour; and he stayed opposite us at least ten minutes, to give us a fair opportunity of admiring his grandeur, and diverting ourselves by the frolicsome gambols of his attendants. Smiling at our wonderment, and gratified with the respect we paid him by discharging our pistols close to his person, he nodded and passed on. The king was mounted on a fine handsome grey horse, sumptuously caparisoned; while he himself is a noble and commanding figure on horseback, and was dressed extremely well, in a red cap and large turban of the same colour, a silk damask tobe of green and crimson, made full and flowing, red cloth trousers and Arab boots. Groups of well-dressed individuals were seated under every tree with spears, quivers of arrows, long bows, and ornamented cows' tails. These latter were flourished about as the people sang; their owners threw them high into the air, and danced at the same time in the most extraordinary manner, and flung their limbs about as though they had been actuated by a supernatural power. Every one was exhilarated and in motion,— both horseman and footman, woman and child. The musicians also, not satisfied by making the whole of Boossa echo with the most grating and outrageous sounds conceivable, both sung, or rather screamed and danced, twisting their mouths, with their exertions, into all manner of wry and comical shapes. The spectacle altogether was odd and grotesque beyond description, and such an one could never enter into the dreams or waking visions of an European. Guns were fired by the king's followers, and other obstreporous and astounding noises were made by the people. Never did we see the king in a happier mood; his satisfaction seemed to be quite complete. He smiled graciously on all around him; and bestowed many an arch and significant look upon us, as if he would have said, 'Can *your* sovereign boast so splendid a retinue as mine, or display so much regal splendour?'

The ceremony was long and fatiguing; and though the king was screened from the sun's rays by two large ponderous umbrellas, and though two men were standing by, constantly fanning him, yet perspiration stood in large drops upon his forehead, and he appeared nearly exhausted. After our curiosity had been amply gratified, the king rode away, preceded by his singing and dancing women, his musicians, his bowmen, and his spearmen, with all their noise and clamour. . . . The king is a graceful rider, and displayed his horsemanship to much advantage by galloping up and down the course; and, owing to his advantageous stature, his appearance was very becoming. The sun was then setting, and as soon as he had disappeared, the amusements ceased. The people, both strangers and inhabitants, were then collected together before the king's house, for the purpose of hearing an oration from their monarch; for, in pursuance of an ancient and established practice, the king of Boossa annually harangues his people on the celebration of this festival. The sovereign is at least a head taller than any of his subjects, so that he was a remarkable and conspicuous object to every one of his audience. If such a comparison may be ventured on, the commencement of his speech was in its nature not much unlike that delivered on the opening of parliament by his Majesty of England. The king of Boossa began by assuring his people of the internal tranquillity of the empire, and of the friendly disposition of foreign powers towards him. He then exhorted his hearers to attend to the cultivation of the soil, to work diligently, and live temperately; and concluded with an injunction for them all to be abstemious in the use of beer. He declared that too much indulgence in it was the source of much evil and wretchedness, and the cause of most of the quarrels and disturbances that had taken place in the city. 'Go; retire to rest soberly and cheerfully,' said the king, 'and do as I have requested you, when you will be an example to your neighbours, and win the good opinion and applause of mankind.' The king's speech lasted for three-quarters of an hour. He spoke vehemently and with much eloquence; his language was forcible and impressive, and his action appropriate and commanding; and he dismissed the assembly with a graceful and noble air. Instead of a sceptre the monarch flourished the tuft of a lion's tail.

*Journal of an expedition to explore the course and termination of the Niger*, 1st edition, vol. II, pp. 162–167

*Leaving Bussa in a canoe, they paddled down the river rapidly and almost without incident until they reached a village named Bocqua, just below the confluence of the Niger and the Benue.*

## 14. AN ATTACK AVERTED

At 10 a.m., we passed a huge and naked white rock, in the form of a perfect dome, arising from the centre of the river. It was about twenty feet high, and covered with an immense quantity of white birds, in consequence of which we named it the Bird Rock: it is about three or four miles distant from Bocqua, on the same side of the river. It is safest to pass it on the south-east side, on which side is also the proper channel of the river, about three miles in width. We passed it on the western side, and were very nearly lost in a whirlpool. It was with the utmost difficulty we preserved the canoe from being carried away, and dashed against the rocks. Fortunately, I saw the danger at first, and finding we could not get clear of it, my brother and I took a paddle, and animating our men, we exerted all our strength, and succeeded in preventing her from turning round. The distance of this rock from the nearest bank is about a quarter of a mile, and the current was running with a velocity of six miles an hour, according to our estimation. Had our canoe become unmanageable, we should inevitably have perished. Shortly after, seeing a convenient place for landing, the men being languid and weary with hunger and exertion, we halted on the right bank of the river, which we imagined was most convenient for our purpose. The course of the river this morning was south-south-west, and its width varied as usual from two to six miles. The angry and scowling appearance of the firmament forewarned us of a heavy shower, or something worse, which induced us hastily to erect an awning of mats under a palm-tree's shade. As soon as we had leisure to look around us, though no habitation could anywhere be seen, yet it was evident the spot had been visited, and that very recently, by numbers of people. We discovered the remains of several extinct fires, with broken calabashes and pieces of earthen vessels, which were scattered around; and our men likewise picked up a quantity of cocoa-nut shells, and three or four staves of a powder-barrel. These discoveries, trifling as they were, filled us with pleasant and hopeful sensations; and we felt assured, from the circumstance of a barrel of powder having found its way hither, that the natives in the neighbourhood maintained some kind of intercourse with Europeans from the sea.

The spot, for a hundred yards, was cleared of grass, underwood, and vegetation of all kinds; and, on a further observation, we came to the conclusion that a market or fair was periodically held thereon. Very shortly afterwards, as three of our men were straggling about in the bush, searching for firewood, a village suddenly opened before them: this did not excite their astonishment, and they entered one of the huts which was nearest them to procure a little fire. However it happened to contain only women; but these were terrified beyond measure at the sudden and abrupt entrance of strange-looking men, whose language they did not know, and whose business they could not understand, and they all ran out in a fright into the woods, to warn their male relatives of them, who were labouring at their usual occupation of husbandry. Meanwhile our men had very composedly taken some burning embers from the fire, and returned to us in a few minutes, with the brief allusion to the circumstance of having discovered a village. They told us also that they had seen cultivated land, and that these women had run away from them as soon as they saw them. This we thought lightly of; but rejoiced that they had seen the village, and immediately sent Pascoe, Abraham, and Jowdie, in company, to obtain some fire, and to purchase a few yams for us. In about ten minutes after, they returned in haste, telling us that they had been to the village, and had asked for some fire, but that the people did not understand them, and instead of attending to their wishes, they looked terrified, and had suddenly disappeared. In consequence of their threatening attitudes, our people had left the village, and rejoined us with all the haste they could. We did not, however, think that they would attack us, and we proceeded to make our fires and then laid ourselves down.

Totally unconscious of danger, we were reclining on our mats,—for we, too, like our people, were wearied with toil, and overcome with drowsiness,—when in about twenty minutes after our men had returned, one of them shouted, with a loud voice, 'War is coming! Oh war is coming!' and ran towards us with a scream of horror, telling us that the natives were hastening to attack us. We started up at this unusual exclamation, and, looking about us, we beheld a large party of men, almost naked, running in a very irregular manner, and with uncouth gestures, towards our little encampment. They were all variously armed with muskets, bows and arrows, knives, cutlasses, barbs, long spears, and other instruments of destruction; and, as we gazed upon this band of wild men, with their ferocious looks and hostile appearance, which was not a little heightened on observing the weapons in their hands, we felt a very uneasy kind of sensation, and wished ourselves safe out of their hands. To persons peaceably inclined, like ourselves, and who had done them no harm, we could look on their preparations with calmness; but as it is impossible to foresee to what extremities such encounters might lead, we waited the result with the most painful anxiety.

Our party was much scattered, but fortunately we could see them coming to us at some distance, and we had time to collect our men. We resolved, however, to prevent bloodshed if possible,—our numbers were too few to leave us a chance of escaping by any other way. The natives were approaching us fast, and had by this time arrived almost close to our palm-tree. Not a moment was to be lost. We desired Pascoe and all our people to follow behind us at a short distance with the loaded muskets and pistols; and we enjoined them strictly not to fire, unless they first fired at us. One of the natives, who proved to be the chief, we perceived a little in advance of his companions; and, throwing down our pistols, which we had snatched up in the first moment of surprise, my brother and I walked very composedly, and unarmed, towards him. As we approached him, we made all the signs and motions we could with our arms, to deter him and his people from firing on us. His quiver was dangling at his side, his bow was bent, and an arrow which was pointed at our breasts, already trembled on the string, when we were within a few yards of his person. This was a highly critical moment—the next might be our last. But the hand of Providence averted the blow; for just as the chief was about to pull the fatal cord, a man that was nearest him rushed forward, and stayed his arm. At that instant we stood before him, and immediately held forth our hands; all of them trembled like aspen leaves; the chief looked up full in our faces, kneeling on the ground—

light seemed to flash from his dark, rolling eyes—his body was convulsed all over, as though he were enduring the utmost torture, and with a timorous, yet undefinable, expression of countenance, in which all the passions of our nature were strangely blended, he drooped his head, eagerly grasped our proffered hands, and burst into tears. This was a sign of friendship—harmony followed, and war and bloodshed were thought of no more. Peace and friendship now reigned among us; and the first thing that we did was to lift the old chief from the ground, and to convey him to our encampment. The behaviour of our men afforded us no little amusement, now that the danger was past. We had now had a fair trial of their courage, and should know who to trust on a future occasion. Pascoe was firm to his post, and stood still with his musket pointed at the chief's breast during the whole time. He is a brave fellow, and said to us as we passed him to our encampment with the old man, 'If the *black* rascals had fired at either of you, I should have brought the old chief down like a guinea-fowl.' It was impossible to avoid smiling at the fellow's honesty, although we were on the best of terms with the old chief,—and we have little doubt that he would have been as good as his word. As for our two brave fellows, Sam and Antonio, they took to their heels, and scampered off as fast as they could directly they saw the natives approaching us over the long grass, nor did they make their appearance again until the chief and all his people were sitting round us; and even when they did return, they were so frightened, they could not speak for some time.

All the armed villagers had now gathered round their leader, and anxiously watched his looks and gestures. The result of the meeting delighted them—every eye sparkled with pleasure—they uttered a shout of joy—they thrust their bloodless arrows into their quivers—they ran about us though they were possessed of evil spirits—they twanged their bowstrings, fired off their muskets, shook their spears, clattered their quivers, danced, put their bodies into all manner of ridiculous positions, laughed, cried, and sung in rapid succession—they were like a troop of maniacs. Never was spectacle more wild and terrific. When this sally of passion to which they had worked themselves had subsided into calmer and more reasonable behaviour, we presented each of the war-men with a quantity of needles, as a further token of our friendly intentions. The chief sat himself down on the turf, with one of us on each side of him, while the men were leaning on their weapons on his right and left. At first no one could understand us; but an old man made his appearance shortly after, who understood the Haussa language. Him the chief employed as an interpreter, and every one listened with anxiety to the following explanation which he gave us:—

'A few minutes after you first landed, one of my people came to me and said, that a number of strange people had arrived at the market-place. I sent him back again to get as near to you as he could, to hear what you intended doing. He soon after returned to me, and said that you spoke in a language which he could not understand. Not doubting that it was your intention to attack my village at night, and carry off my people, I desired them to get ready to fight. We were all prepared and eager to kill you, and came down breathing vengeance and slaughter, supposing that you were my enemies, and had landed from the opposite side of the river. But when you came to meet us unarmed, and we saw your white faces, we were all so frightened that we could not pull our bows, nor move hand or foot; and when you drew near me, and extended your hands towards me, I felt my heart faint within me and believed that you were *"Children of Heaven"* and had dropped from the skies.' Such was the effect we had produced on him; and under this impression he knew not what he did. 'And now,' said he, 'white men, all I want is your forgiveness.' 'That you shall have mos heartily,' we said, as we shook hands with the old chief, and having taken care to assure him we had not come from so good a place as he had imagined, we congratulated ourselves, as well as him, that this affair had ended so happily. For our own parts, we had reason to feel the most unspeakable pleasure at its favourable termination; and we offered up internally to our merciful Creator, a prayer of thanksgiving and praise, for his providential interference in our behalf; for the Almighty had indeed, to use the words of the Psalmist of Israel, 'delivered our soul from death, and our feet from falling; and preserved us from any terror by night, and from the arrow that flieth by day; from the pestilence that walketh in darkness; and from the sickness that destroyeth at noon-day.' We were grateful to find that our blood had not been shed, and that we had been prevented from spilling the blood of others, which we imagined we should have been constrained to do from irremediable necessity. Our guns were all double-loaded with balls and slugs, our men were ready to present them, and a single arrow from a bow would have been the signal for immediate destruction. It was a narrow escape; and God grant we may never be so near a cruel death again. It was happy for us that our white faces and calm behaviour produced the effect it did on these people —in another minute our bodies would have been as full of arrows as a porcupine's is full of quills.

*Journal of an expedition to explore the course and termination of the Niger*, vol. III, pp. 71–80

*The suspiciousness and hostility of the natives increased as they neared the sea: once they were actually attacked, but they escaped with little damage. At length on 15th November they reached Brass*

*Town: after some disagreeable difficulties with the captain of an
English merchant ship, they sailed out of the delta by the Nun mouth
and across to Fernando Po, which they reached on 1st December.
They returned to England by way of Brazil, arriving in July 1831.
Richard was awarded the first Gold Medal of the Royal Geographical
Society (founded in the year of his return); and together the brothers
wrote an account of their journey which appeared in three charming
little volumes in 1832.*[1]

*Richard was not to remain long in England. Early in 1832 he
agreed to join, in the capacity of guide, a commercial expedition to
the Niger organized by Macgregor Laird, a member of the famous
family of Birkenhead shipbuilders. It proved an unfortunate venture
from the beginning. The voyage out (in the brig and two steamships
with which the expedition was provided) was slow; disease began to
attack the white men as soon as they arrived in the delta; the steamers
were not a success on the river; the native chiefs were naturally hostile
to what they considered as an attempt at competing with their trade.
This was the reason for an attack made on Lander and his men at
Angiama on 20th January 1834: Lander was wounded, but managed to
retire to Fernando Po, where he died at the beginning of February—
'a victim', as one of his companions wrote, 'to his too great confidence in the natives'.*

*Lander's books reveal his character and personality very clearly.
By temperament he was gay and light-hearted, though subject to
passing fits of melancholy; his gentleness and good temper never
failed; his humour, if it occasionally degenerates into a rather dated
facetiousness, is most refreshing. Above all, his books give a haunting
impression of his youth—he was not quite thirty when he died.*

---

[1] The preface explains that, although the book is written as if it were the
work of one man, and Richard always appears in it as 'I', the first two volumes
are taken from the journal of John Lander (who had some literary pretensions)
and the last from Richard's. Thus of our three extracts from it, the first two
are from John's part of the work. But this matters little, since the whole book
was edited by a third hand and its style agrees closely with that of *Records of
Captain Clapperton's last expedition*, which was entirely written by Richard.

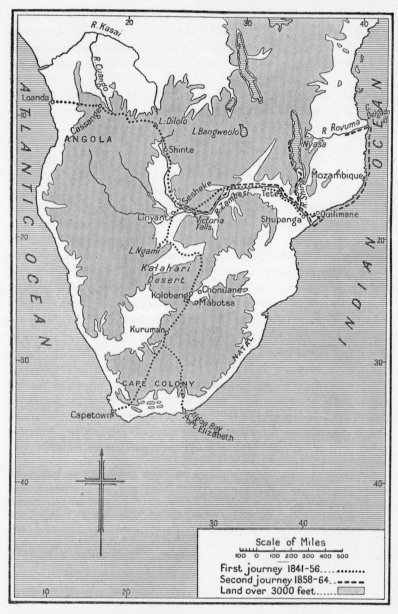

5. THE TRAVELS OF LIVINGSTONE, 1841–64

# IV

# DAVID LIVINGSTONE
## 1813–1873

The story of Livingstone's life before he went out to Africa can be told in a few words. His father was a tea-merchant in a very small way: he was born at Blantyre near Glasgow. At the age of ten he went into a cotton mill, where he remained until 1836: then, fired by the idea of becoming a medical missionary in China, he entered Glasgow University, where he qualified as a doctor in 1840. Meanwhile, he had offered his services to the directors of the London Missionary Society, who accepted them after he had gone through a period of probation. The Opium War making it impossible for him to go to China as he intended, Robert Moffat (whom he met in London and who afterwards became his father-in-law) succeeded in persuading him to turn his thoughts to Africa. In December 1840 he sailed for Capetown.

He made his way up to Kuruman in Bechuanaland, Moffat's headquarters. From here he was instructed by the London Missionary Society to prospect northwards, and in 1843, after prospecting the country in several considerable journeys, he established a new base for himself.

## 15. ENCOUNTER WITH A LION

Returning towards Kuruman, I selected the beautiful valley of Mabotsa (lat. 25° 14′ south, long. 26° 30′ ?) as the site of a missionary station; and thither I removed in 1843. Here an occurrence took place concerning which I have frequently been questioned in England, and which, but for the importunities of friends, I meant to have kept in store to tell my children when in my dotage. The Bakatla of the village Mabotsa were much troubled by lions, which leaped into the cattle-pens by night, and destroyed their cows. They even attacked the herds in open day. This was so unusual an occurrence that the people believed that they were bewitched—'given,' as they said, 'into the power of the lions by a neighbouring tribe.' They went once to attack the animals, but, being rather a cowardly people compared to Bechuanas in general on such occasions, they returned without killing any.

It is well known that if one in a troop of lions is killed the others take the hint and leave that part of the country. So the next time the herds were attacked, I went with the people, in order to encourage them to rid themselves of the annoyance by destroying one of the marauders. We found the lions on a small hill about a quarter of a mile in length, and covered with trees. A circle of men was formed round it, and they gradually closed up, ascending pretty near to each other. Being down below on the plain with a native schoolmaster, named Mebalwe, a most excellent man, I saw one of the lions sitting on a piece of rock within the now closed circle of men. Mebalwe fired at him before I could, and the ball struck the rock on which the animal was sitting. He bit at the spot struck, as a dog does at a stick or stone thrown at him; then leaping away, broke through the opening circle and escaped unhurt. The men were afraid to attack him, perhaps on account of their belief in witchcraft. When the circle was re-formed, we saw two other lions in it; but we were afraid to fire lest we should strike the men, and they allowed the beasts to burst through also. If the Bakatla had acted according to the custom of the country, they would have speared the lions in their attempt to get out. Seeing we could not get them to kill one of the lions, we bent our footsteps towards the village; in going round the end of the hill, however, I saw one of the beasts sitting on a piece of rock as before, but this time he had a little bush in front. Being about thirty yards off, I took a good aim at his body through the bush, and fired both barrels into it. The men then called out, 'He is shot, he is shot!' Others cried, 'He has been shot by another man too; let us go to him!' I did not see any one else shoot at him, but I saw the lion's tail erected in anger behind the bush, and, turning to the people, said, 'Stop a little till I load again.' When in the act of ramming down the bullets I heard a shout. Starting, and looking half round, I saw the lion just in the act of springing upon me. I was upon a little height; he caught my shoulder as he sprang, and we both came to the ground below together. Growling horribly close to my ear, he shook me as a terrier dog does a rat. The shock produced a stupor similar to that which seems to be felt by a mouse after the first shake of the cat. It caused a sort of dreaminess, in which there was no sense of pain nor feeling of terror, though quite conscious of all that was happening. It was like what patients partially under the influence of chloroform describe, who see all the operation, but feel not the knife. This singular condition was not the result of any mental process. The shake annihilated fear, and allowed no sense of horror in looking round at the beast. This peculiar state is probably produced in all animals killed by the carnivora; and if so, is a merciful provision by our benevolent Creator for lessening the pain of death. Turning round to relieve myself of the weight, as he had one paw on the back of my head, I saw his eyes directed to Mebalwe, who was trying to

ENCOUNTER WITH A LION
From Livingstone's *Missionary Travels*

shoot him at a distance of ten or fifteen yards. His gun, a flint one, missed fire in both barrels; the lion immediately left me, and, attacking Mebalwe, bit his thigh. Another man, whose life I had saved before, after he had been tossed by a buffalo, attempted to spear the lion while he was biting Mebalwe. He left Mebalwe and caught this man by the shoulder, but at that moment the bullets he had received took effect, and he fell down dead. The whole was the work of a few moments, and must have been his paroxysm of dying rage. In order to take out the charm from him, the Bakatla on the following day made a huge bonfire over the carcase, which was declared to be that of the largest lion they had ever seen. Besides crunching the bone into splinters, he left eleven teeth wounds in the upper part of my arm.

A wound from this animal's tooth resembles a gun-shot wound; it is generally followed by a great deal of sloughing and discharge, and pains are felt in the part periodically ever afterwards. I had on a tartan jacket on the occasion, and I believed that it wiped off all the virus from the teeth that pierced the flesh, for my two companions in this affray have both suffered from the peculiar pains, while I have escaped with only the inconvenience of a false joint in my limb. The man whose shoulder was wounded showed me his wound actually burst forth afresh in the same month of the following year. This curious point deserves the attention of inquirers.

Missionary Travels, 1st edition, pp. 11–13

*Livingstone remained at Mabotsa until 1846. He was tireless in trying to explain the doctrines of Christianity to the Bakwain tribe among whom he lived, and to Sechele their chief. His methods of argument, and the sort of acute criticism he had to meet, are well illustrated in a conversation with a Bakwain rain-doctor which he set down with striking fairness and detachment.*

## 16. ARGUMENT WITH A RAIN-DOCTOR

The natives, finding it irksome to sit and wait helplessly until God gives them rain from heaven, entertain the more comfortable idea that they can help themselves by a variety of preparations, such as charcoal made of burned bats, inspissated renal deposit of the mountain coney (*Hyrax capensis*) (which by the way is used in the form of pills as a good anti-spasmodic, under the name of 'stone-sweat'), the internal parts of different animals—as jackals' livers, baboons' and lions' hearts, and hairy calculi from the bowels of old cows—serpents' skins and vertebræ, and every kind of tuber, bulb, root, and plant to be found in the country. Although you disbelieve their efficacy in charming the clouds to pour out their refreshing treasures, yet, conscious that civility is useful everywhere, you kindly state that you think they are mistaken as to their power; the rain-doctor selects a particular bulbous root, pounds it, and administers a cold infusion to a sheep, which in five minutes afterwards expires in convulsions. Part of the same bulb is converted into smoke, and ascends towards the sky; rain follows in a day or two. The inference is obvious. Were we as much harassed by droughts, the logic would be irresistible in England in 1857.

As the Bakwains believed that there must be some connection between the presence of 'God's Word' in their town and these successive and distressing droughts, they looked with no good will at the church-bell, but still they invariably treated us with kindness and respect. I am not aware of ever having had an enemy in the tribe. The only avowed cause of dislike was expressed by a very influential and sensible man, the uncle of Sechele. 'We like you as well as if you had been born among us; you are the only white man we can become familiar with; but we wish you to give up that everlasting preaching and praying; we cannot become familiar with that at all. You see we never get rain, while those tribes who never pray as we do obtain abundance.' This was a fact; and we often saw it raining on the hills, ten miles off, while it would not look at us 'even with one eye.' If the Prince of the power of the air had no hand in scorching us up, I fear I often gave him the credit of doing so.

As for the rain-makers, they carried the sympathies of the people along with them, and not without reason. With the following arguments they were all acquainted, and in order to understand their force we must place ourselves in their position, and believe, as they do, that all medicines act by a mysterious charm. The term for cure may be translated 'charm'.

*Medical Doctor.*—Hail, friend! How very many medicines you have about you this morning! Why, you have every medicine in the country here.

*Rain-Doctor.*—Very true, my friend; and I ought; for the whole country needs the rain which I am making.

*M.D.*—So you really believe that you can command the clouds? I think that can be done by God alone.

*R.D.*—We both believe the very same thing. It is God that makes the rain, but I pray to him by means of these medicines, and, the rain coming, of course it is then mine. It was I who made it for the Bakwains for many years, when they were at Shokuane; through my wisdom, too, their women became fat and shining. Ask them; they will tell you the same as I do.

*M.D.*—But we are distinctly told in the parting words of our Saviour that we can pray to God acceptably in His name alone, and not by means of medicines.

*R.D.*—Truly! but God told *us* differently. He made black men first, and did not love us, as he did the white men. He made you beautiful, and gave you clothing, and guns, and gunpowder, and horses, and waggons, and many other things about which we know nothing. But toward us he had no heart. He gave us nothing, except the assegai, and cattle, and rain-making; and he did not give us hearts like yours. We never love each other. Our tribes place medicines about our country to prevent the rain, so that we may be dispersed by hunger, and go to them, and augment their power. We must dissolve their charms by our medicines. God has given us one little thing, which you know nothing of. He has given us the knowledge of certain medicines by which we can make rain. *We* do not despise those things which you possess, though we are ignorant of them. We don't understand your book, but we don't despise it. *You* ought not to despise our little knowledge, though you are ignorant of it.

*M.D.*—I don't despise what I am ignorant of; I only think you are mistaken in saying that you have medicines which can influence the rain at all.

*R.D.*—That's just the way people speak when they talk on a subject of which they have no knowledge. When we first opened our eyes, we found our forefathers making rain, and we follow in their footsteps. You, who send to Kuruman for corn, and irrigate your garden, may do without rain; *we* cannot manage in that way. If we had no rain, the cattle would have no pasture, the cows give no milk, our children become lean and die, our wives run away to other tribes who do make rain, and have corn, and the whole tribe become dispersed and lost; our fire would go out.

*M.D.*—I quite agree with you as to the value of the rain; but you cannot charm the clouds by medicines. You wait till you see the clouds come, then you use your medicines, and take the credit which belongs to God only.

*R.D.*—I use my medicines, and you employ yours; we are both doctors, and doctors are not deceivers. You give a patient medicine. Sometimes God is pleased to heal him by means of your medicine: sometimes not—he dies. When he is cured, you take the credit of what God does. I do the same. Sometimes God grants us rain, sometimes not. When he does, we take the credit of the charm. When a patient dies, you don't give up trust in your medicine, neither do I when rain fails. If you wish me to leave off my medicines, why continue your own?

*M.D.*—I give medicines to living creatures within my reach, and can see the effects though no cure follows; you pretend to charm the clouds, which are so far above us that your medicines never reach them. The clouds usually lie in one direction, and your smoke goes in another. God alone can command the clouds. Only try and wait patiently; God will give us rain without your medicines.

*R.D.*—Mahala-ma-kapa-a-a!! Well, I always thought white men were wise till this morning. Who ever thought of making trial of starvation? Is death pleasant then?

*M.D.*—Could you make it rain on one spot and not on another?

*R.D.*—I wouldn't think of trying. I like to see the whole country green, and all the people glad; the women clapping their hands and giving me their ornaments for thankfulness, and lullilooing for joy.

*M.D.*—I think you deceive both them and yourself.

*R.D.*—Well, then, there is a pair of us (meaning both are rogues).

The above is only a specimen of their way of reasoning, in which, when the language is well understood, they are perceived to be remarkably acute. These arguments are generally known, and I never succeeded in convincing a single individual of their fallacy, though I tried to do so in every way I could think of. Their faith in medicines as charms is unbounded. The general effect of argument is to produce the impression that you are not anxious for rain at all; and it is very undesirable to allow the idea to spread that you do not take a generous interest in their welfare. An angry opponent of rain-making in a tribe would be looked upon as were some Greek merchants in England during the Russian war.[1]

*Missionary travels*, 1st edition, pp. 22–25

*On leaving Mabotsa, Livingstone gradually worked his way northwards, establishing himself successively at Chonuane and Kolobeng. In 1849 he determined to cross the Kalahari Desert and find Lake Ngami, which he knew lay beyond it. With three English friends (one of them W. C. Oswell), he made the journey in exactly two months: they discovered the lake on 1st August, afterwards returning to Kolobeng. He crossed the desert again in each of the two following years, accompanied by his wife and family, and in June 1851 reached the Zambesi at Sesheke: it was on this journey that he came into contact with the slave trade for the first time.*

*He now determined to travel on still further north into the heart of Africa, and in order to be able to do this more easily sent his family home to England, travelling down to the Cape with them. From here he made his way back to Linyanti, the capital of the Makololo people,*

[1] I.e. the Crimean War, which had only just ended when Livingstone wrote.

*where he arrived in May 1853. Their chief Sekeletu welcomed him kindly and lent him twenty-seven porters, without demanding any payment. With them, and with a very small outfit of goods, he left Linyanti on 11th November, travelling up the valley of the Zambesi, striking out past Lake Dilolo and crossing the River Kasai (one of the great tributaries of the Congo) into the territory of the Kioko. Here he met with vexatious demands for tolls: a little further on, in the Chiboque country, he began to hear of slave-traders and—significant conjunction—encountered real hostility from the inhabitants. He then went north and west until he came to a spot above the valley of the Congo which made him think of Langside and Mary, Queen of Scots. On the eastern bank of the river he met a half-caste Portuguese sergeant, who set him on his way to Cassange, an outpost of the colony of Angola. Here he was treated with great kindness and forwarded to Loanda, which he reached on 31st May 1854.*

*Livingstone stayed nearly four months at Loanda, resisting all offers of a passage to England on the grounds that he must take his faithful Makololo porters home. This he accomplished in a march lasting almost a year: the party arrived at Linyanti on 11th September 1855. Seven weeks later Livingstone set out on the third and last part of his journey, that down the Zambesi to the east coast. On 16th November he had his first sight of the Falls which he named after the Queen.*

# 17. DISCOVERY OF THE VICTORIA FALLS

As this was the point from which we intended to strike off to the north-east, I resolved on the following day to visit the falls of Victoria, called by the natives Mosioatunya, or more anciently Shongwe. Of these we had often heard since we came into the country: indeed one of the questions asked by Sebituane [Sekeletu's father] was, 'Have you smoke that sounds in your country?' They did not go near enough to examine them, but, viewing them with awe at a distance, said, in reference to the vapour and noise, 'Mosi oa tunya' (smoke does sound there). It was previously called Shongwe, the meaning of which I could not ascertain. The word for a 'pot' resembles this, and it may mean a seething caldron; but I am not certain of it. Being persuaded that Mr. Oswell and myself were the very first Europeans who ever visited the Zambesi in the centre of the country, and that this is the connecting link between the known and unknown portions of that river, I decided to use the same liberty as the Makololo did, and gave the only English name I have affixed to any part of the country. No better proof of previous ignorance of this river could be desired, than that an untravelled gentleman, who had spent a great part of his life in the study of the geography of Africa, and knew everything written on the subject from the time of Ptolemy downwards, actually asserted in the 'Athenæum,' while I was coming up the Red Sea, that this magnificent river, the Leeambye, had 'no connection with the Zambesi, but flowed under the Kalahari Desert, and became lost;' and 'that, as all the old maps asserted, the Zambesi took its rise in the very hills to which we have now come.' This modest assertion smacks exactly as if a native of Timbuctu should declare, that the 'Thames' and the 'Pool' were different rivers, he having seen neither the one nor the other. Leeambye and Zambesi mean the very same thing, viz. the RIVER.

Sekeletu intended to accompany me, but, one canoe only having come instead of the two he had ordered, he resigned it to me. After twenty minutes' sail from Kalai, we came in sight, for the first time, of the columns of vapour, appropriately called 'smoke,' rising at a distance of five or six miles, exactly as when large tracts of grass are burned in Africa. Five columns now arose, and bending in the direction of the wind, they seemed placed against a low ridge covered with trees; the tops of the columns at this distance appeared to mingle with the clouds. They were white below, and higher up became dark, so as to simulate smoke very closely. The whole scene was extremely beautiful; the banks and islands dotted over the river are adorned with sylvan vegetation of great variety of colour and form. At the period of our visit several trees were spangled over with blossoms. Trees have each their own physiognomy. There, towering above all, stands the great burly baobab, each of whose enormous arms would form the trunk of a large tree, beside groups of graceful palms, which, with their feathery-shaped leaves depicted on the sky, lend their beauty to the scene. As a heiroglyphic they always mean 'far from home,' for one can never get over their foreign air in a picture or landscape. The silvery mohonono, which in the tropics is in form like the cedar of Lebanon, stands in pleasing contrast with the dark colour of the motsouri, whose cypress-form is dotted over at present with its pleasant scarlet fruit. Some trees resemble the great spreading oak, others assume the character of our own elms and chestnuts; but no one can imagine the beauty of the view from anything witnessed in England. It had never been seen before by European eyes; but scenes so lovely must have been gazed upon by angels in their flight. The only want felt, is that of mountains in the background. The falls are bounded on three sides by ridges 300 or 400 feet in height, which are covered with forest, with the red soil appearing among the trees. When about half a mile from the falls, I left the canoe by which we had come down thus far, and embarked in a lighter one, with men well acquainted with the rapids, who, by passing down the centre of the stream in the eddies and still places caused by many jutting rocks, brought me to an island situated in the middle of the river, and on the edge of the lip over which the water rolls. In coming hither, there was danger of being swept down by the streams which rushed along on each side of the island; but the river was now low, and we sailed where it is totally impossible to go when the water is high. But though we had reached the island, and were within a few yards of the spot, a view from which would solve the whole problem, I believe that no one could perceive where the vast body of water went; it seemed to lose itself in the earth, the opposite lip of the fissure into which it disappeared being only 80 feet distant. At least I did not comprehend it until, creeping with awe to the verge, I peered down into a large rent which had been made from bank to bank of the broad Zambesi, and saw that a stream of a thousand yards broad leaped down a hundred feet, and then became suddenly compressed into a space of fifteen or twenty yards. The entire falls are simply a crack made in a hard basaltic rock from the right to the left bank of the Zambesi, and then prolonged from the left bank away through thirty or forty miles of hills. . . . In looking down into the fissure on the right of the island, one sees nothing but a dense white cloud, which, at the time we visited the spot, had two bright rainbows on it. (The sun was on the meridian, and the declination about equal to the latitude of the place.) From this cloud rushed up a great jet of vapour exactly like steam, and it mounted 200 or 300 feet high; there condensing, it changed its hue to that of dark smoke, and came back in a constant shower, which soon wetted us to the skin. This shower falls chiefly on the opposite side of the fissure, and a few yards back from the lip there stands a straight hedge of evergreen trees, whose leaves are always wet. From their roots a number of little rills run back into the gulf; but as they flow down the steep wall there, the column of vapour, in its ascent, licks them up clean off the rock, and away they mount again. They are constantly running down, but never reach the bottom.

On the left of the island we see the water at the bottom, a white rolling mass moving away to the prolongation of the fissure, which branches off near the left bank of the river. A piece of the rock has fallen off a spot on the left of the island, and juts out from the water below, and from it, I judged the distance which the water falls to be about 100 feet. The walls of this gigantic crack are perpendicular, and composed of one homogeneous mass of rock. The edge of that side over which the water falls, is worn off two or three feet, and pieces have fallen away, so as to give it somewhat of a serrated appearance. That over which the water does not fall is quite straight, except at the left corner, where a rent appears, and a piece seems inclined to fall off. Upon the whole, it is nearly in the state in which it was left at the period of its formation. The rock is dark brown in colour, except about ten feet from the bottom, which is discoloured by the annual rise of the water to that or a greater height. On the left side of the island we have a good view of the mass of water which causes one of the columns of vapour to ascend, as it leaps quite clear of the rock, and forms a thick unbroken fleece all the way to the bottom. Its whiteness gave the idea of snow, a sight I had not seen for many a day. As it broke into (if I may use the term) pieces of water, all rushing on in the same direction, each gave off several rays of foam, exactly as bits of steel, when burnt in oxygen gas, give off rays of sparks. The snow-white sheet seemed like myriads of small comets rushing on in one direction, each of which left behind its nucleus rays of foam. I never saw the appearance referred to noticed elsewhere. It seemed to be the effect of the mass of water leaping at once clear of the rock, and but slowly breaking up into spray.

I have mentioned that we saw five columns of vapour ascending from this strange abyss. They are evidently formed by the compression suffered by the force of the water's own fall, into an unyielding wedge-shaped space. Of the five columns, two on the right, and one on the left of the island were the largest, and the streams which formed them seemed each to exceed in size the falls of the Clyde at Stonebyres, when that river is in flood. This was the period of low water in the Leeambye, but, as far as I could guess, there was a flow of five or six hundred yards of water, which, at the edge of the fall, seemed at least three feet deep. I write in the hope that others more capable of judging distances than myself will visit this scene, and I state simply the impressions made on my mind at the time. . . .

The fissure is said by the Makololo to be very much deeper farther to the eastward; there is one part at which the walls are so sloping, that people accustomed to it, can go down by descending in a sitting position. The Makololo on one occasion, pursuing some fugitive Batoka, saw them, unable to stop the impetus of their flight at the edge, literally dashed to pieces at the bottom. They beheld the stream like a 'white cord' at the bottom, and so far down (probably 300 feet) that they became giddy, and were fain to go away, holding on to the ground. . . .

At three spots near these falls, one of them the island in the middle on which we were, three Batoka chiefs offered up prayers and sacrifices to the Barimo. They chose their places of prayer within the sound of the roar of the cataract, and in sight of the bright bows in the cloud. They must have looked upon the scene with awe. Fear may have induced the selection. The river itself is, to them, mysterious. The words of the canoe-song are—

'The Leeambye! Nobody knows,
Whence it comes and whither it goes.'

The play of colours of the double iris on the cloud, seen by them elsewhere only as the rainbow, may have led them to the idea that this was the abode of Deity. Some of the Makololo who went with me near to Gonye, looked upon the same sign with awe. When seen in the heavens it is named 'motse oa barimo'—the pestle of the gods. Here they could approach the emblem, and see it stand steadily above the blustering uproar below—a type of Him who sits supreme—alone unchangeable, though ruling over all changing things. But not aware of His true character, they had no admiration of the beautiful and good in their bosoms. They did not imitate His benevolence, for they were a bloody imperious crew, and Sebituane performed a noble service, in the expulsion from their fastnesses of these cruel 'Lords of the Isles'.

Having feasted my eyes long on the beautiful sight, I returned to my friends at Kalai, and, saying to Sekeletu that he had nothing else worth showing in his country, his curiosity was excited to visit it the next day. . . . Sekeletu acknowledged to feeling a little nervous at the probability of being sucked into the gulf before reaching the island. His companions amused themselves by throwing stones down, and wondered to see them diminishing in size, and even disappearing, before they reached the water at the bottom.

I had another object in view in my return to the island. I observed that it was covered with trees, the seeds of which had probably come down with the stream from the distant north, and several of which I had seen nowhere else; and every now and then the wind wafted a little of the condensed vapour over it, and kept the soil in a state of moisture, which caused a sward of grass, growing as green as on an English lawn. I selected a spot—not too near the chasm, for there the constant deposition of the moisture nourished numbers of polypi of a mushroom shape and fleshy consistence—but somewhat back, and made a little garden. I there planted about a hundred peach and apricot stones, and a quantity of coffee-seeds. I had attempted fruit-trees before, but, when left in charge of my Makololo friends, they were always allowed to wither, after having vegetated, by being forgotten. I bargained for a hedge with one of the Makololo, and if he is faithful, I have great hopes of Mosioatunya's abilities as a nurseryman. My only source of fear is the hippopotami, whose footprints I saw on the island. When the garden was prepared, I cut my initials on a tree, and the date 1855. This was the only instance in which I indulged in this piece of vanity. The garden stands in front, and were there no hippopotami, I have no doubt but this will be the parent of all the gardens, which may yet be in this new country. We then went up to Kalai again.

*Missionary travels*, 1st edition, pp. 518–525

# DAVID LIVINGSTONE

*On 20th November 1855 Livingstone parted from Sekeletu, who added to his former kindnesses by giving him an escort of 114 men. With them he travelled down the Zambesi and so to Quilimane on the sea, where he arrived on 22nd May 1856. He had accomplished, with slender means, one of the greatest journeys on record.*

*When he reached home in the following December he had a great welcome: he quickly found himself a famous man. A little news of his journey had trickled back to England in his reports to the London Missionary Society and the Royal Geographical Society— which had awarded him its Gold Medal in the previous year. But he soon became known to the public as much more than a missionary and much more than an explorer. He made use of his fame in these capacities to put across what we should now call a 'policy for Africa', to open an attack on the slave trade, some of the results of which he had seen both on the eastern borders of Angola and on the lower Zambesi. Livingstone was able—by power of mind as well as by force of character and religious conviction—to make the widest possible appeal. He was listened to by the missionary public, by philanthropists, and by geographers, of course; but also by scientists ('no explorer on record', wrote the Astronomer Royal at the Cape, 'has determined his path with the precision you have accomplished') and even by politicians as cool and wary as Palmerston and Clarendon. This true breadth of mind, together with his deep spiritual power, puts Livingstone far above all other African travellers, in a class by himself.*

*It is not easy to describe the strange power of Livingstone's character in a few words: there is clear proof of it in the deep impression he made upon men of all types who met him, and upon the imagination of his country. His humanity drove him to face and struggle with cruelty rather than to avoid it: his overpowering compassion for the African people, roused by the crushing miseries of the slave trade, drove him to follow a single purpose at the cost of all that most men count as happiness.*

*As a result of his appeals, the British Government decided to send out an elaborately equipped expedition to the Zambesi, under his command. Its task was to see how far the river was navigable to steamers, to see what opening there might be for trade with the natives, and—above all—to discover how the slave trade might best be attacked.*

*With the five Englishmen under his command (one of them his*

138

*brother), Livingstone started in March 1858. After considerable difficulties in entering the Zambesi, the party steamed up to Tete. Their first objective was the exploration of the River Shire: it was reported to rise in a great lake to the north named Nyasa, which Livingstone at last managed to reach on 16th September 1859. After revisiting the Victoria Falls he returned to the Shire–Nyasa area, where he saw more than he ever had before of the terrible activities of the slave-traders. Undeterred by disasters (his wife died at Shupanga in 1862), by disagreements with his English colleagues, with whom he worked far less happily than with Africans, or by the evident failure of the expedition to accomplish its purposes, he worked on feverishly, trying to open up a workable route into the interior either by the Shire or the Rovuma. At length, in July 1863, he received notice of the expedition's recall: he reached England a year later.*

*The rest of 1864 he spent in writing, in collaboration with his brother, the* Narrative of an expedition to the Zambesi and its tributaries. *At the same time, the plan of a third journey took shape in his mind: its course and ending are described in Section IX below.*

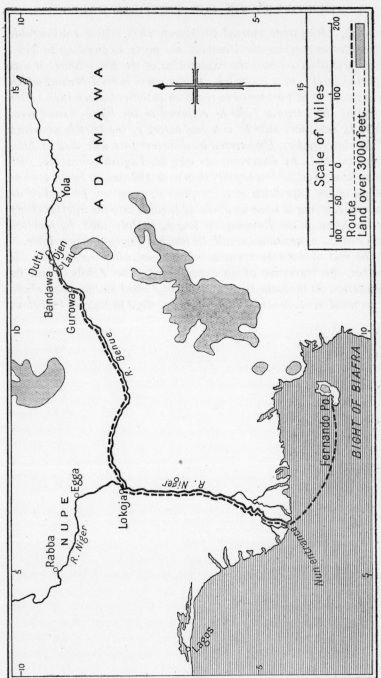

6. Route of the Third Niger Expedition, 1854

# V

# WILLIAM BALFOUR BAIKIE
## 1825–1864

Baikie was the son of a naval captain: he was born at Kirkwall in the Orkneys. After a brilliant career as a medical student at Edinburgh he became an assistant surgeon in the navy. In 1854 he was appointed surgeon and naturalist to the third Niger expedition, on the advice of Sir Roderick Murchison. The leader of the party, Captain Beecroft, died on the way out, at Fernando Po, and the command of it devolved upon Baikie. Under him the expedition was highly successful and did most valuable work, which he described himself in his Narrative of an exploring voyage (1856). In 1857 he went out to Africa again as leader of the fourth Niger expedition. Soon after starting up the river its steamer was wrecked, and most of its members returned to England. Not so Baikie: he established himself at Lokoja, at the meeting of the Rivers Niger and Benue, and made it an unofficial British settlement, entering into relations with the Emir of Nupe and other local chiefs. Lokoja at once became an important commercial centre. Baikie remained there five years: for much of this time he was wholly without white companions. He collected a vast quantity of valuable information on the country, its people and their languages, most of which still remains in manuscript. In 1864 he obtained leave to return home, but he died at Sierra Leone on the way.

He was a man of rather different type from the other great African travellers. His tastes were extremely cultivated (the catalogue of his large library, which was sold after his death, shows this very clearly): by temperament he was a calm and dispassionate scientist—an intellectual, rather than a moral or a spiritual, crusader; cool, humane, above all intelligent.

The two extracts given here are taken from his Narrative of the expedition of 1854: they illustrate his strong nerve, his quiet sense of humour, and his scientist's curiosity. Both episodes occurred on 29th September. Leaving his little steamer the Pleiad further down stream, Baikie had pushed on in a canoe manned by Krumen (those invaluable

141

*sailors from the coast of Liberia), taking with him only one white companion. When they reached Dulti, the village described below (it was some 250 miles from the mouth of the Benue), they decided they must return—not because of the hostile reception they met there, but in order to rejoin the* Pleiad *and take her back to the Niger before the Benue sank too low for navigation. The hurricane described in the second extract took place on the first night of the return voyage.*

# 18. THE GREAT DULTI CHASE

About half-past ten we entered a creek on the north side, running nearly parallel with the river, and shortly afterwards sighted a village, at which we soon arrived. To our astonishment the first thing which brought us up was our running the bow of the gig against a hut, and on looking around we found the whole place to be flooded. We advanced right into the middle of the village, and found no resting place; right and left, before and behind, all was water. People came out of the huts to gaze at the apparition, and standing at the doors of their abodes were, without the smallest exaggeration, immersed nearly to their knees, and one child I particularly observed up to its waist. How the interiors of the huts of these amphibious creatures were constructed I cannot conjecture, but we saw dwellings from which, if inhabited, the natives must have dived like beavers to get outside. We pulled in speechless amazement through this city of waters, wondering greatly that human beings could exist under such conditions. We had heard of wild tribes living in caverns and among rocks, we had read of races in Hindustan roosting in trees, of whole families in China spending their lives on rafts and in boats in their rivers and their canals; we knew, too, of Tuariks[1] and Shanbah roaming over vast sandy deserts, and of Eskimo burrowing in snow retreats, but never had we witnessed or even dreamt of such a spectacle as that of creatures endowed like ourselves, living by choice like a colony of beavers, or after the fashion of the hippopotami and crocodiles of the neighbouring swamps.

A little distance from us we espied a large tree, round the foot of which was a patch of dry land, towards which we pulled, but grounding before reaching quite to it, Mr. May and I waded to it, instruments in hand, to take observations. We were barely allowed to conclude, when nearly the entire population of the place, half-wading, half-swimming across a small creek, came upon us, and stared at us in wild astonishment. A hurried set of sights being taken, we carried our things back into the boat, and as we wished to get another set about three quarters

[1] See p. 88 above.

of an hour after noon, we tried to amuse ourselves and to spend the intervening time as we best could. We were now able to look a little more attentively at our new friends, who in large numbers crowded round, and who, male and female, were nearly all equally destitute of a vestige of clothing. One young man understood a few words of Hausa, and by this means we learnt that this was the Dulti of which we had heard at Djin, and that the inhabitants were of the same stock as at the other villages; but they were by far more rude, more savage, and more naked than any of the other Baibai whom we had encountered. A canoe came near us, lying in the bottom of which was a curious large fish, of which I had just time to make a rough eye sketch, when I had to retreat to the boat, and Mr. May, who had been exploring in another direction, also returned. The behaviour of these wild people now attracted our notice; the men began to draw closer around us, to exhibit their arms, and to send away the women and children. Their attentions became momentarily more and more familiar, and they plainly evidenced a desire to seize and plunder our boat. A sour-looking old gentleman, who was squatting on the branch of a tree, was mentioned as their king; but if so, he made no endeavours to restrain the cupidity of his *sans-culottes*. Part of a red shirt belonging to one of our Krumen was seen peeping out from below a bag, and some advanced to lay hold of it, when suddenly my little dog, who had been lying quietly in the stern sheets, raised her head to see what was causing such a commotion. Her sudden appearance startled the Dulti warriors, who had never seen such an animal before, so they drew back to take counsel together, making signs to me to know if she could bite, to which I replied in the affirmative. Matters were beginning to look serious; our crew, as usual, were timid, and Mr. May and I had only ourselves to depend upon in the midst of three or four hundred armed savages, who were now preparing to make a rush at us. There was no help for it; we had to abandon all hopes of our remaining observations, and of so fixing an exact geographical position. As at Djin, I seized a few trinkets, and handing them hastily to those nearest to us, we shoved off while the people were examining these wondrous treasures.

Still anxious, if possible, to get some further observations not far removed from the spot where the former ones were taken, we pulled about among trees and bushes, but without any success. At length we shoved in among some long grass, hoping to find dry land, but after having proceeded until completely stopped by the thickness of the growth, we still found upwards of a fathom of water. At this moment Mr. May's ear caught a voice not far behind us; so we shoved quietly back, and found a couple of canoes trying to cut off our retreat. Seeing this we paddled vigorously back, there not being room for using our oars, and the canoes did not venture to molest us. We were quickly paddling across the flooded plain, when suddenly a train of canoes in eager pursuit issued out upon us. There were ten canoes, each containing seven or eight men, and they were sufficiently close to us to allow us to see their stores of arms. Our Kruboys worked most energetically, and we went ahead at such a rate that our pursuers had complete occupation found them in paddling, and could not use their weapons. At this moment we were about a couple of hundred yards from the river, towards which we made as straight a course as possible. Not knowing how matters might terminate, we thought it advisable to prepare for defence, so I took our revolver to load it, but now, when it was needed, the ramrod was stiff and quite immoveable. Mr. May got a little pocket-pistol ready, and we had if required a cutlass, and a ship's musket, which the Krumen, by this time in a desperate fright, wished to see prepared, as they kept calling out to us, 'Load de big gun, load de big gun.' Could an unconcerned spectator have witnessed the scene, he would have been struck with the amount of the ludicrous it contained. There were our Kruboys, all as pale as black men could be, the perspiration starting from every pore, exerting to the utmost their powerful muscles, while Mr. May and I were trying to look as unconcerned as possible, and, to lessen the indignity of our retreat, were smiling and bowing to the Dulti people, and beckoning to them to follow us. Their light canoes were very narrow, and the people were obliged to stand upright. The blades of their paddles, instead of being of the usual lozenge shape, were oblong and rectangular, and all curved in the direction of the propelling stroke. It was almost a regatta, our gig taking and keeping the lead. Ahead we saw an opening in the bush, by which we hoped to make our final retreat, but we were prepared, should the boat take the ground, to jump out at once and shove her into deep water. Fortune favoured us, we reached the doubtful spot, and with a single stroke of our paddles shot into the open river. Here we knew we were comparatively safe, as if the natives tried to molest us in the clear water, all we had to do was to give their canoes the stem and so upset them; our only fear had been that of being surrounded by them while entangled among the bushes. Our pursuers apparently guessed that we had now got the advantage, as they declined following us into the river, but turning paddled back to their watery abodes, and so ended the great Dulti chase.

*Narrative of an exploring voyage up the rivers Kwora and Binue,*
pp. 195–200

# 19. HURRICANE ON THE BENUE

Although Mr. May and myself much regretted having so early reached our 'ne plus ultra,' yet our boat's crew took a very different view of the subject. Ever since we had visited Djin, they had been living in fear and trembling; and one Kruman, not content with assuring us that he was destined never again to see his wives and children, in cannibalic horror anticipated his fate and in imagination saw himself slain, cooked, and devoured. During the ascent all hands had been too closely occupied to allow of surveying, so this duty had now to be resumed, the leadsman being stationed in the bows, and Mr. May sketching in the sides of the river with their ever-varying direction, and taking outline views of the mountains. The westerly breeze blew freshly against us, and being opposed to the current caused a considerable ripple; but the stream being the stronger, we went with but little exertion on our part, at the rate of fully three knots an hour. The sun's rays falling nearly directly upon us, through a perfectly cloudless sky, were so powerfully felt, that we were obliged in self-defence to set our awning, although it somewhat impeded our progress. Just before two o'clock we reached Djin, and landing at the scattered huts to the westward of the town, got a set of sights: while thus occupied, many natives came across the swamp and gathering round, were urgent in their entreaties that we should re-visit their city, which however we respectfully declined. As they increased in numbers they showed a disposition to be again troublesome; so our operations being concluded, we gave a small present to our guide of the day previous, and took our departure. While close to a little grassy islet a few miles below this, we came upon a small herd of river horses in a sportive humour, apparently playing at bo-peep or some such analogous game. One suddenly popped up its huge head close to us, but amazed at our interruption, lost no time in again disappearing below the surface. Shortly, Mount Laird and the eastern end of Pleiad Island were made out, and passing along the northern shore of the latter, by half-past four o'clock we reached Bandawa, and by five, Lau; off both which villages we were met by numerous canoes. Below Lau we examined on the south bank what had seemed to us, during our ascent, a rocky cliff; but we now found it to consist of a bank of red clay some fifteen feet high, with a layer of vegetable mould on the top. As long as we could make out the river's sides, we continued our progress, but though now only a few miles from Gurowa, being unwilling to have a blank in our chart, we anchored for the night, although the weather looked very threatening, and distant lightning in the east presaged a storm. We made, accordingly, every preparation, having our awning ready in case of rain.

The moon set shortly after midnight, and was succeeded by intense darkness, every thing around being unnaturally still; the air was hushed, the wind no longer sighed among the branches, and nothing was heard save the rippling of the ceaseless tide. The sky became completely overcast, one by one the stars disappeared, while numerous indications heralded an approaching tornado. A few minutes were left us to make ready to meet it, which we employed to the best advantage we could. More cable was given, all heavy weights and top-hamper were placed in the bottom of the boat, while Mr. May and I gathered our instruments and our few valuables around us, and covered ourselves as we best could with a scanty waterproof sheet we had with us, merely leaving our heads clear, so as to be able to look around. Our Krumen stripped themselves, and wrapping their blankets about them, were ready to attempt to swim for it in case of necessity. Even my little dog seemed to comprehend the coming strife of the elements, and nestled closer beside me. The rudder was shipped, and the yoke-lines laid ready to be seized at a moment's notice. By this time the eastern heavens were brightly illuminated by flashes of vivid lightning, the electric clouds quickly drawing nearer and nearer to us. These flashes issued from strata higher than the pitchy tornado cloud, which, by their light, showed black as ink and rising rapidly above the horizon. Still in our immediate neighbourhood the unearthly quiet reigned, all noise, all motion being ignored, and the very atmosphere seeming a blank. In this state, however, we were not long permitted to rest; already could we distinguish the hissing of the coming whirlwind, and straining our eyes, we fancied we could discern a white line of foam stretching across the river. Presently it burst on us in full fury; the hurricane, sweeping along, enveloped our tiny craft, and large drops of rain struck fiercely against our faces as we attempted to peer into the obscure. Our only fear had been that the gale might catch us on the broadside, as, our boat being but light, it might have upset us, and left us among the crocodiles and river-horses; but, fortunately for us, it blew right a-head, and we rode easily. The rain, which threatened to be a deluge, ceased after a few minutes, and, still more to our astonishment, the wind greatly moderated, but these were succeeded by the most terrific thunderstorm I ever witnessed. Flash followed flash almost instantaneously, until at last the whole sky was lit up with one incessant glow of the most brilliant light. At last the clouds were right over head, and for upwards of an hour every part of the heavens to which we could look, had its own electric bolt. It was impossible to count such creations of the moment, but there must always have been every instant from ten to a dozen flashes, until at last we were utterly unable to distinguish each single thunder-clap, as all were mingled in one prolonged and continued peal, now for a second more faintly rolling, now again grandly swelling, and echoing in deep reverberations from the rugged sides of the mountains. Everything was plainly visible; the island near us, the banks of the river, and the more distant hills, all were distinctly seen.

Above us, around us, the forked lightning unweariedly still pursued its jagged, angular course, while one huge bolt, disdaining the tortuous path followed by its fellows, passed straight towards the earth, piercing

146

the ground opposite to which we lay at anchor. Among the hills the storm raged still more furiously, the lightning playing unceasingly around each mountain summit, while ever and anon a bright spark would suddenly descend into some of the ravines below. Sometimes the passage of the lightning was from cloud to cloud, even at considerable distances; and then the stream of fire would spread, furcate, and divaricate, like the branch of some huge tree. These currents were of a purpler tint, and of smaller diameter, while those which descended were of a brighter red, and showed a much larger body of light. These aerial bolts were quite distinct from the ordinary discharge of two opposite clouds, and were not the mere passage of electricity from one to the other. During the occurrence of a few unusually near and vivid flashes, Mr. May and I were distinctly sensible of a feeling of warmth in our faces. At length there was a kind of lull, and the storm seemed to be decreasing, when a small whitish cloud was observed in the far east. It was a true cumulo-cirro-stratus, and must have been tremendously charged with electricity; for as it passed slowly along, we plainly saw constant powerful discharges. For some miles it continued to scatter around incessant forked bolts, but at length these became gradually fewer, and died away, while the cloud altered its shape to cirro-cumulus. A fresh breeze sprung up from the westward, and for a little time we were apprehensive of a squall up the river, which would not have been so pleasant; but fortunately this did not occur. By a little after three o'clock this magnificent storm had quite ceased, leaving no trace behind, save a distant thunderpeal, or an occasional flash of lightning among the mountains. Intense darkness prevailed; and now that the war of the elements was ended, we could hear about us the snorting of numerous hippopotami, which during the tempest had in fear been cowering among the reeds. Anxiously we waited for the morning; but it was not until half-past five that we could distinguish the river-banks; but these again visible, we weighed anchor, and resumed our voyage and our survey.

*Narrative of an exploring voyage up the rivers Kwora and Binue,* pp. 203–8

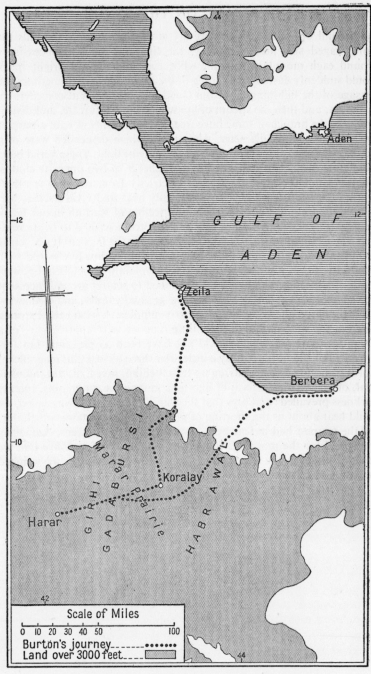

7. Burton's Journey to Harar, 1854-5

# VI

# SIR RICHARD FRANCIS BURTON

## 1821–1890

Burton was the son of a soldier. He was born upon his mother's estate near St. Albans. He had no regular education, but spent a wandering youth and was often on the continent where he became proficient both in languages and swordsmanship. After spending five terms at Oxford, where he studied Arabic, he joined the Indian army in 1842. In India he found opportunities to gratify his lust for travel in remote places and to study more languages and Eastern religions. At this time, also, he gave some offence by consorting closely with Indians and by the unfashionable frankness of his reports upon certain of their customs. This was an anticipation of the public stir he was to make in the 'eighties by his translation of the Arabian Nights with its unexpurgated text and its uncompromising 'anthropological' notes. In 1849 he returned to England where he wrote several books upon India and its languages. In 1853 he undertook in disguise his famous and perilous journey to Mecca, and wrote three volumes upon this expedition.

In October 1854 he arrived in Aden having obtained permission with another officer, Lieutenant Speke (see p. 181), to explore the coastland on the opposite side of the Gulf. Burton went over to Zeila, where he was hospitably received by the Shamarkay, the Governor. While the main expedition was being prepared, Burton decided to strike out alone into the unexplored country of the fanatical Moslem Somali in an attempt to reach the forbidden city of Harar, which stood between Somaliland and Abyssinia and into which no European was ever known to have entered. At Zeila he was warned that the interior was disturbed; that the direct road through the Eesa Somali was closed, and that small-pox was raging in the city. In spite of this he decided to set out, disguised as a Moslem merchant, taking a more southerly route through the country of the Gadabursi and Girhi (or Geri) Somali. He took with him two Somals who had been policemen

149

*in Aden, known as Long Guled and the Hammal, and also a Widad—
which Burton translates 'hedge-priest'—a man of very doubtful
character who was nicknamed 'End of Time'. He left Zeila on 27th
November and the first extract describes his caravan. The opening
words are explained by his having addressed his story to his friend,
J. G. Lumsden.*

## 20. EXPEDITION TO HARAR

You see, dear L., how travelling maketh man *banal*. It is the natural
consequence of being forced to find, in every corner where Fate drops
you for a month, a 'friend of the soul,' and a 'moon-faced beauty.' With
Orientals generally, you *must* be on extreme terms, as in Hibernia, either
an angel of light, or, that failing, a goblin damned. In East Africa
especially, English phlegm, shyness, or pride, will bar every heart and
raise every hand against you, whereas what M. Rochet calls 'a certain
*rondeur* of manner' is a specific for winning affection. You should walk
up to your man, clasp his fist, pat his back, speak some unintelligible
words to him,—if, as is the plan of prudence, you ignore the language,—
laugh a loud guffaw, sit by his side, and begin pipes and coffee. He then
proceeds to utilize you, to beg in one country for your interest, and in
another for your tobacco. You gently but decidedly thrust that subject
out of the way, and choose what is most interesting to yourself. As might
be expected, he will at times revert to his own concerns; your superior
obstinacy will oppose effectual passive resistance to all such efforts; by
degrees the episodes diminish in frequency and duration; at last they
cease altogether. The man is now your own.

You will bear in mind, if you please, that I am a Moslem merchant,
a character not to be confounded with the notable individuals seen on
'Change. Mercator in the East is a compound of tradesman, divine, and
T.G. Usually of gentle birth, he is everywhere welcomed and respected;
and he bears in his mind and manner that, if Allah please, he may
become prime minister a month after he has sold you a yard of cloth.
Commerce appears to be an accident, not an essential, with him; yet he
is by no means deficient in acumen. He is a grave and reverend signior,
with rosary in hand and Koran on lip, is generally a pilgrim, talks at
dreary length about Holy Places, writes a pretty hand, has read and can
recite much poetry, is master of his religion, demeans himself with
respectability, is perfect in all points of ceremony and politeness, and
feels equally at home whether sultan or slave sit upon his counter. He
has a wife and children in his own country, where he intends to spend
the remnant of his days; but 'the world is uncertain'—'Fate descends,

and man's eye seeth it not'—'the earth is a charnel house': briefly, his many wise old saws give him a kind of theoretical consciousness that his bones may moulder in other places but his father-land.

To describe my little caravan. Foremost struts Raghe, our Eesa guide, in all the bravery of Abbanship. He is bareheaded and clothed in Tobe [cloth] and slippers: a long, heavy, horn-hilted dagger is strapped round his waist, outside his dress; in his right hand he grasps a ponderous wire-bound spear which he uses as a staff, and the left forearm supports a round targe of battered hide. Being a man of education, he bears on one shoulder a Musalla or prayer carpet of tanned leather, the article used throughout the Somali country; slung over the other is a Wesi or wicker bottle containing water for religious ablution. He is accompanied by some men who carry a little stock of town goods and drive a camel colt, which by the by they manage to lose before midnight.

My other attendants must now be introduced to you, as they are to be for the next two months companions of our journey. First in the list are Samaweda Yusuf, and Aybla Farih, buxom dames about thirty years old, who presently secured the classical nicknames of Shehrazade and Deenarzade. They look each like three average women rolled into one, and emphatically belong to that race for which the article of feminine attire, called, I believe, 'a bussle' would be quite superfluous. Wonderful, truly, is their endurance of fatigue! During the march they carry pipe and tobacco, lead and flog the camels, adjust the burdens, and will never be induced to ride, in sickness or in health. At the halt they unload the cattle, dispose the parcels in a semicircle, pitch over them the Gurgi or mat tent, cook our food, boil tea and coffee, and make themselves generally useful. They bivouack outside our abode, modesty not permitting the sexes to mingle, and in the severest cold wear no clothing but a head fillet and an old Tobe. They have curious soft voices, which contrast agreeably with the harsh organs of the males. At first they were ashamed to see me; but that feeling soon wore off, and presently they enlivened the way with pleasantries far more naïve than refined. To relieve their greatest fatigue, nothing seems necessary but the 'Jogsi:' they lie at full length, prone, stand upon each other's backs trampling and kneading with the toes, and rise like giants much refreshed. Always attendant upon these dames is Yusuf, a Zayla lad who, being one-eyed, was pitilessly named by my companions the 'Kalendar'; he prays frequently, is strict in his morals, and has conceived, like Mrs. Brownrigg, so exalted an idea of discipline, that, but for our influence, he certainly would have beaten the two female 'prentices to death. They hate him therefore, and he knows it.

Immediately behind Raghe and his party walk Shehrazade and Deenarzade, the former leading the head camel, the latter using my chibouque stick as a staff. She has been at Aden, and sorely suspects me; her little black eyes never meet mine: and frequently, with affected confusion, she turns her sable cheek the clean contrary way. Strung together by their tails, and soundly beaten when disposed to lag, the five camels pace steadily along under their burdens,—bales of Wilyati or American sheetings, Duwwarah or Cutch canvass, with indigo-dyed stuff slung along the animals' sides, and neatly sewn up in a case of matting to keep off dust and rain,—a cow's hide, which serves as a couch, covering the whole. They carry a load of 'Mushakkar' (bad Mocha dates) for the Somal, with a parcel of better quality for ourselves, and a half hundred-weight of coarse Surat tobacco; besides which we have a box of beads, and another of trinkets, mosaic-gold earrings, necklaces, watches and similar nick-nacks. Our private provisions are represented by about 300 lbs. of rice,—here the traveller's staff of life,—a large pot of 'Kawur-meh' [dried meat], dates, salt, clarified butter, tea, coffee, sugar, a box of biscuits in case of famine, 'Halwa' or Arab sweetmeats to be used when driving hard bargains, and a little turmeric for seasoning. A simple batterie de cuisine, and sundry skins full of potable water, dangle from chance rope-ends; and last, but not the least important, is a heavy box of ammunition sufficient for a three month's sporting tour. In the rear of the caravan trudges a Bedouin woman driving a donkey,—the proper 'tail' in these regions, where camels start if followed by a horse or mule. An ill-fated sheep, a parting present from the Hajj, races and frisks about the Cafilah [caravan]. It became so tame, that the Somal received an order not to 'cut' it; one day, however, I found myself dining, and that pet lamb was the menu.

By the side of the camels ride my three attendants, the pink of Somali fashion. Their frizzled wigs are radiant with grease; their Tobes are splendidly white, with borders dazzlingly red; their new shields are covered with canvass cloth; and their two spears, poised over the right shoulder, are freshly scraped, oiled, blackened and polished. They have added my spare rifle, and guns to the camel-load; such weapons are well enough at Aden, in Somali-land men would deride the outlandish tool! I told them that in my country women use bows and arrows, moreover that lancers are generally considered a corps of non-combatants; in vain! they adhered as strongly—so mighty a thing is prejudice—to their partiality for bows, arrows, and lances. Their horsemanship is peculiar, they balance themselves upon little Abyssinian saddles, extending the leg and raising the heel in the Louis Quinze style of equitation, and the stirrup is an iron ring admitting only the big toe. I follow them mounting a fine white mule, which, with its gaudily galonné Arab pad and wrapper cloth, has a certain dignity of look; a double-barrelled gun lies across my lap; and a rude pair of holsters, the work of Hasan Turki, contains my Colt's six-shooters.

Marching in this order, which was to serve as a model, we travelled due south along the coast, over a hard, stoneless, and alluvial plain, here dry, there muddy (where the tide reaches) across boggy creeks, broad water-courses, and warty flats of black mould powdered with nitrous salt, and bristling with the salsolaceous vegetation familiar to the Arab voyager. . . .

My arms were peeled even in the month of December; and my companions, panting with the heat, like the Atlantes of Herodotus, poured forth reproaches upon the rising sun. The townspeople, when forced to hurry across it in the hotter season, cover themselves during the day with Tobes wetted every half hour in sea water; yet they are sometimes killed by the fatal thirst which the Simun engenders. Even the Bedouins are now longing for rain; a few weeks' drought destroys half their herds.

*After a month's riding across the maritime plain and plateau of Somaliland, Burton found himself leaving the end of the true arid Somali country and approaching a transitional belt between 'the desert and the sown' that lay between the Somali hills and those of Harar.*

Early on the 23rd December assembled the Caravan, which we were destined to escort across the Marar Prairie. Upon this neutral ground the Eesa, Berteri, and Habr Awal [three Somali tribes] meet to rob and plunder unhappy travellers. The Somal shuddered at the sight of a wayfarer, who rushed into our encampment *in cuerpo*, having barely run away with his life. Not that our caravan carried much to lose,—a few hides and pots of clarified butter, to be exchanged for the Holcus grain of the Girhi cultivators,—still the smallest contributions are thankfully received by these plunderers. Our material consisted of four or five half-starved camels, about fifty donkeys with ears cropped as a mark, and their eternal accompaniments in Somali-land, old women. The latter seemed to be selected for age, hideousness, and strength: all day they bore their babes smothered in hides upon their backs, and they carried heavy burdens apparently without fatigue. Amongst them was a Bedouin widow, known by her 'Wer,' a strip of the inner bark of a tree tied round the greasy fillet. We were accompanied by three Widads, provided with all the instruments of their craft, and uncommonly tiresome companions. They recited Koran *à tort et à travers*: at every moment they proposed Fatihahs [texts from the first chapter of the Koran], the name of Allah was perpetually upon their lips, and they discussed questions of divinity, like Gil Blas and his friends, with a violence bordering upon frenzy. One of them was celebrated for his skill in the 'Fal', or Omens: he was constantly consulted by my companions, and informed them that we had

153

nought to fear except from wild beasts. The prediction was a good hit: I must own, however, that it was not communicated to me before fulfilment. . . .

Towards evening, as the setting sun sank slowly behind the distant western hills, the colour of the Prairie changed from glaring yellow to a golden hue, mantled with a purple flush inexpressibly lovely. The animals of the waste began to appear. Shy lynxes and jackals, fattened by many sheep's tails, warned my companions that fierce beasts were nigh, ominous anecdotes were whispered, and I was told that a caravan had lately lost nine asses by lions. As night came on, the Bedouin Kafilah, being lightly loaded, preceded us, and our tired camels lagged far behind. We were riding in rear to prevent straggling, when suddenly my mule, the hindermost, pricked his ears uneasily, and attempted to turn his head. Looking backwards, I distinguished the form of a large animal following us with quick and stealthy strides. My companions would not fire, thinking it was a man: at last a rifle-ball, pinging through the air—the moon was too young for correct shooting—put to flight a huge lion. The terror excited by this sort of an adventure was comical to look upon: the valiant Beuh, who, according to himself, had made his *preuves* in a score of foughten fields, threw his arms in the air, wildly shouting 'Libah! Libah! !—the lion! the lion! !'—and nothing else was talked of that evening.

The ghostly western hills seemed to recede as we advanced over the endless rolling plain. Presently the ground became broken and stony, the mules stumbled in deep holes, and the camels could scarcely crawl along. As we advanced, our Widads, who, poor devils! had been 'roasted' by the women all day on account of their poverty, began to recite the Koran with might, in gratitude for having escaped many perils. Night deepening, our attention was rivetted by a strange spectacle; a broad sheet of bright blaze, reminding me of Hanno's fiery river, swept apparently down a hill, and, according to my companions threatened the whole prairie. These accidents are common: a huntsman burns a tree for honey, or cooks his food in the dry grass, the wind rises and the flames spread far and wide. On this occasion no accident occurred; the hills, however, smoked like a Solfatara for two days. . . .

After another delay, and a second vain message to the Gerad Adan [head of a tribe of agricultural Somali, the Girhi], about noon appeared that dignitary's sixth wife, sister to the valiant Beuh. Her arrival disconcerted my companions, who were too proud to be protected by a woman. 'Dahabo,' however, relieved their anxiety by informing us that the Gerad had sent his eldest son Sherwa, as escort. This princess was a gipsy-looking dame, coarsely dressed, about thirty years old, with a gay leer, a jaunty demeanour, and the reputation of being 'fast'; she showed little shamefacedness when I saluted her, and received with noisy joy the appropriate present of a new and handsome Tobe. About 4 p.m. returned our second messenger, bearing with him a reproving message from the Gerad, for not visiting him without delay; in token of sincerity he forwarded his baton, a knobstick about two feet long, painted in rings of Cutch colours, red, black, and yellow alternately, and garnished on the summit with a ball of similar material.

At dawn on the 26th December, mounted upon a little pony, came Sherwa, heir presumptive to the Gerad Adan's knobstick. His father had sent him to us three days before but he feared the Gudabirsi as much as the Gudabirsi feared him, and he probably hung about our camp till certain that it was safe to enter. We received him politely, and he in acknowledgment positively declared that Beuh should not return before eating honey in his cottage. Our Abban's [protector's] heroism now became infectious. Even the End of Time, whose hot valour had long since fallen below zero, was inspired by the occasion, and recited, as usual with him in places and at times of extreme safety, the Arabs' warrior lines—

> 'I have crossed the steed since my eyes saw light,
> I have fronted death till he feared my sight,
> And the cleaving of helm, and the riving of mail
> Were the dreams of my youth—are my manhood's delight.'

As we had finished loading, a mule's bridle was missed. Sherwa ordered instant restitution to his father's stranger, on the ground that all the property now belonged to the Gerad; and we, by no means idle, fiercely threatened to bewitch the kraal. The article was presently found hard by, on a hedge. This was the first and last case of theft which occurred to us in the Somali country;—I have travelled through most civilised lands, and have lost more.

At 8 a.m. we marched towards the north-west, along the southern base of the Gurays hills, and soon arrived at the skirt of the prairie, where a well-trodden path warned us that we were about to quit the desert. After advancing six miles in line we turned to the right, and recited a Fatihah over the heap of rough stones, where, shadowed by venerable trees, lie the remains of the great Shaykh Abd el Malik. A little beyond this spot rises suddenly from the plain a mass of castellated rock, the subject of many a wild superstition. Caravans always encamp beneath it, as whoso sleeps upon the summit loses his senses to evil spirits. At some future day Harar will be destroyed, and 'Jannah Siri' will become a flourishing town. We ascended it, and found no life but hawks, coneys, an owl, and a graceful species of black eagle; there were many traces of buildings, walls, ruined houses, and wells, whilst the sides and summit were tufted with venerable sycamores. This act was an imprudence; the Bedouins at once declared that we were 'prospecting' for a fort, and the evil report preceded us to Harar.

After a mile's march from Jannah Siri, we crossed a ridge of rising ground, and suddenly, as though by magic, the scene shifted.

Before us lay a little Alp; the second step of the Ethiopian Highland. Around were high and jagged hills, their sides black with the Saj [teak] and Somali pine, and their upper brows veiled with a thin growth of cactus. Beneath was a deep valley, in the midst of which ran a serpentine of shining waters, the gladdest spectacle we had yet witnessed: further in front, masses of hill rose abruptly from shady valleys, encircled on the far horizon by a straight blue line of ground, resembling a distant sea. Behind us glared the desert: we had now reached the outskirts of civilization, where man, abandoning his flocks and herds, settles, cultivates, and attends to the comforts of life.

The fields are either terraces upon the hill slopes or the sides of valleys, divided by flowery hedges with lanes between, not unlike those of rustic England, and on a nearer approach the daisy, the thistle, and the sweet briar pleasantly affected my European eyes. The villages are no longer movable: the Kraal and wigwam are replaced by the Gambisa or bell-shaped hut of Middle Africa, circular cottages of holcus wattle, covered with coarse dab and surmounted by a stiff, conical, thatch roof, above which appears the central supporting post, crowned with a gourd or ostrich egg. Strong abbatis of thorns protect these settlements, which stud the hills in all directions: near most of them are clumps of tall trees, to the southern sides of which are hung, like birdcages, long cylinders of matting, the hives of these regions. Yellow crops of holcus rewarded the peasant's toil: in some places the long stems tied in bunches below the ears as piled muskets, stood ready for the reaper; in others, the barer ground showed that the task was done. The boys sat perched upon reed platforms in the trees, and with loud shouts drove away thieving birds, whilst their fathers cut the crop with diminutive sickles, or thrashed heaps of straw with rude flails, or winnowed grain by tossing it with a flat wooden shovel against the wind. The women husked the pineapple-formed heads in mortars composed of a hollowed trunk, smeared the threshing floor with cow-dung and water to defend it from insects, piled the holcus heads into neat yellow heaps, spanned and crossed by streaks of various colours, brick-red and brownish-purple, and stacked the Karbi or straw, which was surrounded like the grain with thorn, as a defence against the wild hog. All seemed to consider it a labour of love: the harvest-home song sounded pleasantly to our ears, and, contrasting with the silent desert, the hum of man's habitation was a music.

Descending the steep slope, we reposed, after a seven miles' march, on the banks of a bright rivulet, which bisects the Kobbo or valley: it runs, according to my guides, from the north towards Ogadayn, and the direction is significant,—about Harar I found neither hill nor stream trending from east to west. The people of the Kutti [cultivated districts] flocked out to gaze upon us; they were unarmed, and did not, like the Bedouins, receive us with cries of 'Bori' [tobacco]. During the halt we bathed in the waters, upon whose banks were a multitude of huge Mantidæ, pink and tender green. Returning to the camels, I shot a kind of crow, afterwards frequently seen. It is about three times the size of our English bird, of a bluish-black with a snow-white poll, and a beak of unnatural proportions; the quantity of lead which it carried off surprised me. A number of Widads assembled to greet us, and some Habr Awal, who were returning with a caravan, gave us the salam, and called my people cousins. 'Verily,' remarked the Hammal, 'amongst friends we cut one another's throats; amongst enemies we become sons of uncles!'

At 3 p.m. we pursued our way over rising ground, dotted with granite blocks fantastically piled, and everywhere in sight of fields and villages and flowing water. A furious wind was blowing, and the End of Time quoted the Somali proverb, 'heat hurts, but cold kills :' the camels were so fatigued, and the air became so raw, that after an hour and a half's march we planted our wigwams near a village distant about seven miles from the Gurays Hills. Till late at night we were kept awake by the crazy Widads: Ao Samattar had proposed the casuistical question, 'Is it lawful to pray upon a mountain when a plain is at hand?' Some took the *pro*, others the *contra*, and the wordy battle raged with uncommon fury.

On Wednesday morning at half-past seven we started down hill towards 'Wilensi,' a small table-mountain at the foot of which we expected to find the Gerad Adan awaiting us in one of his many houses, crossed a fertile valley, and ascended another steep slope by a bad and stony road. Passing the home of Sherwa, who vainly offered hospitality, we toiled onwards, and after a mile and a half's march, which occupied at least two hours, our wayworn beasts arrived at the Gerad's village. On inquiry, it proved that the chief, who was engaged in selecting two horses and two hundred cows, the price of blood claimed by the Amir of Harar for the murder of a citizen, had that day removed to Sagharrah, another settlement.

As we entered the long straggling village of Wilensi, our party was divided by the Gerad's two wives. The Hammal, the Kalendar, Shehrazade, and Deenarzade remained with Beuh and his sister in her Gurgi [hut], whilst Long Guled, the End of Time, and I were conducted to the cottage of the Gerad's prettiest wife, Sudiyah. She was a tall woman, with a light complexion, handsomely dressed in a large Harar Tobe, with silver earrings, and the kind of necklace called Jilbah or Kardas. The Geradah (princess) at once ordered our hides to be spread in a comfortable part of the hut, and then supplied us with food—boiled beef, pumpkin, and Jowari [grain] cakes. During the short time spent in that Gambisa, I had an opportunity, dear L., of seeing the manners and customs of the settled Somal.

The interior of the cottage is simple. Entering the door, a single plank with pins for hinges fitted into sockets above and below the lintel—in fact, as artless a contrivance as ever seen in Spain or Corsica—you find a space, divided by dwarf walls of wattle and dab into three compartments, for the men, women, and cattle. The horses and cows, tethered at night on the left of the door, fill the cottage with the wherewithal to pass many a *nuit blanche*: the wives lie on the right, near a large fireplace of stones and raised clay, and the males occupy the most comfortable part, opposite to and farthest from the entrance. The thatched ceiling shines jetty with smoke, which when intolerable is allowed to escape by a diminutive window: this seldom happens, for smoke, like grease and dirt, keeping man warm, is enjoyed by savages. Equally simple is the furniture: the stem of a tree, with branches hacked into pegs, supports the shields, the assegais are planted against the wall, and divers bits of wood, projecting from the sides and the central roof-tree of the cottage, are hung with clothes and other articles that attract white ants. Gourds smoked inside, and coffee cups of coarse black Harar pottery, with deep wooden platters, and prettily carved spoons of the same material, compose the household supellex. The inmates are the Geradah and her baby, Siddik a Galla serf, the slave girls and sundry Somal: thus we hear at all times three languages spoken within the walls.

Long before dawn the goodwife rises, wakens her handmaidens, lights the fire, and prepares for the Afur or morning meal. The quern is here unknown. A flat, smooth, oval slab, weighing about fifteen pounds, and a stone roller six inches in diameter, worked with both hands, and the weight of the body kneeling ungracefully upon it on 'all fours,' are used to triturate the holcus grain. At times water must be sprinkled over the meal, until a finely powdered paste is ready for the oven: thus several hours' labour is required to prepare a few pounds of bread. About 6 a.m. there appears a substantial breakfast of roast beef and mutton, with scones of Jowari grain, the whole drenched in broth. Of the men few perform any ablutions, but all use the tooth stick before sitting down to eat. After the meal some squat in the sun, others transact business, and drive their cattle to the bush till 11 a.m., the dinner hour. There is no variety in the repasts, which are always flesh and holcus: these people despise fowls, and consider vegetables food for cattle. During the day there is no privacy; men, women, and children enter in crowds, and will not be driven away by the Geradah, who inquires screamingly if they come to stare at a baboon. My kettle especially excites their surprise; some opine that it is an ostrich, others, a serpent: Sudiyah, however, soon discovered its use, and begged irresistibly for the unique article. Throughout the day her slave girls are busied in grinding, cooking, and quarrelling with dissonant voices: the men have little occupation beyond chewing tobacco, chatting, and having their wigs frizzled by a professional coiffeur. In the evening the horses and cattle return home to be milked and stabled: this operation concluded, all apply themselves to supper with a will. They sleep but little, and sit deep into the night trimming the fire, and conversing merrily over their cups of Farshu or millet beer. I tried this mixture several times, and found it detestable: the taste is sour, and it flies directly to the head, in consequence of being mixed with some poisonous bark. It is served up in gourd bottles upon a basket of holcus heads, and strained through a pledget of cotton, fixed across the narrow mouth, into cups of the same primitive material: the drinkers sit around their liquor, and their hilarity argues its intoxicating properties. In the morning they arise with headaches and heavy eyes; but these symptoms, which we, an industrious race, deprecate, are not disliked by the Somal—they promote sleep and give something to occupy the vacant mind.

. . . . . .

On the morning after my arrival at Sagharrah I felt too ill to rise, and was treated with unaffected kindness by all the establishment. The Gerad sent to Harar for millet beer, Ao Samattar went to the gardens in search of Kat [a stimulating vegetable drug], the sons Yusuf Dera and a dwarf insisted upon firing me with such ardour that no refusal could avail: and Khayrah the wife, with her daughters, two tall dark, smiling, and well-favoured girls of thirteen and fifteen, sacrificed a sheep as my Fida, or Expiatory offering. Even the Galla Christians, who flocked to see the stranger, wept for the evil fate which had brought him so far from his fatherland, to die under a tree. Nothing, indeed, would have been easier than such operation: all required was the turning face to the wall, for four or five days. But to expire of an ignoble colic!—the thing was not to be thought of, and a firm resolution to live on sometimes, methinks, effects its object.

On the 1st January, 1855, feeling stronger, I clothed myself in my Arab best, and asked a palaver with the Gerad. We retired to a safe place behind the village, where I read with pomposity the Hajj Sharmarkay's letter. The chief appeared much pleased by our having preferred his country to that of the Eesa: he at once opened the subject of the new fort, and informed me that I was the builder, as his eldest daughter had just dreamed that the stranger would settle in the land. Having discussed the project to the Gerad's satisfaction, we brought out the guns and shot a few birds for the benefit of the vulgar. Whilst engaged in this occupation appeared a party of five strangers, and three mules with ornamented Morocco saddles, bridles, bells, and brass neck ornaments, after the fashion of Harar. Two of these men, Haji Umar and Nur Ambar, were citizens: the others, Ali Hasan, Husayn Araleh, and Haji Mohammed, were Somal of the Habr Awal tribe, high in the Amir's confidence. They had been sent to settle with Adan the weighty matter of Blood-money. After sitting with us almost half-an-hour, during which they exchanged grave salutations with my attendants, inspected our asses with portentous countenances, and asked me a few questions concerning my business in those parts, they went privily to the Gerad, told him that the Arab was not one who bought and sold, that he had no design but to spy out the wealth of the land, and that the whole party should be sent prisoners in their hands to Harar. The chief curtly replied that we were his friends, and bade them 'throw far those words.' Disappointed in their designs, they started late in the afternoon, driving off their 200 cows, and falsely promising to present our salams to the Amir.

It became evident that some decided step must be taken. The Gerad confessed fear of his Harari kinsman, and owned that he had lost all his villages in the immediate neighbourhood of the city. I asked him point-blank to escort us: he as frankly replied that it was impossible. The request was lowered—we begged him to accompany us as far as the frontier: he professed inability to do so, but promised to send his eldest son, Sherwa.

Nothing then remained, dear L., but *payer d'audace*, and, throwing all forethought to the dogs, to rely upon what has made many a small man great, the good star. I addressed my companions in a set speech, advising a mount without delay. They suggested a letter to the Amir, requesting permission to enter his city: this device was rejected for two reasons. In the first place, had a refusal been returned, our journey was cut short, and our labours stultified. Secondly, the End of Time had whispered that my two companions were plotting to prevent the letter reaching its destination. He had charged his own sin upon their shoulders: the Hammal and Long Guled were incapable of such treachery. But our hedge-priest was thoroughly terrified; 'a coward body after a',' his face brightened when ordered to remain with the Gerad at Sagharrah, and though openly taunted with poltroonery, he had not the decency to object. My companions were then informed that hitherto our acts had been those of old women, not soldiers, and that something savouring of manliness must be done before we could return. They saw my determination to start alone, if necessary, and to do them justice, they at once arose. This was the more courageous in them, as alarmists had done their worst: but a day before, some travelling Somali had advised them, as they valued dear life, not to accompany that Turk to Harar. Once in the saddle, they shook off sad thoughts, declaring that if they were slain, I should pay their blood-money, and if they escaped, that their reward was in my hands. When in some danger, the Hammal especially behaved with a sturdiness which produced the most beneficial results. Yet they were true Easterns. Wearied by delay at Harar, I employed myself in meditating flight; they drily declared that after-wit serves no good purpose: whilst I considered the possibility of escape, they looked only at the prospect of being dragged back with pinioned arms by the Amir's guard. Such is generally the effect of the vulgar Moslems' blind fatalism.

I then wrote an English letter from the Political Agent at Aden to the Amir of Harar, proposing to deliver it in person, and throw off my disguise. Two reasons influenced me in adopting this 'neck or nothing' plan. All the races amongst whom my travels lay, hold him nidering who hides his origin in places of danger; and secondly, my white face had converted me into a Turk, a nation more hated and suspected than any Europeans, without our *prestige*. Before leaving Sagharrah, I entrusted to the End of Time a few lines addressed to Lieut. Herne at Berberah, directing him how to act in case of necessity. Our baggage was again decimated: the greater part was left with Adan, and an ass carried only what was absolutely necessary—a change of clothes, a book or two, a few biscuits, ammunition, and a little tobacco. My Girhi escort consisted of Sherwa, the Bedouin Abtidon, and Mad Said mounted on the End of Time's mule.

At 10 a.m. on the 2nd January all the villagers assembled and recited the Fatihah, consoling us with the information that we were dead men. By the worst of foot-paths we ascended the rough and stony hill behind Sagharrah, through bush and burn and over ridges of rock. At the summit was a village, where Sherwa halted, declaring that he dared not advance: a swordsman, however, was sent on to guard us through the Galla Pass. After an hour's ride we reached the foot of a tall Table-mountain called Kondura, where our road, a goat-path rough with rocks or fallen trees, and here and there arched over with giant creepers, was reduced to a narrow ledge, with a forest above and a forest below. I could not but admire the beauty of this Valombrosa, which reminded me of scenes whilome enjoyed in fair Touraine. High up on our left rose the perpendicular walls of the misty hill, fringed with tufted pine, and on the right, the shrub-clad folds fell into a deep valley. The cool wind whistled and sunbeams like golden shafts darted through tall shady trees—

> Bearded with moss, and in garments green—

the ground was clothed with dank grass, and around the trunks grew thistles, daisies, and blue flowers which at a distance might well pass for violets.

Presently we were summarily stopped by half-a-dozen Gallas attending upon one Rabah, the Chief who owns the Pass. This is the African style of toll-taking: the 'pike' appears in the form of a plump of spearmen, and the gate is a pair of lances thrown across the road. Not without trouble, for they feared to depart from the *mos majorum*, we persuaded

L                              161

them that the ass carried no merchandise. Then, rounding Kondura's northern flank, we entered the Amir's territory: about thirty miles distant, and separated by a series of blue valleys, lay a dark speck upon a tawny sheet of stubble—Harar.

Having paused for a moment to savour success, we began the descent. The ground was a slippery black soil—mist ever settles upon Kondura—and frequent springs oozing from the rock formed beds of black mire. A few huge Birbisa trees, the remnant of a forest still thick around the mountain's neck, marked out the road: they were branchy from stem to stern, and many had a girth of from twenty to twenty-five feet.

After an hour's ride amongst thistles, whose flowers of a bright red-like worsted were not less than a child's head, we watered our mules at a rill below the slope. Then remounting, we urged over hill and dale, where Galla peasants were threshing and storing their grain with loud songs of joy: they were easily distinguished by their African features, mere caricatures of the Somal, whose type has been Arabised by repeated immigrations from Yemen and Hadramaut. Late in the afternoon, having gained ten miles in a straight direction, we passed through a hedge of plantains, defending the windward side of Gafra, a village of Midgans who collect the Gerad Adan's grain. They shouted delight on recognizing their old friend, Mad Said, led us to an empty Gambisa, swept and cleaned it, lighted a fire, turned our mules into a field to graze, and went forth to seek food. Their hospitable thoughts, however, were marred by the two citizens of Harar, who privately threatened them with the Amir's wrath if they dared to feed that Turk. . . .

About noon we crossed the Erar River. The bed is about one hundred yards broad, and a thin sheet of clear, cool, and sweet water covered with crystal the greater part of the sand. According to my guides, its course, like that of the hills, is southerly towards the Webbe of Ogadayn: none, however, could satisfy my curiosity concerning the course of the only perennial stream which exists between Harar and the coast.

In the lower valley, a mass of waving holcus, we met a multitude of Galla peasants coming from the city market with new potlids and the empty gourds which had contained their butter, ghee, and milk: all wondered aloud at the Turk, concerning whom they had heard many horrors. As we commenced another ascent appeared a Harar Grandee mounted upon a handsomely caparisoned mule and attended by seven servants who carried gourds and skins of grain. He was a pale-faced senior with a white beard, dressed in a fine Tobe and a snowy turban with scarlet edges: he carried no shield, but an Abyssinian broadsword was slung over his left shoulder. We exchanged courteous salutations, and as I was thirsty he ordered a footman to fill a cup with water. . . .

At 2 p.m. we fell into a narrow fenced lane and halted for a few minutes near a spreading tree, under which sat women selling ghee and unspun cotton. About two miles on the crest of a hill stood the city,—the end of my present travel,—a long sombre line strikingly contrasting with the whitewashed towns of the East. The spectacle, materially speaking, was a disappointment: nothing conspicuous appeared but two grey minarets of rude shape: many would have grudged exposing three lives to win so paltry a prize. But of all that have attempted, none ever succeeded in entering that pile of stones: the thoroughbred traveller, dear L., will understand my exultation, although my two companions exchanged glances of wonder.

Spurring our mules we advanced at a long trot, when Mad Said stopped us to recite a Fatihah in honour of Ao Umar Siyad and Ao Rahmah, two great saints who repose under a clump of trees near the road. The soil on both sides of the path is rich and red: masses of plantains, limes, and pomegranates denote the gardens, which are defended by a bleached cow's skull, stuck upon a short stick, and between them are plantations of coffee, bastard saffron, and the graceful Kat. About half a mile eastward of the town appears a burn called Jalah or the Coffee Water: the crowd crossing it did not prevent my companions bathing, and whilst they donned clean Tobes I retired to the wayside, and sketched the town.

These operations over, we resumed our way up a rough *tranchée* ridged with stone and hedged with tall cactus. This ascends to an open plain. On the right lie the holcus fields, which reach to the town wall: the left is a heap of rude cemetery, and in front are the dark defences of Harar, with groups of citizens loitering about the large gateway, and sitting in chat near the ruined tomb of Ao Abdal. We arrived at 3 p.m. after riding about five hours, which were required to accomplish twenty miles in a straight direction.

Advancing to the gate, Mad Said accosted a warder, known by his long wand of office, and sent our salams to the Amir, saying that we came from Aden, and requested the honor of audience. Whilst he sped upon his errand, we sat at the foot of a round bastion, and were scrutinised, derided, and catechised by the curious of both sexes, especially by that conventionally termed the fair. . . .

After waiting half-an-hour at the gate, we were told by the returned warder to pass the threshold, and, remounting, guided our mules along the main street, a narrow up-hill lane, with rocks cropping out from a surface more irregular than a Perote pavement. Long Guled had given his animal into the hands of our two Bedouins: they did not appear till after our audience, when they informed us that the people at the entrance had advised them to escape with the beasts, an evil fate having been prepared for the proprietors.

Arrived within a hundred yards of the gate of holcus-stalks, which opens into the courtyard of this African St. James, our guide, a blear-eyed, surly-faced, angry-voiced fellow, made signs—none of us understanding his Harari—to dismount. We did so. He then began to trot, and roared out apparently that we must do the same. We looked at one another, the Hammal swore that he would perish foully rather than obey, and—conceive, dear L., the idea of a petticoated pilgrim venerable as to beard and turban breaking into a long 'double!'—I expressed much the same sentiment. Leading our mules leisurely, in spite of the guide's wrath, we entered the gate, strode down the yard, and were placed under a tree in its left corner, close to a low building of rough stone, which the clanking of frequent fetters argued to be a state-prison.

This part of the court was crowded with Gallas, some lounging about, others squatting in the shade under the palace walls. The chiefs were known by their zinc armlets, composed of thin spiral circlets, closely joined, and extending in mass from the wrist almost to the elbow: all appeared to enjoy peculiar privileges—they carried their long spears, wore their sandals, and walked leisurely about the royal precincts. A delay of half-an-hour, during which state-affairs were being transacted within, gave me time to inspect a place of which so many and such different accounts are current. The palace itself is, as Clapperton describes the Fellatah Sultan's state-hall, a mere shed, a long, single-storied, windowless barn of rough stone and reddish clay, with no other insignia but a thin coat of whitewash over the door. This is the royal and vizierial distinction at Harar, where no lesser man may stucco the walls of his house. The courtyard was about eighty yards long by thirty in breadth, irregularly shaped, and surrounded by low buildings: in the centre, opposite the outer entrance, was a circle of masonry, against which were propped divers doors.

Presently the blear-eyed guide with the angry voice returned from within, released us from the importunities of certain forward and inquisitive youth, and motioned us to doff our slippers at a stone step, or rather line, about twelve feet distant from the palace-wall. We grumbled that we were not entering a mosque, but in vain. Then ensued a long dispute, in tongues mutually unintelligible, about giving up our weapons: by dint of obstinacy we retained our daggers and my revolver. The guide raised a door curtain, suggested a bow, and I stood in the presence of the dreaded chief.

The Amir, or, as he styles himself, the Sultan Ahmad bin Sultan Abubakr, sat in a dark room with whitewashed walls, to which hung—significant decorations—rusty matchlocks and polished fetters. His appearance was that of a little Indian Rajah, an etiolated youth twenty-four or twenty-five years old, plain and thin-bearded, with a yellow complexion, wrinkled brows and protruding eyes. His dress was a flowing robe of crimson cloth edged with snowy fur, and a narrow white

turban tightly twisted round a tall conical cap of red velvet, like the old
Turkish headgear of our painters. His throne was a common Indian
Kursi, or raised cot, about five feet long, with back and sides supported
by a dwarf railing: being an invalid he rested his elbow upon
a pillow, under which appeared the hilt of a Cutch sabre. Ranged
in double line, perpendicular to the Amír, stood the 'court', his
cousins and nearest relations, with right arms bared after fashion of
Abyssinia.

I entered the room with a loud 'Peace be upon ye!' to which H.H.
replying graciously, and extending a hand, bony and yellow as a kite's
claw, snapped his thumb and middle finger. Two chamberlains stepping
forward held my forearms, and assisted me to bend low over the fingers,
which however I did not kiss, being naturally averse to performing that
operation upon any but a woman's hand. My two servants then took
their turn: in this case, after the back was saluted, the palm was presented for a repetition. These preliminaries concluded, we were led to
and seated upon a mat in front of the Amir, who directed towards us
a frowning brow and an inquisitive eye.

Some inquiries were made about the chief's health: he shook his head
captiously, and inquired our errand. I drew from my pocket my own
letter: it was carried by a chamberlain, with hands veiled in his Tobe, to
the Amir, who after a brief glance laid it upon the couch, and demanded
further explanation. I then represented in Arabic that we had come from
Aden, bearing the compliments of our Daulah or governor, and that we
had entered Harar to see the light of H.H.'s countenance: this information concluded with a little speech, describing the changes of Political
Agents in Arabia, and alluding to the friendship formerly existing between the English and the deceased chief Abubakr.

The Amir smiled graciously.

This smile I must own, dear L., was a relief. We had been prepared
for the worst, and the aspect of affairs in the palace was by no means
reassuring.

Whispering to his Treasurer, a little ugly man with a badly shaven
head, coarse features, pug nose, angry eyes, and stubby beard, the Amir
made a sign for us to retire. The *baise main* was repeated, and we backed
out of the audience-shed in high favour. According to grandiloquent
Bruce, 'the Court of London and that of Abyssinia are, in their principles, one:' the loiterers in the Harar palace yard, who had before
regarded us with cut-throat looks, now smiled as though they loved us.
Marshalled by the guard, we issued from the precincts, and after walking a hundred yards entered the Amir's second palace, which we were
told to consider our home. There we found the Bedouins, who, scarcely
believing that we had escaped alive, grinned in the joy of their hearts,
and we were at once provided from the chief's kitchen with a dish of

Shabta, holcus cakes soaked in sour milk, and thickly powdered with red pepper, the salt of this inland region. . . .

Returning we inquired anxiously of the treasurer about my servants' arms which had not been returned, and were assured that they had been placed in the safest of store-houses, the palace. I then sent a common six-barrelled revolver as a present to the Amir, explaining its use to the bearer, and we prepared to make ourselves as comfortable as possible. The interior of our new house was a clean room, with plain walls, and a floor of tamped earth; opposite the entrance were two broad steps of masonry, raised about two feet, and a yard above the ground, and covered with hard matting. I contrived to make upon the higher ledge a bed with the cushions which my companions used as shabracques, and, after seeing the mules fed and tethered, lay down to rest, worn out by fatigue and profoundly impressed with the *poésie* of our position. I was under the roof of a bigoted prince whose least word was death; amongst a people who detest foreigners; the only European that had ever passed over their inhospitable threshold, and the fated instrument of their future downfall.

. . . . . .

The ancient capital of Hadiyah shares with Zebid, in Yemen, the reputation of being an Alma Mater, and inundates the surrounding districts with poor scholars and crazy 'Widads.' Where knowledge leads to nothing, says philosophic Volney, nothing is done to acquire it, and the mind remains in a state of barbarism. There are no establishments for learning, no endowments, as generally in the East, and apparently no encouragement to students: books also are rare and costly. None but the religious sciences are cultivated. The chief Ulema [learned men] are the Kabir Khalil, the Kabir Yunis, and the Shaykh Jami: the two former scarcely ever quit their houses, devoting all their time to study and tuition: the latter is a Somali who takes an active part in politics. . . .

Harar has not only its own tongue, unintelligible to any save the citizens; even its little population of about 8000 souls is a distinct race. The Somal say of the city that it is a Paradise inhabited by asses: certainly the exterior of the people is highly unprepossessing. Amongst the men, I did not see a handsome face: their features are coarse and debauched; many of them squint, others have lost an eye by smallpox, and they are disfigured by scrofula and other diseases: the bad expression of their countenances justifies the proverb, 'Hard as the heart of Harar.' Generally the complexion is a yellowish brown, the beard short, stubby and untractable as the hair, and the hands and wrists, feet and ancles, are large and ill-made. The stature is moderate-sized, some of the elders show the 'pudding sides' and the pulpy stomachs of Banyans, whilst others are lank and bony as Arabs or Jews. Their voices are loud and rude. The dress is a mixture of Arab and Abyssinian. They shave the head, and clip the mustachios and imperial close, like the Shafei of Yemen. Many are bareheaded, some wear a cap, generally the embroidered Indian work, or the common cotton Takiyah of Egypt: a few affect white turbans of the fine Harar work, loosely twisted over the ears. The body-garment is the Tobe, worn flowing as in the Somali country or girt with the dagger-strap round the waist: the richer classes bind under it a Futah or loin-cloth and the dignitaries have wide Arab drawers of white calico. Coarse leathern sandals, a rosary and a tooth-stick rendered perpetually necessary by the habit of chewing tobacco complete the costume: and arms being forbidden in the streets, the citizens carry wands five or six feet long.

The women, who, owing probably to the number of female slaves, are much the more numerous, appear beautiful by contrast with their lords. They have small heads, regular profiles, straight noses, large eyes, mouths approaching the Caucasian type, and light yellow complexions. . . .

Silver ornaments are worn only by persons of rank. The ear is decorated with Somali rings or red coral beads, the neck with necklaces of the same material, and the fore-arms with six or seven of the broad circles of buffalo and other dark horns prepared in Western India. Finally, stars are tattooed upon the bosom, the eyebrows are lengthened with dyes, the eyes fringed with Kohl, and the hands and feet stained with henna.

The female voice is harsh and screaming, especially when heard after the delicate organs of the Somal. The fair sex is occupied at home spinning cotton thread for weaving Tobes, sashes, and turbans; carrying their progeny perched upon their backs, they bring water from the wells in large gourds borne on the head; work in the gardens, and—the men considering, like the Abyssinians, such work a disgrace—sit and sell in the long street which here represents the Eastern bazaar. Chewing tobacco enables them to pass much of their time, and the rich diligently anoint themselves with ghee [butter], whilst the poorer classes use remnants of fat from the lamps. Their freedom of manners renders a public flogging occasionally indispensable. Before the operation begins, a few gourds full of cold water are poured over their heads and shoulders, after which a single-thonged whip is applied with vigour.

Both sexes are celebrated for laxity of morals. High and low indulge freely in intoxicating drinks, beer, and mead. The Amir has established strict patrols, who unmercifully bastinado those caught in the streets after a certain hour. They are extremely bigoted, especially against Christians, the effect of their Abyssinian wars, and are fond of 'Jihading' with the Gallas, over whom they boast many a victory. I have seen a letter addressed by the late Amir to the Hajj Sharmarkay, in which he boasts of having slain a thousand infidels, and, by way of bathos, begs for a few pounds of English gunpowder. The Harari hold foreigners in especial hate and contempt, and divide them into two orders, Arabs and Somal. The latter, though nearly one-third of the population, or 2500 souls, are, to use their own phrase, cheap as dust: their natural timidity is increased by the show of pomp and power, whilst the word 'prison' gives them the horrors.

· · · · · ·

After a day's repose, we were summoned by the Treasurer, early in the forenoon, to wait upon the Gerad Mohammed. Sword in hand, and followed by the Hammal and Long Guled, I walked to the 'palace,' and entering a little ground-floor-room on the right of and close to the audience-hall, found the minister sitting upon a large dais covered with Persian carpets. He was surrounded by six of his brother Gerads or councillors, two of them in turbans, the rest with bare and shaven heads: their Tobes, as is customary on such occasions of ceremony, were allowed to fall beneath the waist. The lower part of the hovel was covered with dependents, amongst whom my Somal took their seats: it seemed to be customs' time, for names were being registered, and money changed hands. The Grandees were eating Kat, or as it is here called 'Jat.' One of the party prepared for the Prime Minister the tenderest twigs of the tree, plucking off the points of even the softest leaves. Another pounded the plant with a little water in a wooden mortar: of this paste, called 'El Madkuk,' a bit was handed to each person, who, rolling it into a ball, dropped it into his mouth. All at times, as is the custom, drank cold water from a smoked gourd, and seemed to dwell upon the sweet and pleasant draught. I could not but remark the fine flavour of the plant after the coarser quality grown in Yemen. Europeans perceive but little effect from it—friend S. and I once tried in vain a strong infusion—the Arabs, however, unaccustomed to stimulants and narcotics, declare that, like opium eaters, they cannot live without the excitement. It seems to produce in them a manner of dreamy enjoyment, which, exaggerated by time and distance, may have given rise to that splendid myth the Lotos, and the Lotophagi. It is held by the Ulema here as in Arabia, 'Akl el Salikin,' or the Food of the Pious, and literati remark that it has the singular properties of enlivening the imagination, clearing the ideas, cheering the heart, diminishing sleep, and taking the place of food. The people of Harar eat it every day from 9 a.m. till near noon, when they dine and afterwards indulge in something stronger—millet-beer and mead.

The Gerad, after polite inquiries, seated me by his right hand upon the Dais, where I ate Kat and fingered my rosary, whilst he transacted the business of the day. Then one of the elders took from a little recess

in the wall a large book, and uncovering it, began to recite a long Dua
or Blessing upon the Prophet: at the end of each period all present
intoned the response, 'Allah bless our Lord Mohammed with his Progeny and his Companions, one and all!' This exercise lasting half-an-hour
afforded me the opportunity—much desired—of making an impression.
The reader, misled by a marginal reference, happened to say, 'angels,
Men, and Genii': the Gerad took the book and found written, 'Men,
Angels, and Genii.' Opinions were divided as to the order of beings,
when I explained that human nature, which amongst Moslems is *not* a
little lower than the angelic, ranked highest, because of it were created
prophets, apostles, and saints, whereas the other is but a 'Wasitah' or
connection between the Creator and his creatures. My theology won
general approbation and a few kinder glances from the elders.

Prayer concluded, a chamberlain whispered the Gerad, who arose,
deposited his black coral rosary, took up an inkstand, donned a white
'Badan' or sleeveless Arab cloak over his cotton shirt, shuffled off the
Dais into his slippers, and disappeared. Presently we were summoned to
an interview with the Amir: this time I was allowed to approach the
outer door with covered feet. Entering ceremoniously as before, I was
motioned by the Prince to sit near the Gerad, who occupied a Persian
rug on the ground to the right of the throne: my two attendants squatted
upon the humbler mats in front and at a greater distance. After sundry
inquiries about the changes that had taken place at Aden, the letter was
suddenly produced by the Amir, who looked upon it suspiciously and
bade me explain its contents. I was then asked by the Gerad whether it
was my intention to buy and sell at Harar: the reply was, 'We are no
buyers nor sellers; we have become your guests to pay our respects to
the Amir—whom may Allah preserve!—and that the friendship between
the two powers may endure.' This appearing satisfactory, I added, in
lively remembrance of the proverbial delays of Africa, where two or
three months may elapse before a letter is answered or a verbal message
delivered, that perhaps the Prince would be pleased to dismiss us soon,
as the air of Harar was too dry for me, and my attendants were in danger of the smallpox, then raging in the town. The Amir, who was
chary of words, bent towards the Gerad, who briefly ejaculated, 'The
reply will be vouchsafed:' with this unsatisfactory answer the interview
ended.

Shortly after arrival, I sent my Salam to one of the Ulema, Shaykh
Jami of the Berteri Somal: he accepted the excuse of ill-health, and at
once came to see me. This personage appeared in the form of a little
black man aged about forty, deeply pitted by smallpox, with a protruding brow, a tufty beard and rather delicate features: his hands and feet
were remarkably small. Married to a descendant of the Sherif Yunis, he
had acquired great reputation as an Alim of Savan, a peace-policy-man,

and an ardent Moslem. Though an imperfect Arabic scholar, he proved remarkably well read in the religious sciences, and even the Meccans had, it was said, paid him the respect of kissing his hand during his pilgrimage. In his second character, his success was not remarkable, the principal results being a spear-thrust in the head, and being generally told to read his books and leave men alone. Yet he is always doing good 'lillah,' that is to say, gratis and for Allah's sake: his pugnacity and bluntness—the prerogatives of the 'peaceful'—gave him some authority over the Amir, and he has often been employed on political missions amongst the different chiefs. Nor has his ardour for propagandism been thoroughly gratified. He commenced his travels with an intention of winning the crown of glory without delay, by murdering the British Resident at Aden: struck, however, with the order and justice of our rule, he changed his intentions and offered El Islam to the officer, who received it so urbanely, that the simple Eastern repenting having intended to cut the Kafir's throat, began to pray fervently for his conversion. Since that time he has made it a point of duty to attempt every infidel: I never heard, however, that he succeeded with a soul.

The Shaykh's first visit did not end well. He informed me that the old Usmanlis conquered Stamboul in the days of Umar. I imprudently objected to the date, and he revenged himself for the injury done to his fame by the favourite ecclesiastical process of privily damning me for a heretic, and a worse than heathen. Moreover he had sent me a kind of ritual which I had perused in an hour and returned to him: this prepossessed the Shaykh strongly against me, lightly 'skimming' books being a form of idleness as yet unknown to the ponderous East.

Our days at Harar were monotonous enough. In the morning we looked to the mules, drove out the cats—as great a nuisance here as at Aden—and ate for breakfast lumps of boiled beef with peppered holcusscones. We were kindly looked upon by one Sultan, a sick and decrepit Eunuch, who having served five Amirs, was allowed to remain in the palace. To appearance he was mad: he wore upon his poll a motley scratch wig, half white and half black, like Day and Night in masquerades. But his conduct was sane. At dawn he sent us bad plantains, wheaten crusts, and cups of unpalatable coffee-tea, and, assisted by a crone more decrepit than himself, prepared for me his water-pipe, a gourd fitted with two reeds and a tile of baked clay by way of bowl; now he 'knagged' at the slave-girls, who were slow to work, then burst into a fury because some visitor ate Kat without offering it to him, or crossed the royal threshold in sandal or slipper. The other inmates of the house were Galla slave-girls, a great nuisance, especially one Berille, an unlovely maid, whose shrill voice and shameless manners were a sad scandal to pilgrims and pious Moslems. . . .

Our fate was probably decided by the arrival of a youth of the Ayyal

Gedid clan, who reported that three brothers had landed in the Somali country, that two of them were anxiously awaiting at Berberah the return of the third from Harar, and that, though dressed like Moslems, they were really Englishmen in government employ. Visions of cutting off caravans began to assume a hard and palpable form: the Habr Awal ceased intriguing and the Gerad Mohammed resolved to adopt the *suaviter in modo* whilst dealing with his dangerous guest.

Some days after his first visit, the Shaykh Jami, sending for the Hammal, informed him of an intended trip from Harar: my follower suggested that we might well escort him. The good Shaykh at once offered to apply for leave from the Gerad Mohammed; not, however, finding the minister at home, he asked us to meet him at the palace on the morrow, about the time of Kat-eating.

We had so often been disappointed in our hopes of a final 'lay-public,' that on this occasion much was not expected. However, about 6 a.m., we were all summoned, and entering the Gerad's levee-room were, as usual, courteously received. I had distinguished his complaint—chronic bronchitis—and resolving to make a final impression, related to him all its symptoms, and promised, on reaching Aden, to send the different remedies employed by ourselves. He clung to the hope of escaping his sufferings, whilst the attendant courtiers looked on approvingly, and begged me to lose no time. Presently the Gerad was sent for by the Amir, and after a few minutes I followed him, on this occasion, alone. Ensued a long conversation about the state of Aden, of Zayla, of Berberah, and of Stamboul. The chief put a variety of questions about Arabia, and every object there: the answer was that the necessity of commerce confined us to the gloomy rock. He used some obliging expressions about desiring our friendship, and having considerable respect for a people who built, he understood, large ships. I took the opportunity of praising Harar in cautious phrase, and especially of regretting that its coffee was not better known amongst the Franks. The small wizen-faced man smiled, as Moslems say, the smile of Umar [who smiled only once]: seeing his brow relax for the first time, I told him that being now restored to health, we requested his commands for Aden. He signified consent with a nod, and the Gerad, with many compliments, gave me a letter addressed to the Political Resident, and requested me to take charge of a mule as a present. I then arose, recited a short prayer, the gist of which was that the Amir's days and reign might be long in the land, and that the faces of his foes might be blackened here and hereafter, bent over his hand and retired. Returning to the Gerad's levee-hut, I saw by the countenances of my two attendants that they were not a little anxious about the interview, and comforted them with the whispered word 'Achha'—'all right!'

Presently appeared the Gerad, accompanied by two men, who brought my servants' arms, and the revolver which I had sent to the prince. This was a *contretemps*. It was clearly impossible to take back the present, besides which, I suspected some finesse to discover my feelings towards him: the other course would ensure delay. I told the Gerad that the weapon was intended especially to preserve the Amir's life, and for further effect, snapped caps in rapid succession to the infinite terror of the august company. The minister returned to his master, and soon brought back the information that after a day or two another mule should be given to me. With suitable acknowledgments we arose, blessed the Gerad, bade adieu to the assembly, and departed joyful, the Hammal in his glee speaking broken English, even in the Amir's courtyard.

Returning home, we found the good Shaykh Jami, to whom we communicated the news with many thanks for his friendly aid. I did my best to smooth his temper about Turkish history, and succeeded. Becoming communicative, he informed me that the original object of his visit was the offer of good offices, he having been informed that in the town was a man who brought down the birds from heaven, and the citizens having been thrown into great excitement by the probable intentions of such a personage. Whilst he sat with us, Kabir Khalil, one of the principal Ulema, and one Hajj Abdullah, a Shaykh of distinguished fame who had been dreaming dreams in our favour, sent their salams. This is one of the many occasions in which, during a long residence in the East, I have had reason to be grateful to the learned, whose influence over the people when unbiassed by bigotry is decidedly for good. That evening there was great joy amongst the Somal, who had been alarmed for the safety of my companions: they brought them presents of Harari Tobes, and a feast of fowls, limes, and wheaten bread for the stranger.

On the 11th of January I was sent for by the Gerad and received the second mule. At noon we were visited by the Shaykh Jami, who, after a long discourse upon the subject of Sufiism,[1] invited me to inspect his books. When midday prayer was concluded we walked to his house, which occupies the very centre of the city: in its courtyard is 'Gay Humburti,' the historic rock upon which Saint Nur held converse with the Prophet Khizr. The Shaykh, after seating us in a room about ten feet square, and lined with scholars and dusty tomes, began reading out a treatise upon the genealogies of the Grand Masters, and showed me in half-a-dozen tracts the tenets of the different schools. The only valuable MS. in the place was a fine old copy of the Koran; the Kamus and the Sihah were there, but by no means remarkable for beauty or correctness. Books at Harar are mostly antiques, copyists being exceedingly rare, and the square massive character is more like Cufic with diacritical points, than the graceful modern Naskhi. I could not, however, but admire the bindings: no Eastern country save Persia surpasses

[1] The Eastern parent of Freemasonry. (*Burton's note*.)

172

them in strength and appearance. After some desultory conversation the Shaykh ushered us into an inner room, or rather a dark closet partitioned off from the study, and ranged us around the usual dish of boiled beef, holcus bread, and red pepper. After returning to the study we sat for a few minutes—Easterns rarely remain long after dinner—and took leave, saying that we must call upon the Gerad Mohammed. . . .

Our intention was to mount early on Friday morning. When we awoke, however, a mule had strayed and was not brought back for some hours. Before noon Shaykh Jami called upon us, informed us that he would travel on the most auspicious day—Monday—and exhorted us to patience, deprecating departure upon Friday, the Sabbath. Then he arose to take leave, blessed us at some length, prayed that we might be borne upon the wings of safety, again advised Monday, and promised at all events to meet us at Wilensi.

I fear that the Shaykh's counsel was on this occasion likely to be disregarded. We had been absent from our goods and chattels a whole fortnight: the people of Harar are famously fickle; we knew not what the morrow might bring forth from the Amir's mind—in fact, all these African cities are prisons on a large scale, into which you enter by your own will, and, as the significant proverb says, you leave by another's. However, when the mosque prayers ended, a heavy shower and the stormy aspect of the sky preached patience more effectually than did the divine: we carefully tethered our mules, and unwillingly deferred our departure till next morning.

*First footsteps in East Africa*, 1st edition, pp. 130–140, 247–266, 280–303, 323–330, 346–363

*Burton returned safely to Berbera, but as a result—according to Speke—of the delay and suspicion caused by his journey to Harar, the main expedition had hardly started before it was attacked by the Somali. A spear pierced Burton's face from cheek to cheek, Speke was more seriously wounded, as he was tortured by his captors and speared in eleven places, while a third member, Stroyan, was killed.*

*Both men recovered from their wounds, and upon his return to England Burton gained the support of the Royal Geographical Society, and also a government grant, for an attempt to penetrate the heart of equatorial Africa from Zanzibar in order to clear up the mystery of the reported great lake or lakes. Upon this important journey he took Speke as his second in command.*

*After some preliminary travelling on the coast to find the best*

*route they struck inland along the Arab slavers' line from Bagamoyo
to Kazeh or Tabora, the great inland centre of the slave-trade. They
were accompanied by Bombay, a Swahili who spoke Hindustani. At
Tabora they met the Arab who had been the first to reach Uganda a
few years before, and were told that there were three great lakes.
They then pushed on westwards with increasing difficulty. They met
with opposition from the tribes, while Burton was constantly prostrated with fever and Speke almost blind with ophthalmia. To judge
by Burton's references—and lack of references—to Speke at this
moment of their great achievement in African discovery, the rift
which was to embitter their future lives had already opened between
them. The extract which follows is Burton's account of the discovery
of the first of the great African lakes.*

## 21. DISCOVERY OF LAKE TANGANYIKA

The 10th February saw us crossing the normal sequence of jungly and
stony 'neat's-tongues,' divided by deep and grassy swamps, which, stagnant in the dry weather, drain after rains the northern country to the
Malagarazi River. We passed over by a felled tree-trunk an unfordable
rivulet, hemmed in by a dense and fetid thicket; and the asses summarily
pitched down the muddy bank into the water, swam across and wriggled
up the slimy off-side like cats. Thence a foul swamp of black mire led to
the Ruguvu or Luguvu River, the western boundary of Uvinza and the
eastern frontier of Ukaranga. This stream, which can be forded during
the dry season, had spread out after the rains over its borders of grassy
plain; we were delayed till the next morning in a miserable camping
ground, a mud-bank thinly veiled with vegetation, in order to bridge
it with branching trees. An unusual downfall during the night might
have caused serious consequences;—provisions had now disappeared,
moreover the porters considered the place dangerous.

The 10th February began with the passage of the Ruguvu River,
where again our goods and chattels were fated to be thoroughly sopped.
I obtained a few corn-cobs from a passing caravan of Wanyamwezi, and
charged them with meat and messages for the party left behind. A desert
march, similar to the stage last travelled, led us to the Unguwwe or
Uvungwe River, a shallow, muddy stream, girt in as usual by dense
vegetation; and we found a fine large kraal on its left bank. After a cold
and rainy night, we resumed our march by fording the Unguwwe. Then
came the weary toil of fighting through tiger and spear-grass, with reeds,
rushes, a variety of ferns, before unseen, and other lush and lusty

growths, clothing a succession of rolling hills, monotonous swellings, where the descent was ever a reflection of the ascent. The paths were broken, slippery, and pitted with deep holes; along their sides, where the ground lay exposed to view, a conglomerate of ferruginous red clay— suggesting a resemblance to the superficies of Londa, as described by Dr. Livingstone—took the place of the granites and sandstones of the eastern countries, and the sinking of the land towards the Lake became palpable. In the jungle were extensive clumps of bamboo and rattan; the former small, the latter of poor quality; the bauhinia, or black-wood, and the salsaparilla vine abounded; wild grapes of diminutive size, and of the austerest flavour, appeared for the first time upon the sunny hill-sides which Bacchus ever loves, and in the lower swamps plantains grew almost wild. In parts the surface was broken into small deep hollows, from which sprang pyramidal masses of the hugest trees. Though no sign of man here met the eye, scattered fields and plantations showed that villages must be somewhere near. Sweet water was found in narrow courses of black mud, which sorely tried the sinews of laden man and beast. Long after noon, we saw the caravan halted by fatigue upon a slope beyond a weary swamp: a violent storm was brewing, and whilst half the sky was purple black with nimbus, the sun shone stingingly through the clear portion of the empyrean. But these small troubles were lightly borne; already in the far distance appeared walls of sky-blue cliff with gilded summits, which were as a beacon to the distressed mariner.

On the 13th February we resumed our travel through screens of lofty grass, which thinned out into a straggling forest. After about an hour's march, as we entered a small savannah, I saw the Fundi before alluded to running forward and changing the direction of the caravan. Without supposing that he had taken upon himself this responsibility, I followed him. Presently he breasted a steep and stony hill, sparsely clad with thorny trees: it was the death of my companion's riding-ass. Arrived with toil,—for our fagged beasts now refused to proceed,—we halted for a few minutes upon the summit. 'What is that streak of light which lies below?' I inquired of Seedy Bombay. 'I am of opinion,' quoth Bombay, 'that that is *the* water.' I gazed in dismay; the remains of my blindness, the veil of trees, and a broad ray of sunshine illuminating but one reach of the Lake, had shrunk its fair proportions. Somewhat prematurely I began to lament my folly in having risked life and lost health for so poor a prize, to curse Arab exaggeration, and to propose an immediate return, with the view of exploring the Nyanza, or Northern Lake. Advancing, however, a few yards, the whole scene suddenly burst upon my view, filling me with admiration, wonder, and delight. . . .

Nothing, in sooth, could be more picturesque than this first view of the Tanganyika Lake, as it lay in the lap of the mountains, basking in the gorgeous tropical sunshine. Below and beyond a short foreground of rugged and precipitous hill-fold, down which the foot-path zigzags painfully, a narrow strip of emerald green, never sere and marvellously fertile, shelves towards a ribbon of glistening yellow sand, here bordered by sedgy rushes, there cleanly and clearly cut by the breaking wavelets. Further in front stretch the waters, an expanse of the lightest and softest blue, in breadth varying from thirty to thirty-five miles, and sprinkled by the crisp east-wind with tiny crescents of snowy foam. The background in front is a high and broken wall of steel-coloured mountain, here flecked and capped with pearly mist, there standing sharply pencilled against the azure air; its yawning chasms, marked by a deeper plum-colour, fall towards dwarf hills of mound-like proportions, which apparently dip their feet in the wave. To the south, and opposite the long low point, behind which the Malagarazi River discharges the red loam suspended in its violent stream, lie the bluff headlands and capes of Uguhha, and, as the eye dilates, it falls upon a cluster of outlying islets, speckling a sea-horizon. Villages, cultivated lands, the frequent canoes of the fishermen on the waters, and on a nearer approach the murmurs of the waves breaking upon the shore, give a something of variety, of movement, of life to the landscape, which, like all the fairest prospects in these regions, wants but a little of the neatness and finish of Art,— mosques and kiosks, palaces and villas, gardens and orchards—contrasting with the profuse lavishness and magnificence of nature, and diversifying the unbroken *coup d'œil* of excessive vegetation, to rival, if not to excel, the most admired scenery of the classic regions. The riant shores of this vast crevasse appeared doubly beautiful to me after the silent and spectral mangrove-creeks on the East-African seaboard, and the melancholy, monotonous experience of desert and jungle scenery, tawny rock and sun-parched plain or rank herbage and flats of black mire. Truly it was a revel for soul and sight! Forgetting toils, dangers, and the doubtfulness of return, I felt willing to endure double what I had endured; and all the party seemed to join with me in joy. My purblind companion found nothing to grumble at except the 'mist and glare before his eyes.' Said bin Salim looked exulting,—*he* had procured for me this pleasure,—the monoculous Jemadar grinned his congratulations, and even the surly Baloch made civil salams.

*The lake regions of Central Africa*, vol. II, pp. 40–44

*Speke's temporary blindness upon this occasion led him to describe this incident in his journal in the following words: 'From the summit of the Eastern horn the lovely Tanganyika Lake could be seen in all its glory by everybody but myself.'*

*After a hurried exploration of part of the lake, they returned to Tabora to recuperate. From this point they describe events in somewhat different terms. Speke writes as though, owing to Burton being quite 'done up', he took the initiative in pressing to be allowed to go on alone to look for the lake which the Arabs reported in the north. Burton writes of Speke as 'being a fit person to be detached upon this duty', all the more as his presence was 'by no means desirable at Kazeh. To associate at the same time with Arabs and Anglo-Indians who are ready to take offence when it is least intended, who expect servility as their due and whose morgue of colour induces them to treat all skins a shade darker than their own as "niggers", is even more difficult than to avoid rupture when placed between two friends who have quarrelled with each other'.*

*Speke therefore struck out to the north without Burton. On 30th July 1858 he saw the waters of the southernmost creek of Africa's greatest lake. By little more than intuition and reliance upon Arab information he decided that this lake—to which, following the example set by Livingstone, he gave the somewhat unimaginative name Victoria —must be the source of the Nile, though he could have no conception then of its shape or its immensity. He returned to find Burton inclined to give little welcome or even credence to his news.*

## 22. EXPLORERS DIFFER

At length my companion had been successful, his 'flying trip' had led him to the northern water, and he had found its dimensions surpassing our most sanguine expectations. We had scarcely, however, breakfasted, before he announced to me the startling fact that he had discovered the sources of the White Nile. It was an inspiration perhaps: the moment he sighted the Nyanza, he felt at once no doubt but that the 'Lake at his feet gave birth to the interesting river which had been the subject of so much speculation, and the object of so many explorers.' The fortunate discoverer's conviction was strong, his reasons were weak—were of the category alluded to by the damsel Luceter, when justifying her penchant in favour of 'the lovely gentleman' Sir Proteus:—

> 'I have no other but a woman's reason,
> I think him so because I think him so';

and probably his sources of the Nile grew in his mind as his Mountains of the Moon had grown under his hand....

What tended at the time to make me the more sceptical was the substantial incorrectness of the geographical and other details brought back by my companion. This was natural enough. Bombay, after misunderstanding his master's ill-expressed Hindostani, probably mistranslated the words into Kiswahili to some travelled African, who in turn passed on the question in a wilder dialect to the barbarian or barbarians under examination. During such a journey to and fro words must be liable to severe accidents. . . . And what knowledge of Asiatic customs can be expected from the writer of these lines? 'The Arabs at Unyanyembe had advised my donning their habit for the trip in order to attract less attention, a vain precaution, which I believe they suggested more to gratify their own vanity *in seeing an Englishman lower himself to their position*, than for any benefit I might receive by doing so.' (Blackwood, loco cit). This galamatias of the Arabs!—the haughtiest and the most clannish of all Oriental peoples.

But difference of opinion was allowed to alter companionship. After a few days it became evident to me that not a word could be uttered upon the subject of the Lake, the Nile, and his *trouvaille* generally without offence. By a tacit agreement it was, therefore, avoided, and I should never have resumed it had my companion not stultified the results of the expedition by putting forth a claim which no geographer can admit and which is at the same time so weak and flimsy that no geographer has yet taken the trouble to contradict it.

*The lake regions of Central Africa,*
vol. II, pp. 204–209

*The two men travelled back together on very unhappy terms, which were not improved by Burton having to nurse his companion in a state of delirium. Speke now revealed all the grievances he had accumulated against Burton since a moment during the Somali attack upon them outside Berbera, when Speke believed an exclamation by Burton to have reflected upon his courage.*

*Their future controversy will, however, be more suitably included in the notes upon Speke in the next section. It remains here to summarize the rest of Burton's life, crowded as it was with his travels and with writing the seventy books and other publications which resulted from them. In 1861 he married, without her parents' consent, Isabel Arundel. She had since girlhood been in love with a man whose reputation, virile personality and bronzed and scarred face had appealed to her strong sense of romance. He travelled in North*

*America and was a consul in West Africa, Brazil, Damascus and Trieste. Always regarded as a difficult, and, from some aspects, a dangerous man, he had to wait until 1886 for official recognition, in the form of knighthood, which he had so long desired. At the same time came the fortune which he owed to the pornographic success of his* Arabian Nights. *After his death his wife published an expurgated edition and erected over him a monument in the form of a stone tent.*

8. The Travels of Burton and Speke, 1857–9

# VII
# JOHN HANNING SPEKE
## 1827–1864

*S*peke's home was Ilminster in Somerset, and his parents both came from the landed gentry. He disliked school but developed early a love of natural history and of wandering in the countryside. At seventeen he obtained a commission in the Indian army and saw much fighting with it, spending his leaves exploring and shooting big game. Soon after he reached the age of twenty he began to dream of exploring Africa and finding the Equatorial Nile. In 1854 he obtained permission to traverse Somaliland in company with Burton. The disastrous end of that attempt has been described in the section upon Burton, and also the expedition of 1856–9 when Lakes Tanganyika and Victoria were discovered.

After Speke and Burton, now on bad terms, returned in 1859 to the coast, Burton fell ill again and Speke went on ahead to England to claim the main credit for the discoveries and to obtain funds from the Royal Geographical Society to finance a new expedition—from which Burton was to be excluded—in order to verify the relationship of Lake Victoria to the White Nile.

Upon this new expedition Speke took with him a more congenial companion than Burton, the resolute but gentle James Grant. He had an escort of freed slaves (*Wanguana*) and Baluchi soldiers from the Sultan of Zanzibar with Mabruki and Bombay, who had been with him before when he found the two great lakes, as headmen. In Unyamwezi the Arab traders helped the travellers and gave them information of the country west and north of Lake Victoria. But here their serious troubles began with fever and fatigue, wars between Arabs and natives and the extortions of chiefs, among them Suwarora of Usui. At last, however, the travellers reached the relatively important kingdoms of the Lake region, where the pastoral Hima people had established their rule over the agricultural negroid tribes. They received a great welcome at the court of the king of Karagwe, the intelligent and courteous Rumanika, who is described in the first extract from

181

*Speke's book, while the second gives his visit to the neighbouring kingdom of Uganda.*

# 23. THE EVER-SMILING KING

To do royal honours to the king of this charming land I ordered my men to put down their loads and fire a volley. This was no sooner done than as we went to the palace gate, we received an invitation to come in at once, for the king wished to see us before attending to anything else. Now, leaving our traps outside, both Grant and myself, attended by Bombay and a few of the seniors of my *Wanguana*, entered the vestibule, and walking through extensive enclosures studded with huts of kingly dimensions, were escorted to a pent-roofed baraza, which the Arabs had built as a sort of government office, where the king might conduct his state affairs.

Here, as we entered, we saw sitting cross-legged on the ground Rumanika the king, and his brother Nnanaji, both of them men of noble appearance and size. The king was plainly dressed in an Arab's black choga, and wore, for ornament, dress stockings of rich-coloured beads, and neatly-worked wristlets of copper. Nnanaji, being a doctor of very high pretensions, in addition to a check cloth wrapped round him, was covered with charms. At their sides lay huge pipes of black clay. In their rear, squatting quiet as mice, were all the king's sons, some six or seven lads, who wore leather middle-coverings, and little dream-charms tied under their chins. The first greetings of the king, delivered in good Kisuahili, were warm and affecting, and in an instant we both felt and saw we were in the company of men who were as unlike as they could be to the common order of the natives of the surrounding districts. They had fine oval faces, large eyes, and high noses, denoting the best blood of Abyssinia. Having shaken hands in true English style, which is the peculiar custom of the men of this country, the ever-smiling Rumanika begged us to be seated on the ground opposite to him, and at once wished to know what we thought of Karague, for it had struck him his mountains were the finest in the world; and the lake, too, did we not admire it? Then laughing, he inquired—for he knew all the story—what we thought of Suwarora, and the reception we had met with in Usui. When this was explained to him, I showed him that it was for the interest of his own kingdom to keep a check on Suwarora, whose exorbitant taxations prevented the Arabs from coming to see him and bringing things from all parts of the world. He made inquiries for the purpose of knowing how we found our way all over the world; for on the former expedition a letter had come to him for Musa, who no sooner read it than he said I had called him and he must leave, as I was bound for Ujiji.

This of course led to a long story, describing the world, the proportions of land and water, and the power of ships, which conveyed even elephants and rhinoceros—in fact, all the animals in the world—to fill our menageries at home,—&c. &c.; as well as the strange announcement that we lived to the northward, and had only come this way because his friend Musa had assured me without doubt that he would give us the road on through Uganda. Time flew like magic, the king's mind was so quick and inquiring; but as the day was wasting away, he generously gave us our option to choose a place for our residence in or out of his palace, and allowed us time to select one. We found the view overlooking the lake to be so charming, that we preferred camping outside, and set our men at once to work cutting sticks and long grass to erect themselves sheds.

One of the young princes—for the king ordered them all to be constantly in attendance on us—happening to see me sit on an iron chair, rushed back to his father and told him about it. This set all the royals in the palace in a state of high wonder, and ended by my getting a summons to show off the white man sitting on his throne; for of course I could only be, as all of them called me, a king of great dignity, to indulge in such state. Rather reluctantly I did as I was bid, and allowed myself once more to be dragged into court. Rumanika, as gentle as ever, then burst into a fresh fit of merriment, and after making sundry enlightened remarks of inquiry, which of course were responded to with the greatest satisfaction, finished off by saying, with a very expressive shake of the head, 'Oh, these Wazungu, these Wazungu! (white men) they know and do everything.'

.    .    .    .    .    .

A long theological and historical discussion ensued, which so pleased the king, that he said he would be delighted if I would take two of his sons to England, that they might bring him a knowledge of everything. Then turning again to the old point, his utter amazement that we should spend so much property in travelling, he wished to know what we did it for; when men had such means they would surely sit down and enjoy it. 'Oh no,' was the reply; 'we have had our fill of the luxuries of life; eating, drinking, or sleeping have no charms for us now; we are above trade, therefore require no profits, and seek for enjoyment the run of the world. To observe and admire the beauties of creation are worth much more than beads to us. But what led us this way we have told you before: it was to see your majesty in particular, and the great kings of Africa—and at the same time to open another road to the north, whereby the best manufactures of Europe would find their way to Karague, and you would get so many more guests.' In the highest good humour the king said 'As you have come to see me and see sights, I will order some boats and show you over the lake, with musicians to play before you, or anything else that you like.' Then, after looking over our pictures with intensest delight, and admiring our beds, boxes, and outfit in general, he left for the day.

In the afternoon, as I had heard from Musa that the wives of the king and princes were fattened to such an extent that they could not stand upright, I paid my respects to Wazezeru, the king's eldest brother— who, having been born before his father ascended his throne, did not come in the line of succession—with the hope of being able to see for myself the truth of the story. There was no mistake about it. On entering the hut I found the old man and his chief wife sitting side by side on a bench of earth strewed over with grass, and partitioned like stalls for sleeping apartments, whilst in front of them were placed numerous wooden pots of milk, and hanging from the poles that supported the beehive-shaped hut, a large collection of bows six feet in length, whilst below them were tied an even larger collection of spears, intermixed with a goodly assortment of heavy-headed assagais. I was struck with no small surprise at the way he received me, as well as with the extraordinary dimensions, yet pleasing beauty, of the immoderately fat fair one his wife. She could not rise; and so large were her arms that, between the joints, the flesh hung down like large loose-stuffed puddings. Then in came their children, all models of the Abyssinian type of beauty, and as polite in their manners as thorough-bred gentlemen. They had heard of my picture-books from the king and all wished to see them; which they no sooner did, to their infinite delight, especially when they recognized any of the animals, than the subject was turned by my inquiring what they did with so many milk-pots. This was easily explained by Wazezeru himself, who, pointing to his wife said, 'This is all the product of those pots: from early youth upwards, we keep those pots to their mouths, as it is the fashion at court to have very fat wives.'

27th.—Ever anxious to push on with the journey, as I felt every day's delay only tended to diminish my means—that is my beads and copper wire—I instructed Bombay to take the under-mentioned articles to Rumanika as a small sample of the products of my country;[1] to say I felt quite ashamed of their being so few and so poor, but I hoped he would forgive my shortcomings, as he knew I had been so often robbed on the way to him; and I trusted, in recollection of Musa, he would give me leave to go on to Uganda, for every day's delay was consuming my supplies. Nnanaji, however, it was said, should get something; so, in

[1] *Rumanika's present.* One block-tin box, one Raglan coat, five yards scarlet broadcloth, two coils copper wire, a hundred large blue-egg beads, five bundles best variegated beads, three bundles minute beads—pink, blue and white. (*Speke's note.*)

addition to the king's present I apportioned one out for him, and Bombay took both up to the palace. Everybody, I was pleased to hear, was surprised with both the quantity and the quality of what I had been able to find them; for, after the plundering in Ugogo, the immense consumption caused by long delays on the road, the fearful prices I had had to pay for my porters' wages, the enormous taxes I had been forced to give both in Msalala and Uzinza, besides the constant thievings in camp, all of which was made public by the constantly-recurring tales of my men, nobody thought I had got anything left.

Rumanika, above all, was as delighted as if he had come in for a fortune, and sent to say the Raglan coat was a marvel, and the scarlet broadcloth the finest thing he had ever seen. Nobody but Musa had ever given him such beautiful beads before, and none ever gave with such free liberality. Whatever I wanted I should have in return for it, as it was evident to him I had really done him a great honour in visiting him. Neither his father nor any of his forefathers had had such a great favour shown them. He was alarmed, he confessed, when he heard we were coming to visit him, thinking we might prove some fearful monsters that were not quite human, but now he was delighted beyond all measure with what he saw of us. A messenger should be sent at once to the king of Uganda to inform him of our intention to visit him with his own favourable report of us. This was necessary according to the etiquette of the country. Without such a recommendation our progress would be stopped by the people, whilst with one word from him all would go straight; for was he not the gatekeeper, enjoying the full confidence of Uganda? A month, however, must elapse, as the distance to the palace of Uganda was great; but, in the mean time, he would give me leave to go about in his country to do and see what I liked, Nnanaji and his sons escorting me everywhere. Moreover, when the time came for my going on to Uganda, if I had not enough presents to give the king, he would fill up the complement from his own stores, and either go with me himself or send Nnanaji to conduct me as far as the boundary of Uganda, in order that Rogero might not molest us on the way.

.    .    .    .    .    .

31*st*.—Ever proud of his history since I had traced his descent from Abyssinia and King David whose hair was as straight as my own, Rumanika dwelt on my theological disclosures with the greatest delight, and wished to know what difference existed between the Arabs and ourselves; to which Baraka replied, as the best means of making him understand, that whilst the Arabs had only one Book, we had two; to which I added, Yes that is true in a sense; but the real merits lie in the fact that we have got the better *book*, as may be inferred from the obvious fact that we are more prosperous, and their superiors in all things, as I would prove to him if he would allow me to take one of his sons home to learn that *book*; for then he would find his tribe, after a while, better off than the Arabs are. Much delighted, he said he would be very glad to give me two boys for that purpose.

Then, changing the subject, I pressed Rumanika, as he said he had no idea of a God or future state, to tell me what advantage he expected from sacrificing a cow yearly at his father's grave. He laughingly replied that he did not know, but he hoped he might be favoured with better crops if he did so. He also placed pombe and grain, he said, for the same reason, before a large stone on the hill-side, although it could not eat, or make any use of it; but the coast-men were of the same belief as himself, and so were all the natives. No one in Africa, as far as he knew, doubted the power of magic and spells; and if a fox barked when he was leading an army to battle, he would retire at once, knowing that this prognosticated evil. There were many other animals, and lucky and unlucky birds, which all believed in.

I then told him it was fortunate he had no disbelievers like us to contend with in battle, for we, instead of trusting to luck and such omens, put our faith only in skill and pluck which Baraka elucidated from his military experience in the wars in British India. Lastly, I explained to him how England formerly was as unenlightened as Africa, and believing in the same sort of superstitions, and the inhabitants were all as naked as his skin-wearing Wanyambo; but now, since they had grown wiser, and saw through such impostures, they were the greatest men in the world. He said, for the future, he would disregard what the Arabs said, and trust to my doctrines, for without doubt he had never seen such a wise man as myself; and the Arabs themselves confirmed this when they told him that all their beads and cloths came from the land of the Wazungu or white men. . . .

7*th*.—Our spirits were now further raised by the arrival of a semi-Hindu-Suahili, named Juma, who had just returned from a visit to the king of Uganda, bringing back with him a large present of ivory and slaves; for he said he had heard from the king of our intention to visit him, and that he had despatched officers to call us immediately. This intelligence delighted Rumanika as much as it did us, and he no sooner heard it than he said, with ecstasies, 'I will open Africa, since the white men desire it; for did not Dagara command us to show deference to strangers?' Then, turning to me, he added, 'My only regret is, you will not take something as a return for the great expenses you have been put to in coming to visit me.' The expense was admitted, for I had now been obliged to purchase from the Arabs upwards of £400 worth of beads, to keep such a store in reserve for my return from Uganda as would enable me to push on to Gondokoro. . . .

8*th to* 10*th*.—At last we heard the familiar sound of the Uganda drum.

Maula, a royal officer, with a large escort of smartly-dressed men, women and boys, leading their dogs and playing their reeds, announced to our straining ears the welcome intelligence that their king had sent them to call us. N'yamgundu, who had seen us in Usui, had marched on to inform the king of our advance and desire to see him; and he, intensely delighted at the prospect of having white men for his guests, desired no time should be lost in our coming on. Maula told us that his officers had orders to supply us with everything we wanted whilst passing through his country, and that there would be nothing to pay.

One thing only now embarrassed me—Grant was worse, without hope of recovery for at least one or two months. This large body of Waganda could not be kept waiting. To get on as fast as possible was the only chance of ever bringing the journey to a successful issue; so, unable to help myself, with great remorse at another separation, on the following day I consigned my companion, with several Wanguana, to the care of my friend Rumanika. . . .

This business concluded in camp, I started my men and went to the palace to bid adieu to Rumanika, who appointed Rozaro, one of his officers, to accompany me wherever I went in Uganda, and to bring me back safely again. At Rumanika's request I then gave Mtesa's pages some ammunition to hurry on with to the great king of Uganda, as his majesty had ordered them to bring him, as quickly as possible, some strengthening powder, and also some powder for his gun. Then, finally, to Maula, also under Rumanika's instructions, I gave two copper wires and five bundles of beads; and when all was completed, set out on the march, perfectly sure in my mind that before very long I should settle the great Nile problem for ever; and, with this consciousness, only hoping that Grant would be able to join me before I should have to return again, for it was never supposed for a moment that it was possible I ever could go north from Uganda. Rumanika was the most resolute in this belief, as the kings of Uganda, ever since that country was detached from Unyoro, had been making constant raids, seizing cattle and slaves from the surrounding countries.

*Journal of the discovery of the source of the Nile,* 1st edition, pp. 202–205, 208–211, 240–242, 243–245

# 24. DISCOVERY OF UGANDA

[14 Feb. 1862.] Here I was also brought to a standstill, for N'yamgundu said I must wait for leave to approach the palace. He wished to have a look at the presents I had brought for Mtesa. I declined to gratify it, taking my stand on my dignity; there was no occasion for any distrust

on such a trifling matter as that, for I was not a merchant who sought
for gain, but had come at great expense, to see the king of this region.
I begged, however, he would go as fast as possible to announce my
arrival, explain my motive for coming here, and ask for an early interview, as I had left my brother Grant behind at Karague, and found my
position, for want of a friend to talk to, almost intolerable. It was not
the custom of my country for great men to consort with servants, and
until I saw him, and made friends, I should not be happy. I had a great
deal to tell him about as he was the father of the Nile, which river
drained the N'yanza down to my country to the northward. With this
message N'yamgundu hurried off as fast as possible. . . .

[16 Feb.] I then very much wished to go and see the escape of the
Mwerango river, as I still felt a little sceptical as to its origin, whether
or not it came off those smaller lakes I had seen on the road the day
before I crossed the river; but no one would listen to my project. They
all said I must have the king's sanction first, else people, from not knowing my object, would accuse me of practising witchcraft and would tell
their king so. They still all maintained that the river did come out of the
lake, and said, if I liked to ask the king's leave to visit the spot, then they
would go and show it me. I gave way, thinking it prudent to do so, but
resolved in my mind I would get Grant to see it in boats on his voyage
from Karague. There were no guinea-fowls to be found here, nor a
fowl, in any of the huts, so I requested Rozaro to hurry off to Mtesa,
and ask him to send me something to eat. He simply laughed at my
request, and said I did not know what I was doing. It would be as much
as my life was worth to go one yard in advance of this until the king's
leave was obtained. I said, rather than be starved to death in this
ignominious manner, I would return to Karague; to which he replied,
laughing, 'Whose leave have you got to do that? Do you suppose you
can do as you like in this country?'

[17 Feb.] Next day, in the evening, N'yamgundu returned full of
smirks and smiles, dropped on his knees at my feet and, in company
with his 'children', set to n'yanzigging, according to the form of that
state ceremonial already described (a form of giving thanks to great
men). In his excitement he was hardly able to say all he had to communicate. Bit by bit, however, I learned that he first went to the palace,
and, finding the king had gone off yachting to the Murchison Creek, he
followed him there. The king for a long while would not believe his tale
that I had come, but being assured he danced with delight, swore he
would not taste food until he had seen me. 'Oh,' he said, over and over
again and again, according to my informer, 'can this be true? Can the
white man have come all this way to see me? What a strong man he
must be too, to come so quickly! Here are seven cows, four of them
milch ones, as you say he likes milk, which you will give him; and there

are three for yourself for having brought him so quickly. Now hurry off as fast as you can, and tell him I am more delighted at the prospect of seeing him than he can be to see me. There is no place here fit for his reception. I was on a pilgrimage which would have kept me here seven days longer; but as I am so impatient to see him, I will go off to my palace at once, and will send word for him to advance as soon as I arrive there.'

[18 Feb.] About noon the succeeding day, some pages ran in to say we were to come along without a moment's delay, as their king had ordered it. He would not taste food until he saw me, so that everybody might know what great respect he felt for me. In the meanwhile, however, he wished for some gunpowder. I packed the pages off as fast as I could with some, and then tried myself to follow, but my men were all either sick or out foraging, and therefore we could not get under way until the evening. . . .

[19 Feb.] One march more and we came in sight of the king's kibuga or palace, in the province of Bandawarogo, N. lat. 0° 21' 19", and E. long. 32° 44' 30". It was a magnificent sight. A whole hill was covered with gigantic huts, such as I had never seen in Africa before. I wished to go up to the palace at once, but the officers said, 'No, that would be considered indecent in Uganda; you must draw up your men, and fire your guns off, to let the king know you are here; we will then show you your residence, and to-morrow you will doubtless be sent for, as the king could not now hold a levee whilst it is raining.' I made the men fire, and then was shown into a lot of dirty huts, which they said were built expressly for all the king's visitors. The Arabs, when they came on their visits always put up here, and I must do the same. At first I stuck out on my claims as a foreign prince, whose royal blood could not stand such an indignity. The palace was my sphere, and unless I could get a hut there, I would return without seeing the king.

In a terrible fright at my blustering, N'yamgundu fell at my feet, and implored me not to be hasty. The king did not understand who I was, and could not be spoken to then. He implored me to be content with my lot for the present, after which the king, when he knew all about it, would do as I liked, he was sure, though no strangers had ever yet been allowed to reside within the royal enclosures. I gave way to this good man's appeal, and cleaned my hut by firing the ground, for, like all the huts, in this dog country, it was full of fleas. Once ensconced there, the king's pages darted in to see me, bearing a message from their master, who said he was sorry the rain prevented him from holding a levee that day, but the next he would be delighted to see me. Irungu, with all Suwarora's men, then came to a collection of huts near where I was residing, and whilst I lay in bed that night, Irungu with all his wives came in to see me and beg for beads.

[19 Feb.] To-day the king sent his pages to announce his intention of holding a levee in my honour. I prepared for my first presentation at court, attired in my best, though in it I cut a poor figure in comparison with the display of the dressy Waganda. They wore neat bark cloaks resembling the best yellow corduroy cloth, crimp and well set, as if stiffened with starch, and over that, as upper-cloaks, a patchwork of small antelope skins, which I observed were sewn together as well as any English glovers could have pieced them; whilst their head-dresses, generally, were abrus turbans, set off with highly-polished boar-tusks, stick-charms, seeds, beads, or shells; and on their necks, arms and ankles they wore other charms of wood, or small horns stuffed with magic powder, and fastened on by strings generally covered with snake-skin. N'yamgundu and Maula demanded, as their official privilege, a first peep; and this being refused, they tried to persuade me that the articles comprising the present required to be covered with chintz, for it was considered indecorous to offer anything to his majesty in a naked state. This little interruption over, the articles enumerated below[1] were conveyed to the palace in solemn procession thus:—With N'yamgundu, Maula, the pages, and myself on the flanks, the Union Jack carried by the kirangozi guide led the way followed by twelve men as a guard of honour, dressed in red flannel cloaks, and carrying their arms sloped, with fixed bayonets; whilst in their rear were the rest of my men, each carrying some article as a present.

On the march towards the palace, the admiring courtiers, wonder-struck at such an unusual display, exclaimed in raptures of astonishment, some with both hands at their mouths, and others clasping their heads with their hands 'Irungi! irungi!' which may be translated 'Beautiful! beautiful!' I thought myself everything was going on as well as could be wished; but before entering the royal enclosures, I found, to my disagreeable surprise, that the men with Suwarora's hongo or offering, which consisted of more than a hundred coils of wire, were ordered to lead the procession, and take precedence of me. There was something specially aggravating in this precedence; for it will be remembered that these very brass wires which they saw, I had myself intended for Mtesa, that they were taken from me by Suwarora as far back as Usui, and it would never do, without remonstrance, to have them boastfully paraded before my eyes in this fashion. My protests, however, had no effect upon the escorting Wakungu [nobles]. Resolving to make them catch it, I walked along as if ruminating in anger up the broad highroad into a cleared square, which divides Mtesa's domain on the south from his

[1] 1 block-tin box, 4 rich silk cloths, 1 rifle (Whitworth's), 1 gold chronometer, 1 revolver pistol, 3 rifled carbines, 3 sword bayonets, 1 box ammunition, 1 box bullets, 1 box gun-caps, 1 telescope, 1 iron chair, 10 bundles best beads, 1 set of table-knives, spoons, and forks. (*Speke's note.*)

Kamraviona's or commander-in-chief on the north, and then turned into the court. The palace or entrance quite surprised me by its extraordinary dimensions and the neatness with which it was kept. The whole brow and sides of the hill on which we stood were covered with gigantic grass huts, thatched as neatly as so many heads dressed by a London barber, and fenced all round with the tall yellow reeds of the common Uganda tiger-grass; whilst within the enclosure, the lines of huts were joined together, or partitioned off into courts, with walls of the same grass. It is here most of Mtesa's three or four hundred women are kept, the rest being quartered chiefly with his mother, known by the title of N'yamasore, or queen-dowager. They stood in little groups at the doors, looking at us, and evidently passing their own remarks, and enjoying their own jokes, on the triumphal procession. At each gate as we passed, officers on duty opened and shut it for us, jingling the big bells which are hung upon them, as they sometimes are at shop-doors to prevent a silent stealthy entrance.

The first court passed, I was even more surprised to find the unusual ceremonies that awaited me. There courtiers of high dignity stepped forward to greet me, dressed in the most scrupulously neat fashions. Men, women, bulls, dogs, and goats, were led about by strings; cocks and hens were carried in men's arms; and little pages, with rope-turbans, rushed about, conveying messages, as if their lives depended on their swiftness, everyone holding his skin-cloak tightly round him lest his naked legs might by accident be shown.

This, then, was the ante-reception court; and I might have taken possession of the hut, in which musicians were playing and singing on large nine-stringed harps, like the Nubian tambira, accompanied by harmonicons. By the chief officers in waiting, however, who thought fit to treat us like Arab merchants, I was requested to sit on the ground outside in the sun with my servants. Now, I had made up my mind never to sit upon the ground as the natives and Arabs are obliged to do, nor to make my obeisance in any other manner than is customary in England, though the Arabs had told me that from fear they had always complied with the manners of the court. I felt that if I did not stand up for my social position at once, I should be treated with contempt during the remainder of my visit, and thus lose the vantage-ground I had assumed of appearing rather as a prince than a trader, for the purpose of better gaining the confidence of the king. To avert over-hastiness, however—for my servants began to be alarmed as I demurred against doing as I was bid—I allowed five minutes to the court to give me a proper reception, saying, if it were not conceded I would then walk away.

Nothing, however, was done. My own men, knowing me, feared for me, as they did not know what a 'savage' king would do in case I carried out my threat; whilst the Waganda, lost in amazement at what seemed little less than blasphemy, stood still as posts. The affair ended by my walking straight away home, giving Bombay orders to leave the present on the ground and to follow me.

Although the king is said to be unapproachable, excepting when he chooses to attend court—a ceremony which rarely happens—intelligence of my hot wrath and hasty departure reached him in an instant. He first, it seems, thought of leaving his toilet-room to follow me, but, finding I was walking fast and had gone far, changed his mind, and sent Wakungu running after me. Poor creatures! they caught me up, fell upon their knees, and implored I would return at once, for the king had not tasted food, and would not until he saw me. I felt grieved at their touching appeals; but, as I did not understand all they said, I simply replied by patting my heart and shaking my head, walking if anything all the faster.

On my arrival at my hut, Bombay and others came in, wet through with perspiration, saying the king had heard of all my grievances. Suwarora's hongo was turned out of court, and, if I desired it, I might bring my own chair with me, for he was very anxious to show me great respect—although such a seat was exclusively the attribute of the king, no one else in Uganda daring to sit on an artificial seat.

My point was gained, so I cooled myself with coffee and a pipe, and returned rejoicing in my victory, especially over Suwarora. After returning to the second tier of huts from which I had retired, everybody appeared to be in a hurried, confused state of excitement, not knowing what to make out of so unprecedented an exhibition of temper. In the most polite manner, the officers in waiting begged me to be seated on my iron stool, which I had brought with me, whilst others hurried in to announce my arrival. But for a few minutes only I was kept in suspense, when a band of music, the musicians wearing on their backs long-haired goat-skins, passed me, dancing as they went along, like bears in a fair, and playing on reed instruments worked over with pretty beads in various patterns, from which depended leopard-cat skins—the time being regulated by the beating of long hand drums.

The mighty king was now reported to be sitting on his throne in the state hut of the third tier. I advanced, hat in hand, with my guard of honour following, formed in 'open ranks,' who in their turn were followed by the bearers carrying the present. I did not walk straight up to him as if to shake hands, but went outside the ranks of a three-sided square of squatting Wakungu, all habited in skins, mostly cow-skins; some few of whom had, in addition, leopard-cat skins girt round the waist, the sign of royal blood. Here I was desired to halt and sit in the glaring sun; so I donned my hat, mounted my umbrella, a phenomenon which set them all a-wondering and laughing, ordered the guard to close ranks, and sat gazing at the novel spectacle. A more theatrical sight I never saw. The king, a good-looking, well-figured, tall young man of twenty five, was sitting on a red blanket spread upon a square platform of royal grass, encased in tiger-grass reeds, scrupulously well dressed in a new mbugu [cloth made of bark]. The hair of his head was cut short, excepting on the top, where it was combed up into a high ridge, running from stem to stern like a cockscomb. On his neck was a very neat ornament—a large ring, of beautifully-worked small beads, forming elegant patterns by their various colours. On one arm was another bead ornament, prettily devised; and on the other a wooden charm, tied by a string covered with snake-skin. On every finger and every toe he had alternate brass and copper rings; and above the ankles, half-way up to the calf, a stocking of very pretty beads. Everything was light, neat and elegant in its way; not a fault could be found with the taste of his 'getting up'. For a handkerchief he held a well-folded piece of bark, and a piece of gold-embroidered silk, which he constantly employed to hide his large mouth when laughing, or to wipe it after a drink of plantain-wine, of which he took constant and copious draughts from neat little gourd-cups, administered by his ladies-in-waiting, who were at once his sisters and wives. A white dog, spear, shield and woman—the Uganda cognisance—were by his side, as also a knot of staff officers, with whom he kept up a brisk conversation on one side; and on the other was a band of Wichwezi, or lady-sorcerers, such as I have already described.

I was now asked to draw nearer within the hollow square of squatters, where leopard-skins were strewed upon the ground, and a large copper kettledrum, surmounted with brass bells on arching wires, along with two other smaller drums covered with cowrie-shells, and beads of colour worked into patterns, were placed. I now longed to open conversation, but knew not the language, and no one near me dared speak, or even lift his head from fear of being accused of eyeing the women; so the king and myself sat staring at one another for full an hour—I mute, but he pointing and remarking with those around him on the novelty of my guard and general appearance, and even requiring to see my hat lifted, the umbrellas shut and opened, and the guards face about and show off their red cloaks—for such wonders had never been seen in Uganda.

Then, finding the day waning, he sent Maula on an embassy to ask me if I had seen him; and on receiving my reply, 'Yes, for full one hour,' I was glad to find him rise, spear in hand, lead his dog, and walk unceremoniously away through the enclosure into the fourth tier of huts; for this being a pure levee day, no business was transacted.

The king's gait in retiring was intended to be very majestic, but did not succeed in conveying to me that impression. It was the traditional walk of his race, founded on the step of the lion; but the outward sweep of the legs, intended to represent the stride of the noble beast, appeared to me only to realize a very ludicrous kind of waddle, which made me ask Bombay if anything serious was the matter with the royal person.

I had now to wait for some time, almost as an act of humanity; for I was told the state secret, that the king had retired to break his fast and eat for the first time since hearing of my arrival; but the repast was no sooner over than he prepared for the second act, to show off his splendour, and I was invited in, with all my men, to the exclusion of all his own officers save my two guides. Entering as before, I found him standing on a red blanket, leaning against the right portal of the hut, talking and laughing, handkerchief in hand, to a hundred or more of his admiring wives, who, all squatting on the ground outside, in two groups, were dressed in new mbugus. My men dared not advance upright, nor look upon the women, but, stooping, with lowered heads and averted eyes, came cringing after me. Unconscious myself, I gave loud and impatient orders to my guard, rebuking them for moving like frightened geese, and, with hat in hand, stood gazing on the fair sex till directed to sit and cap.

Mtesa then inquired what messages were brought from Rumanika; to which Maula, delighted with the favour of speaking to royalty, replied by saying, Rumanika had gained intelligence of Englishmen coming up the Nile to Gani and Kidi. The king acknowledged the truthfulness of their story, saying he had heard the same himself; and both Wakungu, as is the custom in Uganda, thanked their lord in a very enthusiastic manner, kneeling on the ground—for no one can stand in the presence of his majesty—in an attitude of prayer, and throwing out their hands as they repeated the words, N'yanzig, N'yanzig, ai N'yanzig Mkahma wangi, &c. &c., for a considerable time; when thinking they had done enough of this, and heated with the exertion, they threw themselves flat upon their stomachs, and, floundering about like fish on land, repeated the same words over and over again, and rose doing the same, with their faces covered with earth; for majesty in Uganda is never satisfied till subjects have grovelled before it like the most abject worms. This conversation over, after gazing at me, and chatting with his women for a considerable time, the second scene ended. The third scene was more easily arranged, for the day was fast declining. He simply moved with his train of women to another hut, where, after seating himself upon his throne, with his women around him, he invited me to approach the nearest limits of propriety, and to sit as before. Again he asked me if I had seen him—evidently desirous of indulging in his regal pride; so I made the most of the opportunity thus afforded me of opening a conversation by telling him of those grand reports I had formerly heard about him, which induced me to come all this way to see him, and the trouble it had cost me to reach the object of my desire; at the same time taking a gold ring from off my finger, and presenting it to him, I said, 'This is a small token of friendship; if you will inspect it, it is made after

KING MTESA'S LEVEE
From Speke's *Journal*

the fashion of a dog-collar, and being the king of metals, gold, is in every respect appropriate to your illustrious race.'

He said, in return, 'If friendship is your desire, what would you say if I showed you a road by which you might reach your home in one month?' Now everything had to be told to Bombay, then to Nasib, my Kiganda interpreter, and then to either Maula, or N'yamgundu, before it was delivered to the king for it was considered indecorous to transmit any message to his majesty excepting through the medium of one of his officers. Hence I could not get an answer put in; for as all Waganda are rapid and impetuous in their conversation, the king probably forgetting he had put a question, hastily changed the conversation and said 'What guns have you got? Let me see the one you shoot with.' I wished still to answer the first question first, as I knew he referred to the direct line to Zanzibar across the Masai and was anxious without delay to open the subject of Petherick and Grant; but no one dared to deliver my statement. Much disappointed, I then said, 'I had brought the best shooting gun in the world—Whitworth's rifle—which I begged he would accept, with a few other trifles; and, with his permission, I would lay them upon a carpet at his feet, as is the custom of my country when visiting sultans.' He assented, sent all his women away, and had an mbugu spread for the purpose, on which Bombay, obeying my order, first spread a red blanket and then opened each article one after the other, when Nasib, according to the usage already mentioned, smoothed them down with his dirty hands, or rubbed them against his sooty face, and handed them to the king to show there was no poison or witchcraft in them. Mtesa appeared quite confused with the various wonders as he handled them, made silly remarks, and pondered over them like a perfect child, until it was quite dark. Torches were then lit, and guns, pistols, powder, boxes, tools, beads—the whole collection, in short—were tossed together topsy-turvy, bundled into mbugus, and carried away by the pages. Mtesa now said, 'It is late, and time to break up; what provision would you wish to have?' I said, 'A little of everything, but no one thing constantly.' 'And would you like to see me to-morrow?' 'Yes, every day.' 'Then you can't to-morrow for I have business; but the next day come if you like. You can now go away, and here are six pots of plantain wine for you; my men will search for food tomorrow.'

[21 Feb.] In the morning, whilst it rained, some pages drove in twenty cows and ten goats, with a polite metaphorical message from their king, to the effect that I had pleased him much, and he hoped I would accept these few 'chickens' until he could send more,—when both Maula and N'yamgundu, charmed with their success in having brought a welcome guest to Uganda, never ceased showering eulogiums on me for my fortune in having gained the countenance of their king. The rain falling was considered at court a good omen, and everybody declared the king mad with delight. Wishing to have a talk with him about Petherick and Grant, I at once started off the Wakungu to thank him for the present, and to beg pardon for my apparent rudeness of yesterday, at the same time requesting I might have an early interview with his majesty, as I had much of importance to communicate; but the solemn court formalities which these African kings affect as much as Oriental emperors, precluded my message from reaching the king. I heard, however, that he had spent the day receiving Suwarora's hongo of wire, and that the officer who brought them was made to sit in an empty court, whilst the king sat behind a screen, never deigning to show his majestic person. I was told, too, that he opened conversation by demanding to know how it happened that Suwarora became possessed of the wires, for they were made by the white men to be given to himself, and Suwarora must therefore have robbed me of them; and it was by such practices he, Mtesa, never could see any visitors. The officer's reply was, Suwarora would not show the white men any respect, because they were wizards who did not sleep in houses at night, but flew up to the tops of hills, and practised sorcery of every abominable kind. The king to this retorted, in a truly African fashion, 'That's a lie; I can see no harm in this white man; and if he had been a bad man, Rumanika would not have sent him on to me.' At night, when in bed, the king sent his pages to say, if I desired his friendship I would lend him one musket to make up six with what I had given him, for he intended visiting his relations the following morning. I sent three, feeling that nothing would be lost by being 'open-handed.'

[22 Feb.] To-day the king went the round of his relations, showing the beautiful things given him by the white man—a clear proof that he was much favoured by the 'spirits,' for neither his father nor any of his forefathers had been so recognized and distinguished by any 'sign' as a rightful inheritor to the Uganda throne: an anti-Christian interpretation of omens, as rife in these dark regions now as it was in the time of King Nebuchadnezzar. At midnight the three muskets were returned, and I was so pleased with the young king's promptitude and honesty, I begged he would accept them.

[23 Feb.] At noon Mtesa sent his pages to invite me to his palace. I went, with my guard of honour and my stool, but found I had to sit waiting in an ante-hut three hours with his commander-in-chief and other high officers before he was ready to see me. During this time Wasoga minstrels, playing on tambira, and accompanied by boys playing on a harmonicon, kept us amused; and a small page, with a large bundle of grass, came to me and said, 'The king hopes you won't be offended if required to sit on it before him; for no person in Uganda, however high in office, is ever allowed to sit upon anything raised above the ground, nor can anybody but himself sit upon such grass as this; it is all that his throne is made of. The first day he only allowed you to sit on your stool to appease your wrath.'

On consenting to do in 'Rome as the Romans do,' when my position was so handsomely acknowledged, I was called in, and found the court sitting much as it was on the first day's interview, only that the number of squatting Wakungu was much diminished; and the king, instead of wearing his ten brass and copper rings, had my gold one on his third finger. This day, however, was cut out for business, as, in addition to the assemblage of officers, there were women, cows, goats, fowls, confiscations, baskets of fish, baskets of small antelopes, porcupines, and curious rats caught by his gamekeepers, bundles of mbugu, &c. &c., made by his linen-drapers, coloured earths and sticks by his magician, all ready for presentation; but, as rain fell, the court broke up, and I had nothing for it but to walk about under my umbrella, indulging in angry reflections against the haughty king for not inviting me into his hut.

When the rain had ceased, and we were again called in, he was found sitting in state as before, but this time with the head of a black bull placed before him, one horn of which, knocked off, was placed alongside, whilst four living cows walked about the court.

I was now requested to shoot the four cows as quickly as possible; but having no bullets for my gun, I borrowed the revolving pistol I had given him, and shot all four in a second of time; but as the last one, only wounded, turned sharply upon me, I gave him the fifth and settled him. Great applause followed this *wonderful* feat, and the cows were given to my men. The king now loaded one of the carbines I had given him with his own hands, and giving it full-cock to a page, told him to go out and shoot a man in the outer court; which was no sooner accomplished than the little urchin returned to announce his success, with a look of glee such as one would see in the face of a boy who had robbed a bird's nest, caught a trout, or done any other boyish trick. The king said to him, 'And did you do it well?' 'Oh yes, capitally.' He spoke the truth, no doubt, for he dared not have trifled with the king; but the affair created hardly any interest. I never heard, and there appeared no curiosity to know, what individual human being the urchin had deprived of life.

. . . . . .

[27 Feb.] To call upon the queen-mother respectfully, as it was the opening visit, I took, besides the medicine-chest, a present of eight brass and copper wire, thirty blue-egg beads, one bundle of diminutive beads, and sixteen cubits of chintz, a small guard, and my throne of royal grass. The palace to be visited lay half a mile beyond the king's, but the high-road to it was forbidden me, as it is considered uncourteous to pass the king's gate without going in. So after winding through back-gardens, the slums of Bandowaroga, I struck upon the highroad close to her majesty's, where everything looked like the royal palace on a miniature scale. A large cleared space divided the queen's residence from her Kamraviona's. The outer enclosures and courts were fenced with tiger-grass; and the huts, though neither so numerous nor so large, were constructed after the same fashion as the king's. Guards also kept the doors, on which large bells were hung to give alarm, and officers in waiting watched the throne-rooms. All the huts were full of women, save those kept as waiting-rooms, where drums and harmonicons were placed for amusement. On first entering, I was required to sit in a waiting-hut till my arrival was announced; but that did not take long, as the queen was prepared to receive me; and being of a more affable disposition than her son, she held rather a levee of amusement than a stiff court of show. I entered the throne-hut as the gate of that court was thrown open, with my hat off, but umbrella held over my head, and walked straight towards her till ordered to sit upon my bundle of grass.

Her majesty—fat, fair, and forty-five—was sitting, plainly garbed in mbugu, upon a carpet spread upon the ground within a curtain of mbugu, her elbow resting on a pillow of the same bark material; the only ornaments on her person being an abrus necklace, and a piece of mbugu tied round her head, whilst a folding looking-glass, much the worse for wear, stood open by her side. An iron rod like a spit, with a cup on the top, charged with magic powder, and other magic wands, were placed before the entrance; and within the room, four Mabandwa sorceresses or devil-drivers, fantastically dressed, as before described, and a mass of other women, formed the company. For a short while we sat at a distance exchanging inquiring glances at one another, when the women were dismissed, and a band of music, with a court full of Wakungu, was ordered in to change the scene. I also got orders to draw near and sit fronting her within the hut. Pombe, the best in Uganda, was then drunk by the queen, and handed to me and to all the high officers about her, when she smoked her pipe, and bade me smoke mine. The musicians, dressed in long-haired Usoga goat-skins, were now ordered to strike up, which they did, with their bodies swaying or dancing like bears in a fair. Different drums were then beat, and I was asked if I could distinguish their different tones.

The queen, full of mirth, now suddenly rose, leaving me sitting, whilst she went to another hut, changed her mbugu for a deole, and came back again for us to admire her, which was no sooner done to her heart's content, than a second time, by her order, the court was cleared, and, when only three or four confidential Wakungu were left, she took up a small faggot of well-trimmed sticks, and, selecting three, told me she had three complaints. 'This stick,' she says, 'represents my stomach, which gives me much uneasiness; this second stick my liver, which causes shooting pains all over my body; and this third one my heart, for I get constant dreams at night about Sunna, my late husband, and they are not pleasant.' The dreams and sleeplessness I told her was a common widow's complaint, and could only be cured by her majesty making up her mind to marry a second time; but before I could advise for the bodily complaints, it would be necessary for me to see her tongue, feel her pulse, and perhaps, also, her sides. Hearing this, the Wakungu said, 'Oh, that can never be allowed without the sanction of the king;' but the queen, rising in her seat, expressed her scorn at the idea of taking advice from a mere stripling, and submitted herself for examination.

I then took out two pills, the powder of which was tasted by the Wakungu to prove that there was no devilry in 'the doctor,' and gave orders for them to be eaten at night, restricting her pombe and food until I saw her again. My game was now advancing, for I found through her I should get the key to an influence that might bear on the king, and was much pleased to hear her express herself delighted with me for everything I had done except stopping her grog, which, naturally enough in this great pombe-drinking country, she said would be a very trying abstinence.

The doctoring over, her majesty expressed herself ready to inspect the honorarium I had brought for her, and the articles were no sooner presented by Bombay and Nasib, with the usual formalities of stroking to insure their purity, than she, boiling with pleasure, showed them all to her officers, who declared, with a voice of most exquisite triumph, that she was indeed the most favoured of queens. Then, in excellent good taste, after saying that nobody had ever given her such treasures, she gave me in return, a beautifully-worked pombe sucking-pipe, which was acknowledged by every one to be the greatest honour she could pay me.

Not satisfied with this, she made me select, though against my desire, a number of sambo, called here gundu, rings of giraffe hair wound round with thin iron or copper wire, and worn as anklets; and crowned all with sundry pots of pombe, a cow, and a bundle of dried fish, of the description given in the woodcut, called by my men Samaki Kambari. This business over, she begged me to show her my picture-books, and was so amused with them that she ordered her sorceresses and all the other women in again to inspect them with her. Then began a warm and complimentary conversation, which ended by an inspection of my rings and all the contents of my pockets, as well as of my watch, which she called Lubari—a term equivalent to a place of worsnip, the object of worship itself, or the iron horn or magic pan. Still she said I had not yet satisfied her; I must return again two days hence, for she liked me much —excessively—she could not say how much; but now the day was gone, I might go. With this queer kind of adieu she rose and walked away, leaving me with my servants to carry the royal present home.

# JOHN HANNING SPEKE

*He describes another visit to the Queen.*

[3 March.] I told her I had visited all the four quarters of the globe, and had seen all colours of people, but wondered where she got her pipe from, for it was much after the Rumish (Turkish) fashion, with a long stick. Greatly tickled at the flattery, she said, 'We hear men like yourself come to Amara from the other side and drive cattle away.' 'The Gallas, or Abyssinians, who are tall and fair, like Rumanika' I said, 'might do so, for they live not far off on the other side of Amara, but we never fight for such paltry objects. If cows fall into our hands when fighting we allow our soldiers to eat them, while we take the government of the country into our own hands.' She then said, 'We hear you don't like the Unyamuezi route, we will open the Ukori one for you.' 'Thank your majesty,' said I, in a figurative kind of speech to please Waganda ears; and turning the advantage of the project on her side. 'You have indeed hit the right nail on the head. I do not like the Unyamuezi route, as you may well imagine, when I tell you I have lost so much property there by mere robbery of the people and their kings. The Waganda do not see me in a true light; but if they have patience for a year or two, until the Ukori road is open, and trade between our respective countries shall commence, they will then see the fruits of my advent; so much so, that every Mganda will say the first Uganda year dates from the arrival of the first Mzungu (white) visitor. As one coffee-seed sown brings forth fruit in plenty, so my coming here may be considered.' All appreciated this speech, saying, 'The white man, he even speaks beautifully! beautifully! beautifully! beautifully!' and, putting their hands to their mouths, they looked askance at me, nodding their admiring approval.

The queen and her ministers then plunged into pombe and became uproarious, laughing with all their might and main. Small bugu cups were not enough to keep up the excitement of the time, so a large wooden trough was placed before the queen and filled with liquor. If any was spilt, the Wakungu instantly fought over it, dabbing their noses on the ground, or grabbing it with their hands, that not one atom of the queen's favour might be lost; for everything must be adored that comes from royalty, whether by design or accident. The queen put her head to the trough and drank like a pig from it, and was followed by her ministers. The band, by order, then struck up a tune called the Milele, playing on a dozen reeds, ornamented with beads and cow-tips, and five drums of various tones and sizes, keeping time. The musicians dancing with zest, were led by four bandmasters, also dancing, but with their backs turned to the company to show off their long, shaggy, goat-skin jackets, sometimes upright, at other times bending and on their heels, like the hornpipe-dancers of western countries.

200

It was a merry scene, but soon became tiresome; when Bombay, by way of flattery, and wishing to see what the queen's wardrobe embraced, told her, Any woman, however ugly, would assume a goodly appearance if prettily dressed; upon which her gracious majesty immediately rose, retired to her toilet hut, and soon returned attired in a common check cloth, an abrus tiara, a bead necklace, and with a folding looking-glass, when she sat, as before, and was handed a blown-glass cup of pombe, with a cork floating on the liquor, and a napkin mbugu covering the top, by a naked virgin. For her condescension in assuming plain raiment, everybody of course, n'yanzigged. Next, she ordered her slave girls to bring a large number of sambo (anklets) and begged me to select the best, for she liked me much. In vain I tried to refuse them: she had given more than enough for a keepsake before, and I was not hungry for property; still I had to choose some, or I would give offence. She then gave me a basket of tobacco, and a nest of hen eggs for her 'son's' breakfast. When this was over, the Mukonderi, another dancing tune with instruments something like clarionets, was ordered; but it had scarcely been struck up, before a drenching rain, with strong wind, set in and spoilt the music, though not the playing—for none dared stop without an order; and the queen, instead of taking pity, laughed most boisterously over the exercise of her savage power as the unfortunate musicians were nearly beaten down by the violence of the weather.

When the rain ceased, her majesty retired a second time to her toilet-hut, and changed her dress for a puce-coloured wrapper, when I, ashamed of having robbed her of so many sambo, asked her if she would allow me to present her with a little English 'wool' to hang up instead of her mbugu curtain on cold days like this. Of course she could not decline, and a large double scarlet blanket was placed before her. 'Oh, wonder of wonders!' exclaimed all the spectators, holding their mouths in both hands at a time—such a 'pattern' had never been seen here before. It stretched across the hut, was higher than the men could reach—indeed it was a perfect marvel; and the man must be a good one who brought such a treasure as this to Uddu. 'And why not say Uganda?' I asked. 'Because all this country is called Uddu. Uganda is personified by Mtesa; and no one can say he has seen Uganda until he has been presented to the king.'

As I had them all in a good humour now, I complained I did not see enough of the Waganda—and as every one dressed so remarkably well, I could not discern the big men from the small; could she not issue some order by which they might call on me, as they did not dare do so without instruction, and then I, in turn, would call on them? Hearing this, she introduced me to her prime minister, chancellor of exchequer, women-keepers, hang-men, and cooks as the first nobles in the land, that I might recognise them again if I met them on the road. All n'yanzigged for this great condescension, and said they were delighted with their guest; then producing a strip of common joho to compare it with my blanket, they asked if I could recognise it. Of course, said I, it is made in my country, of the same material, only of coarser quality, and everything of the same sort is made in Uzungu [white man's country]. Then, indeed, said the whole company, in one voice, we do like you and your cloth too—but you most. I modestly bowed my head, and said their friendship was my chief desire.

This speech also created great hilarity; the queen and councillors all became uproarious. The queen began to sing and the councillors to join in a chorus; then all sang and all drank, and drank and sang, till, in their heated excitement, they turned the palace into a pandemonium; still there was not noise enough, so the band and drums were called again, and tomfool—for Uganda, like the old European monarchies, always keeps a jester—was made to sing in the gruff, hoarse, unnatural voice which he ever affects to maintain his character, and furnished with pombe when his throat was dry.

Now all of a sudden, as if a devil had taken possession of the company, the prime minister with all the courtiers jumped upon their legs, seized their sticks, for nobody can carry a spear when visiting, swore the queen had lost her heart to me, and running into the yard, returned, charging and jabbering at the queen; retreated and returned again, as if they were going to put an end to her for the guilt of loving me, but really to show their devotion and true love to her. The queen professed to take this ceremony with calm indifference, but her face showed that she enjoyed it. I was now getting very tired of sitting on my low stool and begged for leave to depart, but N'yamasore would not hear of it; she loved me a great deal too much to let me go away at this time of day, and forthwith ordered in more pombe. The same roystering scene was repeated; cups were too small, so the trough was employed; and the queen graced it by drinking, pig-fashion, first, and then handing it round to the company.

.    .    .    .    .    .

[12 March.] Immediately after breakfast the king sent his pages in a great hurry to say he was waiting on the hill for me, and begged I would bring all my guns immediately. I prepared, thinking, naturally enough, that some buffaloes had been marked down; for the boys, as usual, were perfectly ignorant of his designs. To my surprise, however, when I mounted the hill half-way to the palace, I found the king standing, dressed in a rich filigreed waistcoat, trimmed with gold embroidery tweedling the loading-rod in his finger, and an alfia cap on his head, whilst his pages held his chair and guns, and a number of officers, with dogs and goats for offerings, squatting before him.

When I arrived, hat in hand, he smiled, examined my firearms, and proceeded for sport, leading the way to a high tree, on which some adjutant birds were nesting, and numerous vultures resting. This was the sport; Bana must shoot a nundo (adjutant) for the king's gratification. I begged him to take a shot himself, as I really could not demean myself by firing at birds sitting on a tree; but it was all of no use—no one could shoot as I could, and they must be shot. I proposed frightening them out with stones, but no stone could reach so high; so, to cut the matter short, I killed an adjutant on the nest, and, as the vultures flew away, brought one down on the wing, which fell in a garden enclosure.

The Waganda were for a minute all spell-bound with astonishment, when the king jumped frantically in the air, clapping his hands above his head, and singing out, 'Woh, woh! woh! what wonders! Oh, Bana, Bana! what miracles he performs!' [Bana=Bwana, Swahili for master]—and all the Wakungu followed in chorus 'Now load, Bana—load, and let us see you do it,' cried the excited king; but before I was half loaded he said, 'Come along, come along, and let us see the bird.' Then directing the officers which way to go—for, by the etiquette of the court of Uganda, every one must precede the king—he sent them through a court where his women, afraid of the gun, had been concealed. Here the rush onward was stopped by newly made fences, but the king roared to the officers to knock them down. This was no sooner said than done, by the attendants in a body shoving on and trampling them under, as an elephant would crush small trees to keep his course. So pushing, floundering through plantain and shrub, pell-mell one upon the other, that the king's pace might not be checked, or any one come in for a royal kick or blow, they came upon the prostrate bird. 'Woh! woh, woh!' cried the king again, 'there he is, sure enough; come here, women—come and look what wonders!' And all the women, in the highest excitement 'woh-wohed' as loud as any of the men. But that was not enough. 'Come along, Bana,' said the king, 'we must have some more sport;' and, saying this, he directed the way towards the queen's palace, the attendants leading, followed by the pages, then the king, next myself—for I never would walk before him—and finally the women, some forty or fifty, who constantly attended him.

.     .     .     .     .     .     .

[24 March.] Then twenty naked virgins, the daughters of Wakungu, all smeared and shining with grease, each holding a small square of mbugu for a fig leaf, marched in a line before us, as a fresh addition to the harem, whilst the happy fathers floundered n'yanzigging on the ground, delighted to find their darlings appreciated by the king. Seeing this done in such a quiet mild way before all my men who dared not lift their heads to see it, made me burst into a roar of laughter, and the king, catching the infection from me, laughed as well: but the laughing did not end there—for the pages for once giving way to nature, kept bursting—my men chuckled in sudden gusts—while even the women, holding their mouths for fear of detection responded—and we all laughed together. Then a sedate old dame rose from the squatting mass, ordered the virgins to right-about, and marched them off, showing their still more naked reverses. I now obtained permission for the Wakungu to call upon me, and fancied I only required my interpreters to speak out like men when I had anything to say, to make my residence in Uganda both amusing and instructive; but though the king, carried off by the prevailing good humour of the scene we had both witnessed, supported me, I found that he had counter-ordered what he had said as soon as I had gone, and in fact, no Mkungu ever dared come near me.

[25 March.] To-day I visited Usungu again, and found him better. He gave pombe and plantains for my people, but would not talk to me, though I told him he had permission to call on me.

I have now been for some time within the court precincts, and have consequently had an opportunity of witnessing court customs. Among these, nearly every day since I have changed my residence, incredible as it may appear to be, I have seen one, two, or three of the wretched palacewomen led away to execution, tied by the hand, and dragged along by one of the body guard, crying out, as she went to premature death, 'Hai Minange!' (O my lord!) 'Kbakka!' (my king!) at the top of her voice, in the utmost despair and lamentation; and yet there was not a soul who dared lift hand to save any of them, though many might be heard privately commenting on their beauty. . . .

[27 March.] After breakfast I started on a visit to Congow; but finding he had gone to the king as usual, called at Masimbi's and he being absent also, I took advantage of my proximity to the queen's palace to call on her majesty. For hours I was kept waiting; firstly, because she was at breakfast; secondly, because she was 'putting on medicine;' and, thirdly, because the sun was too powerful for her complexion; when I became tired of her nonsense, and said, 'If she does not wish to see me, she had better say so at once, else I shall walk away; for the last time I came I saw her but for a minute when she rudely turned her back upon me, and left me sitting by myself.' I was told not to be in a hurry —she would see me in the evening. This promise might probably be fulfilled six blessed hours from the time when it was made; but I thought to myself, every place in Uganda is alike when there is no company at home, and so I resolved to sit the time out, like patience on a monument, hoping something funny might turn up after all.

At last her majesty stumps out, squats behind my red blanket, which is converted into a permanent screen, and says hastily, or rather testily, 'Can't Bana perceive the angry state of the weather?—clouds flying about, and the wind blowing half a gale? Whenever that is the case, I cannot venture out.' Taking her lie without an answer, I said, I had now been fifty days or so doing nothing in Uganda—not one single visitor of my own rank ever came near me, and I could not associate with people far below her condition and mine—in fact, all I had to amuse me at home now was watching a hen lay her eggs upon my spare bed. . . .

The Wakungu than changed the subject by asking, if I married a black woman, would there be any offspring, and what would be their colour? The company now became jovial when the queen improved it by making a significant gesture, and with roars of laughter asking me if I would like to be her son-in-law, for she had some beautiful daughters, either of the Wahuma or Waganda breed. Rather staggered at first by this awful proposal, I consulted Bombay what I should do with one if I got her. He, looking more to number one than my convenience, said, 'By all means accept the offer, for if *you* don't like her, *we* should, and it would be a good means of getting her out of this land of death, for all black people love Zanzibar.' The rest need not be told; as a matter of course I had to appear very much gratified, and as the bowl went round, all became uproarious. I must wait a day or two, however, that a proper selection might be made; and when the marriage came off I was to chain the fair one two or three days, until she became used to me, else, from mere fright, she might run away. . . .

.    .    .    .    .    .

[30 March.] To fulfil my engagement with the queen, I walked off to her palace with stomach medicine, thinking we were now such warm friends, all pride and distant ceremonies would be dispensed with; but, on the contrary, I was kept waiting for hours till I sent in word to say, if she did not want medicine I wished to go home, for I was tired of Uganda and everything belonging to it. This message brought her to her gate, where she stood laughing till the Wahuma girls she had promised me, one of twelve and the other a little older, were brought in and made to squat in front of us. The elder, who was in the prime of youth and beauty, very large of limb, dark in colour, cried considerably; whilst the younger one, though very fair, had a snubby nose and everted lips, and laughed as if she thought the change in her destiny very good fun. I had now to make my selection, and took the smaller one, promising her to Bombay as soon as we arrived on the coast, where, he said, she would be considered a Hubshi or Abyssinian. But when the queen saw what I had done, she gave me the other as well, saying the little one was too young to go alone, and, if separated, she would take fright and run away. Then with a gracious bow I walked off with my two fine specimens of natural history, though I would rather have had princes, that I might

205

have taken them home to be instructed in England; but the queen, as soon as we had cleared the palace, sent word to say that she must have another parting look at her son with his wives. Still laughing, she said, 'That will do; you look beautiful; now go away home,' and off we trotted, the elder sobbing bitterly, the younger laughing.

As soon as we reached home, my first enquiry was concerning their histories, of which they appeared to know but very little. The elder, whom I named Meri (plantains), was obtained by Sunna, the late king, as a wife from Nkole; and though she was a mere Kahala, or girl, when the old king died, he was so attached to her he gave her twenty cows, in order that she might fatten up on milk after her native fashion; but on Sunna's death, when the establishment of women was divided, Meri fell to N'yamasore's (the queen's) lot. The lesser one, who still retains the name of Kahala, said she was seized in Unyoro by the Waganda, who took her to N'yamasore, but what became of her father and mother she could not say.

It was now dinner time, and as the usual sweet potatoes and goat's flesh were put upon my box-table I asked them to dine with me, and we became great friends, for they were assured they would finally get good houses and gardens at Zanzibar; but nothing would induce either of them to touch food that had been cooked with butter. A dish of plantains and goat-flesh was then prepared; but though Kahala wished to eat it, Meri rejected the goat's flesh, and would not allow Kahala to taste it either; and thus began a series of domestic difficulties. On inquiring how I could best deal with my difficult charge, I was told the Wahuma pride was so great, and their tempers so strong, they were more difficult to break in than a phunda, or donkey, though, when once tamed, they became the best of wives.

*On 23rd April Speke accompanied the king on a frolicsome expedition to the lake.*

[26 April.] We started early in the usual manner; but after working up and down the creek, inspecting the inlets for hippopotami, and tiring from want of sport, the king changed his tactics, and, paddling and steering himself with a pair of new white paddles, finally directed the boats to an island occupied by the Mgussa, or Neptune of the N'yanza, not in person —for Mgussa is a spirit—but by his familiar or deputy, the great medium who communicates the secrets of the deep to the king of Uganda. In another sense, he might be said to be the presiding priest of the source of the mighty Nile, and as such was, of course, an interesting person for me to meet. The first operation on shore was picknicking, when many large bugus of pombe were brought for the king; next, the whole party took a walk, winding through the trees, and picking fruit, enjoying themselves amazingly, till, by some unlucky chance, one of the royal wives, a most charming creature, and truly one of the best of the lot, plucked a fruit and offered it to the king, thinking, doubtless, to please him greatly; but he, like a madman, flew into a towering passion, and said it was the first time a woman ever had the impudence to offer him anything, and ordered the pages to seize, bind, and lead her off to execution.

These words were no sooner uttered by the king than the whole bevy of pages slipped their cord turbans from their heads, and rushed like a pack of cupid beagles upon the fairy queen, who, indignant at the little urchins daring to touch her majesty, remonstrated with the king, and tried to beat them off like flies, but was soon captured, overcome, and dragged away, crying, in the names of the Kamraviona and Mzungu (myself) for help and protection; whilst Lubuga, the pet sister, and all the other women, clasped the king by his legs, and, kneeling, implored forgiveness for their sister. The more they craved for mercy, the more brutal he became, till at last he took a heavy stick and began to belabour the poor victim on the head.

Hitherto I had been extremely careful not to interfere with any of the king's acts of arbitrary cruelty knowing that such interference, at an early stage, would produce more harm than good. This last act of barbarism, however, was too much for my English blood to stand; and as I heard my name, Mzungu, imploringly pronounced, I rushed at the king, and, staying his uplifted arm, demanded from him the woman's life. Of course I ran imminent risk of losing my own in thus thwarting the capricious tyrant; but his caprice proved the friend of both. The novelty of interference even made him smile, and the woman was instantly released.

Proceeding on through the trees of this beautiful island, we next turned into the hut of the Mgussa's familiar, which at the farther end was decorated with many mystic symbols—amongst others a paddle, the badge of his high office—and for some time we sat chatting, when pombe was brought, and the spiritual medium arrived. He was dressed Wichwezi fashion, with a little white goat-skin apron, adorned with numerous charms, and used a paddle for a mace or walking-stick. He was not an old man, though he affected to be so—walking very slowly and deliberately, coughing asthmatically, glimmering with his eyes, and mumbling like a witch. With much affected difficulty he sat at the end of the hut beside the symbols alluded to, and continued his coughing full half an hour, when his wife came in in the same manner, without saying a word, and assumed the same affected style. The king jokingly looked at me and laughed, and then at these strange creatures by turn, as much as to say, 'What do you think of them?' but no voice was heard save that of the old wife, who croaked like a frog for water, and, when some was brought, croaked again because it was not the purest of the lake's produce—had the first cup changed, wetted her lips with the second, and hobbled away in the same manner as she came.

At this juncture the Mgussa's familiar motioned the Kamraviona and several officers to draw around him, when in a very low tone, he gave them all the orders of the deep, and walked away. His revelations seemed unpropitious, for we immediately repaired to our boats and returned to our quarters.

.        .        .        .        .        .

[3 May.] I now received a letter from Grant to say he was coming by boat from Kitangule, and at once went to the palace to give the welcome news to the king. The road to the palace I found thronged with people; and in the square outside the entrance there squatted a multitude of attendants, headed by the king, sitting on a cloth, dressed in his national costume, with two spears and a shield by his side. On his right hand the pages sat waiting for orders, while on his left there was a small squatting cluster of women, headed by Wichwezis, or attendant sorceresses, offering pombe. In front of the king, in form of a hollow square, many ranks deep, sat the victorious officers lately returned from the war, variously dressed; the nobles distinguished by their leopard-cat skins and dirks, the commoners by coloured mbugu and cow or antelope skin cloaks; but all their faces and arms were painted, red, black, or smoke-colour. Within the square of men immediately fronting the king, the war arms of Uganda were arranged in three ranks; the great war drum, covered with a leopard skin, and standing on a large carpeting of them, was placed in advance; behind this, propped or hung on a rack of iron, were a variety of the implements of war in common use, offensive and defensive, as spears—of which two were of copper, the rest iron—and shields of wood and leather; whilst in the last row or lot were arranged systematically, with great taste and powerful effect, the supernatural arms, the god of Uganda, consisting of charms of various descriptions and in great numbers. Outside the square again, in a line with the king, were the household arms, a very handsome copper kettledrum, of French manufacture, surmounted on the outer edge with pretty little brass bells depending from swan-neck-shaped copper wire, two new spears, a painted leather shield, and magic wands of various devices, deposited on a carpet of leopard skins—the whole scene giving the effect of true barbarous royalty in its uttermost magnificence.

Approaching, as usual, to take my seat beside the king, some slight sensation was perceptible, and I was directed to sit beyond the women. The whole ceremonies of this grand assemblage were now obvious. Each regimental commandant in turn narrated the whole services of his party

King Mtesa Reviews His Troops
From Speke's *Journal*

distinguishing those subs who executed his orders well and successfully from those who either deserted before the enemy or feared to follow up their success. The king listened attentively, making, let us suppose, very shrewd remarks concerning them; when to the worthy he awarded pombe, helped with gourd-cups from large earthen jars, which was n'yanzigged for vehemently; and to the unworthy, execution. When the fatal sentence was pronounced, a terrible bustle ensued, the convict wrestling and defying, whilst the other men seized, pulled and tore the struggling wretch from the crowd, bound him hands and head together, and led or rather tumbled him away. . . .

*On 27th May Grant arrived from Karagwe. Speke constantly pressed for permission to go north through Unyoro to Gondokoro, where he hoped to meet the trader Petherick. Until 3rd July the king prevaricated.*

[3 July.] The moment of triumph had come at last, and suddenly the road was granted! The king presently let us see the motive by which he had been influenced. He said he did not like having to send to Rumanika for everything: he wanted his visitors to come to him direct: moreover, Rumanika had sent him a message to the effect that we were not to be shown anything out of Uganda, and when we had done with it, were to be returned to him. Rumanika, indeed! who cared about Rumanika? Was not Mtesa the king of the country, to do as he liked? and we all laughed. Then the king, swelling with pride, asked me whom I liked best —Rumanika or himself—an awkward question, which I disposed of by saying I liked Rumanika very much because he spoke well, and was very communicative; but I also liked Mtesa, because his habits were much like my own—fond of shooting and roaming about; whilst he had learnt so many things from my teaching, I must ever feel a yearning towards him.

.    .    .    .    .    .

On the way home, one of the king's favourite women overtook us, walking, with her hands clasped at the back of her head, to execution, crying 'N'yawo!' in the most pitiful manner. A man was preceding her, but did not touch her; for she loved to obey the orders of her king voluntarily, and, in consequence of previous attachment, was permitted as a mark of distinction, to walk free. Wondrous world! it was not ten minutes since we parted from the king, yet he had found time to transact this bloody piece of business.

[7 July.] Early in the morning the king bade us come to him to say farewell. Wishing to leave behind a favourable impression I instantly

o                                209

complied. On the breast of my coat, I suspended the necklace the queen had given me, as well as his knife, and my medals. I talked with him in as friendly and flattering a manner as I could, dwelling on his shooting, the pleasant cruising on the lake, and our sundry picnics, as well as the grand prospect there was now of opening the country to trade, by which his guns, the best in the world, would be fed with powder—and other small matters of a like nature—to which he replied with great feeling and good taste. We then all rose with an English bow, placing the hand on the heart whilst saying adieu; and there was a complete uniformity in the ceremonial, for whatever I did, Mtesa, in an instant, mimicked with the instinct of a monkey.

We had, however, scarcely quitted the palace gate before the king issued himself, with his attendants and his brothers leading, and women bringing up the rear; here K'yengo and all the Wazina joined in the procession with ourselves, they kneeling and clapping their hands after the fashion of their own country. Budja (their guide to the north) just then made me feel very anxious, by pointing out the position of Urondogani, as I thought, too far north. I called the king's attention to it, and in a moment he said he would speak to Budja in such a manner that he would leave no doubts in my mind, for he liked me much, and desired to please me in all things. As the procession now drew close to our camp and Mtesa expressed a wish to have a final look at my men, I ordered them to turn out with their arms and n'yanzig for the many favours they had received. Mtesa, much pleased, complimented them on their goodly appearance, remarking that with such a force I would have no difficulty in reaching Gani, and exhorted them to follow me through fire and water; then, exchanging adieus again, he walked ahead in gigantic strides up the hill, the pretty favourite of his harem, Lubuga—beckoning and waving with her little hands and crying 'Bana! Bana!'—trotting after him conspicuous amongst the rest, though all showed a little feeling at the severance. We saw them no more.

*Journal of the discovery of the source of the Nile*, 1st edition, pp. 280–316, 334–336, 357–370, 394–396, 405–406, 445–452

*After leaving Uganda, Speke sent Grant on to Unyoro with the stores to make contact with its difficult monarch, Kamrasi, while he himself marched eastwards looking for the Nile. He struck it somewhat north of its egress from Lake Victoria and followed it down the left bank, seeking for the essential proof of his theory.*

## 25. DISCOVERY OF THE SOURCE OF THE NILE

[25 July 1862.] I marched up the left bank of the Nile at a considerable distance from the water, to the Isamba Rapids, passing through rich jungle and plantain gardens. Nango, an old friend and district officer of the place, first refreshed us with a dish of plantain-squash and dried fish with pombe. He told us he is often threatened by elephants, but he sedulously keeps them off with charms; for if they ever tasted a plantain they would never leave the garden until they had cleared it out. He then took us to see the nearest falls of the Nile—extremely beautiful but very confined. The water ran deep between its banks, which were covered with fine grass, soft cloudy acacias, and festoons of lilac convolvuli; whilst here and there, where the land had slipped above the rapids, bared places of red earth could be seen, like that of Devonshire; there, too, the waters, impeded by a natural dam, looked like a huge mill-pond, sullen and dark, in which two crocodiles, laving about, were looking out for prey. From the high banks we looked down upon a line of sloping wooded islets lying across the stream, which divide its waters, and, by interrupting them, cause at once both dam and rapids. The whole was more fairylike, wild, and romantic than—I must confess that my thoughts took that shape—anything I ever saw outside of a theatre. It was exactly the sort of place, in fact, where, bridged across from one side-slip to the other, on a moonlight night, brigands would assemble to enact some dreadful tragedy. Even the Wanguana seemed spellbound at the novel beauty of the sight, and no one thought of moving till hunger warned us night was setting in, and we had better look out for lodgings.

[25 July.] Start again, and after drinking pombe with Nango, when we heard that three Wakungu had been seized at Kari, in consequence of the murder, the march was recommenced, but soon after stopped by the mischievous machinations of our guide, who pretended it was too late in the day to cross the jungles on ahead, either by the road to the source or the palace, and therefore would not move till the morning; then, leaving us, on the pretext of business, he vanished, and was never seen again. A small black fly, with thick shoulders and bullet-head, infests the place, and torments the naked arms and legs of the people with its sharp stings to an extent that must render life miserable to them.

[27 July.] After a long struggling march, plodding through huge grasses and jungle, we reached a district which I cannot otherwise describe than by calling it a 'Church Estate'. It is dedicated in some mysterious manner to Lubari (Almighty) and although the king appeared to have authority over some of the inhabitants of it, yet others had apparently a sacred character, exempting them from the civil power, and

211

he had no right to dispose of the land itself. In this territory there are small villages only at every fifth mile, for there is no road, and the lands run high again, whilst, from want of a guide, we often lost the track. It now transpired that Budja, when he told at the palace that there was no road down the banks of the Nile, did so in consequence of his fear that if he sent my whole party here they would rob these church lands, and so bring him into a scrape with the wizards or ecclesiastical authorities. Had my party not been under control, we could not have put up here; but on my being answerable that no thefts should take place, the people kindly consented to provide us with board and lodgings, and we found them very obliging. One elderly man—half-witted—they said the king had driven his senses from him by seizing his house and family—came at once on hearing of our arrival, laughing and singing in a loose jaunty maniacal manner, carrying odd sticks, shells and a bundle of mbugu rags, which he deposited before me, dancing and singing again, then retreating and bringing some more with a few plantains from a garden, which I was to eat, as kings lived upon flesh, and 'poor Tom' wanted some, for he lived with lions and elephants in a hovel beyond the gardens, and his belly was empty. He was precisely a black specimen of the English parish idiot.

[28 July.] At last, with a good push for it, crossing hills and threading huge grasses, as well as extensive village plantations lately devastated by elephants—they had eaten all that was eatable, and what would not serve for food they had destroyed with their trunks, not one plantain or one hut being left entire—we arrived at the extreme end of the journey, the farthest point ever visited by the expedition on the same parallel of latitude as king Mtesa's palace, and just forty miles east of it.

We were well rewarded; for the 'stones,' as the Waganda call the falls, was by far the most interesting sight I had seen in Africa. Everybody ran to see them at once, though the march had been long and fatiguing, and even my sketch-block was called into play. Though beautiful, the scene was not exactly what I expected; for the broad surface of the lake was shut out from view by a spur of hill, and the falls, about 12 feet deep, and 400 to 500 feet broad, were broken by rocks. Still it was a sight that attracted one to it for hours—the roar of the waters, the thousands of passenger-fish, leaping at the falls with all their might, the Wasoga and Waganda fishermen coming out in boats and taking post on all the rocks with rod and hook, hippopotami and crocodiles lying sleepily on the water, the ferry at work above the falls, and cattle driven down to drink at the margin of the lake,—made, in all, with the pretty nature of the country—small hills, grassy-topped, with trees in the folds, and gardens on the lower slopes—as interesting a picture as one could wish to see.

The expedition had now performed its functions. I saw that old father

212

THE RIPON FALLS
From Speke's *Journal*

Nile without any doubt rises in the Victoria N'yanza, and as I had fore-told, that lake is the great source of the holy river which cradled the first expounder of our religious belief. I mourned, however, when I thought how much I had lost by the delays in the journey having deprived me of the pleasure of going to look at the north-east corner of the N'yanza to see what connection there was, by the strait so often spoken of, with it and the other lake where the Waganda went to get their salt, and from which another river flowed to the north, making 'Usoga an island.' But I felt I ought to be content with what I had been spared to accomplish; for I had seen full half of the lake, and had information given me of the other half, by means of which I knew all about the lake, as far, at least, as the chief objects of geographical importance were concerned.

*Journal of the discovery of the source of the Nile,*
1st edition, pp. 464–467

*Speke named these falls Ripon after Lord de Grey and Ripon, President of the Royal Geographical Society. He then endeavoured to follow the course of the Nile northwards. He was, however, forced away from the river by the hostility of some of the natives and was obliged to cut across to Kamrasi's. After being delayed and perse-cuted by this suspicious and greedy king, they moved on to the north. They were unable to keep touch with the Nile and did not find Lake Albert. Coming through the ghastly preserves of the so-called 'Turkish' slave-raiders from Egypt and the Sudan, who were spread-ing their depredations ever further south, they encountered Mr. Samuel Baker walking by the river at Gondokoro. Reference will be made again in the next section to their meeting.*

*We must briefly follow through the rest of Speke's life. Speke and Grant reached England early in 1863. Their great discoveries were acclaimed, though the Government gave Speke no reward except the right to add a hippopotamus and a crocodile to his coat-of-arms. As, however, Speke had failed to trace the course of the Nile northwards from Lake Victoria, Burton challenged his whole theory, both as to the Nile having its source in the lake and as to the size and impor-tance of the lake itself. He even published a map in 1864 in which the lake was marked as 'supposed site' and the connection further west from Lake Tanganyika, through a speculative Lake Albert, main-tained. It was decided that the bitter controversy between the two explorers should be settled by confronting them publicly at the meet-ing of the British Association at Bath.*

*Speke is said to have dreaded the ordeal though, as further exploration was to show, his theories were correct in spite of his incomplete evidence. The meeting did not, however, take place. When Burton was on the platform and the audience had been kept waiting for twenty-five minutes, news came that while Speke, who had gone out shooting that morning, had been climbing over a wall, both barrels of his shot-gun had gone off, and he had died at once. The verdict at the inquest was 'accidental death'.*

# VIII

# SIR SAMUEL WHITE BAKER
## 1821–1893

Baker was born at Enfield and was the son of an English land-owner, member of a Bristol family with estates and commercial connections in the West Indies. He was, for the most part, educated privately and finished his studies in Germany. In 1840 he married the daughter of a rector and shortly afterwards he was attracted by accounts of big-game shooting to visit Ceylon. His connection with the island, where he fostered an experiment in English colonization, lasted until 1855. He then returned to England where his wife died of typhus. After some rather aimless wandering and sport in the Near East in 1859 he took over the supervision of some railway construction on the Danube, during which he learned confidence in handling gangs of men. At this time he married his second wife, Fraülein von Sass.

In 1861 he decided to embark with his new wife upon exploration in Central Africa. A man of great physical strength and powerful build, the greatest big-game hunter of his age, he was naturally attracted by this adventurous enterprise. He hoped that he might meet Speke and Grant upon their way north from Lake Victoria. After a preliminary fourteen months exploring the tributaries flowing from Abyssinia into the Nile, Baker and his wife set out from Khartoum at the end of 1862. They were provided with a firman from the viceroy of Egypt which was only of limited use among the Sudan officials, as these were mostly deep in the terrible slave trade which was being extended every year further south, and were fearful of Baker's revelations.

Baker took three ships and 100 men up the Nile. He had considerable difficulty with both, but managed to reach Gondokoro, the Equatorial headquarters of the mixed Arab and Egyptian slave-traders (generally known as Turks), in February 1863. Here, as a result of the intrigues and opposition of the Arabs and the hostility of the ill-treated tribes in the neighbourhood, the Bakers had an uncomfortable and even dangerous time. A serious mutiny on the part of

215

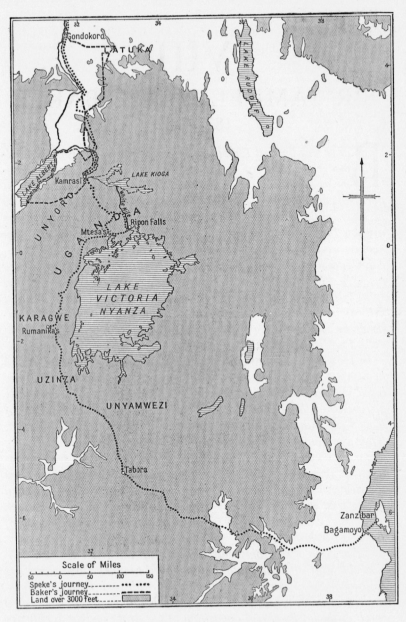

Gondokoro

ATUKA

LAKE RUDOLF

Kamrasi

LAKE KIOGA

UNYORO

LAKE ALBERT

U G A N D A

Mtesa's

Ripon Falls

LAKE
VICTORIA
NYANZA

KARAGWE
or
Rumanika's

UZINZA

UNYAMWEZI

Tabora

Zanzibar

Bagamoyo

Scale of Miles
50    0    50    100    150
Speke's journey --------- ••• ••••
Baker's journey ---------
Land over 3000 feet ---------

9. THE TRAVELS OF SPEKE AND BAKER, 1860–5

*Baker's own men was overcome as much by the outstanding courage and common sense of his wife as by his own vigorous action. The dramatic meeting with Speke and Grant followed, and he was able to replenish their stores. In spite of joy at the meeting, Baker was dashed in his hopes of carrying out his own discoveries until the liberal-minded Speke told him of rumours of the existence of a large undiscovered lake to the south-west connected with the Nile system and generously showed him his own sketch maps to help him. In March 1863 the traveller and his wife struck south upon the most perilous part of their journey. Baker was forced to seek the guidance and company of slave-traders and to endure the brutal and treacherous character of these men who plotted with his own rascally followers, and raised the hostility of the tribes which they massacred and plundered on the way. There were further mutinies and desertions; both travellers suffered from fever and sickness and all their transport animals died.*

*By the beginning of April they had reached the Latuka country and here Baker persuaded the chief to arrange an elephant hunt of which he gives a characteristic account.*

## 26. ENCOUNTER WITH AN ELEPHANT

In about ten minutes we saw the Latookas hurrying towards us, and almost immediately after, I saw two enormous bull elephants with splendid tusks about a hundred yards from us, apparently the leaders of an approaching herd. The ground was exceedingly favourable, being tolerably open, and yet with sufficient bush to afford a slight cover. Presently, several elephants appeared and joined the two leaders—there was evidently a considerable number in the herd, and I was on the point of dismounting to take the first shot on foot, when the Latookas, too eager, approached the herd: their red and blue helmets at once attracted the attention of the elephants, and a tremendous rush took place, the whole herd closing together and tearing off at full speed. 'Follow me!' I hallooed to my men, and touching my horse with the spur I intended to dash into the midst of the herd. Just at that instant, in his start, my horse slipped and fell suddenly upon his side, falling upon my right leg and thus pinning me to the ground. He was not up to my weight, and releasing myself, I immediately mounted my old Abyssinian hunter, 'Tetel,' and followed the tracks of the elephants at full speed, accompanied by two of the Latookas, who ran like hounds. Galloping through the green but thornless bush, I soon came in sight of a grand bull ele-

217

phant, steaming along like a locomotive engine straight before me. Digging in the spurs, I was soon within twenty yards of him; but the ground was so unfavourable, being full of buffalo holes, that I could not pass him. In about a quarter of an hour, after a careful chase over deep ruts and gullies concealed in high grass, I arrived at a level space, and shooting ahead, I gave him a shoulder shot with the Reilly No. 10 rifle. I saw the wound in a good place, but the bull rushed along all the quicker, and again we came into bad ground that made it unwise to close. However, on the first opportunity I made a dash by him, and fired my left-hand barrel at full gallop. He slackened his speed, but I could not halt to reload, lest I should lose sight of him in the high grass and bush.

Not a man was with me to hand a spare rifle. My cowardly fellows, although light-weights and well mounted, were nowhere; the natives were outrun, as of course was Richarn, who, not being a good rider, had preferred to hunt on foot. In vain I shouted for the men; and I followed the elephant with an empty rifle for about ten minutes, until he suddenly turned round, and stood facing me in an open spot in grass about nine or ten feet high. 'Tetel' was a grand horse for elephants, not having the slightest fear, and standing fire like a rock, never even starting under the discharge of the heaviest charge of powder. I now commenced reloading, when presently one of my men, Yaseen, came up upon 'Filfil.' Taking a spare gun from him, I rode rapidly past the elephant and suddenly reining up, I made a good shot exactly behind the bladebone. With a shrill scream, the elephant charged down upon me like a steam-engine. In went the spurs. 'Tetel' knew his work, and away he went over the ruts and gullies, the high dry grass whistling in my ears as we shot along at full speed, closely followed by the enraged bull for about two hundred yards.

The elephant then halted: and turning the horse's head, I again faced him and reloaded. I thought he was dying, as he stood with trunk drooping, and ears closely pressed back upon his neck. Just at this moment I heard the rush of elephants advancing through the green bush upon the rising ground above the hollow formed by the open space of high withered grass in which we were standing facing each other. My man Yaseen had bolted with his fleet horse at the first charge and was not to be seen. Presently, the rushing sound increased, and the heads of a closely packed herd of about eighteen elephants showed above the low bushes, and they broke cover, bearing down directly upon me, both I and my horse being unobserved in the high grass. I never saw a more lovely sight; they were all bulls with immense tusks. Waiting until they were within twenty yards of me, I galloped straight at them, giving a yell that turned them. Away they rushed up the hill, but at so great a pace, that upon the rutty and broken ground I could not overtake them, and they completely distanced me. Tetel, although a wonderfully steady hunter, was an uncommonly slow horse, but upon this day he appeared to be slower than usual, and I was not at the time aware that he was seriously ill. By following three elephants separated from the herd I came up to them by a short cut, and singling out a fellow with enormous tusks, I rode straight at him. Finding himself overhauled, he charged me with such quickness and followed me up so far, that it was with the greatest difficulty that I cleared him. When he turned, I at once returned to the attack; but he entered a thick thorny jungle through which no horse could follow, and I failed to obtain a shot.

I was looking for a path through which I could penetrate the bush, when I suddenly heard natives shouting in the direction where I had left the wounded bull. Galloping towards the spot, I met a few scattered natives; among others, Adda. After shouting for some time, at length Yaseen appeared upon my horse Filfil; he had fled as usual when he saw the troop of elephants advancing and no one knows how far he had ridden before he thought it safe to look behind him. With two mounted gun bearers and five others on foot I had been entirely deserted through the cowardice of my men. The elephant that I had left as dying was gone. One of the Latookas had followed upon his tracks, and we heard this fellow shooting in the distance. I soon overtook him, and he led rapidly upon the track through the thick bushes and high grass. In about a quarter of an hour we came up with the elephant; he was standing in bush, facing us at about fifty yards distance, and immediately perceiving us, he gave a saucy jerk with his head, and charged most determinedly. It was exceedingly difficult to escape, owing to the bushes which impeded the horse, while the elephant crushed them like cobwebs: however, by turning my horse sharp round a tree I managed to evade him after a chase of about a hundred and fifty yards. Disappearing in the jungle after his charge, I immediately followed him. The ground was hard, and so trodden by elephants that it was difficult to single out the track. There was no blood upon the ground, but only on the trees every now and then, where he had rubbed past them in his retreat. After nearly two hours passed in slowly following upon his path, we suddenly broke cover and saw him travelling very quietly through an extensive plain of high grass. The ground was gently inclining upwards on either side the plain, but the level was a mass of deep, hardened ruts, over which no horse could gallop. Knowing my friend's character, I rode up the rising ground to reconnoitre: I found it tolerably clear of holes, and far superior to the rutty bottom. My two mounted gun-bearers had now joined me, and far from enjoying the sport, they were almost green with fright when I ordered them to keep close to me and to advance. I wanted them to attract the elephant's attention, so as to enable me to obtain a good shoulder shot. Riding along the open plain, I at length arrived within about fifty yards of the bull when he slowly turned. Reining 'Tetel' up,

I immediately fired a steady shot at the shoulder with the Reilly No. 10:
—for a moment he fell upon his knees, but, recovering with wonderful
quickness, he was in full charge upon me. Fortunately I had inspected
my ground previous to the attack and away I went up the inclination to
my right, the spurs hard at work and the elephant screaming with rage,
*gaining* on me. My horse felt as though made of wood, and clumsily
rolled along in a sort of cow-gallop;—in vain I dug the spurs into his
flanks, and urged him by rein and voice: not an extra stride could I get
out of him, and he reeled along as though thoroughly exhausted, plunging in and out of the buffalo holes instead of jumping them. Hamed was
on my horse 'Mouse,' who went three to 'Tetel's' one, and instead of
endeavouring to divert the elephant's attention, he shot ahead, and
thought of nothing but getting out of the way. Yaseen, on 'Filfil,' had
fled in another direction, thus I had the pleasure of being hunted down
upon a sick and disabled horse. I kept looking round, thinking that the
elephant would give in:—we had been running for nearly half a mile,
and the brute was overhauling me so fast that he was within ten or
twelve yards of the horse's tail, with his trunk stretched out to catch him.
Screaming like the whistle of an engine, he fortunately so frightened the
horse that he went his best, although badly, and I turned him suddenly
down the hill and doubled back like a hare. The elephant turned up the
hill, and entering the jungle, he relinquished the chase, when another
hundred yards' run would have bagged me.

In a life's experience in elephant-hunting, I never was hunted for such
a distance. Great as were Tetel's good qualities for pluck and steadiness,
he had exhibited such distress and want of speed, that I was sure he
failed through some sudden malady. I immediately dismounted, and the
horse laid down, as I thought to die.

Whistling loudly, I at length recalled Hamed, who had still continued
his rapid flight without once looking back, although the elephant was
out of sight. Yaseen was, of course, nowhere; but after a quarter of an
hour's shouting and whistling, he reappeared, and I mounted Filfil,
ordering Tetel to be led home.

*The Albert N'Yanza*, 1st edition, vol. I, pp. 264–272

On 10th February 1864 they reached the headquarters of Kamrasi,
King of Unyoro, the most northerly of the important African sover-
eigns of the Lake regions, who had just given Speke and Grant a
difficult time. He took advantage of their helpless condition—they
had now only thirteen porters left—to extort from Baker almost
everything he possessed, while Baker desperately tried to obtain his

THE LAST CHARGE
From Baker's *Albert N'Yanza*

*permission and help to discover the great unknown western lake.*
*Kamrasi at length agreed to provide a guide and porters for this*
*expedition.*

# 27. DISCOVERY OF LAKE ALBERT

The day of starting at length arrived; the chief and guide appeared,
and we were led to the Kafoor river, where canoes were in readiness to
transport us to the south side. This was to our old quarters on the marsh.
The direct course to the lake was west and I fully expected some decep-
tion, as it was impossible to trust Kamrasi. I complained to the guide,
and insisted upon his pointing out the direction of the lake, which he did,
in its real position, west; but he explained that we must follow the south
bank of the Kafoor river for some days, as there was an impassable
morass that precluded a direct course. This did not appear satisfactory,
and the whole affair looked suspicious, as we had formerly been de-
ceived by being led across the river in the same spot, and not allowed to
return. We were now led along the banks of the Kafoor for about a
mile, until we arrived at a cluster of huts: here we were to wait for
Kamrasi, who had promised to take leave of us. The sun was overpowering and we dismounted from our oxen, and took shelter in a
blacksmith's shed. In about an hour Kamrasi arrived, attended by a
considerable number of men, and took his seat in our shed. I felt convinced that his visit was simply intended to peel the last skin from the
onion. I had already given him nearly all that I had, but he hoped to
extract the whole before I should depart.

He almost immediately commenced the conversation by asking for a
pretty yellow muslin Turkish handkerchief fringed with silver drops that
Mrs. Baker wore upon her head: one of these had already been given
to him, and I explained that this was the last remaining, and that she
required it. He 'must' have it. It was given. He then demanded other
handkerchiefs. We had literally nothing but a few most ragged towels;
he would accept no excuse, and insisted upon a portmanteau being
unpacked, that he might satisfy himself by actual inspection. The luggage, all ready for the journey, had to be unstrapped and examined, and
the rags were displayed in succession; but so wretched and uninviting
was the exhibition of the family linen, that he simply returned them, and
said 'they did not suit him.' Beads he must have or I was 'his enemy.'
A selection of the best opal beads was immediately given him. I rose
from the stone upon which I was sitting, and declared that we must start
immediately. 'Don't be in a hurry,' he replied, 'you have plenty of time;
but you have not given me that watch you promised me.' This was my

only watch that he had begged for, and had been refused every day during my stay at M'rooli. So pertinacious a beggar I had never seen. I explained to him that, without the watch, my journey would be useless, but that I would give him all that I had except the watch when the exploration should be completed, as I should require nothing on my direct return to Gondokoro. At the same time, I repeated to him the arrangement for the journey that he had promised, begging him not to deceive me, as my wife and I should both die if we were compelled to remain another year in this country by losing the annual boats in Gondokoro. The understanding was this: he was to give me porters to the lake, where I was to be furnished with canoes to take me to Magungo, which was situated at the junction of the Somerset. From Magungo he told me that I should see the Nile issuing from the lake close to the spot where the Somerset entered, and that the canoes should take me down the river, and porters should carry my effects from the nearest point to Shooa and deliver me at my old station without delay. Should he be faithful to this engagement, I trusted to procure porters from Shooa, and to reach Gondokoro in time for the annual boats. I had arranged that a boat should be sent from Khartoum to await me at Gondokoro early in this year, 1864; but I felt sure that should I be long delayed, the boat would return without me, as the people would be afraid to remain alone at Gondokoro after the other boats had quitted.

In our present weak state another year of Central Africa without quinine appeared to warrant death; it was a race against time, all was untrodden ground before us, and the distance quite uncertain. I trembled for my wife, and weighed the risk of another year in this horrible country should we lose the boats. With the self-sacrificing devotion that she had shown in every trial, she implored me not to think of any risks on her account, but to push forward and discover the lake—that she had determined not to return until she herself reached the 'M'wootan N'zige.'

I now requested Kamrasi to allow us to take leave, as we had not an hour to lose. In the coolest manner he replied, 'I will send you to the lake and to Shooa, as I have promised; but, *you must leave your wife with me!*'

At that moment we were surrounded by a great number of natives, and my suspicions of treachery at having been led across the Kafoor river appeared confirmed by this insolent demand. If this were to be the end of the expedition I resolved that it should also be the end of Kamrasi, and, drawing my revolver quietly, I held it within two feet of his chest, and looking at him with undisguised contempt, I told him that if I touched the trigger, not all his men could save him: and that if he dared to repeat the insult I would shoot him on the spot. At the same time I explained to him that in my country such insolence would entail bloodshed, and that I looked upon him as an ignorant ox who knew no better, and that this excuse alone could save him. My wife, naturally indignant, had risen from her seat, and, maddened with the excitement of the moment, she made him a little speech in Arabic (not a word of which he understood), with a countenance almost as amiable as the head of Medusa. Altogether the *mise en scène* utterly astonished him; the woman Bacheeta, although savage, had appropriated the insult to her mistress, and she also fearlessly let fly at Kamrasi, translating as nearly as she could the complimentary address that 'Medusa' had just delivered.

Whether this little *coup de théâtre* had so impressed Kamrasi with British female independence that he wished to be off his bargain, I cannot say, but with an air of complete astonishment, he said, 'Don't be angry! I had no intention of offending you by asking for your wife; I will give you a wife, if you want one, and I thought you might have no objection to give me yours; it is my custom to give visitors pretty wives, and I thought you might exchange. Don't make a fuss about it; if you don't like it, there's an end of it; I will never mention it again.' This very practical apology I received very sternly, and merely insisted upon starting. He seemed rather confused at having committed himself, and to make amends he called his people and ordered them to carry our loads. His men ordered a number of women, who had assembled out of curiosity, to shoulder the luggage and carry it to the next village, where they would be relieved. I assisted my wife upon her ox, and with a very cold adieu to Kamrasi, I turned my back most gladly on M'rooli.

The country was a vast flat of grass land interspersed with small villages and patches of sweet potatoes; these were very inferior, owing to the want of drainage. For about two miles we continued on the banks of the Kafoor river; the women who carried the luggage were straggling in disorder, and my few men were much scattered in their endeavours to collect them. We approached a considerable village, but just as we were nearing it, out rushed about six hundred men with lances and shields, screaming and yelling like so many demons. For the moment, I thought it was an attack, but almost immediately I noticed that women and children were mingled with the men. My men had not taken so cool a view of the excited throng that was now approaching us at full speed, brandishing their spears and engaging with each other in mock combat. 'There's a fight!—there's a fight!' my men exclaimed; 'we are attacked! fire at them, Hawaga.' However, in a few seconds I persuaded them that it was a mere parade, and that there was no danger. With a rush, like a cloud of locusts, the natives closed around us, dancing, gesticulating, and yelling before my ox, feigning to attack us with spears and shields, then engaging in sham fights with each other, and behaving like so many madmen. A very tall chief accompanied them; and one of their men was suddenly knocked down, and attacked by the crowd with sticks and lances, and lay on the ground covered with blood: what his offence had been I did not hear. The entire crowd were most grotesquely got up, being dressed in either leopard or white monkey skins, with cows' tails strapped on behind, and antelopes' horns fitted upon their heads, while their chins were ornamented with false beards, made of the bushy ends of cows' tails sewed together. Altogether, I never saw a more unearthly set of creatures; they were perfect illustrations of my childish ideas of devils—horns, tails, and all, excepting the hoofs; they were our escort! furnished by Kamrasi to accompany us to the lake. Fortunately for all parties the Turks were not with us on that occasion, or the satanic escort would certainly have been received with a volley when they so rashly advanced to compliment us by their absurd performances.

We marched till 7 P.M. over flat, uninteresting country, and then halted at a miserable village which the people had deserted, as they expected our arrival. The following morning I found much difficulty in getting our escort together, as they had been foraging throughout the neighbourhood; these 'devil's own' were a portion of Kamrasi's troops, who considered themselves entitled to plunder *ad libitum* throughout the march; however, after some delay, they collected, and their tall chief approached me, and begged that a gun might be fired as a curiosity. The escort had crowded around us, and as the boy Saat was close to me, I ordered him to fire his gun. This was Saat's greatest delight, and bang went one barrel unexpectedly, close to the tall chief's ear. The effect was charming. The tall chief, thinking himself injured, clasped his head with both hands, and bolted through the crowd, which, struck with a sudden panic, rushed away in all directions, the 'devil's own' tumbling over each other, and utterly scattered by the second barrel which Saat exultantly fired in derision as Kamrasi's warlike regiment dissolved before a sound. I felt quite sure, that in the event of a fight, one scream from the 'baby,' with its charge of forty small bullets, would win the battle, if well delivered into a crowd of Kamrasi's troops.

That afternoon, after a march through a most beautiful forest of large mimosas in full blossom, we arrived at the morass that had necessitated this great *détour* from our direct course to the lake. It was nearly three-quarters of a mile broad, and so deep, that in many places the oxen were obliged to swim; both Mrs. Baker and I were carried across on our angareps [wicker bed-steads] by twelve men with the greatest difficulty; the guide, who waded before us to show the way, suddenly disappeared in a deep hole, and his bundle that he had carried on his head, being of light substance, was seen floating like a buoy upon the surface; after a thorough sousing, the guide reappeared, and scrambled out, and we made a circuit, the men toiling frequently up to their necks through mud and water. On arrival at the opposite side we continued through the same beautiful forest, and slept that night at a deserted village, M'Baze.

I obtained two observations; one of Capella, giving lat. 1° 24′ 47″ N., and of Canopus 1° 23′ 29″.

The next day we were much annoyed by our native escort; instead of attending to us, they employed their time capering and dancing about, screaming and gesticulating, and suddenly rushing off in advance whenever we approached a village, which they plundered before we could arrive. In this manner every place was stripped; nor could we procure anything to eat unless by purchasing it for beads from the native escort. We slept at Karche lat. 1° 19′ 31″ N.

We were both ill, but were obliged to ride through the hottest hours of the sun, as our followers were never ready to start at an early hour in the morning. The native escort were perfectly independent, and so utterly wild and savage in their manner, that they appeared more dangerous than the general inhabitants of the country. My wife was extremely anxious, since the occasion of Kamrasi's 'proposal,' as she was suspicious that so large an escort as three hundred men had been given for some treacherous purpose, and that I should perhaps be way-laid to enable them to steal her for the king. I had not the slightest fear of such an occurrence, as sentries were always on guard during the night, and I was well prepared during the day.

On the following morning we had the usual difficulty in collecting porters, those of the preceding day having absconded, and others were recruited from distant villages by the native escort, who enjoyed the excuse of hunting for porters, as it gave them an opportunity of foraging throughout the neighbourhood. During this time we had to wait until the sun was high; we thus lost the cool hours of morning and it increased our fatigue. Having at length started, we arrived in the afternoon at the Kafoor river, at a bend from the south where it was necessary to cross over in our westerly course. The stream was in the centre of a marsh, and although deep, it was so covered with thickly-matted water-grass and other aquatic plants, that a natural floating bridge was established by a carpet of weeds about two feet thick: upon this waving and unsteady surface the men ran quickly across, sinking merely to the ankles, although beneath the tough vegetation there was deep water. It was equally impossible to ride or to be carried over this treacherous surface; thus I led the way, and begged Mrs. Baker to follow me on foot as quickly as possible, precisely in my track. The river was about eighty yards wide, and I had scarcely completed a fourth of the distance and looked back to see if my wife followed close to me when I was horrified to see her standing in one spot, and sinking gradually through the weeds, while her face was distorted and perfectly purple. Almost as soon as I perceived her, she fell, as though shot dead. In an instant I was by her side; and with the assistance of eight or ten of my men, who were fortunately close to me, I dragged her like a corpse through the yielding

P                    225

vegetations, and up to our waists we scrambled across to the other side, just keeping her head above the water: to have carried her would have been impossible, as we should all have sunk together through the weeds. I laid her under a tree and bathed her head and face with water, as for the moment I thought she had fainted; but she lay perfectly insensible, as though dead, with teeth and hands firmly clenched and her eyes open, but fixed. It was a *coup de soleil*.

Many of the porters had gone on ahead with the baggage; and I started off a man in haste to recall an angarep upon which to carry her, and also for a bag with a change of clothes, as we had dragged her through the river. It was in vain that I rubbed her heart, and the black women rubbed her feet, to endeavour to restore animation. At length the litter came, and after changing her clothes, she was carried mournfully forward as a corpse. Constantly we had to halt and support her head as a painful rattling in the throat betokened suffocation. At length we reached a village and halted for the night.

I laid her carefully in a miserable hut, and watched beside her. I opened her clenched teeth with a small wooden wedge, and inserted a wet rag, upon which I dropped water to moisten her tongue, which was dry as fur. The unfeeling brutes that composed the native escort were yelling and dancing as though all were well, and I ordered their chief at once to return with them to Kamrasi, as I would travel with them no longer. At first they refused to return; until at length I vowed that I would fire into them should they accompany us on the following morning. Day broke, and it was a relief to have got rid of the brutal escort. They had departed, and I had now my own men, and the guides supplied by Kamrasi.

There was nothing to eat in this spot. My wife had never stirred since she fell by the *coup de soleil*, and merely respired about five times in a minute. It was impossible to remain; the people would have starved. She was laid gently upon her litter, and we started forward on our funeral course. I was ill and broken-hearted, and I followed by her side, through the long day's march over wild park-lands and streams, with thick forest and deep marshy bottoms; over undulating hills, and through valleys of tall papyrus rushes, which, as we brushed through them on our melancholy way, waved over the litter like the black plumes of a hearse. We halted at a village, and again the night was passed in watching. I was wet and coated with mud from the swampy marsh, and shivered with ague; but the cold within was greater than all. No change had taken place; she had never moved. I had plenty of fat, and I made four balls of about half a pound, each of which would burn for three hours. A piece of a broken water-jar formed a lamp, several pieces of rag serving for wicks. So in solitude the still calm night passed away as I sat by her side and watched. In the drawn and distorted features that lay before me I could hardly trace the same face that for years had been my comfort through all the difficulties and dangers of my path. Was she to die? Was so terrible a sacrifice to be the result of my selfish exile?

Again the night passed away. Once more the march. Though weak and ill, and for two nights without a moment's sleep, I felt no fatigue, but mechanically followed by the side of the litter as though in a dream. The same wild country diversified with marsh and forest. Again we halted. The night came, and I sat by her side in a miserable hut, with the feeble lamp flickering while she lay as in death. She had never moved a muscle since she fell. My people slept. I was alone, and no sound broke the stillness of the night. The ears ached at the utter silence, till the sudden wild cry of a hyena made me shudder as the horrible thought rushed through my brain, that, should she be buried in this lonely spot, the hyena would . . . disturb her rest.

The morning was not far distant; it was past four o'clock. I had passed the night in replacing wet cloths upon her head and moistening her lips, as she lay apparently lifeless on her litter. I could do nothing more; in solitude and abject misery in that dark hour, in a country of savage heathens, thousands of miles away from a Christian land, I beseeched an aid above all human, trusting alone to Him.

The morning broke; my lamp had just burned out, and cramped with the night's watching, I rose from my low seat, and seeing that she lay in the same unaltered state, I went to the door of the hut to breathe one gasp of the fresh morning air. I was watching the first red streak that heralded the rising sun, when I was startled by the words 'Thank God' faintly uttered behind me. Suddenly she had awoke from her torpor and with a heart overflowing I went to her bedside. Her eyes were full of madness! She spoke; but the brain was gone!

I will not inflict a description of the terrible trial of seven days of brain fever, with its attendant horrors. The rain poured in torrents, and day after day we were forced to travel, for want of provisions, not being able to remain in one position. Every now and then we shot a few guinea-fowl, but rarely; there was no game, although the country was most favourable. In the forest we procured wild honey, but the deserted villages contained no supplies, as we were on the frontier of Uganda, and M'tesa's people had plundered the district. For seven nights I had not slept, and although as weak as a reed, I had marched by the side of her litter. Nature could resist no longer. We reached a village one evening; she had been in violent convulsions successively—it was all but over. I laid her down on her litter within a hut; covered her with a Scotch plaid; and I fell upon my mat insensible, worn out with sorrow and fatigue. My men put a new handle to the pickaxe that evening, and sought for a dry spot to dig her grave!

The sun had risen when I woke. I had slept, and, horrified as the idea flashed upon me that she must be dead, and that I had not been with her, I started up. She lay upon her bed, pale as marble, and with that calm serenity that the features assume when the cares of life no longer act upon the mind, and the body rests in death. The dreadful thought bowed me down; but as I gazed upon her in fear, her chest gently heaved, not with the conclusive throbs of fever, but naturally. She was asleep; and when at a sudden noise she opened her eyes, they were calm and clear. She was saved! When not a ray of hope remained, God alone knows what helped us. The gratitude of that moment I will not attempt to describe.

Fortunately there were many fowls in this village; we found several nests of fresh eggs in the straw which littered the hut; these were most acceptable after our hard fare, and produced a good supply of soup.

Having rested for two days, we again moved forward, Mrs. Baker being carried on a litter. We now continued on elevated ground on the north side of a valley running from west to east, about sixteen miles broad, and exceedingly swampy. The rocks composing the ridge upon which we travelled due west were all gneiss and quartz, with occasional breaks, forming narrow valleys, all of which were swamps choked with immense papyrus rushes, that made the march very fatiguing. In one of these muddy bottoms one of my riding oxen that was ill stuck fast, and we were obliged to abandon it, intending to send a number of natives to drag it out with ropes. On arrival at a village our guide started about fifty men for this purpose, while we continued our journey.

That evening we reached a village belonging to a headman and very superior to most that we had passed on the route from M'rooli: large sugar-canes of the blue variety were growing in the fields, and I had seen coffee growing wild in the forest in the vicinity. I was sitting at the door of the hut about two hours after sunset, smoking a pipe of excellent tobacco, when I suddenly heard a great singing in chorus advancing rapidly from a distance towards the entrance of the courtyard. At first I imagined that the natives intended dancing, which was an infliction that I wished to avoid, as I was tired and feverish; but in a few minutes the boy Saat introduced a headman, who told me that the riding ox had died in the swamp where he had stuck fast in the morning and that the natives had brought his body to me. 'What!' I replied, 'brought his body, the entire ox, to me?' 'The entire ox as he died is delivered at your door,' answered the headman. 'I could not allow any of your property to be lost upon the road. Had the body of the ox not been delivered to you, we might have been suspected of having stolen it.' I went to the entrance of the courtyard and amidst a crowd of natives I found the entire ox exactly as he had died. They had carried him about eight miles on a litter, which they had constructed of two immensely long posts with cross-pieces of bamboo, upon which they had laid the body. They would not eat the flesh, and seemed quite disgusted at the idea, as they replied that 'it had died.'

It is a curious distinction of the Unyoro people, that they are peculiarly clean feeders, and will not touch either the flesh of animals that have died, neither of those that are sick; nor will they eat the crocodile. They asked for no remuneration for bringing their heavy load so great a distance; and they departed in good humour as a matter of course.

Never were such contradictory people as these creatures; they had troubled us dreadfully during the journey, as they would suddenly exclaim against the weight of their loads, and throw them down, and bolt into the high grass; yet now they had of their own free will delivered to me a whole dead ox from a distance of eight miles, precisely as though it had been an object of the greatest value.

The name of this village was Parkani. For several days past our guides had told us that we were very near to the lake, and we were now assured that we should reach it on the morrow. I had noticed a lofty range of mountains at an immense distance west, and I had imagined that the lake lay on the other side of this chain; but I was now informed that those mountains formed the western frontier of the M'wootan N'zige, and that the lake was actually within a march of Parkani. I could not believe it possible that we were so near the object of our search. The guide Rabonga now appeared, and declared that if we started early on the following morning we should be able to wash in the lake by noon!

That night I hardly slept. For years I had striven to reach the 'sources of the Nile.' In my nightly dreams during the arduous voyage I had always failed, but after so much hard work and perseverance the cup was at my very lips, and I was to *drink* at the mysterious fountain before another sun could set—at the great reservoir of Nature that ever since creation had baffled all discovery.

I had hoped, and prayed, and striven through all kinds of difficulties, in sickness, starvation, and fatigue to reach that hidden source; and when it had appeared impossible we had both determined to die upon the road rather than return defeated. Was it possible that it was so near, and that to-morrow we could say, 'the work is accomplished?'

[14 March.] The sun had not risen when I was spurring my ox after the guide, who, having been promised a double handful of beads on arrival at the lake, had caught the enthusiasm of the moment. The day broke beautifully clear, and having crossed a deep valley between the hills, we toiled up the opposite slope. I hurried to the summit. The glory of our prize burst suddenly upon me! There, like a sea of quicksilver, lay far beneath the grand expanse of water—a boundless sea horizon on the south and south-west glittering in the noon-day sun; and on the west, at fifty or sixty miles' distance, blue mountains rose from the bosom of the lake to a height of about 7,000 feet above its level.

It is impossible to describe the triumph of that moment;—here was the reward for all our labour—for the years of tenacity with which we had toiled through Africa. England had won the sources of the Nile! Long before I reached this spot, I had arranged to give three cheers with all our men in English style in honour of the discovery, but now that I looked down upon the great inland sea lying nestled in the very heart of Africa, and thought how vainly mankind had sought these sources throughout so many ages, and reflected that I had been the humble instrument permitted to unravel this portion of the great mystery when so many greater than I had failed, I felt too serious to vent my feelings in vain cheers for victory, and I sincerely thanked God for having guided and supported us through all dangers to the good end. I was about 1,500 feet above the lake, and I looked down from the steep granite cliff upon those welcome waters—upon that vast reservoir which nourished Egypt and brought fertility where all was wilderness—upon that great source so long hidden from mankind; that source of bounty and of blessings to millions of human beings; and as one of the greatest objects in nature, I determined to honour it with a great name. As an imperishable memorial of one loved and mourned by our gracious Queen and deplored by every Englishman, I called this great lake 'the Albert N'yanza.' The Victoria and the Albert lakes are the two sources of the Nile.

*The Albert N'Yanza*, 1st Edition, vol. II, pp. 74–96

*Baker and his wife, after further dangers and privations, returned safely from this expedition. The traveller obtained full recognition and a knighthood for his discovery. He returned to the same scene in 1869, but this time with a well-equipped military expedition and holding from the Khedive of Egypt the appointment of Governor-General of the basin of the Nile. He was charged to extend the frontiers of the Egyptian Empire and to suppress the slave-trade. The brave Lady Baker again accompanied him. He met with serious difficulties and had to fight against the slave-traders, the tribes they raised against him and also against the son of Kamrasi, Kabarega, whose kingdom he nominally annexed to Egypt in 1872. In 1873 he left Equatoria. The account of this expedition is contained in another lively book,* Ismailïa. *His appointment was the precedent for that of a still more distinguished foreigner, General Gordon. After a full, vigorous and successful life, he died in 1893.*

# IX

## DAVID LIVINGSTONE
## and
## SIR HENRY MORTON STANLEY
### 1841–1904

*A*t *the beginning of 1865 Livingstone received a letter from his old friend Sir Roderick Murchison, the President of the Royal Geographical Society, suggesting that he should return to Africa to solve 'a question of intense geographical interest . . . namely the watershed or watersheds of South Africa', and that he should make his way up to the Nile basin by way of the River Rovuma and the Great Lakes. To this proposal Livingstone agreed, while declining to go out solely as an explorer. 'What my inclination leads me to prefer', he characteristically replied, 'is to have intercourse with the people, and do what I can by talking to enlighten them on the slave-trade, and give them some idea of our religion. . . . I shall enjoy myself, and feel that I am doing my duty.' In this spirit he left England for the last time in August 1865.*

*Travelling out by way of India, he reached Zanzibar at the end of the following January: on 4th April 1866 he began his march inland from Mikindani Bay. On this journey he took no Europeans with him. Of his African companions, three, Chumah, Susi and Wikatani, had been rescued from slavery during the Zambesi expedition. He passed round the south end of Lake Nyasa, and then struck out north-north-west, crossing the Loangwa and making for Lake Tanganyika. Shortly before reaching the Chambezi, on 20th January 1867, there occurred the first and greatest of his disasters: one of his porters deserted with a load containing his medicine-chest. He was in a marshy and fever-laden country, in the wet season, entirely without medical supplies. 'I felt as if I had now received the sentence of death,' he wrote in his journal; and he was probably right.*

*On 1st April he sighted Lake Tanganyika. Delayed by much illness and by a war in the country of Itawa, he went on slowly to the north-*

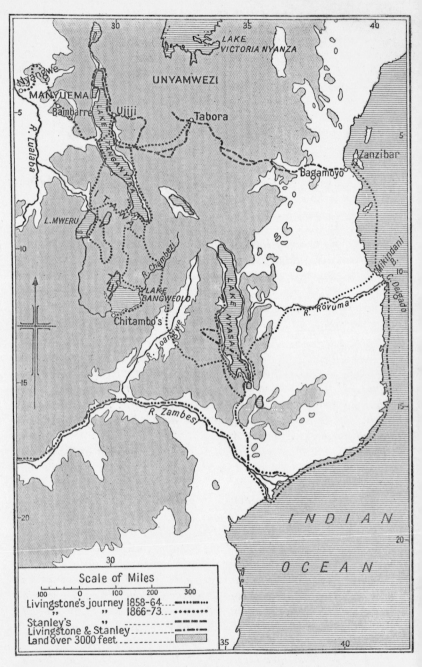

Lake Victoria Nyanza

Nyangwe
MANYUEMA
Baimbarre · Ujiji
Tabora
UNYAMWEZI
R. Lualaba
Zanzibar
Bagamoyo

LAKE TANGANYIKA

L. MWERU
TANA

R. Chambezi
LAKE
BANGWEOLO
Chitambo's
R. Rovuma
C. Delgado
Kikindani
R. Loangwa
LAKE NYASA

R. Zambesi

INDIAN

OCEAN

Scale of Miles
100   0   100   200   300
Livingstone's journey 1858–64 .......
      „        „     1866–73 ....
Stanley's       „
Livingstone & Stanley ..........
Land over 3000 feet ..........

**10. The Travels of Livingstone and Stanley, 1866–73**

*west, discovering Lake Mweru on 8th November: from here he turned south and reached Lake Bangweolo (which he was also the first European to see) on 18th July 1868. He then decided to go across to Ujiji, hoping to find there stores (above all, medicines), which he had previously ordered. But when he arrived there, on 14th March 1869, he discovered that nearly everything had been stolen.*

*Four months later he recrossed the lake and made for Manyuema, a country into which the slave-traders were just beginning to feel their way: he continually saw scenes such as that depicted in the illustration opposite page 234. Here he spent two years and a quarter: his main object during this time was to find the River Lualaba, which took him more than eighteen months, for he was weakened by disease and largely dependent on the whims of the Arab slavers, with whom he was often obliged to travel. He records that he read through the whole Bible four times while he was in Manyuema. To his intense disappointment, he received no answer to his repeated requests for assistance from Zanzibar. When, in February 1871, ten men did reach him, it soon appeared that they had not come to help but to hinder him by their mutinous conduct and intrigues with the Arabs. (They had in reality been sent by the Indian, or Banian, slave-dealers, who were afraid of the disclosures which he might make about their trade.) In the following month he at length reached the Lualaba at Nyangwe. Here, while he was waiting for canoes to take him down the river, he gained further experience of the slave trade.*

# 28. MANYUEMA MASSACRE

*24th May.*—The market is a busy scene—everyone is in dead earnest —little time is lost in friendly greetings; vendors of fish run about with potsherds full of snails or small fishes or young *Clarias capensis* smoke-dried and spitted on twigs, or other relishes to exchange for cassava roots dried after being steeped about three days in water—potatoes, vegetables, or grain, bananas, flour, palm-oil, fowls, salt, pepper; each is intensely eager to barter food for relishes, and makes strong assertions as to the goodness or badness of everything: the sweat stands in beads on their faces—cocks crow briskly, even when slung over the shoulder with their heads hanging down, and pigs squeal. Iron knobs, drawn out at each end to show the goodness of the metal, are exchanged for cloth of the Muabe palm. They have a large funnel of basketwork below the vessel holding the wares, and slip the goods down if they are not to be seen. They deal fairly, and when differences arise they are easily settled by the men interfering or pointing to me; they appeal to each other, and have a strong sense of natural justice. With so much food changing hands amongst the three thousand attendants much benefit is derived; some come from twenty to twenty-five miles. The men flaunt about in gaudy-coloured lambas of many folded kilts—the women work hardest —the potters slap and ring their earthenware all round, to show that there is not a single flaw in them. I bought two finely shaped earthen bottles of porous earthenware, to hold a gallon each, for one string of beads, the women carry huge loads of them in their funnels above the baskets, strapped to the shoulders and forehead, and their hands are full besides; the roundness of the vessels is wonderful, seeing no machine is used: no slaves could be induced to carry half as much as they do willingly. It is a scene of the finest natural acting imaginable. The eagerness with which all sorts of assertions are made—the eager earnestness with which apparently all creation, above, around, and beneath, is called on to attest the truth of what they allege—and then the intense surprise and withering scorn cast on those who despise their goods: but they show no concern when the buyers turn up their noses at them. Little girls run about selling cups of water for a few small fishes to the half-exhausted wordy combatants. To me it was an amusing scene. I could not understand the words that flowed off their glib tongues, but the gestures were too expressive to need interpretation.

27th May.—Hassani told me that since he had come, no Manyuema had ever presented him with a single mouthful of food, not even a potato or banana, and he had made many presents. Going from him into the market I noticed that one man presented a few small fishes, another a sweet potato and a piece of cassava, and a third two small fishes, but the Manyuema are not a liberal people. Old men and women who remained in the half-deserted villages we passed through in coming north, often ran forth to present me with bananas, but it seemed through fear; when I sat down and ate the bananas they brought beer of bananas, and I paid for all. A stranger in the market had ten human under jaw-bones hung by a string over his shoulder: on inquiry he professed to have killed and eaten the owners, and showed with his knife how he cut up his victim. When I expressed disgust he and others laughed. I see new faces every market-day. Two nice girls were trying to sell their venture, which was roasted white ants, called 'Gumbe.'

30th May.—The river fell four inches during the last four days; the colour is very dark brown, and large quantities of aquatic plants and trees float down. Mologhwe, or chief Ndambo, came and mixed blood with the intensely bigoted Moslem Hassani [a slave-trader]: this is to secure the nine canoes. He next went over to have more palaver about them, and they do not hesitate to play me false by detraction. The Man-

THE SLAVERS REVENGING THEIR LOSSES
From Livingstone's *Last Journals*

yuema, too, are untruthful, but very honest; we never lose an article by them: fowls and goats are untouched, and if a fowl is lost, we know that it has been stolen by an Arab slave. When with Mohamad Bogharib [an Arab slave-trader], we had all to keep our fowls at the Manyuema villages to prevent them being stolen by our own slaves, and it is so here. Hassani denies complicity with them, but it is quite apparent that he and others encourage them in mutiny.

*5th June*, 1871.—The river rose again six inches and fell three. Rain nearly ceased, and large masses of fleecy clouds float down here from the north-west, with accompanying cold.

*7th June.*—I fear that I must march on foot, but the mud is forbidding.

*11th June.*—New moon last night, and I believe Dugumbe [another slave-trader] will leave Kasonga's to-day. River down three inches.

*14th June.*—Hassani got nine canoes, and put sixty-three persons in three: I cannot get one. Dugumbe reported near, but detained by his divination, at which he is an expert; hence his native name is 'Molembalemba'—'writer, writing.'

*16th June.*—The high winds and drying of soap and sugar tell that the rains are now over in this part.

*18th June.*—Dugumbe arrived, but passed to Moene Nyangwe's, and found that provisions were so scarce and dear there, as compared with our market, that he was fain to come back to us. He has a large party and 500 guns. He is determined to go into new fields of trade, and has all his family with him, and intends to remain six or seven years, sending regularly to Ujiji for supplies of goods.

*20th June.*—Two of Dugumbe's party brought presents of four large fundos of beads each. All know that my goods are unrighteously detained by Shereef and they show me kindness, which I return by some fine calico which I have. Among the first words Dugumbe said to me were, 'Why, your own slaves are your greatest enemies: I will buy you a canoe, but the Banian slaves' slanders have put all the Manyuema against you.' I knew that this was true, and that they were conscious of the sympathy of the Ujijian traders, who hate to have me here.

*24th June.*—Hassani's canoe party in the river were foiled by narrows, after they had gone down four days. Rocks jut out on both sides, not opposite, but alternate to each other; and the vast mass of water of the great river jammed in, rushes round one promontory on to another, and a frightful whirlpool is formed in which the first canoe went and was overturned, and five lives lost. Had I been there, mine would have been the first canoe, for the traders would have made it a point of honour to give me the precedence (although actually to make a feeler of me), while they looked on in safety. The men in charge of Hassani's canoes were so frightened by this accident that they at once resolved to return, though they had arrived in the country of the ivory: they never looked to see whether the canoes could be dragged past the narrows, as anyone else would have done. No better luck could be expected after all their fraud and duplicity in getting the canoes; no harm lay in obtaining them, but why try to prevent me getting one?

*27th June.*—In answer to my prayers for preservation, I was prevented going down to the narrows, formed by a dyke of mountains cutting across country, and jutting a little ajar, which makes the water in an enormous mass wheel round behind it helplessly, and if the canoes reach the rock against which the water dashes, they are almost certainly over-turned. As this same dyke probably cuts across country to Lomame, my plan of going to the confluence and then up won't do, for I should have to go up rapids again. Again, I was prevented from going down Luamo, and on the north of its confluence another cataract mars navigation in the Lualaba, and my safety is thereby secured. We don't always know the dangers that we are guided past.

*28th June.*—The river has fallen two feet: dark brown water, and still much wreck floating down.

Eight villages are in flames, set afire to by a slave of Syde bin Habib [a slave-trader], called Manilla, who thus shows his blood friends of the Bagenya how well he can fight against the Mohombo, whose country the Bagenya want! The stragglers of this camp are over on the other side helping Manilla, and catching fugitives and goats. The Bagenya are fishermen by taste and profession, and sell the produce of their nets and weirs to those who cultivate the soil, at the different markets. Manilla's foray is for an alleged debt of three slaves, and ten villages are burned. . . .

*7th July.*—I was annoyed by a woman frequently beating a slave near my house, but on my reproving her she came and apologized. I told her to speak softly to her slave, as she was now the only mother the girl had; the slave came from beyond Lomame, and was evidently a lady in her own land: she calls her son Mologwe, or chief, because his father was a headman.

Dugumbe advised my explaining my plan of procedure to the slaves, and he evidently thinks that I wish to carry it towards them with a high hand. I did explain all the exploration I intended to do: for instance, the fountains of Herodotus—beyond Katanga—Katanga itself, and the underground dwellings, and then return. They made no remarks, for they are evidently pleased to have me knuckling down to them; when pressed on the point of proceeding, they say they will only go with Dugumbe's men to the Lomame, and then return. River fallen three inches since the 5th.

*10th July.*—Manyuema children do not creep, as European children do, on their knees, but begin by putting forward one foot and using one knee. Generally a Manyuema child uses both feet and both hands, but never both knees: one Arab child did the same; he never crept, but got up on both feet, holding on till he could walk.

New moon last night of seventh Arab month.

11th July.—I bought the different species of fish brought to market, in order to sketch eight of them, and compare them with those of the Nile lower down: most are the same as in Nyassa. A very active species of Glanis, of dark olive-brown, was not sketched, but a spotted one, armed with offensive spikes in the dorsal and pectoral fins, was taken. Sesamum seed is abundant just now and cakes are made of ground-nuts, as on the West Coast. Dugumbe's horde tried to deal in the market in a domineering way. 'I shall buy that,' said one. 'These are mine,' said another; 'no one must touch them but me,' but the market-women taught them that they could not monopolize, but deal fairly. They are certainly clever traders, and keep each other in countenance, they stand by each other, and will not allow overreaching, and they give food astonishingly cheap: once in the market they have no fear.

12th and 13th July.—The Banian slaves declared before Dugumbe that they would go to the River Lomame, but no further: he spoke long to them, but they will not consent to go further. When told that they would thereby lose all their pay, they replied, 'Yes, but not our lives,' and they walked off from him muttering, which is insulting to one of his rank. I then added, 'I have goods at Ujiji; I don't know how many, but they are considerable, take them all, and give me men to finish my work; if not enough, I will add to them, only do not let me be forced to return now I am so near the end of my undertaking.' He said he would make a plan in conjunction with his associates, and report to me.

14th July.—I am distressed and perplexed what to do so as not to be foiled, but all seems against me.

15th July.—The reports of guns on the other side of the Lualaba all the morning tell of the people of Dugumbe murdering those of Kimburu and others who mixed blood with Manilla. 'Manilla is a slave, and how dares he to mix blood with chiefs who ought only to make friends with free men like us'—this is their complaint. Kimburu gave Manilla three slaves, and he sacked ten villages in token of friendship; he proposed to give Dugumbe nine slaves in the same operation, but Dugumbe's people destroy his villages, and shoot and make his people captives to punish Manilla; to make an impression, in fact, in the country that they alone are to be dealt with—'make friends with us, and not with Manilla or anyone else'—such is what they insist upon.

About 1500 people came to market, though many villages of those that usually come from the other side were now in flames, and every now and then a number of shots were fired on the fugitives.

It was a hot, sultry day, and when I went into the market I saw Adie and Manilla, and three of the men who had lately come with Dugumbe.

237

I was surprised to see these three with their guns, and felt inclined to reprove them, as one of my men did, for bringing weapons into the market, but I attributed it to their ignorance, and, it being very hot, I was walking away to go out of the market, when I saw one of the fellows haggling about a fowl, and seizing hold of it. Before I had got thirty yards out, the discharge of two guns in the middle of the crowd told me that slaughter had begun: crowds dashed off from the place, and threw down their wares in confusion, and ran. At the same time that the three opened fire on the mass of people near the upper end of the market-place volleys were discharged from a party down near the creek on the panic-stricken women, who dashed at the canoes. These, some fifty or more, were jammed in the creek, and the men forgot their paddles in the terror that seized all. The canoes were not to be got out, for the creek was too small for so many; men and women, wounded by the balls, poured into them, and leaped and scrambled into the water, shrieking. A long line of heads in the river showed that great numbers struck out for an island a full mile off: in going towards it they had to put the left shoulder to a current of about two miles an hour; if they had struck away diagonally to the opposite bank, the current would have aided them, and, though nearly three miles off, some would have gained land: as it was, the heads above water showed the long line of those that would inevitably perish.

Shot after shot continued to be fired on the helpless and perishing. Some of the long line of heads disappeared quietly; whilst other poor creatures threw their arms high, as if appealing to the great Father above, and sank. One canoe took in as many as it could hold, and all paddled with hands and arms: three canoes, got out in haste, picked up sinking friends, till all went down together, and disappeared. One man in a long canoe, which could have held forty or fifty, had clearly lost his head; he had been out in the stream before the massacre began, and now paddled up the river nowhere, and never looked to the drowning. By-and-bye all the heads disappeared; some had turned down stream towards the bank, and escaped. Dugumbe put people into one of the deserted vessels to save those in the water, and saved twenty-one, but one woman refused to be taken on board from thinking that she was to be made a slave of; she preferred the chance of life by swimming, to the lot of a slave: the Bagenya women are expert in the water, as they are accustomed to dive for oysters, and those who went down stream may have escaped, but the Arabs themselves estimated the loss of life at between 330 and 400 souls. The shooting-party near the canoes were so reckless, they killed two of their own people; and a Banyamwezi follower, who got into a deserted canoe to plunder, fell into the water, went down, then came up again, and down to rise no more.

My first impulse was to pistol the murderers, but Dugumbe protested against my getting into a blood-feud, and I was thankful afterwards that

I took his advice. Two wretched Moslems asserted 'that the firing was done by the people of the English;' I asked one of them why he lied so, and he could utter no excuse; no other falsehood came to his aid as he stood abashed before me, and so telling him not to tell palpable falsehoods, I left him gaping.

After the terrible affair in the water, the party of Tagamoio, who was the chief perpetrator, continued to fire on the people there and fire their villages. As I write I hear the loud wails on the left bank over those who are there slain, ignorant of their many friends now in the depths of Lualaba. Oh, let Thy kingdom come! No one will ever know the exact loss on this bright sultry summer morning, it gave me the impression of being in Hell. All the slaves in the camp rushed at the fugitives on land, and plundered them: women were for hours collecting and carrying loads of what had been thrown down in terror.

Some escaped to me, and were protected: Dugumbe saved twenty-one, and of his own accord liberated them, they were brought to me, and remained over night near my house. One woman of the saved had a musket-ball through the thigh, another in the arm. I sent men with our flag to save some, for without a flag they might have been victims, for Tagamoio's people were shooting right and left like fiends. I counted twelve villages burning this morning. I asked the question of Dugumbe and others, 'Now for what is all this murder?' All blamed Manilla as its cause, and in one sense he was the cause; but it is hardly credible that they repeat it is in order to be avenged on Manilla for making friends with headmen, he being a slave. I cannot believe it fully. The wish to make an impression in the country as to the importance and greatness of the new comers was the most potent motive; but it was terrible that the murdering of so many should be contemplated at all. It made me sick at heart. Who could accompany the people of Dugumbe and Tagamoio to Lomame and be free from blood-guiltiness?

I proposed to Dugumbe to catch the murderers, and hang them up in the market-place, as our protest against the bloody deeds before the Manyuema. If, as he and others added, the massacre was committed by Manilla's people, he would have consented; but it was done by Tagamoio's people, and others of this party, headed by Dugumbe. This slaughter was peculiarly atrocious, inasmuch as we have always heard that women coming to or from market have never been known to be molested: even when two districts are engaged in actual hostilities, 'the women,' say they, 'pass among us to market unmolested,' nor has one ever been known to be plundered by the men. These Nigger Moslems are inferior to the Manyuema in justice and right. The people under Hassani began the superwickedness of capture and pillage of all indiscriminately. Dugumbe promised to send over men to order Tagamoio's men to cease firing and burning villages; they remained over among the ruins, feasting on goats and fowls all night, and next day (16th) continued their infamous work till twenty-seven villages were destroyed.

*16th July.*—I restored upwards of thirty of the rescued to their friends: Dugumbe seemed to act in good faith, and kept none of them; it was his own free will that guided him. Women are delivered to their husbands, and about thirty-three canoes left in the creek are to be kept for the owners too.

12 a.m.—Shooting still going on on the other side, and many captives caught. At 1 p.m. Tagamoio's people began to cross over in canoes, beating their drums, firing their guns, and shouting, as if to say, 'See the conquering heroes come;' they are answered by the women of Dugumbe's camp lullilooing, and friends then fire off their guns in joy. I count seventeen villages in flames, and the smoke goes straight up and forms clouds at the top of the pillar, showing great heat evolved, for the houses are full of carefully-prepared firewood. Dugumbe denies having sent Tagamoio on this foray, and Tagamoio repeats that he went to punish the friends made by Manilla, who, being a slave, had no right to make war and burn villages; that could only be done by free men. Manilla confesses to me privately that he did wrong in that, and loses all his beads and many friends in consequence.

2 p.m.—An old man, called Kabobo, came for his old wife; I asked her if this were her husband, she went to him, and put her arm lovingly around him, and said 'Yes.' I gave her five strings of beads to buy food, all her stores being destroyed with her house; she bowed down, and put her forehead to the ground as thanks, and old Kabobo did the same: the tears stood in her eyes as she went off. Tagamoio caught 17 women, and other Arabs of his party, 27; dead by gunshot, 25. The heads of two headmen were brought over to be redeemed by their friends with slaves.

3 p.m.—Many of the headmen who have been burned out by the foray came over to me, and begged me to come back with them, and appoint new localities for them to settle in again, but I told them that I was so ashamed of the company in which I found myself, that I could scarcely look the Manyuema in the face. They had believed that I wished to kill them—what did they think now? I could not remain among bloody companions, and would flee away, I said, but they begged me hard not to leave until they were again settled.

The open murder perpetrated on hundreds of unsuspecting women fills me with unspeakable horror: I cannot think of going anywhere with the Tagamoio crew; I must either go down or up Lualaba, whichever the Banian slaves choose.

4 p.m.—Dugumbe saw that by killing the market people he had committed a great error, and speedily got the chiefs who had come over to me to meet him at his house, and forthwith mix blood: they were in bad case. I could not remain to see to their protection, and Dugumbe being

THE MANYUEMA MASSACRE
From Livingstone's *Last Journals*

the best of the whole horde, I advised them to make friends, and then appeal to him as able to restrain to some extent his infamous underlings. One chief asked to have his wife and daughter restored to him first, but generally they were cowed, and the fear of death was on them. Dugumbe said to me, 'I shall do my utmost to get all the captives, but he must make friends now, in order that the market may not be given up.' Blood was mixed, and an essential condition was, 'You must give us chitoka,' or market. He and most others saw that in theoretically punishing Manilla, they had slaughtered the very best friends that strangers had. The Banian slaves openly declare that they will go only to Lomame, and no further. Whatever the Ujijian slavers may pretend, they all hate to have me as a witness of their cold-blooded atrocities. The Banian slaves would like to go with Tagamoio, and share in his rapine and get slaves. I tried to go down Lualaba, then up it, and west, but with bloodhounds it is out of the question. I see nothing for it but to go back to Ujiji for other men, though it will throw me out of the chance of discovering the fourth great Lake in the Lualaba line of drainage, and other things of great value.

At last I said that I would start for Ujiji, in three days, on foot. I wished to speak to Tagamoio about the captive relations of the chiefs, but he always ran away when he saw me coming.

17th July.—All the rest of Dugumbe's party offered me a share of every kind of goods they had, and pressed me not to be ashamed to tell them what I needed. I declined everything save a little gunpowder, but they all made presents of beads, and I was glad to return equivalents in cloth. It is a sore affliction, at least forty-five days in a straight line— equal to 300 miles, or by the turnings and windings 600 English miles— and all after feeding and clothing the Banian slaves for twenty-one months! But it is for the best though; if I do not trust to the riffraff of Ujiji, I must wait for other men at least ten months there. With help from above I shall yet go through Rua, see the underground excavations first, then on to Katanga, and the four ancient fountains eight days beyond, and after that Lake Lincoln.

18th July.—The murderous assault on the market people felt to me like Gehenna, without the fire and brimstone; but the heat was oppressive, and the firearms pouring their iron bullets on the fugitives, was not an inapt representative of burning in the bottomless pit.

The terrible scenes of man's inhumanity to man brought on severe headache, which might have been serious had it not been relieved by a copious discharge of blood; I was laid up all yesterday afternoon, with the depression the bloodshed made,—it filled me with unspeakable horror. 'Don't go away,' say the Manyuema chiefs to me; but I cannot stay here in agony.

*Last journals*, vol. II, pp. 125–139

*After this massacre, which deeply affected Livingstone in mind and health, he felt unable to bear any longer the company of the Arabs. His porters being quite out of hand, he set out with a few servants and carriers for Ujiji. On the way he was nearly killed in an ambush by a chief who mistook him for a slaver. His feet suffered terribly from the rocky track and he was in a sad and emaciated condition ('a mere ruckle of bones' in his own words) when he reached Ujiji. Here he found that the stores which had been sent up from the coast and upon which, after nearly six years' lonely wandering out of touch with civilization, he had been counting so much for food, medicine and clothing, had been plundered by the Arabs, in the hope that he was dead. He was thus in a state of destitution and weakness when he was found by H. M. Stanley, who must now be briefly introduced.*

# SIR HENRY MORTON STANLEY
## 1841–1904

*Stanley was a Welshman, born at Denbigh: his real name was John Rowlands. He passed nine years of his childhood in the St. Asaph workhouse under a sadistic schoolmaster, from whose tyranny he ran away in 1856. Three years later he shipped as a cabin-boy for America: at New Orleans he was adopted by a kindly cotton-broker who gave him the names Henry Stanley. After fighting in the Civil War (first in one army, then in the other, then in the United States navy), he drifted into journalism. He 'covered' Napier's Abyssinian campaign of 1868 for the* New York Herald *with such success that he was taken on to its permanent staff and received from it a number of similar commissions in Europe and the East.*

*One of these was to 'find' Livingstone, whose movements had been a mystery to the outside world since he left for the interior of Africa in March 1866. On this mission Stanley arrived at Zanzibar at the beginning of 1871. Keeping his intention secret, he left Bagamoyo on 21st March, having engaged some of the men who had accompanied Burton and Speke including Mabruki and Bombay. (The latter ended his days in Zanzibar on a pension from the Royal Geographical*

*Society.) Although Stanley was able to provide himself with stores
and porters upon a lavish scale which contrasted strikingly with the
poverty of Livingstone's equipment, it must be admitted that this
journey, the first undertaken by a European by this route since it had
been discovered by Burton and Speke, was an act of enterprise and
courage.*

*After various adventures, he reached the great inland centre of the
Arab slave-traders at Tabora. Here he joined the Arabs in their campaign against Mirambo, a native war-leader who had defied them.
After this he travelled forward with great care, in order to avoid
Mirambo's raiding forces. This extract is taken from that point
when, in great excitement, he was approaching Lake Tanganyika
where he hoped to encounter Livingstone. On 9th November—
Livingstone was so far out as to give the date of the meeting as
24th October—his caravan was almost in sight of the lake. On its
shore at Ujiji was Livingstone, completely ignorant of its approach.*

# 29. STANLEY FINDS LIVINGSTONE

Presently we found the smooth road, and we trod gaily with elastic
steps, with limbs quickened for the march which we all knew to be
drawing near its end. What cared we now for the difficulties we had
encountered—for the rough and cruel forests, for the thorny thickets and
hurtful grass, for the jangle of all savagedom, of which we had been the
joyless audience! To-morrow! Ay, the great day draws nigh, and we may
well laugh and sing while in this triumphant mood. We have been sorely
tried; we have been angry with each other when vexed by troubles, but
we forget all these now, and there is no face but is radiant with the
happiness we have all deserved.

We made a short halt at noon, for rest and refreshment. I was shown
the hills from which the Tanganika could be seen, which bounded the
valley of the Liuche on the east. I could not contain myself at the sight
of them. Even with this short halt I was restless and unsatisfied. We
resumed the march again. I spurred my men forward with the promise
that to-morrow should see their reward. Fish and beer should be given
them, as much as they could eat and drink.

We were in sight of the villages of the Wakaranga; the people caught
sight of us, and manifested considerable excitement. I sent men ahead to
reassure them, and they came forward to greet us. This was so new and
welcome to us, so different from the turbulent Wavinza and the black-
mailers of Uhha, that we were melted. But we had no time to loiter by

the way to indulge our joy. I was impelled onward by my almost uncontrollable feelings. I wished to resolve my doubts and fears. Was HE still there? Had HE heard of my coming? Would HE fly?

How beautiful Ukaranga appears! The green hills are crowned by clusters of straw-thatched cones. The hills rise and fall; here denuded and cultivated, there in pasturage, here timbered, yonder swarming with huts. The country has somewhat the aspect of Maryland.

We cross the Mkuti, a glorious little river! We ascend the opposite bank, and stride through the forest like men who have done a deed of which they may be proud. We have already travelled nine hours, and the sun is sinking rapidly towards the west; yet, apparently, we are not fatigued.

We reach the outskirts of Niamtaga, and we hear drums beat. The people are flying into the woods; they desert their villages, for they take us to be Ruga-Ruga—the forest thieves of Mirambo, who, after conquering the Arabs of Unyanyembe, are coming to fight the Arabs of Ujiji. Even the King flies from his village, and every man, woman, and child, terror-stricken, follows him. We enter into it and quietly take possession, and my tent is set. Finally, the word is bruited about that we are Wangwana, from Unyanyembe.

'Well, then, is Mirambo dead?' they ask.

'No,' we answer.

'Well, how did you come to Ukaranga?'

'By way of Ukonongo, Ukawendi, and Uhha.'

'Oh-hi-le!' Then they laugh heartily at their fright, and begin to make excuses. The King is introduced to me, and he says he had only gone to the woods in order to attack us again—he meant to have come back and killed us all, if we had been Ruga-Ruga. But then we know the poor King was terribly frightened, and would never have dared to return, had we been Ruga-Ruga—not he. We are not, however, in a mood to quarrel with him about an idiomatic phrase peculiar to him, but rather take him by the hand and shake it well, and say we are so very glad to see him. And he shares in our pleasure, and immediately three of the fattest sheep, pots of beer, flour, and honey are brought to us as a gift, and I make him happier still with two of the finest cloths I have in my bales; and thus a friendly pact is entered into between us.

While I write my diary of this day's proceedings, I tell Selim to lay out my new flannel suit, to oil my boots, to chalk my helmet, and fold a new puggaree around it, that I may make as presentable an appearance as possible before the white man with the grey beard, and before the Arabs of Ujiji, for the clothes I have worn through jungle and forest are in tatters. Good-night; only let one day come again, and we shall see what we shall see.

*November* 10*th*. Friday.—The 236th day from Bagamoyo, and the

51st day from Unyanyembe. General direction to Ujiji, west-by-south. Time of march, six hours.

It is a happy, glorious morning. The air is fresh and cool. The sky lovingly smiles on the earth and her children. The deep woods are crowned in bright green leafage; the water of the Mkuti, rushing under the emerald shade afforded by the bearded banks, seems to challenge us for the race to Ujiji, with its continuous brawl.

We are all outside the village cane fence, every man of us looking as spruce, as neat, and happy as when we embarked on the dhows at Zanzibar, which seems to us to have been ages ago—we have witnessed and experienced so much.

'Forward!'

'Ay Wallah, ay Wallah, bana yango!' and the light-hearted braves stride away at a rate which must soon bring us within view of Ujiji. We ascend a hill overgrown with bamboo, descend into a ravine through which dashes an impetuous little torrent, ascend another short hill, then, along a smooth footpath running across the slope of a long ridge, we push on as only eager, light-hearted men can do.

In two hours I am warned to prepare for a view of the Tanganika, for, from the top of a steep mountain the kirangozi [leader of the caravan] says I can see it. I almost vent the feelings of my heart in cries. But wait, we must behold it first. And we press forward and up the hill breathlessly, lest the grand scene hasten away. We are at last on the summit. Ah! not yet can it be seen. A little further on—just yonder, oh! there it is—a silvery gleam. I merely catch sight of it between the trees, and—but here it is at last! True—THE TANGANIKA! and there are the blue-black mountains of Ugoma and Ukaramba. An immense broad sheet, a burnished bed of silver—lucid canopy of blue above—lofty mountains are its valances, palm forests form its fringes! The Tanganika! —Hurrah! and the men respond to the exultant cry of the Anglo-Saxon with the lungs of Stentors, and the great forests and the hills seem to share in our triumph.

'Was this the place where Burton and Speke stood, Bombay, when they saw the lake first?'

'I don't remember, master; it was somewhere about here, I think.'

'Poor fellows! The one was half-paralyzed, the other half-blind,' said Sir Roderick Murchison, when he described Burton and Speke's arrival in view of the Tanganika.

And I? Well, I am so happy that, were I quite paralysed and blinded, I think that at this supreme moment I could take up my bed and walk, and all blindness would cease at once. Fortunately, however, I am quite well; I have not suffered a day's sickness since the day I left Unyanyembe. . . .

We are descending the western slope of the mountain, with the valley

245

of the Liuche before us. Something like an hour before noon we have gained the thick matete brake, which grows on both banks of the river; we wade through the clear stream, arrive on the other side, emerge out of the brake, and the gardens of the Wajiji are around us—a perfect marvel of vegetable wealth. Details escape my hasty and partial observation. I am almost overpowered with my own emotions. I notice the graceful palms, neat plots, green with vegetable plants, and small villages surrounded with frail fences of the matete-cane.

We push on rapidly, lest the news of our coming might reach the people of Bunder Ujiji before we come in sight, and are ready for them. We halt at a little brook, then ascend the long slope of a naked ridge, the very last of the myriads we have crossed. This alone prevents us from seeing the lake in all its vastness. We arrive at the summit, travel across and arrive at its western rim, and—pause, reader—the port of Ujiji is below us, embowered in the palms, only five hundred yards from us! At this grand moment we do not think of the hundreds of miles we have marched, of the hundreds of hills that we have ascended and descended, of the many forests we have traversed, of the jungles and thickets that annoyed us, of the fervid salt plains that blistered our feet, of the hot suns that scorched us, nor of the dangers and difficulties, now happily surmounted. At last the sublime hour has arrived!—our dreams, our hopes, and anticipations are now about to be realized! Our hearts and our feelings are with our eyes, as we peer into the palms and try to make out in which hut or house lives the white man with the grey beard we heard about on the Malagarazi.

'Unfurl the flags, and load your guns!'

'Ay Wallah, ay Wallah, bana!' respond the men, eagerly.

'One, two, three,—fire!'

A volley from nearly fifty guns roars like a salute from a battery of artillery: we shall note its effect presently on the peaceful-looking village below.

'Now, kirangozi, hold the white man's flag up high, and let the Zanzibar flag bring up the rear. And you men keep close together, and keep firing until we halt in the market-place, or before the white man's house. You have said to me often that you could smell the fish of the Tanganika—I can smell the fish of the Tanganika now. There are fish and beer, and a long rest waiting for you. MARCH!'

Before we had gone a hundred yards our repeated volleys had the effect desired. We had awakened Ujiji to the knowledge that a caravan was coming, and the people were witnessed rushing up in hundreds to meet us. The mere sight of the flags informed every one immediately that we were a caravan, but the American flag borne aloft by gigantic Asmani, whose face was one vast smile on this day, rather staggered them at first. However, many of the people who now approached us remembered the flag. They had seen it float above the American Consulate, and from the mast-head of many a ship in the harbor of Zanzibar, and they were soon heard welcoming the beautiful flag with cries of 'Bindera Kisungu!'—a white man's flag! 'Bindera Merikani!'—the American flag!

Then we were surrounded by them: by Wajiji, Wanyamwezi, Wangwana, Warundi, Waguhha, Wamanyuema and Arabs, and were almost deafened with the shouts of 'Yambo, yambo, bana! Yambo, bana! Yambo, bana!' To all and each of my men the welcome was given.

We were now about three hundred yards from the village of Ujiji, and the crowds are dense about me. Suddenly I hear a voice on my right say,

'Good morning, sir!'

Startled at hearing this greeting in the midst of such a crowd of black people, I turn sharply around in search of the man, and see him at my side, with the blackest of faces, but animated and joyous—a man dressed in a long white shirt, with a turban of American sheeting around his woolly head, and I ask:

'Who the mischief are you?'

'I am Susi, the servant of Dr. Livingstone,' said he, smiling, and showing a gleaming row of teeth.

'What! Is Dr. Livingstone here?'

'Yes, sir.'

'In this village?'

'Yes, sir.'

'Are you sure?'

'Sure, sure, sir. Why, I leave him just now.'

'Good morning, sir,' said another voice.

'Hallo,' said I, 'is this another one?'

'Yes, sir.'

'Well, what is your name?'

'My name is Chumah, sir.'

'What! are you Chumah, the friend of Wekotani?'

'Yes, sir.'

'And is the Doctor well?'

'Not very well, sir.'

'Where has he been so long?'

'In Manyuema.'

'Now, you Susi, run, and tell the Doctor I am coming.'

'Yes, sir,' and off he darted like a madman.

But by this time we were within two hundred yards of the village, and the multitude was getting denser, and almost preventing our march. Flags and streamers were out; Arabs and Wangwana were pushing their way through the natives in order to greet us, for according to their account, we belonged to them. But the great wonder of all was, 'How did you come from Unyanyembe?'

Soon Susi came running back, and asked me my name; he had told the Doctor that I was coming, but the Doctor was too surprised to believe him, and, when the Doctor asked him my name, Susi was rather staggered.

But, during Susi's absence, the news had been conveyed to the Doctor that it was surely a white man that was coming, whose guns were firing and whose flag could be seen; and the great Arab magnates of Ujiji—Mohammed bin Sali, Sayd bin Majid, Abid bin Suliman, Mohammed bin Gharib, and others—had gathered together before the Doctor's house, and the Doctor had come out from his veranda to discuss the matter and await my arrival.

In the meantime, the head of the Expedition had halted, and the kirangozi was out of the ranks, holding his flag aloft, and Selim said to me, 'I see the Doctor, sir. Oh, what an old man! He has got a white beard.' And I—what would I not have given for a bit of friendly wilderness, where, unseen, I might vent my joy in some mad freak, such as idiotically biting my hand, turning a somersault, or slashing at trees, in order to allay those exciting feelings that were well-nigh uncontrollable. My heart beats fast, but I must not let my face betray my emotions, lest it shall detract from the dignity of a white man appearing under such extraordinary circumstances.

So I did that which I thought was most dignified. I pushed back the crowds, and, passing from the rear, walked down a living avenue of people, until I came in front of the semicircle of Arabs, in the front of which stood the white man with the grey beard. As I advanced slowly towards him I noticed he was pale, looked wearied, had a grey beard, wore a bluish cap with a faded gold band round it, had on a red-sleeved waistcoat, and a pair of grey tweed trousers. I would have run to him, only I was a coward in the presence of such a mob—would have embraced him, only, he being an Englishman, I did not know how he would receive me;[1] so I did what cowardice and false pride suggested was the

---

[1] 'This Englishman, as I afterwards found, was a military man returning to his country from India, and crossing the Desert at this part in order to go through Palestine. As for me, I had come pretty straight from England, and so here we met in the wilderness at about half-way from our respective starting-points. As we approached each other, it became with me a question whether we should speak; I thought it likely that the stranger would accost me, and in the event of his doing so, I was quite ready to be as sociable and chatty as I could be, according to my nature; but still I could not think of anything particular that I had to say to him; of course among civilized people, the not having anything to say is no excuse at all for not speaking, but I was shy, and indolent, and I felt no great wish to stop, and talk like a morning visitor, in the midst of those broad solitudes. The traveller perhaps felt as I did, for except that we lifted our hands to our caps, and waved our arms in courtesy, we passed each other as if we had passed in Bond Street.'—Kinglake's *Eothen*. (*Stanley's note.*)

best thing—walked deliberately to him, took off my hat, and said:

'Dr. Livingstone, I presume?'

'YES,' said he, with a kind smile, lifting his cap slightly.

I replace my hat on my head, and he puts on his cap, and we both grasp hands, and I then say aloud:

'I thank God, Doctor, I have been permitted to see you.'

He answered, 'I feel thankful that I am here to welcome you.'

I turn to the Arabs, take off my hat to them in response to the saluting chorus of 'Yambos' I receive, and the Doctor introduces them to me by name. Then, oblivious of the crowds, oblivious of the men who shared with me my dangers, we—Livingstone and I—turn our faces towards his tembe [hut]. He points to the veranda, or rather mud platform, under the broad overhanging eaves; he points to his own particular seat, which I see his age and experience in Africa has suggested, namely a straw mat, with a goatskin over it, and another skin nailed against the wall to protect his back from contact with the cold mud. I protest against taking this seat, which so much more befits him than me, but the Doctor will not yield: I must take it.

We are seated—the Doctor and I—with our backs to the wall. The Arabs take seats on our left. More than a thousand natives are in our front, filling the whole square densely, indulging their curiosity, and discussing the fact of two white men meeting at Ujiji—one just come from Manyuema, in the west, the other from Unyanyembe, in the east.

Conversation began. What about? I declare I have forgotten. Oh! we mutually asked questions of one another, such as:

'How did you come here?' and 'Where have you been all this long time?—the world has believed you to be dead.' Yes, that was the way it began; but whatever the Doctor informed me, and that which I communicated to him, I cannot correctly report, for I found myself gazing at him, conning the wonderful man at whose side I now sat in Central Africa. Every hair of his head and beard, every wrinkle of his face, the wanness of his features, and the slightly wearied look he wore, were all imparting intelligence to me—the knowledge I craved for so much ever since I heard the words, 'Take what you want, but find Livingstone.' What I saw was deeply interesting intelligence to me, and unvarnished truth. I was listening and reading at the same time. What did these dumb witnesses relate to me?

Oh, reader, had you been at my side on this day in Ujiji, how eloquently could be told the nature of this man's work! Had you been there but to see and hear! His lips gave me the details; lips that never lie. I cannot repeat what he said; I was too much engrossed to take my notebook out, and begin to stenograph his story. He had so much to say that he began at the end, seemingly oblivious of the fact that five or six years had to be accounted for. But his account was oozing out; it was growing fast into grand proportions—into a most marvellous history of deeds.

The Arabs rose up, with a delicacy I approved, as if they intuitively knew that we ought to be left to ourselves. I sent Bombay with them to give them the news they also wanted so much to know about the affairs at Unyanyembe. Sayd bin Majid was the father of the gallant young man whom I saw at Masange, and who fought with me at Zimbizo, and who soon afterwards was killed by Mirambo's Ruga-Ruga in the forest of Wilyankuru; and, knowing that I had been there, he earnestly desired to hear the tale of the fight; but they had all friends at Unyanyembe, and it was but natural that they should be anxious to hear of what concerned them.

After giving orders to Bombay and Asmani for the provisioning of the men of the Expedition, I called 'Kaif-Halek,' or 'How-do-ye-do,' and introduced him to Dr. Livingstone as one of the soldiers in charge of certain goods left at Unyanyembe, whom I had compelled to accompany me to Ujiji, that he might deliver in person to his master the letter-bag he had been entrusted with by Dr. Kirk [the British vice-consul at Zanzibar]. This was that famous letter-bag marked 'Nov. 1st, 1870,' which was now delivered in the Doctor's hands 365 days after it left Zanzibar! How long, I wonder, had it remained at Unyanyembe had I not been despatched into Central Africa in search of the great traveller?

The Doctor kept the letter-bag on his knee, then, presently, opened it, looked at the letters contained there, and read one or two of his children's letters, his face in the meanwhile lighting up.

He asked me to tell him the news. 'No, Doctor,' said I, 'read your letters first, which I am sure you must be impatient to read.'

'Ah,' said he, 'I have waited years for letters, and I have been taught patience. I can surely afford to wait a few hours longer. No, tell me the general news: how is the world getting along?'

'You probably know much already. Do you know that the Suez Canal is a fact—is opened, and a regular trade carried on between Europe and India through it?'

'I did not hear about the opening of it. Well, that is grand news! What else?'

Shortly I found myself enacting the part of an annual periodical to him. There was no need of exaggeration—of any penny-a-line news, or of any sensationalism. The world had witnessed and experienced much the last few years. The Pacific Railroad had been completed; Grant had been elected President of the United States; Egypt had been flooded with *savants*; the Cretan rebellion had terminated; a Spanish revolution had driven Isabella from the throne of Spain, and a Regent had been appointed; General Prim was assassinated; a Castelar had electrified Europe with his advanced ideas upon the liberty of worship; Prussia had humbled Denmark, and annexed Schleswig-Holstein, and her

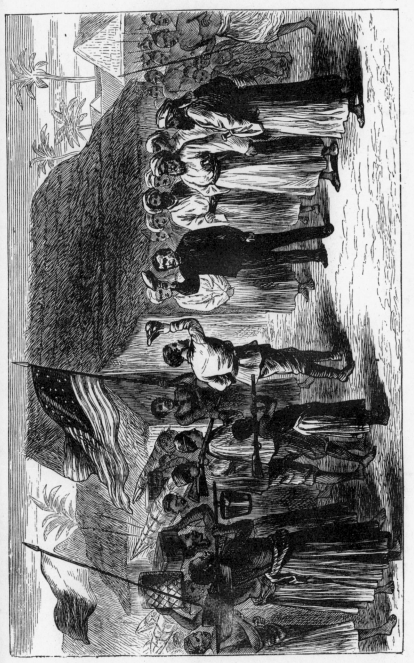

'Dr. Livingstone, I Presume?'
From Stanley's *How I Found Livingstone*

armies were now around Paris; the 'Man of Destiny' was a prisoner at Wilhelmshöhe; the Queen of Fashion and the Empress of the French was a fugitive; and the child born in the purple had lost for ever the Imperial crown intended for his head; the Napoleon dynasty was extinguished by the Prussians, Bismarck and Von Moltke; and France, the proud empire, was humbled to the dust.

What could a man have exaggerated of these facts? What a budget of news it was to one who had emerged from the depths of the primeval forests of Manyuema! The reflection of the dazzling light of civilization was cast on him while Livingstone was thus listening in wonder to one of the most exciting pages of history ever repeated. How the puny deeds of barbarism paled before these! Who could tell under what new phases of uneasy life Europe was laboring even then, while we, two of her lonely children, rehearsed the tale of her late woes and glories? More worthily, perhaps, had the tongue of a lyric Demodocus recounted them; but, in the absence of the poet, the newspaper correspondent performed his part as well and truthfully as he could.

Not long after the Arabs had departed, a dishful of hot hashed-meat cakes was sent to us by Sayd bin Majid, and a curried chicken was received from Mohammed bin Sali, and Moeni Kheri sent a dishful of stewed goat-meat and rice; and thus presents of food came in succession, and as fast as they were brought we set to. I had a healthy, stubborn digestion—the exercise I had taken had put it in prime order; but Livingstone—he had been complaining that he had no appetite, that his stomach refused everything but a cup of tea now and then—he ate also —ate like a vigorous, hungry man; and, as he vied with me in demolishing the pancakes, he kept repeating, 'You have brought me new life. You have brought me new life.'

'Oh, by George!' I said, 'I have forgotten something. Hasten, Selim, and bring that bottle; you know which; and bring me the silver goblets. I brought this bottle on purpose for this event, which I hoped would come to pass, though often it seemed useless to expect it.'

Selim knew where the bottle was, and he soon returned with it—a bottle of Sillery champagne; and, handing the Doctor a silver goblet brimful of the exhilarating wine, and pouring a small quantity into my own, I said,

'Dr. Livingstone, to your very good health, sir.'

'And to yours,' he responded.

And the champagne I had treasured for this happy meeting was drunk with hearty good wishes to each other.

But we kept on talking and talking, and prepared food was being brought to us all that afternoon; and we kept on eating every time it was brought, until I had eaten even to repletion and the Doctor was obliged to confess that he had eaten enough. Still, Halimah, the female cook of the Doctor's establishment, was in a state of the greatest excitement. She had been protruding her head out of the cookhouse to make sure that there were really two white men sitting down in the veranda, when there used to be only one, who would not, because he could not, eat anything; and she had been considerably exercised in her mind about this fact. She was afraid the Doctor did not properly appreciate her culinary abilities; but now she was amazed at the extraordinary quantity of food eaten, and she was in a state of delightful excitement. We could hear her tongue rolling off a tremendous volume of clatter to the wondering crowds who halted before the kitchen to hear the current of news with which she edified them. Poor, faithful soul! While we listened to the noise of her furious gossip, the Doctor related her faithful services, and the terrible anxiety she evinced when the guns first announced the arrival of another white man in Ujiji; how she had been flying about in a state of the utmost excitement, from the kitchen into his presence, and out again into the square, asking all sorts of questions; how she was in despair at the scantiness of the general larder and treasury of the strange household; how she was anxious to make up for their poverty by a grand appearance—to make up a sort of Barmecide feast to welcome the white man. 'Why,' said she, 'is he not one of us? Does he not bring plenty of cloth and beads? Talk about the Arabs! Who are they that they should be compared to white men? Arabs, indeed!'

The Doctor and I conversed upon many things, especially upon his own immediate troubles, and his disappointment, upon his arrival in Ujiji, when told that all his goods had been sold, and he was reduced to poverty. He had but twenty cloths or so left of the stock he had deposited with the man called Sherif, the half-caste drunken tailor, who was sent by the British Consul in charge of the goods. Besides which he had been suffering from an attack of dysentery, and his condition was most deplorable. He was but little improved on this day though he had eaten well, and already began to feel stronger and better.

This day, like all others, though big with happiness to me, at last was fading away. We, sitting with our faces looking to the east, as Livingstone had been sitting for days preceding my arrival, noted the dark shadows which crept up above the grove of palms beyond the village, and above the rampart of mountains which we had crossed that day, now looming through the fast approaching darkness; and we listened with our hearts full of gratitude to the great Giver of Good and Dispenser of all Happiness, to the sonorous thunder of the surf of the Tanganika, and to the chorus which the night insects sang. Hours passed, and we were still sitting there with our minds busy upon the day's remarkable events, when I remembered that the traveller had not yet read his letters.

'Doctor,' I said, 'you had better read your letters. I will not keep you up any longer.'

'Yes,' he answered, 'it is getting late; and I will go and read my friends' letters. Good-night, and God bless you.'

'Good-night, my dear Doctor; and let me hope that your news will be such as you desire.'

And now, dear reader, having related succinctly 'How I found Livingstone,' I bid you also 'Good-night.'

I woke up early next morning with a sudden start. The room was strange! It was a house, and not my tent! Ah, yes! I recollected I had discovered Livingstone, and I was in his house. I listened, that the knowledge dawning on me might be confirmed by the sound of his voice. I heard nothing but the sullen roar of the surf.

I lay quietly in bed. Bed! Yes, it was a primitive four-poster, with the leaves of the palm-tree spread upon it instead of down, and horsehair and my bearskin spread over this serving me in place of linen. I began to put myself under a rigid mental cross-examination, and to an analysation of my position.

'What was I sent for?'

'To find Livingstone.'

'Have you found him?'

'Yes, of course; am I not in his house? Whose compass is that hanging on a peg there? Whose clothes, whose boots, are those? Who reads those newspapers, those "Saturday Reviews" and numbers of "Punch" lying on the floor?'

'Well, what are you going to do now?'

'I shall tell him this morning who sent me, and what brought me here. I will then ask him to write a letter to Mr. Bennett, and to give what news he can spare. I did not come here to rob him of his news. Sufficient for me is it that I have found him. It is a complete success so far. But it will be a greater one if he gives me letters for Mr. Bennett, and an acknowledgment that he has seen me.'

'Do you think he will do so?'

'Why not? I have come here to do him a service. He has no goods. I have. He has no men with him. I have. If I do a friendly part by him, will he not do a friendly part by me? What says the poet?—

> Nor hope to find
> A friend, but who has found a friend in thee.
> All like the purchase; few the price will pay:
> And this makes friends such *wonders* here below.

I have paid the purchase, by coming so far to do him a service. But I think, from what I have seen of him last night, that he is not such a

253

niggard and misanthrope as I was told he was by a man who said he knew him. He exhibited considerable emotion despite the monosyllabic greeting, when he shook my hand. Neither did he run away, as I was told he would; though perhaps that was because he had no time. Still, if he was a man to feel annoyance at any person coming after him, he would not have received me as he did, nor would he ask me to live with him, but he would have surlily refused to see me, and told me to mind my own business, and he would mind his. Neither does he mind my nationality; for "here," said he, "Americans and Englishmen are the same people. We speak the same language and have the same ideas." Just so, Doctor; I agree with you. Here at least, Americans and Englishmen shall be brothers, and whatever I can do for you, you may command me as freely as if I were flesh of your flesh, bone of your bone.'

I dressed myself quietly, intending to take a stroll along the Tanganika before the Doctor should rise; opened the door, which creaked horribly on its hinges, and walked out to the veranda.

'Halloa, Doctor!—you up already? I hope you have slept well?'

'Good morning, Mr. Stanley! I am glad to see you. Hope you rested well. I sat up late reading my letters. You have brought me good and bad news. But sit down.' He made a place for me by his side. 'Yes, many of my friends are dead. My eldest son has met with a sad accident—that is, my boy Tom; my second son, Oswell, is at college studying medicine, and is doing well, I am told. Agnes, my eldest daughter, has been enjoying herself in a yacht, with "Sir Paraffine" Young and his family. Sir Roderick, also, is well, and expresses a hope that he will soon see me. You have brought me quite a budget.'

The man was not an apparition, then, and yesterday's scenes were not the result of a dream! and I gazed on him intently, for thus I was assured he had not run away, which was the great fear that constantly haunted me as I was journeying to Ujiji.

'Now, Doctor,' said I, 'you are, probably, wondering why I came here?'

'It is true,' said he; 'I have been wondering. I thought you, at first, an emissary of the French Government, in the place of Lieutenant Le Saint, who died a few miles above Gondokoro. I heard you had boats, plenty of men, and stores, and I really believed you were some French officer, until I saw the American flag; and, to tell you the truth, I was rather glad it was so, because I could not have talked to him in French; and if he did not know English, we had been a pretty pair of white men in Ujiji! I did not like to ask you yesterday, because it was none of my business.'

'Well,' said I, laughing, 'for your sake I am glad that I am an American, and not a Frenchman, and that we can understand each other perfectly without an interpreter. I see that the Arabs are wondering that you, an Englishman, and I, an American, understand each other. We must take care not to tell them that the English and Americans have fought, and that there are "Alabama" claims left unsettled, and that we have such people as Fenians in America, who hate you. But seriously, Doctor—now don't be frightened when I tell you that I have come after —YOU!'

'After me?'

'Yes.'

'How?'

'Well. You have heard of the "New York Herald"?'

'Oh—who has not heard of that newspaper?'

'Sh-sh! Without his father's knowledge or consent, Mr. James Gordon Bennett, son of Mr. James Gordon Bennett, the proprietor of the "Herald," has commissioned me to find you—to get whatever news of your discoveries you like to give—and to assist you, if I can, with means.'

'Young Mr. Bennett told you to come after me, to find me out, and help me! It is no wonder, then, you praised Mr. Bennett so much last night.'

'I know him—I am proud to say—to be just what I say he is. He is an ardent, generous, and true man.'

'Well, indeed! I am very much obliged to him; and it makes me feel proud to think that you Americans think so much of me. You have just come in the proper time; for I was beginning to think that I should have to beg from the Arabs. Even they are in want of cloth, and there are but few beads in Ujiji. That fellow Sherif has robbed me of all. I wish I could embody my thanks to Mr. Bennett in suitable words; but if I fail to do so, do not, I beg of you, believe me the less grateful.'

'And now, Doctor, having disposed of this little affair, Ferajji shall bring breakfast; if you have no objection.'

'You have given me an appetite,' he said. 'Halimah is my cook, but she never can tell the difference between tea and coffee.'

Ferajji, the cook, was ready as usual with excellent tea, and a dish of smoking cakes; 'dampers', as the Doctor called them. I never did care much for this kind of a cake fried in a pan, but they were necessary to the Doctor, who had nearly lost all his teeth from the hard fare of Lunda. He had been compelled to subsist on green ears of Indian corn; there was no meat in that district; and the effort to gnaw at the corn ears had loosened all his teeth. I preferred the corn scones of Virginia, which, to my mind, were the nearest approach to palatable bread obtainable in Central Africa.

The Doctor said he had thought me a most luxurious and rich man when he saw my great bath-tub carried on the shoulders of one of my men; but he thought me still more luxurious this morning, when my knives and forks, and plates, and cups, saucers, silver spoons, and silver tea-pot were brought forth shining and bright, spread on a rich Persian carpet, and observed that I was well attended to by my yellow and ebon Mercuries.

This was the beginning of our life at Ujiji. I knew him not as a friend before my arrival. He was only an object to me—a great item for a daily newspaper, as much as other subjects in which the voracious news-loving public delight. I had gone over battlefields, witnessed revolutions, civil wars, rebellions, émeutes and massacres; stood close to the condemned murderer to record his last struggles and last sighs; but never had I been called to record anything that moved me so much as this man's woes and sufferings, his privations and disappointments, which now were poured into my ear. Verily did I begin to perceive that 'the Gods above do with just eyes survey the affairs of men.' I began to recognize the hand of an overruling and kindly Providence.

*How I found Livingstone*, 2nd edition, pp. 402–425

*Stanley's visit, though recorded in Livingstone's journal with a reserve which contrasts with Stanley's expressive record, was very beneficial to the Doctor. Stanley's company, his stores, especially his food and his medicine, helped to restore a little the Doctor's spirits, though his constitution must have been too deeply overstrained to be radically improved by this temporary refreshment.*

*The two men made an expedition up Lake Tanganyika in canoes. They were attacked by tribes maddened by the injuries of the slavers, but were saved by the calm, unprovocative behaviour of Livingstone which astonished and impressed his companion, if only for the moment. They reached a point further north than that attained by Burton and Speke and they were thus able to settle a very important question about the source of the Nile by ascertaining that, contrary to Burton's opinion, the Rusizi river flowed into, not out of, the Lake.*

*Livingstone steadily refused all Stanley's pleas that he should return with him. He was determined to verify the connection between the 'fountains' mentioned by Herodotus, which he believed to be in the region of Lake Bangweolo, and the Nile. He thought this connection might be west of Tanganyika, possibly through the Lualaba river, and another lake to the north. Accordingly the two men travelled together to Tabora, and Stanley offered to hurry to the coast and to send back to Livingstone, who now had only Susi, Chumah, and a few other faithful servants, a band of porters to enable him to continue his exploration.*

*At last, after four months together, all Stanley's preparations being made and all Livingstone's letters written, the time came when Stanley must set out for the coast.*

## 30. THE PARTING

*March 13th.*—The last day of my stay with Livingstone has come and gone, and the last night we shall be together is present, and I cannot evade the morrow! I feel as though I would rebel against the fate which drives me away from him. The minutes beat fast, and grow into hours. Our door is closed, and we are both of us busy with our own thoughts. What his thoughts are I know not. Mine are sad. My days seem to have been spent in an Elysian field; otherwise, why should I so keenly regret the near approach of the parting hour? Have I not been battered by successive fevers, prostrate with agony day after day lately? Have I not raved and stormed in madness? Have I not clenched my fists in fury, and fought with the wild strength of despair, when in delirium? Yet, I regret to surrender the pleasure I have felt in this man's society, though so dearly purchased. And I cannot resist the sure advance of time, which flies this night as if it mocked me, and gloated on the misery it created! Be it so! How many times have I not suffered the pang of parting with friends! I wished to linger longer, but the inevitable would come—Fate sundered us. This is the same regretful feeling, only it is more poignant, and the farewell may be for ever! For ever? And 'For ever,' echo the reverberations of a woful whisper.

I have noted down all he has said to-night; but the reader shall not share it with me. It is mine!

I am jealous as he is himself of his Journal; and I have written in German text, and in round hand, on either side of it, on the waterproof canvas cover, 'POSITIVELY NOT TO BE OPENED;' to which he has affixed his signature. I have stenographed every word he has said to me respecting the equable distribution of certain curiosities among his friends and children, and his last wish about 'his dear old friend, Sir Roderick Murchison,' because he has been getting anxious about him ever since we received the newspapers at Uganda, when we read that the old man was suffering from a paralytic stroke. I must be sure to send him the news, as soon as I get to Aden; and I have promised that he will receive the message from me quicker than anything was ever received in Central Africa.

'To-morrow night, Doctor, you will be alone!'

'Yes; the house will look as though a death had taken place. You had better stop until the rains, which are now near, are over.'

'I would to God I could, my dear Doctor; but every day I stop here.

now that there is no necessity for me to stay longer, keeps you from your work and home.'

'I know; but consider your health—you are not fit to travel. What is it? Only a few weeks longer. You will travel to the coast just as quickly when the rains are over as you will by going now. The plains will be inundated between here and the coast.'

'You think so; but I will reach the coast in forty days; if not in forty, I will in fifty—certain. The thought that I am doing you an important service will spur me on.'

*March 14th.*—At dawn we were up, the bales and baggage were taken outside of the building, and the men prepared themselves for the first march towards home.

We had a sad breakfast together. I could not eat, my heart was too full; neither did my companion seem to have an appetite. We found something to do which kept us longer together. At 8 o'clock I was not gone, and I had thought to have been off at 5 a.m.

'Doctor,' said I, 'I will leave two men with you, who will stop to-day and to-morrow with you, for it may be that you have forgotten something in the hurry of my departure. I will halt a day at Tura, on the frontier of Unyamwezi, for your last word, and your last wish; and now we must part—there is no help for it. Good-bye.'

'Oh, I am coming with you a little way. I must see you off on the road.'

'Thank you. Now, my men, Home! Kirangozi, lift the flag, and MARCH!'

The house looked desolate—it faded from our view. Old times, and the memories of my aspirations and kindling hopes, came strong on me. The old hills round about, that I once thought tame and uninteresting, had become invested with histories and reminiscences for me. On that burzani I have sat hour after hour, dreaming, and hoping, and sighing. On that col I stood, watching the battle and the destruction of Tabora. Under that roof I have sickened and been delirious, and cried out like a child at the fate that threatened my mission. Under that banian tree lay my dead comrade—poor Shaw! I would have given a fortune to have had him by my side at this time. From that house I started on my journey to Ujiji; to it I returned as to a friend, with a newer and dearer companion; and now I leave all. Already it all appears like a strange dream.

We walked side by side; the men lifted their voices in a song. I took long looks at Livingstone, to impress his features thoroughly on my memory.

'The thing is, Doctor, so far as I can understand it, you do not intend to return home until you have satisfied yourself about the "Source of the Nile." When you have satisfied yourself, you will come home and satisfy others. Is it not so?'

258

'That is it, exactly. When your men come back, I shall immediately start for Ufipa; then, crossing the Rungwa River, I shall strike south, and round the extremity of the Tanganika. Then, a south-east course will take me to Chicumbi's, on the Luapula. On crossing the Luapula, I shall go direct west to the copper-mines of Katanga. Eight days south of Katanga, the natives declare the fountains to be. When I have found them, I shall return by Katanga to the underground houses of Rua. From the caverns, ten days north-east will take me to Lake Kamolondo. I shall be able to travel from the lake, in your boat, up the River Lufira, to Lake Lincoln. Then, coming down again, I can proceed north, by the Lualaba, to the fourth lake—which, I think, will explain the whole problem; and I will probably find that it is either Chowambe (Baker's lake), or Piaggia's lake.'

'And how long do you think this little journey will take you?'

'A year and a half, at the furthest, from the day I leave Unyanyembe.'

'Suppose you say two years; contingencies might arise, you know. It will be well for me to hire these new men for two years; the day of their engagement to begin from their arrival at Unyanyembe.'

'Yes, that will do excellently well.'

'Now, my dear Doctor, the best friends must part. You have come far enough; let me beg of you to turn back.'

'Well, I will say this to you: you have done what few men could do—far better than some great travellers I know. And I am grateful to you for what you have done for me. God guide you safe home and bless you, my friend.'

'And may God bring you safe back to us all, my dear friend. Farewell!'

'Farewell!'

We wrung each other's hands, and I had to tear myself away before I unmanned myself; but Susi, and Chumah, and. Hamoydah—the Doctor's faithful fellows—they must all shake and kiss my hands before I could quite turn away. I betrayed myself!

'Good-bye, Doctor—dear friend!'

'Good-bye!'

'MARCH! Why do you stop? Go on! Are you not going home?' And my people were driven before me. No more weakness. I shall show them such marching as will make them remember me. In forty days I shall do what took me three months to perform before.

My friendly reader, I wrote the above extracts in my Diary on the evening of each day. I look at them now after six months have passed away; yet I am not ashamed of them; my eyes feel somewhat dimmed at the recollection of the parting. I dared not erase, nor modify what I had penned, while my feelings were strong. God grant that if ever you take to travelling in Africa you will get as noble and true a man for your companion as David Livingstone! For four months and four days I lived with him in the same house, or in the same boat, or in the same tent, and I never found a fault in him. I am a man of a quick temper, and often without sufficient cause, I dare say, have broken ties of friendship; but with Livingstone I never had cause for resentment, but each day's life with him added to my admiration for him.

*How I found Livingstone*, 2nd edition, pp. 622–628

*Stanley's journey back to the coast was quick and uneventful. Staying at Zanzibar only to arrange for the dispatch of porters up to Ujiji, he returned to England with his news and with the letters and papers he had brought from Livingstone. Here he met with a mortifying reception; for though Livingstone's family and Granville, the Foreign Secretary, believed what he said, many people (including the President of the Royal Geographical Society) were incredulous. In due course his story came to be accepted, even by the doubters: but he never forgot their mistrust. It was another step in the process of disillusionment which had been begun by the cruelties of his childhood and which ended by making him a bitter and lonely man. Though he was one of the greatest of African travellers, he was also one of the most ruthless and brutal.*

*Between 1874 and 1889 he made three more journeys in Africa: the first led directly to the founding of the Congo Free State; the second was undertaken in the service of King Leopold II of the Belgians, for the purpose of establishing the Free State's government; the third, the 'Emin Pasha Relief Expedition', helped to make Uganda a British sphere of influence. From 1895 to 1900 he was a Liberal Unionist M.P.: in 1899 he was created a G.C.B. But he never quite lived down the mistrust and dislike he so often inspired: it followed him even to the grave; for Dean Robinson refused permission for him to be buried in Westminster Abbey.*

*Livingstone's refusal, after nearly six years of lonely wandering, to return with Stanley to health and safety must always excite wonder. It was the more astonishing in view of the severe sufferings he had endured and their effect upon his physique. He appears to have been moved by two great purposes that were closely linked in his mind, to reveal the full ravages of the Arab slave-trade and to find the ultimate sources of the Nile.*

*He set off from Tabora in August 1872 and after skirting the southern shore of Lake Tanganyika he struck south-west. Almost from the first he was ill with fever and dysentery and soon his caravan ran into heavy rains and country almost bare of food. He struggled on and at last reached the network of streams flowing into the marshy rim of Lake Bangweolo. It is at this point that the final extract from his journal begins. It has been given almost in full, as it did not seem possible to break it up into shorter extracts without marring the picture of the man and his task and blurring the cumulative effect of the difficulties and sufferings which led to the end.*

# 31. THE DEATH OF LIVINGSTONE

*9th February.*—Slept in a most unwholesome, ruined village. Rank vegetation had run over all, and the soil smelled offensively. Crossed a sponge [a marsh], then a rivulet, and sponge running into the Miwale River, then by a rocky passage we crossed the Mofiri, or great Tinga-tinga, a water running strongly waist and breast deep, above thirty feet broad here, but very much broader below. After this we passed two more rills and the River Methonua, but we built a camp above our former one. The human ticks called 'papasi' by the Suaheli, and 'kara-patos' by the Portuguese, made even the natives call out against their numbers and ferocity.

*10th February.*—Back again to our old camp on the Lovu or Lofu by the bridge. We left in a drizzle, which continued from 4 a.m. to 1 p.m. We were three hours in it, and all wetted, just on reaching camp, by 200 yards of flood mid-deep; but we have food.

*11th February.*—Our guides took us across country, where we saw tracks of buffaloes, and in a meadow, the head of a sponge, we saw a herd of Hartebeests. A drizzly night was followed by a morning of cold wet fog, but in three hours we reached our old camp: it took us six hours to do this distance before, and five on our return. We camped on a deep bridged stream, called the Kiachibwe.

*12th February.*—We crossed the Kasoso, which joins the Mokisya, a river we afterwards crossed: it flows N.W., then over the Mofungwe. The same sponges everywhere.

*13th February.*—In four hours we came within sight of the Luena and Lake, and saw plenty of elephants and other game, but very shy. The forest trees are larger. The guides are more at a loss than we are, as they

261

always go in canoes in the flat rivers and rivulets. Went E., then S.E. round to S.

14*th February*.—Public punishment to Chirango for stealing beads, fifteen cuts; diminished his load to 40 lbs., giving him blue and white beads to be strung. The water stands so high in the paths that I cannot walk dryshod, and I found in the large bougas or prairies in front, that it lay knee deep, so I sent on two men to go to the first villages of Matipa for large canoes to navigate the Lake, or give us a guide to go east to the Chambeze, to go round on foot. It was Halima who informed on Chirango, as he offered her beads for a cloth of a kind which she knew had not hitherto been taken out of the baggage. This was so far faithful in her, but she has an outrageous tongue. I remain because of an excessive hæmorrhagic discharge.

If the good Lord gives me favour, and permits me to finish my work, I shall thank and bless Him, though it has cost me untold toil, pain, and travel; this trip has made my hair all grey.

15*th February*, Sunday.—Service. Killed our last goat while waiting for messengers to return from Matipa's. Evening: the messenger came back, having been foiled by deep tinga-tinga and bouga. He fired his gun three times, but no answer came, so as he had slept one night away he turned, but found some men hunting, whom he brought with him. They say that Matipa is on Chirube islet, a good man too, but far off from this.

16*th February*.—Sent men by the hunter's canoe to Chirube, with a request to Matipa to convey us west if he has canoes, but, if not, to tell us truly, and we will go east and cross the Chambeze where it is small. Chitunkubwe's men ran away, refusing to wait till he had communicated with Matipa. Here the water stands underground about eighteen inches from the surface. The guides played us false, and this is why they escaped.

17*th February*.—The men will return to-morrow, but they have to go all the way out to the islet of Chirube to Matipa's.

Suffered a furious attack at midnight from the red Sirafu or Driver ants. Our cook fled first at their onset. I lighted a candle, and remembering Dr. Van der Kemp's idea that no animal will attack man unprovoked, I lay still. The first came on my foot quietly, then some began to bite between the toes, then the larger ones swarmed over the foot and bit furiously, and made the blood start out. I then went out of the tent, and my whole person was instantly covered as close as small-pox (not confluent) on a patient. Grass fires were lighted, and my men picked some off my limbs and tried to save me. After battling for an hour or two they took me into a hut not yet invaded, and I rested till they came, the pests, and routed me out there too! Then came on a steady pour of rain, which held on till noon, as if trying to make us miserable. At 9 a.m. I got back into my tent. The large Sirafu have mandibles curved like reaping-

'The Water Came up to Susi's Mouth'
From Livingstone's *Last Journals*

sickles, and very sharp—as fine at the point as the finest needle or a bee's sting. Their office is to remove all animal refuse, cockroaches, &c., and they took all my fat. Their appearance sets every cockroach in a flurry, and all ants, white and black, get into a panic. On man they insert the sharp curved mandibles, and then with six legs push their bodies round so as to force the points by lever power. They collect in masses in their runs and stand with mandibles extended, as if defying attack. The large ones stand thus at bay whilst the youngsters hollow out a run half an inch wide, and about an inch deep. They remained with us till late in the afternoon, and we put hot ashes on the defiant hordes. They retire to enjoy the fruits of their raid, and come out fresh another day.

*18th February.*—We wait hungry and cold for the return of the men who have gone to Matipa, and hope the good Lord will grant us influence with this man.

*4th March.*—Sent canoes off to bring our men over to the island of Matipa. They brought ten, but the donkey could not come as far through the 'tinga-tinga' as they, so they took it back for fear that it should perish. I spoke to Matipa this morning to send more canoes, and he consented. We move outside, as the town swarms with mice, and is very closely built and disagreeable. I found mosquitoes in the town.

*5th March.*—Time runs on quickly. The real name of this island is Masumbo, and the position may be probably long. 31° 3′; lat. 10° 11′ S. Men not arrived yet. Matipa very slow.

*6th March.*—Building a camp outside the town for quiet and cleanliness, and no mice to run over us at night. This islet is some twenty or thirty feet above the general flat country and adjacent water.

At 3 p.m. we moved up to the highest part of the island where we can see around us and have the fresh breeze from the Lake. Rainy as we went up, as usual.

*7th March.*—We expect some men to-day. I tremble for the donkey! Camp sweet and clean, but it, too, has mosquitoes, from which a curtain protects me completely—a great luxury, but unknown to the Arabs, to whom I have spoken about it. Abed was overjoyed by one I made for him; others are used to their bites, as was the man who said that he would get used to a nail through the heel of his shoe. The men came at 3 p.m., but eight had to remain, the canoes being too small. The donkey had to be tied down, as he rolled about on his legs and would have forced his way out. He bit Mabruki Speke's lame hand, and came in stiff from lying tied all day. We had him shampooed all over, but he could not eat dura—he feels sore. Susi did well under the circumstances, and we had plenty of flour ready for all. Chanza is near Kabinga, and this last chief is coming to visit me in a day or two.

*8th March.*—I press Matipa to get a fleet of canoes equal to our number, but he complains of their being stolen by rebel subjects. He tells me his brother Kabinga would have been here some days ago but for having lost a son, who was killed by an elephant: he is mourning for him but will come soon. Kabinga is on the other side of the Chambeze. A party of male and female drummers and dancers is sure to turn up at every village; the first here had a leader that used such violent antics perspiration ran off his whole frame. I gave a few strings of beads, and the performance is repeated to-day by another lot, but I rebel and allow them to dance unheeded. We got a sheep for a wonder for a doti; fowls and fish alone could be bought, but Kabinga has plenty of cattle. . . .

The eight men came from Motovinza this afternoon, and now all our party is united. The donkey shows many sores inflicted by the careless people, who think that force alone can be used to inferior animals.

*11th March.*—Matipa says 'Wait; Kabinga is coming, and he has canoes.' Time is of no value to him. His wife is making him pombe, and will drown all his cares, but mine increase and plague me. Matipa and his wife each sent me a huge calabash of pombe; I wanted only a little to make bread with.

By putting leaven in a bottle and keeping it from one baking to another (or three days) good bread is made, and the dough being surrounded by banana leaves or maize leaves (or even forest leaves of hard texture and no taste, or simply by broad leafy grass), is preserved from burning in an iron pot. The inside of the pot is greased, then the leaves put in all round, and the dough poured in to stand and rise in the sun.

Better news comes: the son of Kabinga is to be here to-night, and we shall concoct plans together.

*12th March.*—The news was false, no one came from Kabinga. The men strung beads to-day, and I wrote part of my despatch for Earl Granville.

*13th March.*—I went to Matipa, and proposed to begin the embarkation of my men at once, as they are many, and the canoes are only sufficient to take a few at a time. He has sent off a big canoe to reap his millet, when it returns he will send us over to see for ourselves where we can go. I explained the danger of setting my men astray.

*14th March.*—Rains have ceased for a few days. Went down to Matipa and tried to take his likeness for the sake of the curious hat he wears.

*15th March.*—Finish my despatch so far.

*16th March*, Sunday.—Service. I spoke sharply to Matipa for his duplicity. He promises everything and does nothing: he has in fact no power over his people. Matipa says that a large canoe will come to-morrow, and next day men will go to Kabinga to reconnoitre. There may be a hitch there which he did not take into account; Kabinga's son, killed by an elephant, may have raised complications: blame may be attached to Matipa, and in their dark minds it may appear all important to settle the affair before having communication with him. Ill all day with my old complaint.

17th March.—The delay is most trying. So many detentions have occurred they ought to have made me of a patient spirit.

As I thought, Matipa told us to-day that it is reported he has some Arabs with him who will attack all the Lake people forthwith, and he is anxious that we shall go over to show them that we are peaceful.

18th March.—Sent off men to reconnoitre at Kabinga's and to make a camp there. Rain began again after nine days' dry weather, N.W. wind, but in the morning fleecy clouds came from S.E. in patches. Matipa is acting the villain, and my men are afraid of him: they are all cowards, and say that they are afraid of me, but this is only an excuse for their cowardice.

19th March [his birthday].—Thanks to the Almighty Preserver of men for sparing me thus far on the journey of life. Can I hope for ultimate success? So many obstacles have arisen. Let not Satan prevail over me, Oh! my good Lord Jesus.

8 a.m. Got about 20 people off to canoes. Matipa not friendly. They go over to Kabinga on S.W. side of the Chambeze, and thence we go overland. 9 a.m. Men came back and reported Matipa false again; only one canoe had come. I made a demonstration by taking quiet possession of his village and house; fired a pistol through the roof and called my men, ten being left to guard the camp; Matipa fled to another village. The people sent off at once and brought three canoes, so at 11 a.m. my men embarked quietly. They go across the Chambeze and build a camp in its left bank. All Kabinga's cattle are kept on an island called Kalilo, near the mouth of the Chambeze, and are perfectly wild: they are driven into the water like buffaloes, and pursued when one is wanted for meat. No milk is ever obtained of course.

20th March.—Cold N.W. weather, but the rainfall is small, as the S.E. stratum comes down below the N.W. by day. Matipa sent two large baskets of flour (cassava), a sheep, and a cock. He hoped that we should remain with him till the water of the over-flood dried, and help him to fight his enemies, but I explained our delays, and our desire to complete our work and meet Baker.

21st March.—Very heavy N.W. rain and thunder by night, and by morning. I gave Matipa a coil of thick brass wire, and his wife a string of large neck beads, and explained my hurry to be off. He is now all fair, and promises largely: he has been much frightened by our warlike demonstration. I am glad I had to do nothing but make a show of force.

22nd March.—Susi not returned from Kabinga. I hope that he is getting canoes, and men also, to transport us all at one voyage. It is flood as far as the eye can reach; flood four and six feet deep, and more, with three species of rushes, two kinds of lotus, or sacred lily, papyrus, arum, &c. One does not know where land ends, and Lake begins: the presence of land-grass proves that this is not always overflowed.

*23rd March.*—Men returned at noon. Kabinga is mourning for his son killed by an elephant, and keeps in seclusion. The camp is formed on the left bank of the Chambeze.

*24th March.*—The people took the canoes away, but in fear sent for them. I got four, and started with all our goods, first giving a present that no blame should follow me. We punted six hours to a little islet without a tree, and no sooner did we land than a pitiless pelting rain came on. We turned up a canoe to get shelter. We shall reach the Chambeze to-morrow. The wind tore the tent out of our hands, and damaged it too; the loads are all soaked, and with the cold it is bitterly uncomfortable. A man put my bed into the bilge, and never said, 'Bale out,' so I was safe for a wet night, but it turned out better than I expected. No grass, but we made a bed of the loads, and a blanket fortunately put into a bag.

*25th March.*—Nothing earthly will make me give up my work in despair. I encourage myself in the Lord my God, and go forward.

We got off from our miserably small islet of ten yards at 7 a.m., a grassy sea on all sides, with a few islets in the far distance. Four varieties of rushes around us, triangular and fluted, rise from eighteen inches to two feet above the water. The caterpillars seem to eat each other, and a web is made round others; the numerous spiders may have been the workmen of the nest. The wind on the rushes makes a sound like the waves of the sea. The flood extends out in slightly depressed arms of the Lake for twenty or thirty miles, and far too broad to be seen across; fish abound, and ant-hills alone lift up their heads; they have trees on them. Lukutu flows from E. to W. to the Chambeze, as does the Lubanseusi also. After another six hours' punting, over the same wearisome prairie or Bouga, we heard the merry voices of children. It was a large village, on a flat, which seems flooded at times, but much cassava is planted on mounds, made to protect the plants from the water, which stood in places in the village, but we got a dry spot for the tent. The people offered us huts. We had as usual a smart shower on the way to Kasenga, where we slept. We passed the Islet Luangwa.

*26th March.*—We started at 7.30, and got into a large stream out of the Chambeze, called Mabziwa. One canoe sank in it, and we lost a slave girl of Amoda. Fished up three boxes, and two guns, but the boxes being full of cartridges were much injured; we lost the donkey's saddle too. After this mishap we crossed the Lubanseusi, near its confluence with the Chambeze, 300 yards wide and three fathoms deep, and a slow current. We crossed the Chambeze. It is about 400 yards wide, with a quick clear current of two knots, and three fathoms deep, like the Lubanseusi; but that was slow in current, but clear also. There is one great lock after another, with thick mats of hedges, formed of aquatic plants between. The volume of water is enormous. We punted five hours, and then camped.

*27th March.*—I sent canoes and men back to Matipa's to bring all the men that remained, telling them to ship them at once on arriving, and not to make any talk about it. Kabinga keeps his distance from us, and food is scarce; at noon he sent a man to salute me in his name.

*28th March.*—Making a pad for a donkey, to serve instead of a saddle. Kabinga attempts to sell a sheep at an exorbitant price, and says that he is weeping over his dead child. Mabruki Speke's hut caught fire at night, and his cartridge box was burned.

*29th March.*—I bought a sheep for 100 strings of beads. I wished to begin the exchange by being generous, and told his messenger so; then a small quantity of maize was brought, and I grumbled at the meanness of the present: there is no use in being bashful, as they are not ashamed to grumble too. The man said that Kabinga would send more when he had collected it.

*30th March*, Sunday.—A lion roars mightily. The fish-hawk utters his weird voice in the morning, as if he lifted up to a friend at a great distance, in a sort of falsetto key.

5 p.m. Men returned, but the large canoe having been broken by the donkey, we have to go back and pay for it, and take away about twenty men now left. Matipa kept all the payment from his own people, and so left us in the lurch; thus another five days is lost.

*31st March.*—I sent the men back to Matipa's for all our party. I give two dotis to repair the canoe. Islanders are always troublesome, from a sense of security in their fastnesses. Made stirrups of thick brass wire four-fold; they promise to do well. Sent Kabinga a cloth, and a message, but he is evidently a niggard, like Matipa: we must take him as we find him, there is no use in growling. Seven of our men returned, having got a canoe from one of Matipa's men. Kabinga, it seems, was pleased with the cloth, and says that he will ask for maize from his people, and cut it for me; he has rice growing. He will send a canoe to carry me over the next river.

*3rd April*, 1873.—Very heavy rain last night. Six inches fell in a short time. The men at last have come from Matipa's.

*4th April.*—Sent over to Kabinga to buy a cow, and got a fat one for 2½ dotis, to give the party a feast ere we start. The kambari fish of the Chambeze is three feet three inches in length.

Two others, the 'polwe' and 'lopatakwao,' all go up the Chambeze to spawn when the rains begin. Casembe's people make caviare of the spawn of the 'pumbo.'

*5th April.*—March from Kabinga's on the Chambeze, our luggage in canoes, and men on land. We punted on flood six feet deep, with many ant-hills all about, covered with trees. Course S.S.E. for five miles, across the River Lobingela, sluggish, and about 300 yards wide.

*6th April.*—Leave in the same way, but men were sent from Kabinga to steal the canoes, which we paid his brother Mateysa handsomely for. A stupid drummer, beating the alarm in the distance, called us inland; we found the main body of our people had gone on, and so by this, our party got separated, and we pulled and punted six or seven hours S.W. in great difficulty, as the fishermen we saw refused to show us where the deep water lay. The whole country S. of the Lake was covered with water thickly dotted over with lotus-leaves and rushes. It has a greenish appearance, and it might be well on a map to show the spaces annually flooded by a broad wavy band, twenty, thirty, and even forty miles out from the permanent banks of the Lake: it might be coloured light green. The broad estuaries, fifty or more miles, into which the rivers form themselves, might be coloured blue, but it is quite impossible at present to tell where land ends, and Lake begins; it is all water, water everywhere, which seems to be kept from flowing quickly off by the narrow bed of the Luapula, which has perpendicular banks, worn deep down in new red sandstone. It is the Nile apparently enacting its inundations, even at its sources. The amount of water spread out over the country constantly excites my wonder; it is prodigious. Many of the ant-hills are cultivated and covered with dura, pumpkins, beans, maize, but the waters yield food plenteously in fish and lotus-roots. A species of wild rice grows, but the people neither need it nor know it. A party of fishermen fled from us, but by coaxing we got them to show us deep water. They then showed us an islet, about thirty yards square, without wood, and desired us to sleep there. We went on, and then they decamped.

Pitiless pelting showers wetted everything; but near sunset we saw two fishermen paddling quickly off from an ant-hill, where we found a hut, plenty of fish, and some firewood. There we spent the night, and watched by turns, lest thieves should come and haul away our canoes and goods. Heavy rain. One canoe sank, wetting everything in her. The leaks in her had been stopped with clay, and a man sleeping near the stern had displaced this frail caulking. We did not touch the fish, and I cannot conjecture who has inspired fear in all the inhabitants.

*7th April.*—Went on S.W., and saw two men, who guided us to the River Muanakazi, which forms a connecting link between the River Lotingila and the Lolotikila, about the southern borders of the flood. Men were hunting, and we passed near large herds of antelopes, which made a rushing, plunging sound as they ran and sprang away among the waters. A lion had wandered into this world of water and ant-hills, and roared night and morning, as if very much disgusted: we could sympathise with him! Near to the Muanakazi at a broad bank in shallow water near the river, we had to unload and haul. Our guides left us, well pleased with the payment we had given them. The natives beating a drum on our east made us believe them to be our party, and some thought that they heard two shots. This misled us, and we went towards the sound through papyrus, tall rushes, arums, and grass, till tired out, and took refuge on an ant-hill for the night. Lion roaring. We were lost in stiff grassy prairies, from three to four feet deep in water, for five hours. We fired a gun in the stillness of the night, but received no answer; so on the 8*th* we sent a small canoe at daybreak to ask for information and guides from the village where the drums had been beaten. Two men came, and they thought likewise that our party was south-east; but in that direction the water was about fifteen inches in spots and three feet in others, which caused constant dragging of the large canoe all day, and at last we unloaded at another branch of the Muanakazi with a village of friendly people. We slept there.

All hands at the large canoe could move her only a few feet. Putting all their strength to her, she stopped at every haul with a jerk, as if in a bank of adhesive plaister. I measured the crown of a papyrus plant or palm, it was three feet across horizontally, its stalk eight feet in height. Hundreds of a large dark-grey hairy caterpillar have nearly cleared off the rushes in spots, and now live on each other. They can make only the smallest progress by swimming or rather wriggling in the water: their motion is that of a watch-spring thrown down, dilating and contracting.

*9th April.*—After two hours' threading the very winding, deep channel of this southern branch of the Muanakazi, we came to where our land party had crossed it and gone on to Gandochite, a chief on the Lolotikila. My men were all done up, so I hired a man to call some of his friends to take the loads; but he was stopped by his relations in the way, saying, 'You ought to have one of the traveller's own people with you.' He returned, but did not tell us plainly or truly till this morning.

*10th April.*—The headman of the village explained, and we sent two of our men, who had a night's rest with the turnagain fellow of yesterday. I am pale, bloodless, and weak from bleeding profusely ever since the 31st of March last: an artery gives off a copious stream, and takes away my strength. Oh, how I long to be permitted by the Over Power to finish my work.

*12th April.*—Cross the Muanakazi. It is about 100 or 130 yards broad, and deep. Great loss of αἷμα made me so weak I could hardly walk, but tottered along nearly two hours, and then lay down quite done. Cooked coffee—our last—and went on, but in an hour I was compelled to lie down. Very unwilling to be carried, but on being pressed I allowed the men to help me along by relays to Chinama, where there is much cultivation. We camped in a garden of dura.

*13th April.*—Found that we had slept on the right bank of the Lolo-tikila, a sluggish, marshy-looking river, very winding, but here going about south-west. The country is all so very flat that the rivers down here are of necessity tortuous. Fish and other food abundant, and the people civil and reasonable. They usually partake largely of the character of the chief, and this one, Gondochite, is polite. The sky is clearing, and the S.E. wind is the lower stratum now. It is the dry season well begun. Seventy-three inches is a higher rainfall than has been observed anywhere else, even in northern Manyuema; it was lower by inches than here far south on the watershed. In fact, this is the very heaviest rainfall known in these latitudes; between fifty and sixty is the maximum.

One sees interminable grassy prairies with lines of trees, occupying quarters of miles in breadth, and these give way to bouga or prairie again. The bouga is flooded annually, but its vegetation consists of dry land grasses. Other bouga extend out from the Lake up to forty miles, and are known by aquatic vegetation, such as lotus, papyrus, arums, rushes of different species, and many kinds of purely aquatic subaqueous plants which send up their flowers only to fructify in the sun, and then sink to ripen one bunch after another. Others, with great cabbage-looking leaves, seem to remain always at the bottom. The young of fish swarm, and bob in and out from the leaves. A species of soft moss grows on most plants, and seems to be good fodder for fishes, fitted by hooked or turned-up noses to guide it into their maws.

One species of fish has the lower jaw turned down into a hook, which enables the animal to hold its mouth close to the plant as it glides up and down, sucking in all the soft pulpy food. The superabundance of gelatinous nutriment makes these swarmers increase in bulk with extraordinary rapidity, and the food supply of the people is plenteous in consequence. The number of fish caught by weirs, baskets, and nets now, as the waters decline, is prodigious. The fish feel their element becoming insufficient for comfort, and retire from one bouga to another towards the Lake; the narrower parts are duly prepared by weirs to take advantage of their necessities; the sun heat seems to oppress them and force them to flee. With the south-east aerial current comes heat and sultriness. A blanket is scarcely needed till the early hours of the morning, and here, after the turtle doves and cocks give out their warning calls to the watchful, the fish-eagle lifts up his remarkable voice. It is pitched in a high falsetto key, very loud, and seems as if he were calling to some one in the other world. Once heard, his weird unearthly voice can never be forgotten—it sticks to one through life.

We were four hours in being ferried over the Loitikila, or Lolotikila, in four small canoes, and then two hours south-west down its left bank to another river, where our camp has been formed. I sent over a present to the headman, and a man returned with the information that he was ill at another village, but his wife would send canoes to-morrow to transport us over and set us on our way to Muanazambamba, south-west, and over Lolotikila again.

*14th April.*—At a branch of the Lolotikila.

*15th April.*—Cross Lolotikila again (where it is only fifty yards) by canoes, and went south-west an hour. I, being very weak, had to be carried part of the way. Am glad of resting; αῖμα flowed copiously last night. A woman, the wife of the chief, gave a present of a goat and maize.

*16th April.*—West south-west two and a half hours, and crossed the Lombatwa River of 100 yards in width, rush deep, and flowing fast in aquatic vegetation, papyrus, &c., into the Loitikila. In all about three hours south-west.

*17th April.*—A tremendous rain after dark burst all our now rotten tents to shreds. Went on at 6.35 a.m. for three hours, and I, who was suffering severely all night, had to rest. We got water near the surface by digging in yellow sand. Three hills now appear in the distance. Our course, S.W. three and three-quarters hours to a village on the Kazya River. A Nyassa man declared that his father had brought the heavy rain of the 16th on us. We crossed three sponges.

*18th April.*—On leaving the village on the Kazya, we forded it and found it seventy yards broad, waist to breast deep all over. A large weir spanned it, and we went on the lower side of that. Much papyrus and other aquatic plants in it. Fish are returning now with the falling waters, and are guided into the rush-cones set for them. Crossed two large sponges, and I was forced to stop at a village after travelling S.W. for two hours: very ill all night, but remembered that the bleeding and most other ailments in this land are forms of fever. Took two scruple doses of quinine, and stopped it quite.

*19th April.*—A fine bracing S.E. breeze kept me on the donkey across a broad sponge and over flats of white sandy soil and much cultivation for an hour and a half, when we stopped at a large village on the right bank of [Livingstone leaves a blank here], and men went over to the chief Muanzambamba to ask canoes to cross to-morrow. I am excessively weak, and but for the donkey could not move a hundred yards. It is not all pleasure this exploration. The Lavusi hills are a relief to the eye in this flat upland. Their forms show an igneous origin. The river Kazya comes from them and goes direct into the Lake. No observations now, owing to great weakness; I can scarcely hold the pencil, and my stick is a burden. Tent gone; the men build a good hut for me and the luggage. S.W. one and a half hour.

*20th April,* Sunday.—Service. Cross over the sponge, Moenda, for food and to be near the headman of these parts, Moanzambamba. I am excessively weak. Village on Moenda sponge, 7 a.m. Cross Lokulu in a canoe. The river is about thirty yards broad, very deep, and flowing in marshes two knots from S.S.E. to N.N.W. into Lake.

21*st*.—Tried to ride, but was forced to lie down, and they carried me back to vil. exhausted.

*Last Journals*, vol. II, pp. 274–303

*The last entries reproduced in the facsimile require some explanation. On 21st April he was too weak to sit upon his donkey and fell to the ground. He was carried back to the village, and the next day a bed-like litter (Kitanda) was made of poles and he was taken a short distance. He was carried like this for three more days, suffering terrible pain from acute dysentery and from the movement of the litter. On the 25th, still pursuing his quest, he asked the villagers if they knew of a hill which was the source of four rivers. The facsimile shows that he was too weak to write anything but the date and the hours of travel. On 27th April comes the last entry:*

*'27. Knocked up quite and remain—recover sent to buy milch goats. We are on the banks of the Molilamo.'*

*What happened afterwards was pieced together into a story from the accounts of his servants, and published by the editor of the* Last Journals, *the Rev. Horace Waller. Two days later, on the 29th, his men managed to get him across a river in a small canoe, though every movement was pain and they frequently had to put down the litter on the other side to let him lie still. They had a hut built for him in the next village. Here he lay all day in great weakness and suffering. That night the boy told off to watch saw that Livingstone was kneeling by his bed. After sleeping for some time he looked in again and saw his master in the same position. He called Susi and Chumah, and they and others of the men came into the hut. A candle was burning and by its light they saw the Doctor kneeling with his head in his hands. He was dead.*

*At dawn the men met to decide what to do in their leaderless condition, separated from their base at the coast by a journey of 1,500 miles through difficult and dangerous country. Their decision was remarkable. They resolved to hold together and to carry back their master's remains and all his property, including his journals, to the coast. They buried his heart under a tree, embalmed the emaciated form and wrapped it up so as to look like one of the long bales they carried. They thus triumphed not only over physical fear but also over their superstitious dread of a dead body, an attitude which was certain to be shared by the tribes through which they must pass and which did upon at least one occasion seriously endanger them.*

*The journey back took them nine months and on its course some of the party died and others nearly died. They were attacked by wild animals: they were blackmailed for tolls: once they had to fight their way out from a hostile tribe. That they maintained their courage and their discipline is shown by their safe arrival at last at Tabora. Here they met Lieutenant Cameron, on his way inland to relieve Livingstone. He did everything he could to persuade the men to bury their master there, pointing out to them the great danger of the rest of the journey. They absolutely refused, and went on until they reached the coast and finally handed over their burden to the British Consul. Livingstone was buried in Westminster Abbey on 18th April 1874 and Susi, Chumah and another of his servants came to England and were present at the funeral.*

# LIST OF BOOKS

The following list gives the chief works relating to Africa written by the travellers who are represented in this book, together with such biographies or other sources of information about them as have been published. Only the dates of the first editions have been given; but where cheap modern reprints are available, they have been mentioned. The books which appear under the heading 'General Works' may be recommended as authoritative introductions to the subjects with which they deal: to them, and to the *Dictionary of National Biography*, we are indebted for much of the information contained in our editorial matter. As some of these works have been extensively revised since their first publication, we have cited the latest and best editions of them.

## BRUCE

*Travels to discover the source of the Nile* (5 vols., 1790).
SEE ALSO:
A. MURRAY, *Account of the life and writings of James Bruce* (1808).
SIR F. B. HEAD, *The life of Bruce, the African traveller* (1830).
SIR R. L. PLAYFAIR, *Travels in the footsteps of Bruce* (1877). Deals with Bruce's travels in North Africa and reproduces some of his drawings.

## PARK

*Travels in the interior districts of Africa* (1799). Reissued in 'Everyman's Library', 1907.
*Journal of a mission to the interior of Africa in 1805* (1815).
SEE ALSO:
J. THOMSON, *Mungo Park and the Niger* (1890).
S. GWYNN, *Mungo Park and the Niger* (1934).

## CLAPPERTON

D. DENHAM, H. CLAPPERTON and W. OUDNEY, *Travels and discoveries in Northern and Central Africa in 1822-4* (1826).
*Journal of a second expedition into the interior of Africa . . . by the late Commander Clapperton, of the Royal Navy. To which is added, the journal of Richard Lander from Kano to the sea-coast* (1829).

# LIST OF BOOKS

SEE ALSO:

R. LANDER, *Records of Captain Clapperton's last expedition* (2 vols., 1829).

T. NELSON, *A biographical memoir of the late Dr. W. Oudney, Captain H. Clapperton, and Major A. G. Laing* (1830).

## LANDER

(For his two works published in 1829, see under Clapperton)

*Journal of an expedition to explore the course and termination of the Niger* (3 vols., 1832). Written in collaboration with his brother John.

SEE ALSO:

M. LAIRD and R. A. K. OLDFIELD, *Narrative of an expedition into the interior of Africa, by the River Niger* (2 vols., 1837).

W. TREGELLAS, *Cornish worthies* (1884), vol. II, pp. 199–218.

## LIVINGSTONE

*Missionary travels and researches in South Africa* (1857).

*Narrative of an expedition to the Zambesi and its tributaries* (1865). Written in collaboration with his brother Charles.

*The last journals of David Livingstone in Central Africa*, ed. H. Waller (2 vols., 1874).

SEE ALSO:

W. G. BLAIKIE, *The personal life of David Livingstone* (1880).

R. COUPLAND, *Kirk on the Zambesi* (1928). Deals with Livingstone's second (Zambesi) expedition.

R. J. CAMPBELL, *Livingstone* (1929).

J. I. MACNAIR, *Livingstone the liberator* ('Collins Classics', 1940).

*Some Letters from Livingstone, 1840–1872*, ed. D. Chamberlin (1940).

## BAIKIE

*Narrative of an exploring voyage up the Rivers Kwora and Binue* (1856).

SEE ALSO:

S. A. CROWTHER, *Journal of an expedition up the Niger and Tshadda Rivers* (1855).

A. G. C. HASTINGS, *The voyage of the* Dayspring (1926).

## BURTON

*First footsteps in East Africa; or, an exploration of Harar* (1856). Re-issued in 'Everyman's Library', 1910.

*The lake regions of Central Africa* (2 vols., 1860).

*Abeokuta and the Camaroons mountains* (2 vols., 1863).

*Wanderings in West Africa, by a F.R.G.S.* [i.e. Burton] (2 vols., 1863).

# LIST OF BOOKS

*A mission to Gelele, King of Dahome* (2 vols., 1864).

*The Nile basin* (1864).

*Zanzibar; city, island, and coast* (2 vols., 1872).

*The lands of Cazembe. Lacerda's journey to Cazembe in 1798* (1873).
Translated and annotated by Burton.

*Two trips to gorilla land and the cataracts of the Congo* (2 vols., 1876).

*To the Gold Coast for gold* (2 vols., 1883). Written in collaboration with
V. L. Cameron.

SEE ALSO:

I. BURTON, *The life of Captain Sir Richd. F. Burton* (2 vols., 1893).

H. J. SCHONFIELD, *Richard Burton, explorer* (1936).

J. BURTON, *Sir Richard Burton's wife* (1942).


## SPEKE

'Journal of a cruise on the Tanganyika Lake, Central Africa' and
'Captain J. H. Speke's discovery of the Victoria Nyanza Lake, the
supposed source of the Nile. From his journal' in *Blackwood's Magazine*, vol. LXXXVI (1859), pp. 339–357, 391–419, 565–582.

*Journal of the discovery of the source of the Nile* (1863). Reissued in
'Everyman's Library', 1906.

*What led to the discovery of the source of the Nile* (1864).


## BAKER

*The Albert N'Yanza, great basin of the Nile* (2 vols., 1866).

*The Nile tributaries of Abyssinia* (1867).

*Ismailïa* (2 vols., 1874).

SEE ALSO:

T. D. MURRAY and A. S. WHITE, *Sir Samuel Baker. A memoir* (1895).


## STANLEY

*How I found Livingstone in Central Africa* (1872).

*My Kalulu, prince, king, and slave; a story of Central Africa* (1873).

*Coomassie and Magdala: the story of two British campaigns in Africa*
(1874).

*Through the dark continent* (2 vols., 1878).

*The Congo and the founding of its Free State* (2 vols., 1885).

*In darkest Africa, or the quest, rescue and retreat of Emin, Governor of
Equatoria* (2 vols., 1890).

*My dark companions and their strange stories* (1893).

*The autobiography of Sir Henry Morton Stanley*, ed. D. Stanley (1909).

SEE ALSO:

A. J. A. SYMONS, *H. M. Stanley* ('Great Lives' series, 1933).

# LIST OF BOOKS
## GENERAL WORKS

J. N. L. BAKER, *A history of geographical discovery and exploration* (ed. 2, 1937).

*Cambridge history of the British Empire*, vol. II (1940), ch. xvii, 'The Exploration of Africa' (by E. Henwood), and ch. xviii, 'British Enterprise in Tropical Africa' (by A. P. Newton).

SIR H. H. JOHNSTON, *The Nile quest* (1903), *The opening up of Africa* ('Home University Library'), and *A history of the colonization of Africa by alien races* (ed. 2, 1913).

SIR J. S. KELTIE, *The partition of Africa* (ed. 2, 1895).

R. COUPLAND, *The British anti-slavery movement* ('Home University Library', 1933).

E. W. BOVILL, *Caravans of the old Sahara: an introduction to the history of the Western Sudan* (1933).

W. FITZGERALD, *Africa: a social, economic and political geography of its main regions* (ed. 3, 1940).

C. G. SELIGMAN, *The races of Africa* ('Home University Library': ed. 2, 1939).

# INDEX

Abyssinia: see *Ethiopia*

Africa, physical geography of, 23; history of exploration of, 23–33; Partition of, 32–3

African Association, 25–6, 32

Albert, Lake, 217, 221, 229–30

Arabs, exploration of Africa by, 23n; Clapperton and, 106, 108, 109, 110; Speke and, 177, 178, 185–6, 191; Livingstone and, 233, 234–42, 248, 251, 261; Stanley and, 243, 244, 248, 250, 251: see also *Slave Trade*

Ashanti, 91

Baikie, W. B., 29; biography, 141; attacked by people of Dulti, 142–4; in hurricane on River Benue, 144–147; writings, 275

Baker, Sir Samuel, 14, 31, 213; early life and beginning of expedition to Lake Albert, 215, 217; elephant-hunting, 217–20; and Kamrasi, King of Unyoro, 220–3; discovers Lake Albert, 229–30; later life, 230; writings, 276

Baker, Lady, 215, 217, 221–8, 230

Bangweolo, Lake, 233, 261

Barth, Heinrich, 28, 88

Bathurst, Lord, 97, 115

Beecroft, John, 29

Bello, Sultan of Sokoto, 27, 89, 97, 105–6

Benue, River, 141–7

Bruce, James, 14, 24–5; early life, 35–6; received by Ras Michael, 36–7; quarrel with Guebra Mascal, 39–44; shoots before the King of Ethiopia, 44–7; discovers source of the Blue Nile, 47–55; and Ethiopian cruelty, 64–5; returns to England, 70; writings, 274

Burton, Sir R. F., 17, 21, 30–1, 181, 213–4, 245; early life, 149; journey to Harar, 149–73; end of Harar expedition and beginning of journey to Lake Tanganyika, 173–4; discovers Lake Tanganyika, 174–6; differences with Speke, 177–8, 213–4; later life, 178–9; writings, 275–6

Bussa, 85, 97, 102–3: King of, see under *Kings*

Buxton, Sir T. F., 27–8

Caillié, René, 26

Cameron, V. L., 273

Chumah, 231, 247, 256, 272–3

Clapperton, Hugh, 26–7, 164; early life, 87; at Kano, 88–95; end of first journey and beginning of second, 97; at Wawa, 97–105; travels on to Sokoto, 105–7; illness, death and burial of, 107–14; writings, 274

Congo Free State, 33

Dakar, 25n

Denham, Dixon, 26, 87, 97

Dickens, Charles, 28

Ethiopia, 17, 156, 165, 167, 182, 200, 205, 215; Bruce in, 35–70; punishment of rebels in, 55–66: King of, see *Tecla Haimonot II*

Faidherbe, L. L. C., 31

Fulani, 71, 90

Galla, 21, 35, 67–70, 161, 162, 164

Gondar, 35–6, 58–9

Grant, J. A., 31, 181, 183, 187, 188, 208, 209, 210, 213, 217

# INDEX

421-N
6909

UNIVERSITY OF NOTTINGHAM
51 0078466 X

WITHDRAWN
FROM THE LIBRARY

D1436352

# SCOTTISH FARMING

## PAST AND PRESENT

# SCOTTISH FARMING

## PAST AND PRESENT

J. A. SYMON

NOTTINGHAM
UNIVERSITY
SCHOOL OF
AGRICULTURE
LIBRARY

OLIVER AND BOYD

EDINBURGH AND LONDON

1959

OLIVER AND BOYD LTD

Tweeddale Court
Edinburgh 1

39A Welbeck Street
London W 1

First published 1959

Copyright © J. A. Symon

Printed in Great Britain by
Oliver and Boyd Ltd., Edinburgh

# PREFACE

THE IMPULSE to attempt the story of Scottish agriculture from its early beginnings seized me one day in 1950 at a Glasgow conference, when a speaker was deploring the fact that a history of the kind was not available.

I realised, of course, the immensity and complexity of the task which confronted me, but boyhood memories acted as a spur. My youthful imagination had often been stirred by tales of the cattle raids by the " cateran " in Glenshee and Glenisla and how the grim spectre of starvation stalked these glens in times of famine. I remembered stories of how horses used to be harnessed by their tails to harrows (or their rude equivalents), of the vast reclamation schemes carried out last century, of the dire visitations of rinderpest and pleuro-pneumonia, which so sorely taxed the resources of my great-grandparents, and of the disastrous harvest of 1879. In my native parish of Strachan, Kincardineshire, old men still talked of the droving days when long stretches of the Cairn o' Mount road would be blocked by beasts heading southwards for the Falkirk trysts. Nor, while memory holds the door, can I forget the great " consumption " stone dykes and the water-embankments on the farm where I was reared and which later I myself farmed. In some parts of that farm stones seemed, indeed, to be the most prolific crop.

While the compiling of this book has been an absorbing task, a major difficulty at once encountered was that Scottish historians for the most part seem to have concerned themselves more with stories of wars and political trends than with such matters as social environment or farming affairs. On this latter issue their generalities are often too vague to find acceptance, nor can travellers' tales and the life stories of many of our saints and warriors written long after their deaths always be accepted at their face value. Although Edward I of England robbed Scotland of many invaluable records I have become increasingly conscious in the course of my enquiries of the vast amount of material stored in private and public premises that could shed much light on farming in Scotland in former times.

I would humbly add, however, that, to the best of my ability, I have tried to record the main events as I have understood them, and to give appropriate emphasis in the narrative to the parts played by leading personalities and institutions.

In the production of this book I have been much indebted to a number of my former colleagues in the Department of Agriculture for Scotland and particularly so to Mr G. F. Porthouse. I am also greatly indebted to Sir James Scott Watson, to Dr I. F. Grant, to Mr G. C. Millar, to Mr R. L. Scarlett, to Dr Gregor of the Scottish Society for Research in Plant Breeding, for their constructive and helpful advice and criticisms, to Dr Stewart Mechie for reading the proofs, and to my publishers Oliver and Boyd. Plates I, II, IV, V, VI and VII are reproduced by permission of The Scotsman Publications Ltd. I am grateful to Miss Megan Munro for preparing the index.

Finally, I desire to record my thanks to the Royal Highland and Agricultural Society, whose generosity has made possible the publication of this book, and who have graciously allowed me to make use of a chapter which has already been published in their *Transactions*.

# CONTENTS

# ILLUSTRATIONS

## PLATES

## TEXT

CHAPTER I

# THE EVOLUTION OF AGRICULTURE

The need for food and clothing...Domestication of animals...
Cultivation of soil, systems...First British colonists...Stone,
Bronze and Iron Ages...Introduction of cereals and farm
animals...Celtic and Roman influences...Lynchets and
Terraces...Domestic fowls...Rabbits...Festival Days.

MAN'S FUNDAMENTAL NEEDS are food and clothing, which
he gets from wild or domestic animals and from plants.
Search for these essentials had been his main motive
in life. It is not surprising, therefore, to find that the story of his
development provides us with a picture of conflicts between individuals, tribes, or nations, the underlying causes of which were
almost invariably the desire for more of the fruits of the earth. Some
achieved this by robbing their weaker neighbours, some by exploiting
their wealthier, while others, to whom their own country offered
no adequate future, endured hardships by sea and land in search of
plenty. But none of these fretful happenings could compare in
importance with the efforts of those men whose aim it was to produce
more from the land on which they lived. Their history is the history
of agriculture; indeed, it is the story of civilisation itself.

In the dawn of history progress was undoubtedly slow, but even
in prehistoric times there were important and far-reaching
discoveries, for example, the art of making a fire and the domestication
of animals. The latter may well have occurred when the helpless
young of a beast killed in the chase were brought to the hunter's
home to be reared in captivity. Mated to others similarly reared
these animals would in due time lose their fear of man. Domesticated
cattle, goats and sheep would provide milk, meat and skins, and
the two latter animals also gave materials for weaving into cloth.
Our earliest domesticated dogs would assist in the chase and in
the herding of animals, give warning of the approach of enemies
and aid in defence against attack. Domesticated hens would provide
eggs, flesh and feathers; pigs, meat and skin; horses, their backs
to ride upon, while along with cattle they would be used for draught

A

1

purposes as well as for meat and milk. And so, instead of being dependent on the spoils of the chase, or on the chance gatherings of shell-fish, insects, the smaller animals, eggs, nuts, berries and edible roots, man was able to rely on his animals to supply him with various articles of food and clothing and to help in the transport of his family and goods. This change involved a new way of life. Instead of living in caves and looking for food for himself, man became the wanderer, searching for food for his animals, and dwelling in tents or rudimentary shelters. To prevent his animals from straying, and to protect them from robbers or beasts of prey, he would unite with bands of his fellows and so the family or tribe became established.

Our knowledge of present-day primitive communities suggests that the domestication and herding of animals always preceded the cultivation of the soil. Man's food-gathering habits had familiarised him with plants that bore edible fruits or seeds. Thus the seeds of certain plants of the grass family would be found to be nourishing; they could, moreover, be stored in dry places and crushed and eaten when other foods were scarce. At some time or other it was noticed that these seeds sometimes germinated when scattered and produced plants similar to those from which they had been gathered. Another discovery, no doubt, was that germination occurred more readily on bare or disturbed earth, where fires had taken place, where pigs had rutted, or on land from which floods had receded and left a coating of mud.

Chance discoveries of this kind led, with the passage of time, to a knowledge of the art of growing such cereals as wheat, barley, oats and rice. How the more prolific grain-bearing types were first produced must remain a mystery. Methods were slowly evolved of seed-sowing, harvesting, threshing and storing grain and grinding it into meal. It was discovered, too, which plants were the more prolific grain producers and from them seeds were obtained for further production. To provide the resultant plants with suitable conditions of growth there had to be artificial disturbance of the soil, and, for the sown seeds, a sufficient covering of loose earth to hide them from birds and to induce germination.

The first implements used to disturb the soil in preparation for seed-sowing must have been simple ; they may have been the antlers of deer or pointed sticks shod with flint. In time this process of scratching the soil would doubtless be so extended that two persons could be employed, one to pull, the other to shove the implement used. A further development was the employment of animals to do the pulling while the man guided. As Tyler quaintly observed, " The first man who made his cow instead of his wife draw the plough was a great benefactor ". The discovery of bronze and later of iron, together with the principle of the lever, were great factors in the development of the plough. Another discovery was that a fierce bull could be converted by emasculation into a patient and tractable ox.[1]

The methods of cultivation in this country in prehistoric times were substantially the same as those employed in undeveloped countries today. A sufficient extent of virgin land to satisfy the cereal needs of the following year was prepared and sown. Cropping of the same land was continued until through decrease of fertility and increased incidence of weeds, diseases and pests, yields so declined as to make further cropping unprofitable. That particular piece of land was then abandoned and a fresh piece prepared and cropped; it, too, in course of time was abandoned.

This system is known by the term " wild field grass " husbandry, and could only be used where fresh virgin land was available. In old settled countries in Europe it had largely been abandoned before the dawn of the Christian era. Any suitable virgin soil within easy reach of the cultivators would eventually be used up, and so, unless they migrated, the cultivators would be forced to return to and make use of land previously cropped and abandoned as unprofitable. They might well have found, in such instances, that the fertility of the soil had in the interval largely been restored. Other methods of maintaining or restoring fertility to land were to top-dress it with dung or waste vegetable matter or to bare-fallow it. This latter process ensured the destruction of weeds, reduced the incidence of certain crop diseases and pests, while biochemical processes which released fertility were set in motion. A further development was the separation of arable from pasture land.

Scotland, however, was no pioneer in the development of these processes and none of its native grasses became the progenitors of wheat and barley,[2] or for that matter of oats. The domestication of animals, the discovery of different kinds of suitable cereals and root crops, the implements used and the methods of farming pursued, all had their origin elsewhere. The cradle of European agriculture based upon the above cereals seems to have been the Middle East. The development of the American and of the Chinese systems was

[1] J. M. Tyler, *The New Stone Age in Northern Europe*, London 1921, p. 111.
[2] V. Gordon Childe, *The Prehistory of Scotland*, London 1935, p. 21.

evidently separate and individualistic and was founded on the use of different plants, *e.g.* maize and potatoes in the American countries of Mexico and Peru, rice and millet in China. Basically the story of agriculture in Scotland is, in its early stages at any rate, one of discovering when some particular class of stock, plant or method was introduced from the Continent of Europe.

Archæologists believe that the first colonists appeared in Scotland some eight to ten thousand years ago. The sea level was then twenty-five feet higher than it is today,[3] while the estuary of the Forth stretched to a point five miles west of Stirling. Midden heaps of shells found on the line of the old beaches of that time suggest that these first colonists lived largely on shell-fish.[4] They gathered fruit and nuts, harpooned fish and, with the aid of trained dogs, hunted wild animals; they lived in caves on the walls of which they drew pictures of men and animals. Their contribution to civilisation was meagre—fire, the art of speech and the fashioning of rude weapons. There was little else to distinguish their lives from those of the beasts they hunted.

The colonists who brought cereals and domesticated animals to Britain probably arrived somewhere about 2000 B.C.[5] Initially they had no knowledge of metals. It appears that possibly the first to arrive had come from the Near East by the Mediterranean and the west coasts of France and Spain. Little, dark, slender men, travelling in frail coracles, they came to Scotland by the west coast of England and, proceeding northwards, established colonies on the shores and inland river terraces of our west coast, the Hebrides, Orkney and round by Caithness as far south as the Moray Firth. They buried their dead collectively in chambered tombs and so have become known as the Collectivists.

It seems that other immigrants crossed the North Sea from the Low Countries and settled along the eastern seaboard. Descendants of nomadic Asiatic shepherds, these newcomers were taller and fairer in appearance and more pastoral and warlike in habit than the Collectivists. They were wont to bury their dead singly, a distinctive pottery drinking vessel being placed in the grave. Because of this practice they are known as Beaker-folk. Our knowledge of both these races of colonists is derived almost exclusively from their

[3] Childe, *Prehistory of Scotland*, p. 13.
[4] Stuart Piggott, in *A Scientific Survey of South-East Scotland*, British Association Survey, 1951, p. 45.
[5] Childe, *Prehistory of Scotland*, p. 265.

graves where goods and food for use of the deceased in a future state were placed, for these primitive farmers were concerned with the mysteries of life and death.[6] When the use of metals became known the Beaker-folk were evidently the first of the two groups to benefit and eventually were able to dominate the Collectivists except in the north-west and the Islands.

Excavations at the prehistoric sand-covered hamlet of Skara Brae in Orkney have provided a classical example of early pastoral settlement in the Stone Age, probably about 2000 B.C. The people lived in stone-built houses, roofed over with slabs. They used flagstone furniture presumably because there were no trees in Orkney; they possessed cattle and sheep and evidently practised gelding since certain skulls of cattle had horns intermediate in size between those of cows and bulls. This centre has provided no evidence of grain having been grown,[7] but at Jarlshof (Bronze Age) in Shetland there is distinct evidence of bere or bear (a six-rowed variety of barley) having been grown and of the probable existence of pigs and ponies in addition to cattle, sheep, and dogs.[8] In a paper read to the Society of Antiquaries of Scotland on 14th February 1955, and reported in *The Scotsman* of the following day, it was stated that recent excavations of houses in the Gruting district of Shetland revealed that in the late Stone Age both hulled and naked varieties of barley had been grown, that each house represented a self-supporting croft and that food supplies may have been supplemented by fishing. The predominance of the skeletons of young animals found in settlements of this and later ages points to their having been killed to ease the problem of winter feed.[9] The art of haymaking was unknown and probably all that the animals could eat, beyond what they could pick up from the pasture in winter, was the straw from the grain crops and seaweed. The excavations in Shetland also disclose the fact that houses were provided for cattle.

Evidence of grain being grown in the later Stone Age period is supported but by no means proved through the finding of a saddle quern at Rothesay.[10] The Bronze Age period has furnished a

---

[6] Childe, *Prehistory of Scotland*, p. 22.

[7] *op. cit.*, p. 179.

[8] A. O. Curle, " Account of further investigations in 1932 of the prehistoric township at Jarlshof, Shetland ", in *Proceedings of the Society of Antiquaries of Scotland*, henceforth cited as *P.S.A.S.*, LXVII (1932-33), pp. 112, 128.

[9] Childe, *Prehistory of Scotland*, p. 225.

[10] *op. cit.*, p. 67.

bronze sickle and pieces of pottery with imprints of grains on them.[11]

The men of these ages had their day; other invasions from Europe followed; new races were on the march and five or more centuries before the birth of Christ Celtic invaders from Europe began to cross to Britain. The first band had settled in Orkney and the north by the fourth century B.C. They blended readily with the local inhabitants and formed the nucleus of the historic Picts. Other Celtic invasions followed. About 220 B.C. other groups of Celts landed on the east coast and spread over much of the country. They brought with them iron tools and probably a new breed of cattle, and also introduced new methods of cultivation. With their tools they began to clear the land of trees and to develop its agriculture. Many of their settlements were sited on the tops of the lower hills. There they built their forts and on the underlying slopes they grew their grain crops. In England the many small square-shaped fields in the drier parts of the south tell the story of the Celtic methods of cultivating land. At only one centre in Scotland, Torwoodlee near Galashiels in Selkirkshire,[12] has it been possible to obtain definite evidence of their particular system of farming. Lake dwellings, hill-top towns, forts, earth houses and brochs are all associated with the Pictish or Celtic peoples of this period. It would be unwise, however, to generalise too much on their habits and customs, their stock, their mode of agriculture, their skill in weaving and in working metals, since the period in question covered a whole series of developments. Generally speaking, however, the Celts of the Iron Age reached a fairly advanced stage of civilisation and social culture. They were skilled in the art of working metals and had knowledge of spinning and weaving. Of their mode of farming we know little. Probably much of their cultivation was carried out by the hoe or with a wooden spade shod with iron with a notch for the foot on the right-hand side, or by one shaped and mounted with iron like the Highland *càschrom*. The lynchets at Torwoodlee suggest, however, that stirring ploughs drawn by animals were used in cultivation. Such ploughs merely made a shallow groove in the earth. To ensure that the soil would be properly torn up land had to be cultivated both longways and

[11] J. E. Cree, " Notice of a prehistoric kitchen-midden and superimposed mediæval stone floor found at Tusculum, North Berwick ", in *P.S.A.S.*, XLII (1907-08), p. 288.

[12] H. E. Kilbride-Jones and M. E. Crichton Mitchell, " Primitive agriculture in Scotland ", in *P.S.A.S.*, LXVII (1932-33), pp. 70-81.

broadways. The small fields were thus as broad as they were long. Denuded soil from the upper part of the plot gradually found its way to the lower part, where it was arrested by the grass strip which acted as boundary, thus giving it the lynchet formation.

These Celtic peoples were far from being as ignorant of the arts of cultivation as Roman writers would have us believe. The descriptive term " barbarians " need not be taken too seriously

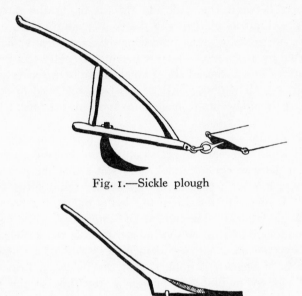

Fig. 1.—Sickle plough

Fig. 2.—*Càschrom* or plough-spade

since this designation was applied to all people not under Roman rule. The evidence of barley in the Shetland excavations, the remains of charred grain found in the Broch of Dunbeath, numerous querns found in other brochs and the fact that the brochs were always situated near reasonably good cultivable land suggest that the art of tillage had long been understood and practised.

Some time before the birth of Christ another Celtic people, the Belgae, had established themselves in the south-east and mid-land regions of England. Compared with other Celtic races already in Britain they seem to have been more civilised and agriculturally-minded.[13] They apparently brought with them the true plough,

[13] M. E. Seebohm, *The Evolution of the English Farm*, henceforth cited as Seebohm, *English Farm*, London 1927, p. 54.

one with a coulter, a ploughshare, a mouldboard and possibly wheels. The new science of pollen analysis suggests that about 400 B.C. a marked change had come over the climate of the northern countries of western Europe. The warm and dry phase prevalent until then gave way to a somewhat wet and moist period which induced a change in vegetation. Swards formed and stirring ploughs could not properly dispose of the turf to provide a bare seed bed. Somewhere between Denmark and Bavaria or, at any rate, north of the Alps, the true plough with the coulter cutting vertically and the share horizontally—thus producing a furrow slice which could be inverted by a mouldboard—was invented to solve this problem. Fragments of one of these heavy ploughs have been recovered from a Danish bog. The date of its use has been reckoned to be about the early part of the pre-Roman Iron Age (say the fourth century B.C.).

Pliny mentions the recent invention in Rhaetia of the wheeled plough [14] while a recent Bavarian publication drawing attention to significant dates in agricultural history states that the mouldboard plough was in use in that region about the time of the birth of Christ.[15] Evidence of the use of this heavy plough has been found at the Belgic fortress of Bigbury near Canterbury, while part of a coulter and signs of strip cultivation attributable to the Belgae have been discovered on a hill near Winchester.[16] Slender though this evidence is, it seems not unlikely that the Belgae in Britain were using the heavy mouldboard plough at the time of the Roman invasion. There are no signs of its having reached Scotland until much later.

The people encountered by the Romans on their invasion of Scotland in A.D. 80 were described as a fierce and warlike race, much more dependent on their herds and the spoils of the chase than on cultivated crops. Indeed, some Roman writers assert that the soil was not cultivated, but this is a mis-statement. Doubtless the Romans found Scotland a land whose flat and potentially fertile tracts were either covered with trees or scrub or else were morasses. It follows that there was little land which could conveniently be cultivated. To the Romans northern Britain was a formidable country of impenetrable forests, great lakes, huge morasses, deep-cut valleys, and high frowning mountains.

[14] E. C. Curwen, *Plough and Pasture*, London 1946, p. 68.
[15] *Hauptdaten der Bayerischen Agrargeschichte*, Munich n.d., p. 2.
[16] Curwen, *Plough and Pasture*, p. 68.

While the Roman occupation of England influenced the agriculture of that country, it had little or no effect in Scotland. The
Perthshire fort at Fendoch had a barn which was probably filled
with supplies grown elsewhere. Their forces were evidently preoccupied in maintaining lines of defence and communications. The
more settled condition of the southern part of Great Britain permitted
the establishment of Roman farms centred on villas and worked by
semi-slaves. Roman farmers drained morasses, won land from the
sea, reclaimed flooded lands and cleared great tracts of forests.
Considerable doubt exists as to the type of plough used. The
Roman plough of the period was of the light stirring type and its
use in Britain has been suggested by the finding of a little bronze
model in Yorkshire.

The land was worked in blocks rather than in strips, but indications of cultivation on these Roman farms have been so much
obliterated that it would be unwise to dogmatise on the type of
plough used. Doubtless what happened was that in the centuries
between the departure of the Romans in the fifth century A.D. and
the year 1066, the use of the heavy mouldboard plough became
general and had spread to Scotland.

Apart from the lynchets at Torwoodlee there is other evidence
of ancient hill-top or hill-side cultivation in Scotland. Rising up
above Duddingston Loch on the slopes of Arthur's Seat in Edinburgh
are traces of terrace cultivation in long strips running parallel to
the contour lines.[17] Similar traces of terraces are to be found in the
counties of Berwick and Roxburgh and at not less than five different
places in Peeblesshire, one of the most conspicuous being at
Romanno Bridge. It is significant that most traces of such cultivation found in Scotland are in the areas which came under the
control of the Angles after the Anglo-Saxon invasion. This suggests
but by no means proves that they were Anglian and not Celtic
in origin.

The fact that these terraces are on hill-sides indicates that at
that time the lower lands could not be cultivated because they were
either tree-covered or too wet. Whether cultivation was by hand
or by ploughs drawn by animals has not been determined, but the
length and narrowness of the strips suggests the use of draught
animals. The terracing was probably done to prevent erosion.
Tradition has attributed the formation of such terraces to spade

[17] R. B. K. Stevenson, " Farms and fortifications in the King's Park, Edinburgh ", in *P.S.A.S.*, LXXXI (1946-47), pp. 158-65.

culture, but nothing as to the date or manner of their formation is known for certain.[18] It would seem, however, that at the time of their use cultivators were forced, through scarcity of suitable land, to cultivate the same ground year after year.

As has been noted, none of Britain's native grasses could have been the progenitors of our cultivated varieties of wheat and barley. The wheats and barleys evidently came from the Near or Middle East. In countries like Denmark, it would seem that in the late Stone and Early Bronze Ages wheat and barley were grown to the exclusion of other cereals. Wheat at that time was the dominant grain. Later, with the marked change in climate some time before the birth of Christ, there occurred a fundamental change in the kind of cereal grown.[19] The suitability of oats, introduced as an impurity of wheat and barley, for growing in a cool and damp climate became recognised in time, but it is not known when the switch-over to oat-growing took place in Scotland. Rye appears to have been little grown in Britain in the early days.

Flint sickles used in Neolithic times to cut off the heads of the different cereals were later replaced by bronze types. The grain had thereafter to be stored in a dry place. What was ground into meal had to be artificially dried, and this may have been done in the Highland way described by Martin in 1703. When small quantities were required a bunch of unthreshed oats was held in the hands and the ears were fired. At the right moment the fire was beaten out and the hot grain fell out readily and was ground into meal.[20] This custom was called " graddan ".

In the Shetlands there are still to be seen former kiln buildings where the unthreshed corn was supported above a smouldering fire and so dried. These kilns at one time were common throughout the country. The approximate date when kiln drying was introduced is unknown, but was probably some time during the Roman period. Corn was ground into meal by the saddle-stone or merely by being pounded in a mortar. The revolving hand quern was probably introduced into Britain about 100 B.C.;[21] and until comparatively recently it was commonly used in the Highlands. Water and wind-operated grinding mills were used by the Romans but the date of

---

[18] R. E. Prothero, Lord Ernle, *English Farming, Past and Present*, henceforth cited as Ernle, *English Farming*, 5th edn. ed. Sir A. D. Hall, London 1936, p. 2.

[19] Curwen, *Plough and Pasture*, pp. 43-4.

[20] Martin Martin, *A Description of the Western Islands of Scotland*, ed. Donald J. Macleod, henceforth cited as Martin, *Western Islands*, Stirling 1934, pp. 243-4.

[21] Curwen, *Plough and Pasture*, p. 109.

their introduction to Scotland is uncertain, probably between A.D. 500 and 600.

So far as can be learned domesticated animals first came to Britain in early Neolithic times, but how they came is a matter of conjecture. Unless they came on foot by means of a land bridge, which seems unlikely, they would have had to be brought over in hollowed-out canoes. It is interesting that their remains have been found in Shetland and at Skara Brae in the Orkneys, for by the late Stone and early Bronze Age periods boats were probably built. The first domesticated food animals to be introduced to Britain were cattle, sheep and pigs. Horses arrived later, not in fact until towards the end of the Neolithic period. The domestic hen, which had originated somewhere in India or the East Indies, came here still later and was probably introduced by the Belgae about the beginning of the Christian era. With the hens came geese, but domesticated ducks were then unknown. The date of introduction of poultry to Scotland can only be guessed, but since there was some coastwise trading they probably came not long after the Belgae had arrived in Britain. As guardians of the barn domestic cats were much esteemed.[22] They are thought to have been introduced by the Romans. Domestic bee-keeping, thoroughly understood by the Romans, may not have been practised in Britain in pre-Roman days. Wild bees were no man's property and any person finding trees in which they lodged was at liberty to take both honey and wax. Mead, which was partly made from honey, was drunk on feast days. Wild rabbits were probably introduced by the Normans.[23]

Four days in the year were celebrated by Celtic farmers and all were related to the sun and the period of growth. The first was Beltane, when vegetation awoke from its winter sleep. The next was Midsummer Day, then followed Lammas, when crops began to ripen and vegetation declined. Samhain, the last day of October later known as Halloween, marked the time when the sun bade a relative farewell.

[22] Seebohm, *English Farm*, pp. 55-61.
[23] E. W. Fenton, in *Scientific Survey of South-East Scotland*, British Association Survey, 1951, p. 91.

## CHAPTER II

# MEDIEVAL DEVELOPMENTS

Introduction of Christianity to Scotland...Influence of early
missionaries...Racial struggles...Consolidation of kingdom...
Mouldboard plough...Lay-out of the land...Self-sufficiency...
English open-field system...Scottish system...Infield and outfield...Methods of cultivation and weed control...Difficulties
of providing food for stock...Housing...Celtic, Anglian and
Norwegian terms for land division.

DESPITE DILIGENT HISTORICAL RESEARCH very little is known
about developments in British agriculture during the six
centuries—the so-called Dark Ages—between the departure
of the Romans and the Norman Conquest of England. This applies
particularly to Scotland which early in the period was converted to
Christianity. The followers of St Ninian (fifth century) and St
Columba (A.D. 521-97) travelled throughout the land preaching the
Gospel and promoting more peaceful ways amongst its unruly
inhabitants. Miracles attributed to some of the saints of the period
and concerned with the ploughing of the land and the growing and
ripening of grain crops suggest that there was a measure of cultivation at that time and that the plough then in use was of the small
stirring type drawn by two animals.

From Adamnan's *Life of St Columba* we learn that at Iona grain
was grown, winnowed, kiln-dried and ground presumably by hand
querns. It may just be possible that a water-power mill was
used for grinding at Iona in St Columba's time. According to Findlay
this mill was introduced about A.D. 500-600.[1] A white pony carried
milk in wooden milk pails from the byre to the monastery. The
aged saint himself rode about in some sort of cart, the wheels of
which were secured to the axle by linch-pins. Beehive-shaped
houses made of wood and wattle provided shelter for monks and
laymen. Barley, evidently bere, was grown, hens were kept, and

[1] W. M. Findlay, *Oats, their Cultivation and Use from Ancient Times to the
Present Day*, henceforth cited as Findlay, *Oats*, Aberdeen University Studies
No. 137, Edinburgh 1956, p. 177.

cattle were esteemed more for their milk and for draught purposes than for meat. A number of miraculous events connected with farming were recorded, but the author's tendency to invest even the ordinary acts of everyday life with the supernatural, and the fact that he must have depended a great deal on tradition for his information, make him in certain respects none too reliable a biographer.

Great racial struggles were a feature of the fourth, fifth and sixth centuries after Christ. Different branches of the Nordic race were on the march. The fierce warlike Saxons, feeling the pressure of the peoples behind them, left their mud flats to invade the southern part of England where they settled, eliminating rather than absorbing the original inhabitants. Further north the Angles, an allied race of like disposition, in due time dominated the territory from Norfolk and the Wash to the natural barrier of the Forth estuary. They brought with them their customs, their cattle—incidentally a larger breed—and their implements. Boorish savages as they were, they were nevertheless great farmers. They began to clear the forests, lay out their farm lands and establish their villages. So complete was their dominance that in most parts where they settled the older place names disappeared.

The Scots had meantime come over from Ireland and settled in Argyllshire, while on the coastal areas of the west and north and in the Islands the fierce Norsemen established colonies at a later date. Traces of these Norse settlements have survived in surnames and place names, measures and customs. Elsewhere, on the east coast, their mission was merely to plunder and to harry. For long the Picts, Celts, Scots and Angles fought each other but by the eleventh century Scotland had been fused more or less into a kingdom. The Scots gave to the country its name and its race of kings, but it was the Angles whose language and customs were in due time largely adopted in the more fertile parts of the country.

Unlike the Celts, who in a sense were people of the hills, the Angles were dwellers in the plains. To them settlement involved clearing trees from the wooded valleys, tilling the more level and fertile portions of land, and separating the arable from the pasture land. Long before the Norman Conquest a well-defined land system had been evolved by these newcomers to Britain. Their cultivation was done by the mouldboard plough. Introduced from England in the first instance, and known as the " old Scots plough " or in Aberdeenshire as the " twal owsen plough ", this cumbersome wooden implement, with only its share, coulter and " cheek rack " or bridle made of iron, largely determined how the land in the lowland areas of Scotland was to be laid out, measured and farmed. Even the social customs, structure and economy of the people were centred round its use.   As it was built by local plough-wrights its design must have varied considerably, though it conformed to a broad general pattern.   In districts where boulders and earthfast stones

## TYPES OF PLOUGHS

Fig. 3.—Twal-owsen plough, Aberdeenshire

Fig. 4.—Small's chain plough

abounded it was vitally important that the beam should be strong. There were also considerable variations in the number and kind of animals required to draw it.   In the south-west it was commonly drawn by horses; in eastern districts by oxen or mixed teams of oxen and horses.   Thus in Berwickshire four oxen and two horses appear to have been a team; commonly eight oxen were employed. But in Aberdeenshire, whether it was that the oxen were undersized or undernourished, particularly in winter, or whether because of the numerous boulders and earthfast stones found in many parts of that county, twelve were used.   The texture of the land also influenced the size of the team.

In the Highlands and Islands, however, a much lighter, shorter and less effective plough known as the Highland one- or two-stilted plough—usually the one-stilted article—was used. A rudimentary mouldboard was strapped to one side. Unlike the old Scots plough it was drawn exclusively by horses, four garrons being yoked abreast and preceded by a driver walking backwards and striking the animals in the face to urge them forward. Three men were employed, one to hold the stilt or stilts, one, as mentioned, to urge on the horses, and one to lay any upturned portions of turf face downwards. So ineffective was this plough that it had often to be preceded by a light plough which merely made a vertical cut in the ground. This latter plough was appropriately called the sickle or ristle plough and was often used in conjunction with the *càschrom* or Highland plough spade.

Now that a plough which could invert the furrow and leave it ready for the harrows was being used, cross ploughing, necessary when stirring ploughs were used, could be dispensed with in cultivating the land. The longer the furrow, therefore, the less time would be lost in turning the ox-team. But even the length of the furrow had to conform to some practical requirements. After about 220 yards or so oxen were apt to need a rest, and so, where practicable, the plough-land was laid out in long strips of not more than 220 yards or a furlong in length.[2] Obstacles such as streams, springs, bogs, rock outcrops and changes in direction of the rigs to conform with the slope often prevented this length from being attained in Scotland.

Since much of the flatter land both in England and in Scotland was too wet for successful cereal growing some form of drainage had to be devised. Underground drainage, though known in Roman times and mentioned by Palladius in his *De re rustica*, was rarely practised. The usual plan was to imitate nature by providing miniature hills and valleys to encourage the surplus water to flow away quickly. This was effected by using the mouldboard plough, the land being laid out in narrow strips running perpendicularly to the contours. By beginning to plough in the centre of these strips or " rigs "—the term used in Scotland—gathering the successive furrows on either side towards the centre, and ploughing all the loose earth from the baulks or balks (as the soil-denuded, weed-infested hollows between the rigs were called) inwards towards the centre the rig was given a hump-backed appearance, high in the

[2] Curwen, *Plough and Pasture*, pp. 49, 71.

centre and low at the sides. Incidentally many writers have concluded that the baulks were unploughed strips of grass but there
is insufficient evidence to support this view although sometimes
this was the case. This method ensured that much of the rain ran
towards the baulks, and these being sited up and down the steepest
slopes quickly conveyed the surface water away from the ploughed
portions.

Two considerations governed the breadth of the rig, viz. the
desirability of having a convenient and uniformly-sized area of land
contained within each rig and the relative degree of the natural
dryness or wetness of the land. In England rigs or ridges were
often made to contain a day's work of ploughing. Many were 220
yards long and 22 yards wide—in fact, acre plots.[3] Where the
land was naturally wet the 22 yards' width might be reduced to a
half or even a quarter. In Scotland the old rigs varied from 20 to
40 feet in width and like the English ones were somewhat bent.
The commonly accepted explanation for this curvature is that it
was done to facilitate turning the long plough-team on a narrow
headland. Obviously, if the plough was to be drawn straight out
a very wide headland would be necessary. If, however, the rig
was curved at the ends the team could continue pulling the plough
much further and emerge on a narrower headland.[4] The turning
of the team at the ends had, however, to be done in such a way
that the crested form of the ridge could be preserved. Accordingly
the oxen were turned left-handed, *i.e.* against the way the furrow
was being turned. Since it had to be turned against the slope the
tail end of the mouldboard had to press against the furrow
which otherwise would have been apt to fall back. This assumes
that the mouldboard was on the right side of the plough.
The ox-team had thereafter to be reversed on the headland to allow
them to enter on the opposite side of the rig.[5] The gentle bends
on many of the old roads in England are relics of the time when
these roads followed the direction of the plough ridges.

The transition from a community system of land cultivation and
of sharing the produce to one of individuals cultivating and harvesting their own crops was a long-drawn-out process involving many
evolutionary changes. Until farming for profit became customary,

---

[3] Seebohm, *English Farm*, p. 88.
[4] C. S. and C. S. Orwin, *The Open Fields*, Oxford 1938, p. 34.
[5] S. R. Eyre, " The curving plough stick and its historical implications ", in
*Agricultural History Review*, III (1955), pp. 80 ff.

equality, first of all of distribution of the produce within a community, and later of sharing the good and the poor land, was the guiding principle. Even towards the end of the nineteenth century the system of sharing the land equally was meticulously observed in some of the Uist townships, and the rigs, after being measured and laid out in the fairest manner possible, were allocated by lot.[6] But this stage of self-sufficiency in land cultivation—that in Uist largely carried out by individual crofters equipped with *càschroms*—and in sowing and harvesting the crops, had to be modified when the heavy mouldboard plough was introduced. The cultivator, possessing at the most only two work oxen, had to co-operate with his neighbours to get his land ploughed. Accordingly plough teams had to be organised.

This led to group cultivation, the arable land being portioned off in the first instance into blocks corresponding with what a plough team could conveniently turn over in a year, or more correctly the land pertaining to a one-plough holding. Such blocks were variously termed ploughs, ploughlands, ploughgates, carucates and hides. In Scotland they became the " ferme toons " or simply the " toons " or " touns " where the various members of a plough team dwelt. But, if co-operation in ploughing was enforced through sheer necessity, that principle was carried no further. Each cultivator sowed his own land and harvested his own crops on the scattered rigs allocated to him, the object of scattering the rigs being to ensure that each partner in the team had his fair share of the good and the bad land. This was usually done in sequence—hence the term " run-rig ".

For simplicity we may assume that eight partners, each possessing one ox, constituted a plough team. When ploughing began each partner would assemble at the rendezvous with his ox. The work was done by ploughing the first rig of number one of the team, then the corresponding rig of number two of the team and so on, until all the rigs were ploughed in sequence. This ensured that no one had an undue advantage in having his land ploughed early or in good season. In practice, however, such an exact division on so small a scale rarely occurred; many cultivators possessed two oxen and occupied a quarter of a ploughgate. Such men were termed husbandmen and the portions so occupied were called

---

[6] *Report of Her Majesty's Commissioners appointed to inquire into the conditions of the Crofters and Cottars in the Highlands and Islands of Scotland*, henceforth cited as *Crofters Commission Report*, Edinburgh 1884, pp. 466-7.

B

husbandlands, each husbandland being theoretically the equivalent of 26 acres Scots. Both these terms were, however, loosely used. In Aberdeenshire the husbandland was often only 6½ acres in extent [7] and on Kincardineshire estates husbandmen might occupy 52 acres.[8] Men occupying only an eighth share of the plough-gate and possessing only one ox were allocated an oxgate of land. The same principle of dividing the ploughgates applied to England as well as to Scotland although different terms—usually Latin ones—were customary in the former country. The number of acres in the various divisions were, as shown below, different. But as the Scots acre was about a quarter larger than the English one, the area of the larger units did not differ greatly in size.

|  | Scotland | | | | England | |
|---|---|---|---|---|---|---|
| Oxgate | . | . | 13 acres Scots | Bovate . | . | 15 acres |
| Husbandland | . | 26 | ,,    ,, | Virgate | . | 30 ,, |
| Ploughgate | . | . 104 | ,,    ,, | Carucate | . | 120 ,, |

According to Seebohm the early English cultivator normally possessed besides his two work oxen, a cow, presumably with followers, six sheep, some pigs and poultry.[9] Probably the numbers of stock possessed by the Scottish husbandmen were somewhat similar.

With the passage of time modifications in land distribution took place. The chief men in a community, who at first held their land in run-rig, would doubtless wish to consolidate their scattered portions into one block. Such blocks formed the nucleus of the home farms, the acreage of which could be gradually extended either by further rearrangement of the scattered rigs or by re-clamation. Men skilled in iron, wood, leather work, etc. might find it profitable to give up part of their share so as to devote more time to their trade. In that case they would claim a smaller share of the land and barter their labour for produce. Death without heirs, misfortune, or the desire of a father to portion out his shares amongst his sons, necessitated redistribution from time to time. The fact that the land lay in unfenced rigs made this a comparatively simple matter. Still another complication arose through increases

[7] G. Skene Keith, *A General View of the Agriculture of Aberdeenshire*, hence-forth cited as Keith, *Agric. Aberdeenshire*, Aberdeen 1811, p. 76.

[8] *The Court Book of the Barony of Urie*, ed. Douglas Barron, henceforth cited as *Urie Court Book*, Scottish History Society, VOL. XII, Edinburgh 1892, p. xli.

[9] Seebohm, *English Farm*, p. 107.

in the number of families associated with townships and lack of husbandlands or oxgates to accommodate all.

This difficulty was solved by main tenants letting part of their share to sub-tenants, variously termed cottars, pendiclers, and grassmen, the former two having possibly two or three acres of land and the grassmen a house and garden. Usually these sub-tenants paid their rent in the form of services, and for occupancy they were at the mercy of the main tenant.

While in principle similar methods of allocating the scattered strips of a ploughgate were followed on both sides of the Border, the systems of land settlement and management differed. In Scotland the various members of a plough team usually dwelt in scattered hamlets, each the headquarters of one or possibly two plough teams, whereas in England they lived in nucleated villages along with the members of other plough teams. From these villages they worked their arable land which lay in large open fields between their village and the next. Such villages, even in Saxon times, were self-governing communities, regulating, through the instrument of village law, the systems of cultivation and even to a large extent the lives of the people. So satisfactorily did this system operate that William the Conqueror, realising its value, had the good sense to leave it alone. Under Norman rule and through the services of the manor court, village and Common Law were strengthened and developed.[10] In their isolated hamlets the Scottish cultivators enjoyed less protection and social intercourse, but although subject to the decrees of the barons' courts, they were more free to do as they pleased.

There were other similarities and differences. In both countries the pasture land was separated from the arable and the stubble lands after harvest became, like the commons, common pasture to the stock of the community. But here the similarity ended. In much of England flat lands next the streams were set aside for growing hay,[11] in Scotland little hay was grown. Furthermore, whereas in England each cultivator was compelled to do his share in fencing the arable from the pasture land to prevent stock from damaging the crops,[12] no such regulation was generally observed in Scotland, the animals being herded by day and folded by night. Another difference lay in the fact that Scotland, in common with

[10] Arthur Bryant, *The Story of England*, London 1953, p. 167.
[11] Ernle, *English Farming*, pp. 2-3.
[12] *op. cit.*, p. 25.

such hilly countries as Norway and Switzerland, made use of the shieling system, *i.e.* sending the cattle away in summer to graze on distant hill pastures. Even in the comparative lowland areas of Berwickshire and the Lothians the occurrence of " shiel " in place names and the fact that some of the parishes have long narrow portions extending well into the hills, goes to show that the system, often deemed to be practised only in the Highlands, also applied in the Lowlands.

But the main difference in methods of agriculture lay in the cropping systems. In England fallowing the land every second or third year was an established practice in medieval times whereas in Scotland it was unknown.[13] While fallowing prevented crops being grown on the land for one particular year, its disadvantage in that respect was more than offset by the soil being freed from weeds and rendered more fertile by means of the biochemical processes set in motion. Furthermore, in a wheat-growing country like England, the fallow land could be prepared well before the seed was sown in the autumn so that the wheat crop was given the best possible chance. Originally the land was fallowed in alternate years, but doubtless the pressure of an expanding population and the realisation that the more fertile land would not be unduly harmed by yielding two crops in three years led to the system of following the winter wheat or the winter rye crop by a spring-sown crop like barley, leaving the fallow till the third year. So generally sound was this Open Field system with its three-year rotation that, despite modern developments, it is still adhered to in all its purity at Laxton in the county of Nottingham.[14]

In Scotland an entirely different system—Infield and Outfield —was practised.[15] The infield portion of the arable land usually occupied the best and most conveniently situated land of the ferme-toun. It was kept constantly under crop, the sequence of crops varying—in many parts it was oats, oats, bere (a variety of barley). Thereafter the process was repeated. Before the bere crop was put down the land was manured with such farmyard manure as was available. Manure was applied at no other time. The rest of

[13] Ernle, *English Farming*, pp. 23, 33.

[14] C. S. Orwin, *A History of English Farming*, henceforth cited as Orwin, *English Farming*, London 1940, p. 14.

[15] James Wilson, " Farming in Aberdeenshire, ancient and modern ", henceforth cited as Wilson, " Farming in Aberdeenshire ", in *Transactions of the Highland and Agricultural Society of Scotland*, henceforth cited as *T.H.A.S.*, 5th ser. XIV (1902), p. 78.

the arable land was termed outfield. Intermittently cropped, it usually occupied the highest and steepest slopes or comprised the more mossy and moorish parts of the ferme-touns. Portions of these were cropped year after year so long as they produced an adequate return for seed and labour. Thereafter they were abandoned until nature and the dung of the animals grazing the

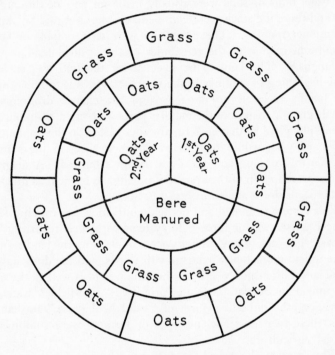

Fig. 5.—Diagrammatic representation of infield and outfield, after Wilson

| Outer circle | *Faughs* |
| Middle circle | *Folds* |
| Inner circle | *Infield* |

self-sown pastures had restored enough fertility to justify the resumption of cropping.

The proportion of infield to outfield varied according to the natural fertility of the soil. The rental roll of Coupar Abbey (1443-1538) supports the view that some of the smaller holdings in that fertile area were all infield. On some of the less fertile Aberdeenshire lands the outfield was four times larger than the infield. " Six times larger than the ' infield ' was the ' outfield '," wrote Graham,[16] but his statement was too sweeping to be always true.  Writing of the central Highlands Skene states that of the average township extending to 90 acres within the head dyke 20 were infield and 15 outfield.[17]

While only the infield land received farmyard dung, enclosures with walls built of sods were usually made on part of the outfield land and there the stock were confined at night or at midday during the summer months.  These portions were termed folds or faulds in contradistinction to the remainder of the outfield land, termed the faughs.[18]  The land to be selected for the fold was enclosed at the beginning of summer in the year before it was to be cropped.  The faughs received no dung beyond the chance droppings of animals grazing them, but the mossier parts were often rib-ploughed, *i.e.* half ploughed so that each furrow slice rested on the unploughed portion of what would have been the next slice, in the summer previous to cropping and the dried furrows burned.  A diagrammatic representation of the system of infield and outfield as practised in Aberdeenshire is shown in Fig. 5.

This system of infield and outfield cultivation was much inferior to the English two- or three-field systems with their recurring bare fallows.  The lack of any proper system of cleaning the land resulted in the infield crops being overrun with weeds, and the dung applied to the land every third year nourished the weeds as well as the crop.  The infield in Scotland was the primitive " one-field " system of cultivation, the outfield a form of " wild field grass " husbandry.  Thus these two most ancient types of farming were combined in Scottish agriculture.

Why, it may be asked, was there this divergence from the English system ?  The principles upon which the land was set out were much the same in both countries and the heavy mouldboard plough was, except in the Highlands, common to both.  The Anglian influence in Scotland had to contend with the Celtic, but so little arable cultivation was done by the Celts that the explanation does not seem to lie in that direction.  In any case infield and outfield were practised in the Lothians where Anglian influence prevailed.  The answer seems partly to lie in the general local

[16] H. G. Graham, *The Social Life of Scotland in the Eighteenth Century*, henceforth cited as Graham, *Social Life*, 4th edn. London 1937, p. 154.
[17] W. Skene, *Celtic Scotland*, 2nd edn. VOL. III, Edinburgh 1890, p. 370.
[18] Wilson, " Farming in Aberdeenshire ", pp. 78-9.

inequalities of Scotland's soils. The best land was cropped continually, the poorer land only intermittently. In the poorer districts of England and Wales, such as Northumberland [19] and even in Norfolk, the same procedure of cropping the poorer land intermittently seems to have been observed. Another probable reason lies in the fact that before the Norman Conquest fallowing and the three-field system was well established in England, while under Norman rule the systematised manorial procedure had the effect of forcing all cultivators in a village community to observe recognised standards of husbandry : moreover, the more peaceful internal conditions enjoyed in the south tended to promote advances in methods. Distracted for centuries by external and internal strife, and with no strong unifying influence such as was administered by English Common Law through the manor court, Scotland, in her independence, discouraged all friendly contact with England and neglected her agriculture, and differences in systems of farming tended to increase rather than to disappear. Nevertheless, in view of the Roman Church's unifying influence in agriculture as well as in religion, the whole matter is distinctly puzzling.

Although bare fallowing was unknown in Scotland in early times and the infield was kept constantly under crop, it should not be assumed that weed control was ignored. In fact strong measures were taken even in medieval times against cultivators who allowed " guld " (corn marigold), a troublesome weed, to infest their land. In an early law of uncertain date, guilty persons were to be punished according to their social rank. The " malar " (lord) was to be dealt with as if he were a traitor ("as he that lades ane host in the king's lands ") while the " bonde " (bondman tenant) was to be fined a sheep for every plant found).[20] Why this weed should have been singled out for special legislation is somewhat difficult to appreciate. Its prevalence in those days seems to have been due to its tolerance of acidity in the soil—Scotland's soils being at that time extremely acid. For centuries it was regarded as Scotland's worst weed, for not only did it seriously repress grain crops but its succulent stem also prevented rapid drying of the cut grain. It has been stated that badly infested crops yielded

[19] I. F. Grant, *Social and Economic Development of Scotland before 1603*, henceforth cited as Grant, *Social Development*, Edinburgh 1930, pp. 102-03.

[20] *Acts of the Parliaments of Scotland*, henceforth cited as *A.P.S.*, 12 vols. London 1814-75, Edinburgh 1875, VOL. I, ed. C. Innes, pp. 750-1.

only one-tenth of the grain returned by clean crops.[21]  On many estates men designated " gool riders " were appointed to inspect crops during the growing season and report offenders.  Two of the tenants of the Coupar Abbey estate, Symon Kergill and Symon Tailzoure, were fined in the year 1497 for allowing guld to grow on their land [22] and stern measures taken by the estate against this weed are said to have been reflected in its sales of surplus grain. The custom of gool riding was practised in the Perthshire parish of Cargill right down to the eighteenth century,[23] when Grierson of Lagg also held special gool courts to punish offenders.[24]  The abhorrence in which the weed was held may be judged from the old rhyme :—

> The guell, the Gordon and the hoodie craw
> are the three warst faes Moray ever saw.

The prominence given to the control of this weed in these early days suggests that considerable attention might have been given to the suppression of other annual weeds such as charlock and spurrey which, according to Garden, writing of Lower Banffshire in 1683, were the worst weeds in that district.  Hand-weeding may have been practised as was the case in England, but the general impression given by descriptions by travellers of Scottish grain crops, particularly in the Highlands, is that they were badly infested with weeds.  A report on Tiree in 1737 [25] states that scarcely a tenth part of the crops grown there were grain, while Marshall, an Englishman, writing of the Central Highlands in 1794, commented on the prevalence of weeds in the crops.[26]  Nevertheless, methods of weed control described in an essay published in 1735 and reprinted in Souter's *General View of the Agriculture of the County of Banff*[27] seem to have long been in vogue.  Such were the harrowing of the young braird of the cereal crop to destroy the seedlings of annual weeds, the

[21] T. Bedford Franklin, *A History of Scottish Farming*, henceforth cited as Franklin, *Scottish Farming*, London 1952, p. 44.

[22] *Rental Book of the Cistercian Abbey of Cupar-Angus*, ed. C. Rogers, henceforth cited as *Coupar Abbey Rental Book*, Grampian Club, London 1879-80, VOL. I, p. 228.

[23] *First Statistical Account of Scotland*, ed. Sir J. Sinclair, henceforth cited as *F.S.A.*, Edinburgh 1791-9, VOL. XIII, p. 537.

[24] *op. cit.*, VOL. II, p. 4.

[25] *Crofters Commission Report*, p. 392.

[26] W. Marshall, *General View of the Agriculture of the Central Highlands of Scotland*, henceforth cited as Marshall, *Agric. Central Highlands*, London 1794, p. 36.

[27] D. Souter, *General View of the Agriculture of the County of Banff*, henceforth cited as Souter, *Agric. Banff*, Edinburgh 1812, Appendix, pp. 33-85.

sowing of the bere seeds on freshly turned ground late in the spring, and the grazing of the corn brairds by young cattle in late May and the first half of June. These latter expedients were resorted to in order to give the sown crop a better chance of competing against the weeds. The ploughing of the bere crop land was intentionally delayed until late in the spring. This was done partly to check the weeds and partly to ensure that the seed would germinate rapidly and the braird get a good start over the weeds. Furthermore, before the land was ploughed with a light furrow, a top dressing of dung was applied. With ready access to the dung the young bere plants were thus afforded a good lead over the perennial weeds. By grazing the braird the leaves of the grassy weeds were cropped down to the level of those of the braird. Young cattle were used because their sharp incisor teeth could cut cleanly across the leaves of the weeds instead of pulling them up, in which case the braird would have been pulled up as well. Advantage was taken of the fact that wild oats flowered earlier than the sown kinds. This enabled the heads, when newly out, to be cut off without injury to the crop. Mossy land was often rib-ploughed and, when the furrows were dried out, set on fire.

Of the methods of keeping farm animals in these early days we know little except that the animals were grazed on the commons, their food being supplemented in autumn and winter by stubble grazing, straw from the grain crops, and loppings of broom bushes and trees. Indeed broom parks used to be common features of the farms of Angus and the Mearns. Furze does not appear to have been used for animal feed in Scotland until the latter half of the eighteenth century. Little hay was made, but it would be a mistake to assert that haymaking was unknown. The phrase " in pratis and pascuis " ("pratis " meaning hay meadows) occurs in many legal documents. What hay was made was derived from the rough vegetation found in marshes. Only riding horses received oats and even then the amount given was sometimes restricted by law according to the rank of the rider. So long as woods abounded pigs were fed on the beech mast and acorns. The keeping of so many work oxen was a sore burden on the stock feed resources of farms, as may be instanced by the fact that Rossie Island at Montrose, which extended to 63 acres of land of which 23 were arable, had to support a team of six work-oxen and four horses.[28] So reduced

---

[28] J. A. S. Watson, " The agricultural revolution in Scotland ", in *T.H.A.S.*, 5th ser. XLI (1929), p. 4.

did the animals become in severe winters that many died and those that survived were so emaciated that many had to be " lifted " to the pastures, a practice which gave rise to the terms Lifting and Lifting Day.   In many parts of Scotland sheep had to be kept indoors at night for fear of wolves.   Starved in winter and stinted of grass in summer—even thistles were valued for horse feed and gratitude to Providence was sometimes expressed for their abundance [29]—the farm animals of medieval times were by modern standards poor specimens—undersized with gaunt frames, and heads, horns and tails disproportionate to the size of their bodies. A constructive livestock policy under these conditions was out of the question; the quality most eagerly prized was an animal's ability to survive on the least possible amount of food.

From early times considerations of shelter, available building materials and protection from enemies had dictated the type of human dwelling.   In Scotland the broch, the underground dwelling, the hill fort and the lake dwelling all tell of the need for protection from enemies in Celtic or even earlier times.   Later, when the woods were being cut down and the flatter lands settled, the need for protection was exemplified by people dwelling in clusters of houses.   Lack of suitable transport and materials and of orderly rule, however, precluded the erection of substantial dwelling houses. As already mentioned, in St Columba's time houses at Iona were built of wood and wattle, and right down to the end of the eighteenth century, rooms, the walls of which were built of turf and covered over inside with plaited wicker, served as bedrooms at the so-called Highland inns.[30]

In the choice of sites for houses certain considerations had to be observed.   Proximity to the arable land, to a good water supply, and to such building material as turf and stone, timber, clay and some sort of thatching-heather, rushes, broom, straw, bracken or even divots were important factors.

The cuppled house was a development of the wattle house.   To make the cupples two tree trunks were tied together at the top and their straddled legs firmly set into the ground at an appropriate distance from each other, thus forming an inverted V, the base being the width of the house.   One set of cupples was at one end

[29] Graham, *Social Life*, p. 171 *n*.

[30] Samuel Johnson and James Boswell, *Journey to the Western Islands of Scotland, and Journal of a Tour to the Hebrides*, ed. R. W. Chapman, Oxford 1930, p. 246.

of the house, another set at the other, with a number of others at regular intervals in between, usually from three to five in all. The

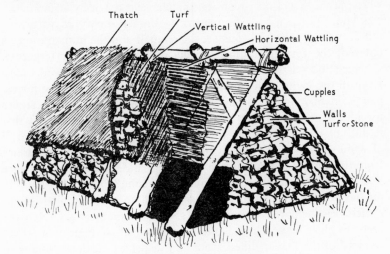

Fig. 6.—the cuppled house

Fig. 7.—An eighteenth-century Jura " Sheelin ", after Pennant

tops were joined by the roof-tree which extended the whole length of the house. The spaces between the lower parts of the cupples up to a certain height were filled in with turf or unhewn stones plastered with clay. These formed the walls but did not support the roof; the cupples performed that function. Wattle binders placed horizontally over the cupples were used to connect them and to form the foundation for other roofing material like smaller wattle sticks placed at right angles to the first laid wattle. On top were placed divots on which the thatch, held down by straw ropes, was laid. Often a rude framework of branches covered with hide did duty for a door. Through it the animals and the human inmates entered, the former confined to one part by hurdles or tethering.

Such indeed were the houses of the people in medieval times. Even in the eighteenth century we read of the houses of the poorer people in Scotland being low and mean, consisting of a few stones jumbled together without mortar to cement them, so ordered that it did not take much more time to erect than to pull them down;[31] of some of the Skye houses being indistinguishable at a distance from the natural mounds in the vicinity;[32] and of one Aberdeenshire house having "no dor, no windo, no lum."[33] In England in medieval times the dwelling house was often a clay-walled, open-roofed, earth-floored, chimneyless shed with one room. Even the early English manor house often consisted of a single hall where the lord of the manor dined, slept and dispensed justice. The need for some place to store grain safely often made it imperative that the barn in Scotland should be more weather-proof than the dwelling house.

It may seem strange that, in an age of stately cathedrals and beautiful churches, and in a country where stone was plentiful, people were content to live in hovels. But so long as war and unrest prevailed there was little or no incentive to build better houses except in towns with walled protection. In the country districts on the approach of an enemy the inhabitants retreated to the hills, driving their livestock before them and leaving their crops, stackyards and houses to the mercy of the invader. Returning probably to find them burned to the ground they would philosophically set about the task of rebuilding. Another reason for the poverty of their houses was insecurity of tenure. Once the lower classes gained their freedom and became tenants of their lords, they were at his mercy in regard to land occupancy, the lord himself being in similar case with the king. As explained later it was not until 1449 that steps were taken to protect even the rights of lease-holders.

[31] Graham, *Social Life*, pp. 181-2.
[32] A. Nicolson, *History of Skye*, Glasgow 1930, p. 330.
[33] *Selections from the Monymusk Papers 1713-1755*, ed. H. Hamilton, henceforth cited as *Monymusk Papers*, Scottish History Society, 3rd ser. VOL. XXXIX, Edinburgh 1945, p. 15.

The mode of life in those days was simple in the extreme. Cleanliness could not be practised in smoke-begrimed, chimneyless houses, which admitted daylight via the open door or through holes at the gable end of the roof, and in which domestic animals were accommodated, the hens probably roosting on the " cupples " above where the people ate and slept. Burns in the " Vision " described the poorer houses of his time thus:

> There lonely by the ingle cheek
> I sat and ey'd the spewing reek
> That filled wi' hoast-provokin' smeek
>     The auld clay biggin',
> An' heard the restless rattons squeak
>     Abune the riggin'.

Little wonder then that infectious and contagious diseases spread alarmingly, infant mortality being particularly high. For artificial light the people depended on the pith of a rush inserted in oil, or on splinters of resinous fir from mosses. Under such conditions hours of rest were largely those of darkness. At first every man was his own tradesman but in time specialisation became the rule, although tradesmen still retained some land, usually sufficient to keep a cow and produce some grain.

Some of the features of medieval times were the gradual substitution of services for serfdom, the evolution of the grange farm on Church estates and of the home farm on those of the lay lords. The time when landlords first sought to consolidate, enclose and cultivate their own home farms in Scotland is not known. In England the movement seems to have taken place towards the end of the twelfth century, and since there was at that time much coming and going between the two countries we may surmise that many of the home farms belonging to the Scottish lay lords were first established in the thirteenth century. For the support of themselves and their families, household servants and armed and other retainers, the Scottish landlords of the time depended largely on rents in kind paid by their tenants and the home farm was doubtless largely used as the depot where the grain and livestock provided by way of rent could be stored or accommodated until required. To consume the produce of their lands the great lords frequently changed their abodes. At first all the cultivation and harvesting operations associated with the grain crops were done by tenants and serfs bound to the estate, but gradually services tended to be replaced by rents in grain, in livestock, or actual cash. Doubtless the need for fenced parks to accommodate stock received as rent partly explains why, in the sixteenth and seventeenth centuries, only the home farms were enclosed.

Most of what has been written about systems of cultivation and housing was probably true, not merely of the twelfth and thirteenth centuries, but of all centuries down to the eighteenth. For the four hundred years after Bannockburn little or no improvement was effected in the way of life, the standard of living, or the systems of managing stock or land.

While Scottish units of land measurement were equated roughly with the English, some units were also equated to certain old Celtic units and these in turn with Scandinavian ones. The old Celtic term " davoch " was a case in point. Originally it appears to have been applied to a vessel of a specified capacity which, when filled with seed, was sufficient to sow a certain area of land to which the the term davoch was then related.[34] Presumably the extent of land embraced by the original davochs was no exact area of measurement but included within its bounds so much cultivated land as, along with the associated pastures, could support a given number of families. Its size would vary with the quality of the land and its shape would be determined by natural boundaries.

The idea that the davoch was associated with the seed required for a given area was evidently perpetuated, for we find, in the eighteenth century in the counties of Inverness and Moray, " daughs " as units of land measurement, representing forty-eight bolls, approximately the quantity of seed needed to sow forty-eight Scots acres or roughly the area that would normally be cropped in a ploughgate of land in any one year. So here the Celtic " davoch " was equated with the Saxon "plough" or "ploughgate". But in Strathbogie the davoch represented not one but four " ploughs " each consisting of 104 Scots acres or 416 acres in all[35]—the " auld aucht and forty o' Huntly", the forty-eight " daughs " into which this district was divided, being a favourite toast at meetings.[36]

It would be unwise, however, to conclude from this that the davoch in that area was always 416 acres in extent. In a broken and hilly country like Strathbogie it would be difficult to fashion

[34] William Mackay, *Urquhart and Glenmoriston*, 2nd edn. Inverness 1914, p. 440.

[35] Cosmo Innes, *Lectures on Scotch Legal Antiquities*, henceforth cited as Innes, *Legal Antiquities*, Edinburgh 1872, p. 273.

[36] *Illustrations of the Topography and Antiquities of the Shires of Aberdeen and Banff*, ed. J. Robertson, VOL. II, Spalding Club, Aberdeen 1847, p. 164.

out blocks or farms of an exact size. Probably what had happened was that with the development of arable farming it became possible in many instances to operate four ploughs instead of one in a davoch. Instances of the extent of the arable land in a davoch being more than doubled through wood clearance, and again of the land requiring three times the number of oxen to labour it are given by McKerral in the *Proceedings of the Society of Antiquaries*.[37] At the end of the eighteenth century Kirkmichael, a Banffshire parish measuring 1550 acres arable and 29,500 acres in all, was divided into ten davochs. In parts of Inverness-shire land at this time was let not by the acre, but by the lump, thus indicating that measure by production had still a strong hold on the people.[38]

The position becomes even more confusing in districts where the Celtic davoch came to be related to the Norwegian valuation terms " merklands " and " ouncelands " with subdivisions into penny, halfpenny and farthing lands.[39] In Badenoch the Davoch of Dunachton was said to be the " greatest pennyworth " in the Lordship of that area. As the merk consisted of 160 pennies the above saying may not have been intended to be taken too literally, but in other instances glaring anomalies were met with. At times the ounceland, *i.e.* twenty pennylands, was equal to a davoch, at other times the merkland was considered to be the equivalent of the husbandland of which there were sixteen to the davoch; at other times again we find that through the relationship of the davoch to the obsolete measurement term " tierunga " of which it was the equivalent, there were only six merklands to a davoch.[40] It is only fair to add that the merkland was at first a valuation measure and although supposed at a later stage to be the equivalent of 34⅔ acres,[41] was very variable in size. Thus in Shetland this term, retained until the eighteenth century, sometimes represented only half an acre.[42] This confusion in area measurements was doubtless the result of trying to superimpose one system of land measurement over another in a country where barriers of race and terrain inhibited easy communication, and where the supporting capacity of restricted

[37] A. McKerral, " Ancient denominations of agricultural land in Scotland ", in *P.S.A.S.*, LXXVIII (1943-4), pp. 39-80.

[38] *F.S.A.*, VOL. XII, pp. 426-7 ; VOL. VIII, p. 507.

[39] Innes, *Legal Antiquities*, pp. 275-7.

[40] Grant, *Social Development*, pp. 46-7.

[41] Innes, *Legal Antiquities*, p. 270.

[42] *F.S.A.*, VOL. III, p. 420 ; VOL. VII, p. 580 ; VOL. XII, p. 352.

areas, whether reckoned in terms of stock or people, or of both, meant far more than precise area measurements.

A puzzling feature about rentals in these medieval times is that they were sometimes stated in pounds or merks and sometimes in even multiples of 8s. 4d., thus 16s. 8d. and 33s. 4d. As the merk was the equivalent of 160 pennies, or 13s. 4d., the above amounts did not correspond with one another.[43] It has been suggested that an attempt to relate a possible earlier system of land measurement to a later led, as in the cases cited, to such anomalies.

Mention has already been made of land being valued for revenue purposes, the Norse merkland being an instance. In the time of Alexander III a valuation was made of the land to ascertain the dues to the Crown and to assess public taxes.[44] But later on it became necessary, owing to money changes in land and produce values, to make another valuation.[45] This explains why, when the term valuation is used, it was often necessary to add the words " Old Extent " to distinguish it from the " New Extent " valuation. The unit used was the ploughgate, which in the time of the Alexanders was rentalled at 40 shillings or 3 merks. It was taken as the basis for franchise, the owner of a ploughgate held of the Crown having a vote for a member of Parliament.[46] It was also used at a later date to define those who were allowed to kill game. By an Act of 1621 only the owner of a ploughgate or more was permitted to exercise this right.[47]

It was in the twelfth and thirteenth centuries that the characteristic system of Scottish agriculture prevalent until the agricultural revolution of the eighteenth century was evolved. The race of powerful kings that ruled Scotland in these centuries created conditions under which agriculture could prosper. A law of Alexander II [48] relating the extent of the land to be cultivated to the number of cattle owned by a man suggests that the population was increasing and that in order to provide enough food more land had to be cultivated —in short, that arable was replacing pastoral farming.

The Church at this period was, as explained in a later chapter, exerting her powerful influence in the promotion of better methods of agriculture.[49] The thirteenth century was termed Scotland's Golden Age, but that was probably an over-statement. The cultivators had not yet learned how to win from Scotland's poor, wet

[43] Innes, *Legal Antiquities*, p. 278.          [44] *A.P.S.*, VOL. I, pp. 11, 52.
[45] *op. cit.*, VOL. II, ed. T. Thomson, p. 4.          [46] Innes, *Legal Antiquities*, p. 270.
[47] *A.P.S.*, VOL. IV, ed. T. Thomson, p. 629.          [48] See p. 50.
                    [49] See Chapter IV.

and acid, weed-infested soils more than three or four times the seed sown; indeed their returns were often much less, but golden in retrospect the times must have been in the dark days that were to follow the outbreak of the Wars of Independence. Little wonder that the following plaintive lines were inspired:

Quhen Alysandyr oure Kyng was dede,
That Scotland led in luve and lé,               lé   = law
Away wes sons off ale and brede,               sons = plenty
Off wyne and wax, off gamyn and glé         glé  = wassail cake
Oure gold wes changyd in to lede.
Cryste borne in to Virginytie
Succour Scotland and remede
That stad in hir pirplexyte.

C

# CHAPTER III

# FEUDALISM

Celtic feudalism...Tanistry...Land ownership...Introduction
of Norman-French feudalism...Grades of society...Emancipa-
tion of serfs...Influence of Church...Wars of Independence...
Administration of justice...Duties of Sheriff and of clerical
and lay lords...Barons' courts...Church Estates...Charters,
Ownership of commons, Leases ... Thirlage ... Feudal
casualties...Laws...Weights and measures.

WHEN SCOTLAND FIRST EMERGED from her inter-racial struggles
to form a united kingdom traces of an elementary feudalism
already existed. The thane was overlord of his vassals,
from whom he could demand specific services and payments; he
could summon them to assist him in war; he could insist on their
being properly trained for that purpose, on their providing him
with certain peace-time services, and he could exact a proportion
of the produce of the land for the upkeep of himself, his family and
his immediate followers. Amongst the earlier people of Scotland
were two types of non-freemen similar to the slave and gebur of the
Saxons and the serf and villein of the Normans. Every Saxon word
connected with the feudalistic practices of exacting dues or fines
was matched by a corresponding word in the Gaelic which, at the
time of Malcolm Canmore, was commonly spoken everywhere in
Scotland except in the Lothians.

Although actual ownership of land was recognised in St
Columba's time the idea of one man possessing exclusive rights
over definite wide areas did not generally emerge until feudalism,
as interpreted by the Norman French overlords, was adopted in the
twelfth and thirteenth centuries and legal titles conferred on one
individual. While in a sense it was true that the Celtic overlords
had dominion over certain territories, they were regarded less as
landowners than as trustees for the people whom they led in war
and guided and ruled in times of peace. The social unit was the
tribe, family or clan, headship of which was by no means hereditary.
The people exercised the right to appoint as leader and governor

the man most suitable for the purpose. It was even customary to appoint a successor to the chief while he was still alive. This custom avoided any possible disadvantage should the chief die while his eldest son was still a child or was otherwise unsuitable. Usually some near relation to the chief, often a brother, might be appointed to succeed him. For instance, on the death of Malcolm Canmore, the kingship was disputed between Donald, a brother of the late King, and Duncan, a son by his first wife. Frequently a man from a collateral branch of the chief's family, *i.e.* descended from a common ancestor, might be appointed, as being nearer in degree to that ancestor, in preference to the chief's own sons or near relations. This was a perpetuation of the old Irish custom of tanistry. The people also had an inherent conviction that the land they occupied was owned by them for their welfare, and that the chief was merely their leader and spokesman. This idea, in marked contrast to the feudalistic conception of land ownership introduced into Scotland by the Norman French lords, persisted in the Highlands right down to the eighteenth century.

The Norman French lords had acquired an unrivalled reputation for conquest in war and firm rule in peace. Attracted by their brilliance and anxious that all the turbulent portions of the land should be brought under complete dominance, the kings of Malcolm Canmore's line induced many of them to settle in Scotland. Confiscated estates were made over to some of them as gifts while others acquired land through marriage. In a surprisingly short time large portions of the country came to be owned by these lords, a development in the nature of a bloodless Norman French conquest of Scotland. Their idea of feudalism was based on the procedure adopted by conquering armies after settling on newly-won territories. The land would first of all be divided by the commander amongst his followers. Two aims were kept in view, one to ensure that there was an adequate force to keep the conquered territory, the other to reward the soldiers for their services.[1] Accordingly, when the commander divided the land among his chief officers, the latter would be required to supply him on demand with a certain number of trained men-at-arms. These chief officers would in turn distribute their lands amongst their under-officers, obliging them in like manner to supply trained men as occasion required. The rank and file would be allowed to settle as lesser vassals on condition that

---

[1] Cosmo Innes, *Scotland in the Middle Ages*, henceforth cited as Innes, *Middle Ages*, Edinburgh 1860, pp. 36-7.

they supplied such services—military and otherwise—as might be required by their immediate superiors. The original inhabitants, if not eliminated, would be allowed to remain as bondmen and serfs.

The king, however, remained ultimate owner of the land; he could confiscate and gift land and when a lord died without an heir the estates reverted to the Crown. Under the king, according to the interpretation of feudalism as practised in Scotland, the lord did not merely own the cultivated, the meadow and the waste land, *i.e.* the moors, heaths, mosses, woods, rivers, fishing ponds, mountains and roads, but also had rights over the people of the land " *cum tenentibus, tenandriis,*" " *cum bondis et bondagiis,*" " *cum nativis* " or " *cum hominibus* " as deeds of the time expressed it.[2] The first of these terms was apparently applied to the lord's free tenants and would include the right to receive from them certain services and payments in kind in return for the privilege of occupying their holdings. Unlike the other two classes mentioned the freemen were not personally tied to an estate but they were so bound in respect of their enjoyment of a heritable occupancy. They could not sell their land because the lord would be deprived of their services.[3]

The bondmen, the second group mentioned, were tied to the estates. In the legal language of the time they were described as " *adscripti glebae* ", the object being to ensure that enough of the lord's lands would be cultivated, that his harvests would be reaped, that there would be a sufficiency of trained men-at-arms and that defence works would be erected and maintained. Their services, in contrast to those of the serfs, were stipulated. The bondman was thus an indispensable unit; he could not leave the estate without a licence from his lord which involved the payment of a fine. The loss of the services of a son who became a priest, or of a daughter who married, had to be compensated by the payment of another fine. Although he could own property his goods were liable to be seized by his lord.[4] Even a son could not inherit his father's property or succeed his father in his tenancy without buying a licence or paying yet another fine. When an estate was transferred the bond-men were transferred with it. Instances of how bondmen were transferred with estates are to be found in legal documents. For example, when the lands of Gordun were gifted to Kelso Abbey

[2] Innes, *Legal Antiquities*, pp. 49-50.
[3] *A.P.S.*, VOL. I, p. 731.
[4] Ernle, *English Farming*, p. 21.

in the year 1280, two crofts held by Adam of the Hog and John, son of Lethe, were included in the deed of gift, which further included the name of Adam himself with all his following.[5] In a deed relating to the transfer of certain lands in connexion with Scone Abbey the " *nativi homines* " were transferred with the lands.[6]

Beneath the bondmen were the serfs, the descendants probably of the original conquered inhabitants. In law they had no rights. They and their families were the property of their masters. They were born into serfdom and genealogies like modern stud books were kept, even on Church estates, so that ownership could be proved.[7] They performed the more menial services connected with running the lord's household or farm and they evidently could not own any property, though there is some doubt on this matter, presumably because the period was one of transition. Yet, although there was no hard and fast distinction betweeen freedom and slavery such as existed in the United States before the Civil War, out-and-out serfs could on occasion be sold or transferred. Thus in a transaction between Richard de Morevill and Henry de St Clair two serfs, Edmund son of Bonda and Gillemichel, his brother, with their families changed hands for the sum of three merks,[8] while the Prior of Coldingham purchased Turkill Hog and his sons and daughters for a similar sum.[9] The terms of this latter transaction show that the sale was made a matter of urgency. We may infer from this that it was unusual to sell a serf apart from the estate.

An inherent principle of Norman French feudalism introduced to Scotland by David I was that no man should be without a lord. This was effected by a law *De homine invento sine domino*, by the terms of which anyone without a lord had to find one within fifteen days or be fined.[10] This law was designed to afford protection to both person and property. It would be easy to misinterpret the meaning of this statute by suggesting that men, in order to protect themselves, had to become abject slaves or serfs of a particular lord; it was rather in the nature of a bargain between protector and protected for their mutual benefit. The lord, as protector, was entitled to certain services from the bondman he protected. The king, for his part, saw in this law the means to enforce firm and

---

[5] *Liber Sancte Marie de Calchou, Registrum cartorum abbacie Tironensis de Calchou*, ed. C. Innes, henceforth cited as *Liber de Calchou*, Bannatyne Club, Edinburgh 1846, p. xxxvi.

[6] *A.P.S.*, VOL. I, p. 365.

[7] Innes, *Middle Ages*, p. 142.      [8] *A.P.S.*, VOL. I, p. 94.

[9] Innes, *Legal Antiquities*, p. 52.      [10] *A.P.S.*, VOL. I, p. 321.

just rule throughout his realm. That, in his view, was more important than some slight degree of bondage to be borne by the individual.
But a man thus voluntarily bound to a lord could not buy back his
freedom,[11] the reason being that the serf or bondman had in law
no money of his own and therefore could not buy his freedom with
his lord's money.[12]    Laws were also passed to enable owners to
reclaim runaway slaves.    Yet imperceptibly serfdom was on the
decline by the thirteenth century;   by the fourteenth it was
practically dead.    The last known instance of a Scottish serf being
reclaimed was in 1364 when the Bishop of Moray successfully
proved the servility of a slave in the Sheriff Court at Banff.[13]   An
instance of the same kind is known to have taken place at Norwich
as late as 1561.

One of the foremost agencies in the emancipation of slaves was
the Church,[14] but the reason why has never been fully determined.
It may be that in time slavery came to be considered a violation of
Christian principles or that, in practice, slave labour was more
costly than free labour.    The Wars of Independence accelerated
the process.    Men would ask: "Why fight for mutual freedom when
individual freedom is withheld?"    In the prevailing unsettled
conditions serfs would seize the opportunity to run away from their
owners and join bands of soldiers.    No questions would be asked
since commanders would be only too glad of men to augment their
forces.    At the end of the fighting these serfs would probably drift
into towns and, as there was a law enabling a serf who could own
a house in town for a year and a day to be emancipated, many would
become free.    Even the fact that freemen and serfs fought side by
side in a common cause would make men wonder why they tolerated
serfdom.    The Black Death in the fourteenth century probably put
an end to the practice.    Yet emancipation had probably gone on
for at least three centuries, for the Abbot of Kelso about the year
1160 granted half a ploughgate of land in heritage to a man named
Hosbern, who had evidently once been in some kind of bondage,
in return for certain services and a yearly payment of 8s., a considerable sum at that time.[15]   This apparently meant perpetual hereditary
occupancy of the land and, if so, provided an early example of a
bonnet laird.    Serfs could become freemen in various ways, e.g.

---

[11] *A.P.S.*, VOL. I, p. 607.              [12] *op. cit.*, p. 608.
[13] Innes, *Middle Ages*, p. 145.    Mention is made of the Wolf of Badenoch's
"nativi" in 1389 : Mackay, *Urquhart and Glenmoriston*, p. 442.
[14] Innes, *Middle Ages*, p. 145.          [15] *Liber de Calchou*, p. xxxix.

the master might give a serf freedom, a third party might purchase a serf to free him, a serf might have held property in a town for a year and a day or have remained unchallenged for seven years, a lord might refuse to stand pledge for a serf or have drawn blood from him or committed adultery with a serf's wife.[16]

It may be asked how Hosbern or any freed slave managed to acquire capital to run a holding, for he would need livestock, seed corn, implements, and sufficient food to nourish his family until his grain crop was harvested. This point is discussed in Chapter IV. Evidently in such cases landlords rented their land and stock to tenants under what was known as the " stuht " or " steelbow " form of tenure.[17] By this means tenants in time acquired sufficient capital to provide their own equipment. Presumably the Abbey selected only the more promising serfs to become steelbow tenants. The present " bowing " system of dairying is a survival of this steelbow system, the bowing tenant renting the stock, the buildings and the food to maintain the animals for the season. Many serfs on being freed no doubt became mere labourers or cottars. The latter—usually subtenants—occupied an acre or two of land which they could dig and crop for themselves and in such a semi-independent state could choose to some extent when they would work for men other than the tenant from whom they rented their land.

It must not be supposed that this division of the cultivators of the land into three groups—freemen, bondmen and serfs—is an exact one. To judge from the dozen or more different terms used in legal documents in describing the people as opposed to the landed classes, there appear to have been several social grades, one merging imperceptibly into the other. Nor can we be certain of the relative proportion which any one class bore to another. There seem, however, to have been relatively few men of the freemen class.

A law relating to the cultivation of land, passed in 1214 in the time of Alexander II, is interesting from several points of view. It apparently legislates for cultivators *en masse*. All bondmen possessing more than four cattle had to take land from their lord and plough and sow it, while all with less than five cattle had to dig the land to sustain themselves. Lords were forced to provide their vassals with land. Even the date when ploughing was to commence (18th January Old Style) was laid down.[18] The statute

---

[16] *A.P.S.*, VOL. I, pp. 608-09.  [17] Grant, *Social Development*, p. 86.
[18] *A.P.S.*, VOL. I, p. 397.

suggests that while the population was still largely in a semi-servile state, many of the lower classes had acquired property, and that the needs of a growing population were making the cultivation of more land imperative.

The process of emancipation in Scotland seems to have been slow and imperceptible. Cosmo Innes has called it a great, peaceful, silent revolution which has never found its way into the pages of our historians.[19] No Emancipation Act was passed. The serfdom system was replaced first of all by services and then by rents in money and kind and finally by rents in money only. Yet it is note-worthy that Scotland, backward as she then was in comparison with England or other European countries, freed her serfs much earlier. Her air had become too pure to admit its continuance. Great changes such as the emancipation of the serfs cannot be accomplished, however, without dislocation of time-honoured practices. An instance of the changing relationship between lord and vassal is afforded by a petition presented in the year 1320 by certain men who had belonged to the Abbot of Dunfermline. There were four claims.[20] They wished to be represented in the Abbot's Court and not in what they considered to be the more oppressive lay courts; they asked to be supported if they were in want through poverty or old age; they petitioned for the privilege of sanctuary should any of them slay a man, and, if any of them should commit homicide and be fined, that the Abbey should contribute twelve merks towards the fine. The jury assented to the first three petitions but refused the fourth. To us the chief interest of this claim is that serfdom was now coming to an end, that superiors had consider-able obligations towards their vassals, and that the Church's or Abbot's Courts were thought to give fairer and more humanitarian decisions than the lay courts.

When feudalism, as interpreted by the Normans, was introduced into Scotland, it had two objectives. The king wished to have at his command loyal lords who could provide him with a definite number of trained men-at-arms to protect the kingdom, or, if so desired, to extend its boundaries. He also sought to bring law and order on a uniform basis to bear on its people. To this latter end the country was parcelled out by David I into sheriffdoms and sheriffs were appointed. The sheriff had many duties to perform, such as keeping the royal castles and fortifications in proper repair, ensuring the training of a sufficient number of men-at-arms in his

[19] Innes, *Legal Antiquities*, p. 159.          [20] Innes, *Middle Ages*, p. 143.

area, settling bequests, collecting Crown dues, disbursing whatever payments had to be made, fixing prices on occasion and regulating fairs.[21] His court was intended to be the most important in the sheriffdom, but obviously he could deal with only the more serious offences. Nevertheless in theory he had powers of jurisdiction over lesser courts. The less serious cases were dealt with by local courts, whether run by the Church or by the laity. Barons in early medieval times boasted of the power of " pit and gallows " and were allowed to deal with all crimes save treason. By the seventeenth century, however, they could pass sentence of death only where homicides were caught in the act, or where a thief had stolen property in his or her possession and was within the bounds of the barony, the legal term used being " infangthefe ". On 25th August 1679 the Gordonstoun Court, Moray, sentenced Janet Grant to be drowned in Spynie Loch for stealing a web of cloth.[22]

Thus the abbot's or the baron's court became the local instrument for enforcing law and order, and from records of the baron's court at Ury, Kincardineshire, or at Stichill in the Borders, we learn that some at least discharged their duties most seriously. Drunkenness, rioting, swearing, spreading of scandalous stories, theft. bloodwyt (shedding of blood), pursuit for debt and assault, all came under notice. Convicted offenders were usually fined, the payment finding its way into the lord's pocket. Whatever King David I's intention as to the extent to which the sheriff for each area would dispense justice and how far the landlord would so act, it soon became evident that it was to the landlord's interest to try as many offences as possible in his court since the fines imposed on offenders found their way into his pocket and not the King's. There was thus conflict between lord and sheriff.

Besides trying and punishing offenders these local courts settled all disputes between landlord and tenant or between neighbours. In latter days the courts stipulated the amount of money to be collected for poor relief or for the upkeep of the schoolmaster or local smithy. In their books were recorded the rents and services which tenants had to pay and the conditions they had to observe; they also regulated the rather troubled transactions and conflicts between the miller and the tenants. In a sense they corresponded

[21] Grant, *Social Development*, pp. 29, 30.
[22] E. Dunbar, *Social Life in Former Days, chiefly in the Province of Moray*, henceforth cited as Dunbar, *Social Life in Moray*, 2nd series, Edinburgh 1866, pp. 141 ff.

to the manorial courts in England, but they were far less uniform, orderly and fair in their administration of rules and regulations, their conduct of affairs and their times of meeting. Outwardly they were democratic, since verdicts were supposed to be given by a jury—usually of fifteen—drawn from the ranks of the cultivators,[23] but in reality they were largely autocratic since they were dominated by the barons. Far too often these lords were both prosecutors and judges and in their judgments often used no precedent to guide them as was the case in England. They were in fact laws unto themselves.

At the outset feudalism undoubtedly had a very pronounced effect in promoting law and order, justice and fair dealing. In the twelfth and thirteenth centuries Scotland was fortunate in her race of strong kings, but in the unhappy centuries that followed Bannockburn, when the central government was weak, feudalism became a two-edged weapon. The powers given to the barons were often sadly abused. It was no wonder that the men belonging to the Abbot of Dunfermline petitioned to be heard in the Abbot's rather than in the more oppressive lay court.

As ultimate owner the king could make and revoke gifts of land. Many of the Norman French lords were granted estates which had been confiscated. After Bannockburn many estates were confiscated and given to prominent leaders who had assisted Robert the Bruce in freeing Scotland from the power of England. The earldom of Moray was a notable example of this procedure. When these transfers of property were first made only the name of the territory was mentioned and no precise legal documents were drawn up. In course of time, however, written records of gifts and possession of land were deemed necessary and these took the form of charters.

The earliest known Scottish charter, made in King Duncan's reign (1094-97),[24] conveyed the East Lothian lands of Tyningham, Auldhame, Scoughall, Hedderwick Hill and Broxmouth (modern spellings) to the monks of St Cuthbert. No boundaries were mentioned but the lands in question were doubtless well-defined areas separated by wastes belonging to no particular owner. But with the development of feudalistic ideas a new conception of the

---

[23] Innes, *Legal Antiquities*, p. 59. At Urie, however, the number of jurymen was always less than 15.

[24] George Douglas Campbell, Duke of Argyll, *Scotland as it was and as it is*, henceforth cited as Argyll, *Scotland*, 2nd edn. Edinburgh 1887, p. 40.

ownership of waste lands materialised. The lords regarded themselves as owners of all land whether cultivated or uncultivated, and
boundaries began to be recorded in more specific terms. Common
grazings were considered to be the undivided property of adjoining
landowners. Should an exact division be required all that was
necessary was agreement between these owners.[25] To facilitate this
the General Enclosure Act of 1695 was passed. In England the
procedure was different for no division of the commons could take
place unless by Act of Parliament.[26]

Towns were given the same privileges as owners of land. In
their charters so much land would be granted for cropping and so
much for grazing, but the process of determining boundaries of the
land presented considerable difficulty. King David I and his
kinsmen spent much time personally surveying the marches of the
granted lands so that proper boundaries might be recorded. With
the development of charters came leases or written agreements
giving to cultivators a legal security of occupancy of land on certain
conditions for a definite number of years. In 1190 the monks of
Kelso are known to have had leased a certain amount of land.[27]

In the Highlands the introduction of Norman feudalism met
with special difficulties. So strong was the idea that the land was
owned by the people, and so attached were they to their leaders,
that even when estates were confiscated and granted to new owners
the people often refused to recognise their new lords. Nevertheless,
in a surprisingly short time Norman French feudal ideas were
grafted on to Celtic ideas in the eastern Highlands. The process
was probably rendered easier because of the old Celtic custom of
tanistry in selecting a good leader for chief. Furthermore, bondship
of blood was not always interpreted in the narrow sense of blood
relationship but of blood mingled in a common cause such as battle,
Non-Celtic families, like the Frasers, Stewarts, Chisholms, Sinclairs
and Grants, attained great prominence in parts of the Highlands.[28]
Amongst the Norman French the principle of primogeniture
had always been practised and now it was to prevail in the eastern
Highlands as it did later throughout most of the Highlands.

During the twelfth and thirteenth centuries a great wave of
religious fervour, manifested by the building of cathedrals and

[25] *A.P.S.*, VOL. IX, ed. T. Thomson, p. 462.
[26] Grant, *Social Development*, p. 68. However, the Statute of Merton (Henry
III) and the Statute of Westminster (Edward I) allowed lords to enclose waste
land provided enough pasture was kept.
[27] Argyll, *Scotland*, p. 93.          [28] Grant, *Social Development*, p. 496.

churches, the founding of monasteries, and the establishment and
endowment of parish churches, swept over Britain. Much land
was given to the Church, but the question arose as to how, or
to what extent, such land should be relieved from the service of
men-at-arms. That service had enabled the lords to build up a
military organisation which could be used to combat invasion,
suppress insurrections and impose the king's will throughout the
realm.

The difficulty could be overcome by granting lands largely
free from secular services, frankalmoign tenure as it was called.[29]
It became apparent, however, that by this process the king's power
might in time become seriously weakened, and so in donating lands
to the Church the obligation to provide trained men-at-arms was
largely retained. Instances of Church lands providing men for
military service are given on pp. 55-6, and it may be pointed out that
men from the Arbroath Abbey lands fought as an organised force
at Bannockburn. Other Church lands were assessed at so many
knights' fees.[30]

Thirlage, introduced in early medieval times, provided a striking
example of a practice intended to benefit the community at large
becoming in course of time a form of private abuse. Grinding
grain into meal by hand querns was slow and cumbrous. Accordingly, the introduction of grinding mills, driven either by wind or
water, saved much labour. To justify its erection and maintenance
a power-operated mill had to have enough custom.[31] Hence,
when an estate owner erected a mill he made sure that all his tenants
would send their grain (except rent, teind, seed and horse corn)
to be ground at the estate mill. This practice was called thirlage.
Certain scales of duties payable by the tenants for milling were laid
down. These scales usually allowed a considerable margin of
profit, so much so that millers, because of the monopoly they
enjoyed, offered high rents for the lease of a mill. Thus the miller
came to be regarded as a cheat and a parasite. The tenants got no
redress from their lord since his purse benefited from the high rents
offered by the miller for the monopoly of exacting his dues on the
grain grown in the area forming what was called the mill " sucken ".
In addition to paying thirlage, often a seventeenth part of the grain,

[29] Franklin, *Scottish Farming*, p. 24.
[30] *Coupar Abbey Rental Book*, VOL. II, p. 54.
[31] George Robertson, *General View of the Agriculture of Kincardineshire or the
Mearns*, henceforth cited as Robertson, *Agric. Kincardineshire*, London 1810,
p. 459.

tenants might have to pay a thirty-second part for grinding it, and
if the mill-owner employed a hired man as miller he often demanded
and was expected to get a "lick" as a gratuity. In sum total the
amount exacted for milling was often an eleventh part and in
Ross-shire even an eighth part was rendered.[32]

Some tenants even had to pay multure on horse corn, bere and
wheat. A tenant suspected of selling oats instead of delivering
them to the mill to which he was thirled was reported by the miller
to the baron's or abbot's court. On the Paisley Abbey Estate fines
of £5 were exacted from tenants who had their corn ground elsewhere than at the mill to which they were thirled.[33] In 1604 tenants
on the Ury estate were liable to be fined £2 and to pay double
multure for a like offence.[34] In the eighteenth century, when great
improvements took place in farming and much higher yields per
acre were obtained, the millers claimed thirlage dues not on the
former amount of grain sent to the mill but on the larger amount
grown on the farm, less the seed and horse corn. This form of
injustice brought matters to a head and led to the virtual abolition
of thirlage. Thirlage was instituted when farming was for self-
sufficiency; it was inappropriate to farms being run for profit, and
was a definite deterrent to land reclamation and improvement.

Another grievance of the tenants was that a man might have
to pass one or two mills before reaching the mill to which he was
thirled. If the mill were out of action, as it might be in time of
drought, or if the mill lade became frozen up, the tenant was not
allowed to put his corn to another mill unless he paid his own miller
the appropriate dues. Tenants were obliged to keep the mill lade
in repair and to bring home the new millstones when required.
The stones might have to be fetched from quarries long distances
away. Many of the Aberdeenshire and Banffshire mills got their
millstones from the coarse sandstone quarry at Pennan on the coast
between Banff and Fraserburgh. The mode of bringing home these
stones in times when there were no proper roads or wheeled vehicles
capable of carrying so heavy a load, was to trundle them on edge
all the way. A long spar, projecting two to three feet at one side
and possibly fifteen on the other, was put through the eye of the
stone. The longer projection was designed to keep the stone on

---

[32] William Alexander, *Notes and Sketches, being Illustrations of Northern
Rural Life*, henceforth cited as Alexander, *Notes and Sketches*, Aberdeen 1876,
p. 148.
[33] Franklin, *Scottish Farming*, p. 34.      [34] *Urie Court Book*, p. 10.

its edge, the shorter to guide it.  A rough wooden frame was fixed
over the stone and to it four to six horses were attached.  A considerable body of men armed with ropes followed behind to prevent
the stone running away on downhill stretches.[35]

The relationship between miller and " suckeners " as the tenants
thirled to the mill were called, was hostile.  It was customary for
tenants to kiln-dry their grain before sending it to the mill, but
once there the miller could make either a good or a bad job of
milling it, and the tenants had no redress.  Commenting on thirlage
at the end of the eighteenth century, Dr Anderson observed that
" the millers in many cases exercise their power with the most
wanton influence "—" I have myself seen poor farmers, by vexation
and despair, reduced to tears to supplicate what they ought to have
commanded from him." [36]  By this time thirlage had long outlived
its original purpose.  Instead of providing cultivators with means
to ease their lot it had become a barrier to farming progress.  In
the Highlands the use of hand querns for grinding grain continued
until the end of the eighteenth century.  But as early as 1284 the
Scottish legislature tried to supersede the quern by the water mill.
The use of the quern was allowed only where there were no mills
or when, as in time of storm, the mill was unworkable.[37]  But in
the Highlands, where small amounts of grain were grown, it was
impracticable to enforce this law.

Another feature of feudalism was the custom of exacting
casualties.  The king or superior could exact casualties from his
vassals in respect of wardship, marriage and relief.  These formed
one of their chief, if rather uncertain, sources of income.[38]  The
lords for their part exacted feudal casualties from their tenants
when, for instance, the eldest son was knighted or the eldest daughter
married.  When a tenant died they could claim, in respect of what
was known as " herezelde " or " heriot ", the best horse or ox,
provided the tenant had occupied at least the eighth part of a davoch,
otherwise the heirs were not required to pay.  When the letting of
land on lease became customary they could exact a grassum or

[35] Alexander, *Notes and Sketches*, p. 147.

[36] James Anderson, *General View of the Agriculture of the County of Aberdeen*,
Edinburgh 1794, pp. 47-8.

[37] *A.P.S.*, VOL. I, p. 435.

[38] *A.P.S.*, VOL. I, pp. 11, 616.  If the heir to an estate was a minor the feudal
superior had the right to be his guardian, and could administer the estate until the
minor was recognised as fit to succeed (*i.e.* till he came of age), when he had to
pay the casualty of relief.  The superior was thus as a rule greatly in pocket
over the business.

renewal fee. If a vassal died without an heir the lord could resume possession of the land. Some of these burdens operated very heavily against cultivators.

Feudalism, as has been noted, had two main objectives— protection of the kingdom from enemies and the administration of law and order. In his efforts towards this latter end David I, Scotland's greatest organiser, was indefatigable and many laws based on principles of justice and equity are attributed to him. They were administered through appropriate courts and if, as so often happened in later centuries, these courts failed to administer them, the fault lay with the Government and not with the law. Many of these laws were either directly or indirectly related to agriculture and a study of some of the more important is appropriate. In such a study it must be borne in mind that the times were primitive, that personal rights in land and property were often unlike those of the present day, and that the whole structure of society was materially different.

The first known systematic attempt to standardise weights and measures throughout the kingdom appears to have been made by David I. Doubtless to give effect to a long established custom it was decreed that the length of an inch could be determined in either of two ways—by finding out the average length of the thumbs " messurit at the rut of the nail " of three men—a little, a tall, and an average sized man—or by placing three barley grains on end.[39] Thirty-seven of these inches made an ell. In the Fragmentary Collection of old laws we find that the length of a rood of land was equal to 18 feet of a " middlin " man. An oxgate was given as 13 acres and a ploughgate as eight oxgates. An acre consisted of 4 roods and each rood of 40 falls.[40] Obviously in those early days measurements were at best approximate and remained so until certain burghs were entrusted at a later date with the custody of standard measures. Edinburgh had the custody of the ell, Stirling of the stoup, Lanark of the stone and Linlithgow of the firlot.[41]

The first mention of the old Scottish dry measures occurs in the *Assisa de ponderibus* of David I. The size of the gallon was stated in terms of a round vessel 6½ in. deep, 8½ in. broad, 27 in. in circumference at the top and 23 at the bottom " with the thickness of the tree on both sides ".[42] The boll, which also had to conform to certain dimensions, was equivalent to 12 gallons and the chalder

---

[39] *A.P.S.*, VOL. I, pp. 673-4.      [40] *op. cit.*, pp. 586-7.
[41] *op. cit.*, p. 751.      [42] *op. cit.*, p. 674.

to 16 bolls. At a later stage the size of the boll was varied; an Act
passed in 1425 decreed that it should be larger than one fixed by
David I, but even then the matter was not finally settled and, in
spite of subsequent Acts determining how grain should be sold, we
find that as late as 1807 a committee of the Justices of the Peace in
Kincardineshire reported that three different measures were being
used within the county for the sale of bere, barley, oats and malt,[43]
and that such variations were prejudicing the grain trade. Different counties had bolls which varied in size, some containing
four firlots (the Scots name for bushels), others six and others ten.
Furthermore, replicas of the standard measures kept at Stirling
and Linlithgow were found to differ in size owing to faulty workmanship. Even the Scots firlot, which was intended to be of the
same size as the English bushel, had slightly different dimensions.[44]
King David I also decreed that the ounce, formerly 20 pennies, was
to weigh 21 pennies, and that there were 25 ounces in the pound.[45]
The weight of the stone varied according to the material weighed ; a
stone of wool in the early days weighed 15 pounds troy. But in spite
of these early laws the question of ensuring the use of standardised
weights and measures for long engaged the attention of the Scottish
Parliament.

Amongst the laws applicable to the four burghs—Edinburgh,
Stirling, Berwick and Roxburgh (*Leges quatuor burgorum*)—attributed
to the reign of King David I several related to land. A burgess,
for instance, could during his lifetime dispose as he wished of land
acquired either by conquest or purchase, but on his deathbed he
could not bequeath land past his heirs.[46] Heirs were to succeed to
their father's property on the day he died. If a burgess were
compelled through poverty to sell land he had to offer it first of all
to the nearest heir.[47] A man in unchallenged possession of land
for a year and a day was deemed to be the owner.[48] Some laws were
related to land in wadset and in feu ferm [49] while others defined the
relationship between lord and vassal and master and serf.[50]

In his *Assisi Regis* King David I stipulated that owners of lands
were to use them and were not to waste lands of others or to enter

[43] Robertson, *Agric. Kincardineshire*, pp. 454-5.
[44] G. Skene Keith goes very fully into the variations in the size of the bushel,
pint, etc. *Agric. Aberdeenshire*, pp. 554-60.
[45] *A.P.S.*, VOL. I, pp. 673-4.
[46] *op. cit.*, pp. 336-7.
[47] *op. cit.*, p. 340.                      [48] *op. cit.*, p. 334.
[49] *op. cit.*, pp. 349-50.                  [50] *op. cit.*, p. 609.

another man's land without his leave.[51] The latter provision was doubtless to underline the idea that the moors and wastes previously deemed to be no man's property in particular were the undivided property of adjoining lords. Other laws decreed that freemen could not sell land, because their lords would thus be deprived of their services. Landowners convicted of treason had their lands confiscated. Where an owner had been put out of his land illegally it was to be restored to him together with its fruits from the time of the seizure.[52] Land could not be seized for debt so long as there were other movables. Heirs who were minors could not come into possession of land until they came of age,[53] and could only do so after paying the casualty of relief.

The desire to dispense justice and fair dealing to poor as well as to rich is evidenced time and again in many of King David's laws. In the *Leges quatuor burgorum* and the *Assize of Bread* measures were taken to prevent forestalling and to regulate the price of meal and bread. Standard weights and measures had to be used.[54] This King's humanitarian spirit was revealed in his new law to protect the interests of " pur folk and waik ".[55] The same idea is seen in the law compelling every man to have a lord or protector.[56] The procedure to be followed when a man killed another man's house dog, which obliged the former to keep watch over the latter's property for a year and a day, indicates that he must have drawn upon old Celtic as well as Norman French rules and customs in framing his code of laws.[57] His partiality towards feudalism must be interpreted in light of the fact that Norman French feudalism was regarded as the best means of imposing rule and order on an unruly people. His example in law-making was followed by succeeding monarchs. The law of " claremathan " is attributed to King William I. It details the procedure to be taken in the recovery of stolen cattle which had passed into the possession of a third party.[58] Laws were made about mills and multures [59] and about the procedure of baron's courts.[60] It is generally supposed that the Forest Laws were passed in his reign. These were based on the laws applicable to England but were less harsh in character.[61] The laws of this period are interesting in that they provide us

---

[51] *A.P.S.*, VOL. I, p. 323.

[52] For such a claim see p. 123.

[53] *A.P.S.*, VOL. I, pp. 604, 650, 730, 734.

[54] *op. cit.*, pp. 342, 346.

[55] *op. cit.*, p. 324.

[56] *op. cit.*, p. 321.

[57] *op. cit.*, pp. 279 ff.

[58] *op. cit.*, p. 372.

[59] *op. cit.*, pp. 435, 437.

[60] *op. cit.*, pp. 374-5.

[61] *op. cit.*, pp. 687-92.

D

with some insight into the status of the different classes of people, for the penalties were regulated by social grade, degree of responsibility, and seeming ability to pay. The old law about "guld" clearly shows this; the lord with guld on his land was to be dealt with as a traitor, the "bonde" or "natiff" man was fined a sheep for every plant found. The law of Alexander II (1214) requiring land to be ploughed or dug by the occupier in accordance with the number of cattle owned contains this same distinction. The lord who refused to give land to his tenant was to be fined eight cattle, while the bondman or husbandman who refused to obey, was to be fined a cow or a sheep.[62] The varying terms applied to the lower grades imply subtle distinctions not always easy to comprehend. Life in these early days was cheap but it is interesting to note that a man convicted of sheep-stealing was liable to be hanged only if he had stolen two or more.[63]

In assessing the influence of feudalism on agriculture in early medieval times it is difficult to weigh its good against its bad features. Feudalism widened the difference between the two great classes— the so-called well-born and the so-called base-born—but, to begin with at any rate, it promoted the observance of law and order. Yet in time the powers which the King granted to his nobles, in the interests of the nation as a whole, were turned against him and became fertile causes of unrest and disorder. For centuries, largely as a result of this, no advance in farming was possible. Nor can it be said that the feudal lords at any time did much to develop agriculture, for they held agricultural pursuits in contempt. Their interests lay in hunting, tilts and tournaments and in preparing themselves for war. What they did was merely to create conditions under which agriculture could develop. In the eighteenth century this order of things was reversed, but the survival of outmoded feudalistic practices largely accounted for the great stagnation of agriculture in Scotland which persisted from Bannockburn to Culloden.

[62] *A.P.S.*, VOL. I, p. 397.          [63] *op. cit.*, p. 375.

# CHAPTER IV

# THE CHURCH AND AGRICULTURE

Influence of the Church...Cistercians and Benedictines...
Establishment of monasteries...Acquisition and division of
Church lands...Granges—description and management...
Sheep and cattle farming...Crops grown...Ecclesiastical
improvements of land...Teinds.

FROM THE TIME OF ST NINIAN and St Columba to the Industrial
Age the Christian Church exercised a potent and beneficent
influence on Scottish agriculture. It stood for peace and
promoted conditions under which agriculture could thrive and
develop. Many of the early missionaries and medieval churchmen
were either natives of other lands or, by reason of their wide travels,
had become familiar with methods of farming more advanced than
those practised in the districts where they worked. They could
thus combine preaching of the Gospel with the teaching of better
husbandry. In the Middle Ages the humanising influence of the
Church did much to ease the burden of the downtrodden, to free
the serf from bondage and the cultivator from onerous servitudes.

Although the ancient Celtic Church had done much to promote
agriculture, it was under the Roman organisation that the Church
exercised the most beneficent influence on early Scottish agriculture.
Celtic priests and monks were both clerics and farmers. In addition
to performing their religious offices they ploughed the land, sowed
and reaped the grain crops, threshed, winnowed and ground the
grain and attended to farm animals. These divided interests
probably led in time to the decay of the Celtic Church, for decayed
it certainly was in the time of David I. Under the Roman system
the monks confined themselves largely to spiritual matters and
directed temporal affairs in only a general way. The actual work
of farming the land and of looking after the wide estates which the
Church soon acquired was done by the lay brethren assisted by
serfs and by all classes of tenants. These lay brethren were men
who, in the period of great religious fervour in the twelfth and
thirteenth centuries, voluntarily withdrew from the world and

51

undertook vows of chastity, obedience and poverty.[1] Precluded by their ignorance of Latin from becoming monks and so performing religious duties, they farmed the granges, as the arable and pasture lands occupied by the Church itself were called, and looked after the woods, fishings, salt pans, coal pits and such other property on Church estates as might be worked by the monasteries and their staffs or let to tenants. Their wide knowledge of farming, often acquired outside Scotland, stood them in good stead and had a beneficent influence on early Scottish agriculture.

Of the two European monastic orders most prominent in Scottish farming, the Cistercians exerted the wider influence.[2] They possessed more of the large abbeys than the Benedictines who, besides being fewer in numbers, were more disposed to settle in towns. The former usually founded their abbeys on comparatively unknown and at that time unsettled pieces of land—often in river valleys—which, though possibly swampy and tree- or scrub-covered, were potentially fertile and particularly well suited for vegetable and fruit growing. From such centres the Church lands could expand without undue disturbance of other occupiers. Abbeys such as Melrose, Coupar, Newbattle, Deer, Dundrennan, Kinloss, Sweetheart and Balmerino, belonged to this Order. Kelso, Arbroath and Dunfermline Abbeys belonged to the Benedictines; Pluscardine Abbey and Beauly Priory, which were prominent in the north, were linked to the Valliscaulians, and other abbeys belonged either to the Augustinians or to the Premonstratensians.

From France, where the order originated, the Cistercians crossed to England and in 1132 founded the Yorkshire abbeys of Rievaulx and Fountains. From the former a band came in 1146 to Melrose where, on the potentially fertile soil of the Tweed basin and on the nearby hill pastures, they pursued farming with enterprise and zeal. Horses, cattle, sheep and swine were kept, the art of cheese-making was developed, wet land was drained, tree-covered and scrub land was brought into cultivation and orchards and vegetable gardens established. Through industry and bequest acre was added to acre and field to field. The agricultural methods learned in Yorkshire and elsewhere were introduced as experience dictated. King David I, designated " the sair sanct " because of his generosity to the Church and zeal in all religious matters, was the founder of many abbeys. He established them partly for their religious impact

---

[1] Franklin, *Scottish Farming*, pp. 22, 26.    [2] *op. cit.*, pp. 21 ff.

on life and partly as a means of bringing law and order, justice and fair dealing, peace, progress and prosperity to the then backward and unruly inhabitants.[3] Of him a contemporary wrote: " The land which was uncultivated and barren he has made productive and fertile." [4] Such fulsome praise was not undeserved.

At first, with the help of serfs and bondmen, the lay brethren of the newly-founded abbeys were doubtless able to cultivate all the tillage land in the neighbourhood of the monastery and attend to stock grazed on the hills.[5] But as more arable land was won from marsh, moor, scrub and forest, and as the area of Church lands gradually grew through generous gifts, it became impossible in course of time for all the land owned by a particular monastery to be conveniently worked from a central focus. Land, it may be mentioned, was practically the only method in early medieval times of conveying large gifts to Church institutions; consequently, in an age when religious fervour was high and the threat of Hell and promise of Heaven confronted credulous mankind, much land was gifted to the Church.

The policy followed by the Cistercians was to consolidate their land as far as possible into compact blocks and divide them into estates with their own granges, which were at least three miles apart.[6] Where this was impossible isolated granges were formed or the land was let to tenants. The Church was always careful to ensure that it had a right of way to its lands. Kelso Abbey (Benedictine) apparently had fourteen granges while Coupar (Cistercian) had nine.[7] The buildings at each grange included besides the dwelling houses and administrative offices, barns, store and brew houses, stables, byres and pigsties, while in some nearby hollow, where water from a stream could be used to turn a mill wheel, would be found the estate meal mill to which the tenants would be thirled.[8]

Dwelling houses at the grange would accommodate the lay brother or brethren and the many workers required for the routine farm duties and for the gardens and stores. For the most part these workers were at first of the more servile type, people born into serfdom and to whom strict law assigned no rights. Nearby would be the cottars, men with a little land, a cow or two and perhaps a brood sow; they paid a small rent, performed limited seasonal

[3] Grant, *Social Development*, pp. 36-8.  [4] Innes, *Middle Ages*, pp. 114-16.
[5] *op. cit.*, p. 138.  [6] Franklin, *Scottish Farming*, p. 26.
[7] *op. cit.*, pp. 37, 52.  [8] Innes, *Middle Ages*, pp. 138-9.

service and enjoyed some greater degree of freedom than the out-and-out serf. On the perimeter of the grange lands would be the husbandmen—tenants tied to the estate, each, in theory, with two work oxen and occupying a husbandland. For the most part they lived in groups but some may have farmed individual holdings. It would be a mistake, however, to regard this description of the layout of a grange estate as typical throughout the period under consideration. The period was one of evolution, in which the various grades of people connected with the land were gradually throwing off their bonds and servitudes and emerging as rent-paying tenants, subtenants, cottars and free labourers,[9] while the arable land was being extended by reclamation. For instance, a charter conferring a gift of land from the King to the Church, records that arrangements had been made with the tenants of each plough of land for the payment in rent of half a merk in silver yearly—incidentally a sign of commutation of services. Included in the gift were some draught animals for the purpose of reclaiming the land.[10]

In the book known as the *Liber S. Marie de Calchou* we get a very interesting picture of the estate administration of Kelso Abbey estate in 1290. Besides its fourteen granges great stretches of pasture owned by the Abbey were farmed as cattle and sheep walks, while considerable areas of land were rented to private individuals for cash rents. Certain other lands had been attached to the parish churches in their gift and smaller parcels were set aside for the use of specialised workers such as millers and shepherds. This rent roll of 1290 fortunately contains a list of the services which the tenants had formerly rendered and which just before that date had been commuted into cash payments.[11]

Many cottars on this estate seem to have previously paid between one and six shillings yearly in rent and to have given from six to nine days' labour as service rents. Some were allowed to keep two cows, while the Clarilaw cottars each had three acres of land less a rood. These cottars paid no cash rent but rendered instead two bolls of meal, the boll at this period probably consisting of two bushels.[12] The Clarilaw tenants were also required to shear the

    [9] Grant, *Social Development*, p. 79.
    [10] Argyll, *Scotland*, p. 45.
    [11] Grant, *Social Development*, p. 86.
    [12] It was not until 1696 that the boll of meal was standardised at 140 lb. by weight. *A.P.S.*, VOL. x, ed. T. Thomson, p. 34.

whole of the grain crop at Newton. At Bolden there were twenty-eight husbandmen, thirty-six cottars, one miller and four brewers. Each husbandman paid in rent 6s. 8d. or half a merk yearly, and each cottar about 1s. 6d., exclusive of services, for approximately half an acre. Cottars were allowed the right of common pasture for their cows. Pannage, i.e. feeding on nuts in the forest for a sow and her young, was also allowed. The miller's rent, possibly because he could exact more than a fair price for the right of grinding the tenants' corn, was fixed at eight merks, and each brewer paid 10d. sterling a year and supplied the abbot with ale.[13] In addition to the half merk which the Bolden husbandmen paid as rent they had to perform the following services: [14]

> 5 days' reaping in harvest, four of them with wife and family, and one with two men.
> 1 day carting peats.
> 1 day with horse and cart performing cartages to Berwick.
> Tilling of 1½ acres and 1 day's harrowing with a horse.
> 1 day's sheep shearing, 1 sheep washing and 1 in harvest with waggon.
> Transport of wool to the Abbey and certain carriages to Lesmahagow (which then belonged to the Abbey).

Thus precise details were set out and it was even specified that the Abbey was to provide food when the tenant was engaged in transporting goods to and from Berwick-on-Tweed. In the latter case the Abbey itself was responsible. The load was defined as consisting of three bolls of oats or two of salt or one and a half of coals.[15] As the boll of grain was then much less than it became later, it may well be that by modern standards the load was extremely small, probably not more than six bushels. Most roads in those days were unsuitable for wheeled traffic; in any case most carts or wains were at that time rudimentary structures without properly spoked wheels; accordingly a load was what a horse could carry on its back. In this rental roll it is noteworthy that no mention is made of farm work being done by women except during harvest.

As has been pointed out above, many Church lands were free of secular obligations, but where military service was required the Church passed on the duty to the tenants. For instance, the Bolden tenants had to furnish a captain and thirty archers,[16] while in a lease contracted in 1549 Patrick Hering, the tenant of Arthurstane on the

[13] *Liber de Calchou*, p. xxxix.  [14] *op. cit.*, p. xxxvii.
[15] *op. cit.*, p. xxxviii.  [16] *op. cit.*, p. xl.

Coupar Abbey estate, had to " fynd ane furnish spere " so as " to ryde in our [the Abbot's] company in the Quenis service ".[17]

But in general the military burdens attached to Church lands in Scotland were light compared with those connected with land owned by lay lords, and much lighter than those applicable to Church lands in England. This privileged position enjoyed by the Scottish Church lands became an important factor affecting the relative prosperity, progress and development of agriculture on Church lands during the twelfth, thirteenth and subsequent centuries. While cultivation on secular lands was often interrupted by men being called up for military purposes, such interference was rarer on Church lands. Furthermore, invading armies might lay waste the land, houses and crops of their enemies, but up to the fourteenth century to do so on Church lands, even within the confines of an enemy's country, laid the invaders open to stiff claims for damages. So great was the power and prestige of the Church that these damages had to be paid, although in the process Peter was often robbed to pay Paul. Thus more stock would be taken from the enemy's country to replace stock seized from Church lands.

Many changes were taking place towards the end of the thirteenth century. Serfs were gradually being emancipated and acquiring capital of their own : at Revelden on the Kelso Abbey estate each emancipated serf selected to become a tenant was provided with two oxen, a horse, three chalders of oats, six bolls of barley and three of wheat, with the necessary implements.[18] This stock remained the property of the Abbey, which required as rent half of the produce of the holding. From the remaining half the tenant was able gradually to acquire capital. In course of time this Stuht or Steelbow form of tenure was withdrawn and the land was let in the usual way. About the year 1290 service rents at this grange were withdrawn and commuted into a cash rent payment of 18s.[19]

By this time the Border abbeys were keeping large numbers of sheep. Kelso Abbey had 6600 exclusive of some unnumbered flocks; the grange at Newton had 1000 ewes, that of Sprouston 300 hoggs, while at Colpinhope there were 500 ewes and 200 dinmonts.[20] The Lammermoor estate of Spertildon and Bothkill carried 1400 sheep and Melrose Abbey is said to have owned 12,000.

---

[17] *Coupar Abbey Rental Book*, VOL. II, p. 54.
[18] *Liber de Calchou*, p. xxxiv.
[19] *ibid.*        [20] *op. cit.*, p. xxxiii.

From the numbers kept, the careful arrangements of folds on the grazings and the various terms used in these old documents, it may be surmised that sheep farming was then well understood. The wool was purchased by Italian, French and Flemish buyers and was a considerable source of revenue to these Border monasteries. So much importance was attached to the wool trade of the two countries in the thirteenth century that Italian merchants compiled a register of the total yearly amount of sacks of wool that might be purchased from monastic houses in England and Scotland.[21]

Sheep on the Border hills would seem to have been folded at night, but many may have been housed as was the case in the Highlands where all were housed. Incidentally wolves—the main reason for sheep being housed—were not exterminated in the Highlands until about 1743. Sheep suffered at that time from many of our present-day diseases. Scab, a common trouble, was mistakenly attributed to hoar frosts and so sheep were not allowed outside the fold until the sun had melted the frost. Probably there was some confusion between braxy and scab. About 1296 exports of wool and skins from the Border abbeys dropped to one-sixth of their former value. This was largely ascribed to a bad outbreak of scab, but the unsettling effect of the Wars of Independence undoubtedly contributed. Liver rot was rightly ascribed to grazing on marshy areas; it was thought, however, that the sheep contracted the trouble through eating the water snail. Technical knowledge of sheep husbandry was surprisingly high in the Borders.

Cattle were mainly kept for draught purposes, the chief function of the cow being to breed plough oxen. Kelso Abbey, for instance, had 80 cows at Witelaw. In William the Lion's time the monks of Melrose were allowed a vaccarium of 100 cattle at Threpwood,[22] while at Bolden the numbers exceeded 400.[23] For tenants, husbandmen and cottars, cattle were more important than sheep. The latter were kept largely for their milk and wool, which was spun and woven in the homes of the tenants, but the Abbeys were often glad to buy surplus wool from their tenants. They sometimes sold wool for forward delivery and in bad years may have had difficulty in fulfilling orders. The customary clip of a sheep was then very much smaller than it is now and amounted probably to not more than $1\frac{1}{2}$ lb. The monks of Melrose also kept a stud of horses, for

[21] Franklin, *Scottish Farming*, pp. 77-81.
[22] *A.P.S.*, VOL. I, p. 387.
[23] Franklin, *Scottish Farming*, p. 52.

we read that Patrick, Earl of Dunbar, in preparation for his departure to the Holy Land in the thirteenth century, sold to the monks of Melrose his stud of brood mares in Lauderdale for the then considerable sum of one hundred merks sterling.[24]

Wheat, barley, rye and oats were all grown on monastery lands in the Borders. Evidence of this is furnished in a claim made by the Abbot of Coldingham against the invading army of Edward I. The claim was for 48 quarters of wheat, 40 of rye, 56 of barley and 80 of oats. Such was the prestige and power of the Church that the claim was admitted and the grain losses made good with grain and malt from England. Other losses in livestock were also made good.[25] The figures for the damaged crops of Coldingham Abbey afford some indication of the proportions which the various cereals bore to one another at this centre. From other sources we learn that, except in some areas south of the Forth, wheat was not extensively grown, but even in those early days it was grown in Moray.[26]

The oat commonly grown was the grey oat, *Avena strigosa*. It had long awns, small grains and a larger percentage of husk to kernel than the white oat which tradition says was introduced in the seventeenth century. It must, however, have been introduced before that time, for as early as the year 1548 John Thome, a tenant on the Coupar Abbey estate, had to provide five bolls of " quhyt aitis " (white oats) as part of his rent.[27] Probably the grey oats, in those days when the land was invariably dirty and impoverished, suited farmers better than the white varieties. Most of the grain described in records as barley was probably the six-rowed variety known as bere or bear. Being more tolerant of soil acidity, it was then more suitable for Scottish conditions than the two-row variety which apparently did not come into common use until liming was practised.

In these medieval times the monks were pioneers in land improvement and had sufficient knowledge, wealth and command of labour to enable them to embark on extensive projects. In the early part of the thirteenth century an ambitious drainage scheme to convert an extensive morass into dry land was successfully undertaken at Inchaffray in Perthshire. At Holyrood another scheme freed the

---

[24] Innes, *Middle Ages*, p. 131.
[25] Franklin, *Scottish Farming*, p. 42.
[26] Innes, *Middle Ages*, p. 145.
[27] *Coupar Abbey Rental Book*, VOL. II, pp. 47, 48, 122.

wet land in the vicinity from water.[28]  At Bele in East Lothian a stream was straightened to prevent flooding.[29]  Ettrick Forest, described by Alexander II who donated it in 1235 to Melrose Abbey as "my whole waste of Ettrick," was later so improved that it commanded a rent of £66—a considerable sum in those days—for sheep pasture.[30]  We shall see later[31] how careful the Coupar Abbey estate was to ensure that ditches were kept clean and land not spoiled by being too wet, and how land was to be won from the mire by being drained under the supervision of the Abbey drainage expert.[32]  But land reclamation in medieval times was not the sole prerogative of the Church.  Trees were being cut down by lay landlords and tenants for building and for fuel, while fresh virgin land was being broken up and added to the arable acreage.  For instance, land at Ednam in the Merse was being broken in by a man called Thor, who had received it in gift from King Edgar about the year 1105.  In the deed of gift the land was described as desert.[33]  The Act of Alexander II in 1214 about the ploughing and digging of land suggests that private reclamation was under way in the thirteenth century and that Scotland was gradually passing from a pastoral to a more arable form of agriculture.

Fruit and vegetables were actively cultivated in the gardens attached to abbeys and priories.  Many of the monks hailed from countries where horticulture was well developed and so would miss their apples, pears, and lettuces and their herbs, medicinal or flavorous.  Kinloss Abbey engaged a French gardener about 1540.[34]  Some monks were skilled in bee-keeping, the bees providing wax for candles and also honey, which was the principal sweetening agent for food.  Although some of the kings were interested in gardening, notably David I and Alexander III, the nobility as a rule were so occupied with field sports and preparations for war that they had little or no interest in horticulture.  Indeed at their grim castles gardening would have been strangely out of place, so the Church alone was left to promote developments.  The nobility's contempt of bucolic pursuits is reflected in their heraldry.

In another direction the monks seem to have acted as pioneers.  By the thirteenth century the forests that had at one time covered

---

[28] G. G. Coulton, *Scottish Abbeys and Social Life*, henceforth cited as Coulton, *Scottish Abbeys*, Cambridge 1933, p. 122.

[29] Innes, *Middle Ages*, p. 147.

[30] Franklin, *Scottish Farming*, p. 28.  [31] See p. 75.

[32] *Coupar Abbey Rental Book*, VOL. I, pp. 142, 172.

[33] Coulton, *Scottish Abbeys*, p. 122.  [34] *op. cit.*, p. 120.

most of Scotland's surface were being thinned out.  The monks had used much of the best timber to build their fine cathedrals, abbeys etc., while both the Church and the common people had cut down trees to clear land for crops and to provide firewood.  The practice of allowing stock to graze the common pastures meant that there could be little natural regeneration of woods.  A tree cut down was not usually replaced, and it was therefore to the credit of the monks, who realised that in time Scotland would become treeless, that steps were taken not merely to protect existing woods but also to plant trees.  These measures, however, relate more particularly to the fifteenth and sixteenth centuries.[35]

Accordingly in a variety of ways the Church in the twelfth and thirteenth centuries did much to stimulate agriculture.  It drained and reclaimed land, provided buildings laid out in orderly fashion, and enabled the lower ranks of rural society to shake off the bonds of serfdom.  It eased the burden of servitude and assisted emancipated slaves to acquire capital and become independent.[36]  Through the Church courts the laws of the land were administered and disputes settled.  We have seen how one law was concerned with the cultivation of land and another with the destruction of that troublesome weed, the " gule ".  It was probably largely due to the representation of the Church in Parliament at a later date that measures designed to further agricultural interests were passed.  When through lack of lay brethren and servile workers most of the granges of Church estates had to be let out to tenants, the same helpful attitude towards agriculture was observed.  This matter will be dealt with in Chapter V, but meantime it may be mentioned that on the extensive estates of Coupar Abbey everything possible was done to promote good farming as then understood.  Drainage and reclamations were encouraged; measures were taken to suppress certain weeds and harmful birds and animals; tenants were given leases of holdings at reasonable rents; aged tenants were helped; the planting of trees, including fruit trees and hedges, was encouraged and even the consolidation of scattered run-rig land was commended.

We now come to the question of teinds.  The early Christian Church had commended the old Jewish custom of setting aside for

---

[35] Franklin, *Scottish Farming*, pp. 59-60.

[36] In this respect, however, its influence may have been overstressed.  Coulton has pointed out that the Church clung longest to lordship over the persons of tillers of the soil : *Scottish Abbeys*, p. 124.

religious purposes the tenth part of the produce of the land, whether in the form of grain, fruit, stock or stock products. In Scotland this tenth or tithe was known as teind. When the Norman nobles whom David I invited to Scotland founded or erected churches on their estates they assigned to them the teinds. The manor or land tithed to its church became a parish. It became the custom, however, to grant parish churches to monasteries or cathedral chapters. For instance in 1150 Holyrood Abbey was made the recipient of half the teinds of Argyll, while it has been calculated that 678 of the 940 parishes in Scotland had by the Reformation been annexed to larger Church institutions, *e.g.* the abbeys, leaving only about 262 as independent parsonages.[37] Such an arrangement was far from satisfactory. It meant that the collecting body—the owners of the teinds—often distributed the proceeds of the teinds as they saw fit : so much, and often too little, for the upkeep of the parish churches and their incumbents, the vicars ; so much for other parish purposes as, for instance, the poor ; so much for bishops' dues and so much for their own particular purposes. Even in the thirteenth century, when the larger institutions like the abbeys were being supported most generously and there was no excuse for owners of teinds—usually these institutions—to withhold a proper share of the teind income from the parish priests, we find William the Lion decreeing that the revenues of parish churches should be used for the proper remuneration of the incumbents and for the payment of the bishops' dues.[38] So poorly paid were the parish priests that illiterate men were often appointed, and we learn that Pope Innocent III complained about this procedure.

Probably to ensure a fair means of distribution teinds were classified in three categories, the Greater, the Small and the Mixed teinds,[39] the proceeds of each often being specifically earmarked. Thus the proceeds of the Greater Teinds, the tenth sheaf of grain or produce of the crop (*decimae bladi*) might be allocated to the rector, or the cathedral or monastery, *i.e.* some person or body outside the parish. The Small Teinds—the tenth part of the young of animals and of the produce of farm animals—butter, cheese, eggs, wool—were usually earmarked for the parish incumbent. To obviate the difficulty of collecting the young animals when fewer than ten of a kind had been produced within the year, a system of

[37] Ninian Hill, *The Story of the Scottish Church from the Earliest Times,* Glasgow 1919, p. 140.

[38] *A.P.S.*, VOL. I, p. 90.          [39] Franklin, *Scottish Farming*, p. 49.

cash and kind equivalents was used. Thus a man whose stock had
produced only one foal or three calves or six lambs within the year
might find it convenient to pay his Small Teinds in the form of
cash, etc. If there were eight lambs an eighth lamb might be taken
but the farmer was allowed two-tenths of the value of a lamb.
However, information on the exact procedure is scanty.[40] The
Mixed Teinds consisted of fish, spoils of the chase, proceeds from
the mills, peats, etc.[41] For instance Arbroath Abbey, which owned
the teinds of Inverness, derived a considerable income from the
herring caught by Inverness fishermen.

While the above allocation of the teinds may have been generally
adopted, it was unfortunately true that time and again in later
centuries the vicars or parish priests were often shabbily dealt with.
Doubtless, following representations, the distribution might sometimes be rearranged. Cosmo Innes gives details of such a rearrangement between the vicar of Inverness and the Abbey of Arbroath,
the owner of the teinds. The vicar was to have the Small Teinds,
the Abbot the Great Teinds along with the teinds of the mill and
herrings, three merks from the Lent offerings and the income from
the lands belonging to the Church at Inverness. But the Abbot
was bound to see to the proper service of the church at Inverness
and of its chapels at Petty, etc. This latter condition was somewhat
ambiguous in its terms.[42]

The method of collecting teinds often caused much disagree-
ment and resentment. Every tenth sheaf had to be set aside and,
as may be imagined, the size of the sheaf was often in dispute,
particularly when the collection was done by a " tacksman of the
teinds ", i.e. someone who rented the privilege of collecting them.
But the manner of collection aroused even greater resentment. No
sheaves could be stacked until the teind sheaves had been collected.
The poor cultivators were thus often chagrined to find that they
could not rick their crops when the weather was good. They had
to await the convenience of the collector and so the grain crop was
often damaged before it could be secured. To obviate this difficulty
the Coupar Abbey estate, who owned their own teinds, often

[40] It would appear that tithes of eggs were calculated on the assumption
that a hen laid, exclusive of hatching eggs, twenty in a year. In that case two eggs
were paid. The tithe for cheese was often 14 out of 140 days' cheese making.
John Dowden, *The Medieval Church in Scotland*, Glasgow 1910, pp. 171-2.

[41] Franklin, *Scottish Farming*, p. 49.

[42] Innes, *Legal Antiquities*, pp. 194-5.

stipulated that they should be collected in the form of grain, definite amounts being stated in the leases.[43]

At the Reformation there was much discontent concerning the ownership, manner of collection and distribution of teinds. The story of the teinds for the first sixty or seventy years after that event —a story that makes shameful reading—is discussed in Chapter V.

[43] *Coupar Abbey Rental Book*, VOL. II, pp. 211-20.

CHAPTER V

# THE FOURTEENTH TO SIXTEENTH CENTURIES

Unrest after Bannockburn...Confiscation of estates...Tenure
of tenants...An early lease...Tacksmen, Kindly tenants...
Crown and Church leases...Grassums...Monastic estate
administration...Division of former granges...Establishment
of self-contained unit farms...Cash, kind and service rents...
Laws relating to agriculture...Church estate regulations...
Rack-renting...Evictions...Frequency of dearth years...
Teinds...Feuing system...Development on Church and Crown
estates...Causes of disorder...Complaints by tenants...Effects
of Reformation...Negligible advances in agriculture...Gradual
drift from self-sufficiency towards production for sale.

THE PERIOD FOLLOWING the twelfth and thirteenth centuries
—the so-called Golden Age of Scotland—was one of great
turmoil, unrest and lawlessness and saw little progress in
agriculture.    At its beginning Scotland was engaged in a long and
bitter struggle with England which, though it quickened the patriotic
fervour of the Scots, aroused passions not easily quelled.   Bannockburn, while securing independence for Scotland, was not the
harbinger of stable government or progress in agriculture.    For
the next three centuries the country was in a state of almost constant
disorder.   The three kings who followed Robert the Bruce were
weaklings and allowed the nobles to get out of hand.   Feudalism,
which in the preceding centuries had done so much to promote law
and order, was far too often by this time having the opposite effect.
The nobles frequently abused their powers; they oppressed their
inferiors, ignored their superiors and quarrelled with each other.
If they were not at variance with their King they were frequently
on bad terms with their neighbours.

   In the wars with England the land as far north as Edinburgh
was repeatedly pillaged and laid waste.   In 1544 over 10,000 cattle
were seized by English soldiers; ripe but uncut fields of grain were
methodically set on fire and even the abbeys, practically sacrosanct
in earlier days, were sacked and destroyed.   In 1523 Lord Dacre

burned Kelso Abbey, which was further maltreated in 1545 by that
" scourge of Scotland " the Earl of Hertford. At that time Melrose,
Dryburgh, Jedburgh and Kelso Abbeys, and Coldingham Priory
were destroyed, along with 5 towns, 243 villages and 16 fortified
places. In the intervals between the wars Border adventurers
habitually raided the land of their traditional enemies; and raiding
was not confined to the pillaging of stock belonging to owners on
the other side of the Border; the Border lairds would steal stock
from each other, and it was reckoned a feat for stolen animals to be
safely hidden before daybreak in some secluded hollow in the hills.
Many Border men subsisted by plunder. James V hanged forty-
eight notable Border thieves in June 1529, one of them the notorious
Johnnie Armstrong. Cattle-lifting in the Highlands was even
esteemed a gentleman's occupation. No thought of breaking the
Eighth Commandment disturbed the " wild wikkid Highlandmen "
who raided the Lowlands, driving back animals that could travel
fast and maiming those that could not.

After Bannockburn the estates of the Comyns, the Balliols and
other nobles who had sided with the English were confiscated and
granted by Robert the Bruce to his most prominent and loyal
followers.[1] These new owners had the right to dispossess tenants
who had occupied land by arrangement with the previous owners.
This right of dispossession is shown in the first preserved specimen
of a written lease in Scotland. It was a thirty years' lease between
the Abbot of Scone and two men, a father and son of the name
of De Hay del Leys.[2] The subject in question was the lands of
Balgarvie in Perthshire and the date of the lease was 1312. One
of its clauses runs as follows:—" And if our Lord the King shall
happen to revoke the gift of the said land from the said Abbot and
convent, the said Edmund, William, heirs of the said William, and
their husbandmen [i.e. their subtenants] shall quit without having
to pay the rent of the year of their quitting ". Besides underlining
the uncertainty of tenure [3] this lease has other significant features.
For instance, it is what might be termed an improving lease. The
rent payable for the first two years was to be two merks a year; it
then rose to three and by gradations to ten merks a year at which
it remained from the twenty-first year until the lease ended. The

[1] Innes, *Legal Antiquities*, p. 39.
[2] Argyll, *Scotland*, p. 96.
[3] Tenants could also be evicted for non-fulfilment of services, and for committing
certain offences, *e.g.* murder and in some cases adultery. When a tenant died
without heirs his land reverted to his lord.

E

object of this lease was not stated, but doubtless it was granted for the purpose of reclaiming land. It would thus appear that much of the potential arable land in Scotland at this period was marsh, moorland or scrub wood. The monks had certainly done much to reclaim land on their estates during the previous century, so also had Alexander II and Alexander III, grain in their reigns being plentiful and cheap. But evidently the work had not been completed.

Another feature of the lease was that the tenant had husbandmen as subtenants, thus providing an example of what was afterwards known as a tacksman's lease. A tacksman was one who normally rented a considerable area of land, and who was allowed to have subtenants from whom he collected rents and arranged terms of occupancy without reference to the owner. Usually he was responsible for settling disputes and maintaining law and order amongst his own tenantry, and in this case the Hays were obliged to settle all minor disputes, etc. among their tenants. In a sense many husbandmen of the time were small tacksmen, since they often accommodated subtenants and cottars on their holdings. All tenants, including the Hays themselves, had to have their grain ground at the Abbey mill, but the rates of multure (miller's fees) varied as between the Hays and their subtenants. The former, being specially privileged, paid as milling dues only one twenty-fourth part, the latter one-sixteenth part. The lease stipulated that all tenants were to do suit at the Abbot's Court three times a year. There they acted as jurymen in disputes and such offences as could be appropriately dealt with. The Hays were to provide competent buildings for themselves and their husbandmen and to leave them in proper condition without compensation at way-go. Probably the houses were made largely of turf, undressed stone, clay, wood and wattle. This stipulation is interesting since the practice of a Scottish landlord to provide houses for his tenants did not become customary until fully five centuries later. The rights and privileges of the procurement of fuel were at this period jealously guarded. So scarce had trees become in most parts that peat and turf were used exclusively for fuel. This explains why the tenants and subtenants were to be allowed to procure fuel for their own use but not for sale.

This lease provides an interesting picture of the definitiveness of an early contract of the kind. All the essential features are there —tenure, the rent payable, the provision of permanent equipment and its disposal at way-go, thirlage to the Abbot's mill, forensic services at his court, provision for the settlement of disputes, fuel rights and restrictions on rights of occupancy. The area of land covered by the lease is not disclosed, but the fact that the final rent amounted to only ten merks a year, considered in relation to rents ruling for husbandlands elsewhere about that time, suggests that the extent was at least a ploughgate. Probably part was divided into husbandlands and part retained by the Hays for their own occupation.

Most leases in these early times were merely recorded in estate rental books. Their terms were disclosed at the meetings of the abbot's or baron's courts. But certain symbolic features in the granting or breaking off of a lease were observed. Thus the giving of an unbroken wand to a new tenant meant that he was entitled to occupy the land, whereas the breaking of a wand in his presence meant that his period of tenure was to end.[4] Thatch and turf (thayk and dyffat) were also given to denote the right of occupancy. When leases were made they were usually for short terms.[5] Most tenants in the fourteenth century and for long afterwards were entitled to remain on their holdings purely at the owner's will and most subtenants at the will of the main tenants. Once agreed the lease gave a somewhat limited security of tenure, and since many tenants had no leases, and those who had had to renew them at short intervals, it behoved all tenants to remain on good terms with their lords, to be friendly with their neighbours and to pay promptly their dues in cash, kind and services.

Notice to quit was often served on tenants with little warning and with unfortunate results. Rude and comfortless as were the houses of husbandmen and cottars they were at least habitations; meagre as was the living they extracted from their impoverished holdings, they at least provided a means of livelihood. Beggary was far too often the only alternative to occupancy of a holding.

Even though evictions, as we shall see later, were common there were also many instances of the same family remaining on the same holding for several generations. Although this was particularly the case on Church estates it was by no means confined to them. In such cases the families came in time to consider that, while they did not possess the legal right to own land, they at least possessed a moral right to occupy their holdings. They claimed that their families had occupied the same land past memory of man

---

[4] *A.P.S.*, VOL. II, pp. 17, 22, 35.
[5] Grant, *Social Development*, pp. 253-4.

and wished to be treated "kindly";[6] hence the term "kindly tenant". The exact significance of this term "kindly" is not at all clear. Some kindly tenants undoubtedly possessed legal rights to occupy land and to sell or bequeath those rights. Such were the kindly tenants of Lochmaben who, by virtue of services said to have been rendered to Robert the Bruce, had been granted these heritable rights, which from time to time were renewed by special charter. On many Church lands in the west there were tenants whose rights of occupancy could be bequeathed, but to what extent, if any, these rights had a legal basis is unknown. So it was with certain Carstairs tenants, mentioned in the Diocesan Register of Glasgow and whose right was probably more moral than legal.[7] Usually the male heir would succeed his father as tenant and long residence of a family on a holding would thus be regarded as conferring the rights of occupancy on that family. So when the Mackintosh tenants were evicted from their holdings by the Earl of Moray there was great resentment.[8] At the time of the Reformation, when the Church lands of Dunblane came into the possession of the Earl of Montrose, the old-established tenant families successfully petitioned Parliament, greatly to Montrose's annoyance, to be allowed to remain in their holdings.[9] Many such tenants evidently managed at a later stage to secure sufficient legal rights to remain on in their holdings. They became the "bonnet lairds," *i.e.* landlords of their own holdings, the bonnet signifying that the extent of land owned was small.

By the middle of the fifteenth century leases had become common enough to warrant action by Parliament to ensure that when estates changed hands, which they frequently did through confiscation, reversion to the Crown, sale, etc., leaseholders would continue to enjoy occupancy until the end of the arranged period. In 1449 under the caption "the Buyer of landis suld keepe the Tackes [leases] set [arranged] before the Bying" it was ordained for the "sauftie and favour of the pure pepil that labouris the grunde that thai and all utheris, that has takyn or sal tak landis in tym to come fra lordis and has termes and yeris thereof, that, suppose the lordis sell or analy [transfer] thai landis that the tackaris [leaseholders] sall remayne with thare tackis unto the ische [end] of thare termes".[10]

---

[6] *A.P.S.*, VOL. II, pp. 248, 253.        [7] *op. cit.*, pp. 249, 252.
[8] A. M. Mackintosh, *The Mackintoshes and Clan Chattan*, Edinburgh 1903, p. 218.
[9] *A.P.S.*, VOL. III, ed. T. Thomson, pp. 111-12.
[10] *op. cit.*, VOL. II, p. 35.

On Crown lands the system of letting varied. Until the end of the fifteenth century there were no leases in Bute[11] and the tenure was uncertain. On most other Crown lands, however, careful letting on lease was the rule, commissioners being generally empowered to grant leases for either three or five years, but they might be for varying periods of seven or fifteen years, or even for life. Where tenants either had short leases or none at all, as was usual, there was no incentive to embark on any policy of improvements. Major, a shrewd sixteenth-century observer, attributed the treeless and hedgeless condition of the countryside and the poor state of Scotland's agriculture to short leases and lack of security of tenure.[12] Good building stone, he pointed out, was abundant but no tenant felt justified in erecting a good dwelling house for himself or improving his land unless he could be assured of reaping the reward of his labours. There were, however, other reasons, for even security of tenure through feuing brought about no marked improvement in farming, standards of living, etc.

Another custom of the times was the exacting of a grassum or lump sum at the beginning of a lease. In a sense a feudal casualty, the grassum was the price of the privilege of occupancy as distinct from the yearly rent; usually the amount payable was a year's rent, although when feus were taken the entry fee might be several times this amount.[13] Although rents were arranged in the light of the amount of grassum, and vice versa, the custom had little to commend and indeed much to condemn it. For new tenants it tied up capital which they probably could ill spare; for existing tenants, inability to pay the grassum on the renewal of a lease provided the landlord with an excuse for evicting them.

In the Rental Book of Coupar Abbey there is fortunately preserved much information concerning the running of a Church estate between the years 1443 and 1538. At the beginning of this period most of the former estate granges had been divided and let to tenants. We surmise this from the fact that the last mention of services being required in harvest time, presumably for crops grown on granges, was in 1456,[14] and the fact that the various granges were let in fractional parts, thirds, quarters, sixths, twelfths, sixteenths, and even twenty-fourths, with no consistent division except that the

[11] Grant, *Social Development*, p. 254.
[12] John Major, *History of Greater Britain*, trans. A. Constable, Edinburgh 1892, p. 31.
[13] Grant, *Social Development*, pp. 255, 268.
[14] *Coupar Abbey Rental Book*, VOL. I, p. 137.

portions were fractions of a half or a third. Some grange farms
might be let at first to a single tenant; later they might be divided
and farmed either singly or conjointly by a number of tenants; still
later portions might be regrouped and reallocated, the absence of
enclosures and the layout of the land in run-rig facilitating the
process. The variations are most puzzling and we can only surmise
the causes by following events on certain of the old grange
farms.

In 1438 the grange farm of Tullyfergus was held on life lease
by a tenant, Gilbert Ratre.[15] Four years later Patrick, evidently one
of his sons, got the lease on the death of his father. Seven years
still later three of Gilbert's sons, two possibly boys when the father
died, leased the farm. In 1456, John Ratre, one of Gilbert's sons,
leased one half of the farm, the other half being let to tenants other
than people of the name of Ratre. In 1464 a curious fact emerges
for, while one half of the farm was let to one tenant, and two quarter
portions to other tenants, mention is made of an additional eighth
portion. Further complications followed for in 1470 two men each
leased one third of one of the quarters. Then in 1474 an entirely new
arrangement was made. The holding was divided into two main
parts—the east and the west portions, the east in turn being subdivided into thirds and the west into quarters. There were thus
seven portions, an arrangement which apparently held good until
1508, since in that year there were still seven tenants, one of them
being a Ratre. After 1524 there is no further mention of this family
in connexion with Tullyfergus.

In the absence of more definite information we may surmise
that when a tenant had two or more sons the holding might be
subdivided to provide each with a share. Such an arrangement,
should there be a rise in the population, would mean recurring
subdivisions of holdings into progressively smaller portions. But
in those days life, particularly amongst children, was very uncertain
and tenants were often cut off in their prime, leaving no heirs. Thus
although on occasion holdings were subdivided, at other times they
had to be regrouped for lack of tenants. Where, however, provision
had to be made to meet an increase in population and it was deemed
inadvisable to subdivide holdings beyond certain limits, the expedient
of quartering cottars on tenants was presumably adopted.[16] The
association of the Ratre family with Tullyfergus for at least

[15] *Coupar Abbey Rental Book*, VOL. I, pp. 119, 123, 136, 140, 150, 158, 200, 245, 268.
[16] Marshall, *Agric. Central Highlands*, p. 33.

eighty-six years suggests that on this Church estate consideration was shown to families associated with certain holdings.

Tenants on the Coupar Abbey estate were allowed to have cottars, *i.e.* subtenants who, for the privilege of occupying a small portion of land from the main tenant, bound themselves to carry out a certain amount of work for him. The Abbey insisted, however, on limiting the number of cottars a tenant should have;[17] in some cases one was allowed, in others two. This arrangement was doubtless made to ensure that the food, and possibly the fuel resources of a holding were not over-taxed by its having to support too many families. These subtenants, or cottars, enjoyed much less security of tenure than the main tenants who could, subject to the above provisions as regards numbers, take them in or dismiss them at will. Cottars, however, had to be given land, kail yards, and proper fuel rights and, save in exceptional circumstances, tenants were forbidden to evict them.[18]

In addition to the cottars who were subtenants of the main tenants, there were instances of cottars holding small portions of land, either jointly or severally, direct from the estate. Thus, on the Coupar Abbey estate, the holding of Baitscheill, extending to thirty-nine acres, was let jointly in cottery to fourteen tenants, the number of acres allocated to each varying from one to four,[19] each cottar paying his rent and performing his services " as he has number of acres ". Whether this implied working the land and harvesting the crop in common, thereafter sharing it according to each cottar's number of acres, or each cottar harvesting his own acres is not made clear. In other cases holdings of three and four acres were let direct to tenants. Doubtless cottars holding land direct from the estate could work for whom they pleased and would be largely employed as blacksmiths, carpenters, masons, workers in leather, weavers, tailors, thatchers, millers, etc. A village of cottars at Balgersho[20] on the estate had by 1492 become the burgh of barony of Keithock.

Another feature of the management of this estate was that although many holdings were let to joint tenants on the run-rig system, joint tenants were sometimes given the option of dividing their land into separate portions. Thus when Coupar Grange was repartitioned in 1473 it was stipulated that " ilke man sal kepe

---

[17] *Coupar Abbey Rental Book*, VOL. I, pp. 123, 143, 227, 235.
[18] *op. cit.*, p. xxviii.  [19] *op. cit.*, p. 177.
[20] Franklin, *Scottish Farming*, p. 56.

his pairt of his malyn [farmland] and his toft [site of house and buildings] that his nichbur be nocht injuryt and the toun sal be partit gife nede be ".[21] The two tenants of Cotsyards were given the option of working their land in run-rig or in " twa " separate parts. This movement towards separate divisions of holdings was apparently none too popular, probably because the run-rig system ensured a fairer method of land distribution and cultivation. Until Small's plough with its two-horse team became popular in the late eighteenth century, holders had to co-operate in providing animals for a joint plough team and it seemed fairer to have the ploughing done rig about than to incur the chance of one partner's block field being ploughed early and in good season and another's ploughed too late or in bad season, thereby prejudicing the success of the crop. The Acts of Parliament of 1426 and 1457[22] requiring the sowing of wheat, beans and peas, and the sowing to be done in one " sched " also made it desirable that the portions of land devoted to these crops should be grouped.

In drawing up leases the Coupar Abbey estate was careful to specify for the larger holdings exact details about the length of the lease, the rent and teinds, whether in money or kind, the services to be rendered and general conditions regarding the regulations of Acts of Parliament or rules peculiar to the estate. The preamble to the lease was often framed in most courteous terms. Old and trusted tenants in renewing their leases might be described as " our loved " or even " our familiar " or "our well-beloved " familiar or servant,[23] proportionate honours being paid. There was no consistent rule about money rents, whether in merks or in pounds, shillings and pence. The amount of rent payable in kind varied according to the nature of the farm. On the more fertile farms it was usual to stipulate for so many chalders—a chalder being 16 bushels—or bolls of oats, bere and meal—the boll of oats being usually 6 bushels—and on one Carse farm the rent was largely paid in wheat. Usually poultry were included in the rent and on the Glenisla holdings, where little grain was grown, the " kind " portion of the rent consisted of calves, kids, venison, butter, cheese, hens and geese. Certain tenants near to the Isla or the Tay had to provide fresh or kippered salmon. Some tenants were obliged to supply fodder for the Abbey stock, others had to take in stock for

---

[21] *Coupar Abbey Rental Book*, VOL. I, pp. 165, 171.
[22] *A.P.S.*, VOL. II, pp. 13, 51.
[23] *Coupar Abbey Rental Book*, VOL. II, p. 136.

summering or wintering.   By detailing the produce of the land to be
paid as teinds the Abbey followed an enlightened policy, for no
question would arise of the grain harvest being held up until the
tenth sheaf could be collected.   Incidentally here, in common with
other Cistercian estates, there were no teinds of young stock, but in
letting the Church of Glenisla in 1557 on the eve of the Reformation
Abbot Donald Campbell evidently withdrew this privilege.[24]  Rents
were usually related to special features connected with the holdings.
Thus the tenant of Dalsack in the parish of Birse, Aberdeenshire,
had to render to the proprietor, the Bishop of Aberdeen, four
dozen plates, four dozen dishes, four dozen salvers, eight chargers
and four basins, all to be made of dry wood, in addition to his money
rent.   At that time large areas of the district were covered with
wood and the turning industry long associated with the parish was
practised.   Tenants in the adjoining Forest of Birse paid their
rents partly in wood and partly in hazel nuts.[25]

The services rendered by the tenants on the Coupar Abbey estate
varied in character.   In most instances carriages had to be performed.
The letting of the grange farms had obviated the need for the former
sowing and harvesting services but peats, firewood, the carriage of
sand for building, etc.—all designated " short carriage " because of
the short distances involved—had to be provided.   When long-
distance transport had to be rendered, e.g. taking coal, salt, slates,
lime, from Dundee or some other distant place it was termed " long
carriage ".   Individual tenants might be required to maintain fences
and sheep cots, to protect woods from stock, look after the fisheries
and erect drainage works; the tenant of the gardens had to supply
the Abbey with fruit and vegetables and the other tenants with
young trees.   Officials such as the head forester, the cattle keeper,
the porter, the cunyngar (keeper of rabbit warrens) received a
holding as part wages.   Certain offices appear to have been hereditary,
doubtless because a son had a better chance than anyone else of
becoming familiar with his father's work.

By following the main conditions of let in the case of the holding
of Adhory certain features of the times may be noted.[26]

Points to be noted are the change from merks to pounds, the
range in the amount of kind and cash rents, the former being greatly
increased in twelve years: the marches being ridden, a necessity

[24]  *Coupar Abbey Rental Book*, VOL. I, pp. xxvi-xxvii ;  VOL. II, p. 136.
[25]  Innes, *Legal Antiquities*, pp. 252-4.
[26]  *Coupar Abbey Rental Book*, VOL. I, pp. 140, 159, 163, 204, 222, 245.

in a period when land was unenclosed and boundary marks were easily removed; and a new lease twice being entered into before the expiry of the old one.  Incidentally the period between 1360 and 1603 was one of great inflation, the Scottish pound dropping to a twelfth of the value of the English one, which in itself had fallen greatly in value.  Without knowledge of the full circumstances it would be unwise to assume that the area of the holding remained unchanged throughout the period—the riding of the marches and the rearrangement in rent in 1476 imply some enlargement.  It was often customary to arrange for a new lease two years before the old one was due to expire.  It may be noted also that a life lease was

| Date of Lease | Tenant | Duration of Lease | Rent in cash | Kind rent. Grain, poultry |
|---|---|---|---|---|
| 1464 | James Karmag | 5 years | 5 merks | 12 capons |
| 1470 | ,, ,, | 5 ,, | 6 ,, | 4 bolls horse corn, 12 capons |
| 1472 | ,, ,, | 5 ,, | 6 ,, | 4 bolls horse corn, 12 capons or 24 cocks and hens, and 12 geese |
| 1476 | ,, ,, | Life | £5 0 0 | Marches to be ridden |
| 1476 | ,, ,, | ,, | ,, | 4 bolls horse corn, 12 capons |
| 1493 | Patrick Karmag (son) | 5 years.  No rent disclosed, but evidently the above rent was paid ;  40s. fabric money had to be rendered at the renewal | | |
| 1504 | New tenant | Occupies all land | | |

arranged in 1476.  This form of lease was often granted to older tenants on the estate.  In the circumstances of the times this Church estate would appear to have been almost a model landlord—compassionate, fair-minded, enlightened, yet firm in its dealings with tenants in regard to land use.  Its compassion is evidenced by certain new tenants being allowed to lease holdings on condition that they looked after predecessors who had become old and infirm, its forbearance in the matter of arrears of rent through occasional forgiving of defaulters in the hope that matters would improve, and its sense of fair play in allowing widows and heirs to succeed to tenancies as a matter of course.  It was stipulated, however, that if a widow were to remarry she must have the consent of the abbot.[27]  In the interests of good husbandry and to comply with an Act of Parliament the estate fined tenants who allowed " guld " to grow on their land, supplied " guld-free " seed to those who required it, and

[27] *Coupar Abbey Rental Book*, VOL. I, p. 159 ; VOL. II, pp. 238, 243, 250.  In certain instances a fee was exacted for giving consent to the remarriage of a widow.

provided young fruit trees or ash, osier and willow so that the planting Act of 1457 could be observed. Other Acts of Parliament such as those governing the sowing of wheat, peas and beans, the destruction of rooks' nests, the keeping of hounds to kill foxes and wolves, and the arrangement of wolf hunts were enforced. Estate regulations provided for the carrying out of drainage schemes, erection of embankments alongside watercourses, the proper treatment of moss land when digging for peats, the preservation of woods, and the periodical laying down of certain parks to grass (presumably self-seeded natural pastures) and broom. Broom parks were established to provide fuel for the Abbey ovens, cover for rabbits and fodder for stock in winter. In England, where hay was made to feed stock in winter, it was customary to supplement the hay with tree loppings. Certain tenants had to hain specified pastures—" and thai sall kepe our medewis and brume parks fra thaim self and thair catell "; others had to preserve woods. Tenants were thirled to certain mills; they were encouraged or even compelled to build houses, reclaim land, divide joint holdings into separate parts or sometimes to refrain from doing so. Through the Abbot's court most kinds of offences were dealt with.

Tenants had to be decently clothed, attend wapinshaws four times a year and keep on friendly terms with each other. Arbiters were appointed by the people themselves to settle disputes; pundlers took charge of trespassing stock and should a man fail to cultivate all his land the Abbot could nominate some one to do so. Refractory tenants were informed that they might " tyn their tacks ", *i.e.* lose their leases, if they became " uncorrigebil ". Some tenants were enjoined to keep a sufficient number of stock, and husbandmen at Coupar Grange were at one time limited to keeping one pig although two were allowed subsequently. The influence of enlightened landlords such as this Church estate went far beyond ensuring that rents were promptly paid or land properly cultivated; it permeated the lives of the people. One tenant was warned that he must be obedient to his mother; others, who kept an inn, that they had to be " sweet and gentle " to all who came. As the time of the Reformation drew near heresy clauses were inserted in the leases. The near approach of this momentous event greatly influenced the Abbey's land policy. Feuing was increasingly practised; longer leases were arranged and considerable sums of money by way, or in lieu, of grassums (compositions) were handed over to the Church by prospective life renters and feuars.

Rents varied according to the fertility and extent of the land. John Pilmour, occupying three Scots acres of land at Newcassey, paid in rent two bolls of bere, one of meal, and one truss of fodder, exclusive of the sum of 20 shillings.[28] The relatively large amount of grain rent suggests that he held a particularly fertile holding and had all his land in infield. Many holdings on this estate were rented, as in Pilmour's case, for a cash rent exclusive of services and payments in kind, of half a merk per acre.

From a document dated 1536 and dealing with the feuing of Drygrange on the Melrose Abbey estate, we get another interesting sidelight on the state of agriculture at that time and the relationship between another Church estate and its tenants.[29] Here a tenant petitioned the estate for a reduction of rent on the ground that it had been fixed just after the land had been reclaimed from woodland and was yielding very good crops. Unfortunately the land through persistent cropping quickly became so unfertile that the yields sunk to those of the adjoining cultivated (but apparently exhausted) lands. It seems evident that at this period reclamation was still going on in Scotland but that the system of farming practised robbed land so quickly of its fertility that crop yields soon sank to very low levels. While the Church in this case appears to have rack-rented the tenant on the improvements effected by his family the petition was nevertheless granted. It may be noted that after 1532, when King James V in conjunction with the Pope placed a heavy tax on monasteries, the Church estates were forced to exact more from their tenants than they had previously done. This may have explained the high rent placed on Drygrange.

In general, Church tenants were treated with much more consideration than tenants on other estates. The policy followed on Church estates was more consistent and the tenants were less subject to the caprices of a single individual; they were not liable to be called upon to fight a lord's private battles, were more immune from raids and less subject to rack-renting and evictions. The general tenor of an Act passed in 1568 after many Church lands had become secularised is unmistakable. After a preamble stating the reasons—people being subjected to beggary and unable to serve in the wars—the Act goes on to state—" Therefore it will be necessary to statute that no mailer, farmer or other occupier of lands, who

---

[28] *Coupar Abbey Rental Book*, VOL. II, p. 88.
[29] G. Neilson, " The feuing of Drygrange from the Monastery of Melrose ", in *Scottish Historical Review*, VII (1909-10), pp. 358-9.

pay their duties shall be removed for the space of certain years so that order may be taken for the relief of the poor and better forth setting of the King's service." [30]   Many people, who formerly had enjoyed security of tenure under the Church, were now in danger of being reduced to beggary following eviction by their new land-lords.   But quite apart from this aspect of insecurity it would be wrong to suppose that tenants on other Scottish estates enjoyed the same degree of prosperity as those at Coupar Abbey.   Most holdings on that estate were favoured in having a good soil and climate.   Years of scarcity were less frequent and the degree of want in such years was felt less acutely than elsewhere in Scotland.   It was largely the small returns from the cultivated crops, coupled with the impoverished state of the kingdom, that made landlords so grasping and tenants so poor.   The graceless King David II had, first of all by making the kingdom pay for his ransom and then by his extravagances, reduced Scotland, already bled white by the Wars of Independence, to utter impoverishment.   Landlords were desperate for money and to raise it they resorted to several expedients. Services were commuted into cash rents; casualties were demanded as was customary under the feudal system when the eldest son of a lord was knighted or his eldest daughter married; rack-renting was practised and under threats of eviction grassums were exacted whenever a lease was renewed or a new one made.   When a tenant holding half a ploughgate or more of land died, the lord, under the old custom of herezelde or heriot, was entitled to the best beast, often a calving cow.   Although this was not supposed to apply to tenants occupying less than two husbandlands there is reason to believe that on smaller holdings heriot was exacted.   Even as late as about 1750 a somewhat similar custom " calpa " was practised in a Skye parish.[31]

Against the background of the prevailing wretched state of agriculture, the frequently recurring poor seasons, the general scarcity of money and its gradually decreasing purchasing power, these exactions were bitterly resented.   Much discontent found expression in gatherings of the people on the frequent occasions when evictions and " punding for malis and annualis " were carried

---

[30] *A.P.S.*, VOL. III, p. 45.

[31] *New Statistical Account of Scotland*, henceforth cited as *N.S.A.*, Edinburgh 1845, VOL. XVI, Inverness-shire p. 315 :   the origin of the custom is obscure, but it seems to have been associated with the lord's protection of the vassal during his lifetime, and on his death with a claim to the steed and harness with which the vassal rode to battle.

out and the tenant was often deprived of his home and his living.[32] So much rioting took place on the holy days of Whitsunday and Martinmas that an Act passed in 1469 decreed that poindings for rent should take place three days after these festivals.

But this Act did not deal with the root cause of the trouble, the wretched state of Scottish agriculture at the time. The average three- to four-fold increase on the seed sown left little margin to occupiers even in ordinary years after seed, rent and teind grain had been set aside. From that margin and any contribution made by stock the tenant had to provide himself and his family with the means of subsistence. When in bad years that margin largely disappeared he had no sufficient reserve of food on which to fall back. The conditioned surplus animal that was killed and salted at Martinmas—the " mart " or " mairt "—was not available to all families. Sometimes in periods of scarcity, in the interests of preserving human life, resort had to be made to the bleeding of animals, while the fleshy roots of plants, like docks and dandelions, and shell fish were eaten. Years of scarcity with ransom prices for meal were of frequent occurrence. Such were the years of 1562-63 and 1571-72 when meal sold from £2. 3s. 0d. to £3. 6s. 8d. per boll.[33] In 1568 the price ranged from 20 in Perth to 30 shillings in Fife. The customary average price for meal at that period was about 7s. 6d. a boll.[34]

How real was the fear of famine may be judged by the many Acts relating to food in the fifteenth and sixteenth centuries. For instance, the practice of forestalling or withholding food from sale in the hope of getting a still higher price was forbidden by Acts passed in 1449, 1482, 1535, 1540, 1551, 1579, 1587, 1592 and 1594. Every man who grew grain had also, by the Act of 1452, to have it all threshed by the end of May; in 1563 this date was extended to 10th July.[35] The export of grain was prohibited by Acts passed in 1535, 1555, 1585, that of cattle and sheep by Acts of 1468, 1535, 1555, 1581, 1585 and 1592, while imports of grain from Ireland were allowed only in years of great scarcity. A system of food rationing was introduced in 1551. In 1584 the eating of meat was

---

[32] John Mackintosh, *History of Civilisation in Scotland*, 2nd edn. VOL. II, Paisley 1893, p. 238.

[33] Cosmo Innes, *Sketches of Early Scottish History and Social Progress*, Edinburgh 1861, p. 353.

[34] Franklin, *Scottish Farming*, p. 102.

[35] *A.P.S.*, VOL. II, pp. 36, 41, 144, 346, 376, 538; VOL. III, pp. 146, 452; VOL. IV, p. 86.

forbidden on three days of the week and during Lent. In certain other years price restrictions were placed on foods. During some of these years of scarcity so many of the young of sheep and of game were killed that fears were expressed that an insufficient number would be left to replenish the flocks. Accordingly, in 1551 and 1555, Acts were passed forbidding the killing of young lambs. Since riding horses competed with human beings for grain they were not allowed to have hard feed in summer; a lord was exempted, however, to the extent of two horses, and a baron to that of one horse.[36] To prevent damage to crops Acts were passed in 1366, 1540 and 1555 forbidding riders to pass through cropped land in the growing season. Wilful burning of ricks (Acts of 1525, 1540 and 1567), and the maiming of farm animals (Act of 1581) were capital offences. Acts of 1424 and 1457 were aimed at the destruction of predatory birds and animals; game laws were passed to preserve game for the use of the landed classes, and although tenants were not allowed to kill pigeons, these birds did so much damage that Parliament in 1617 restricted the erection of dovecots. An Act passed in 1469 forbade the seizure of a tenant's goods for his lord's debts, another (1503) the distraint of plough gear for debt; Acts of 1426 and 1457 required the sowing of so much wheat, beans and peas, and one passed in 1424 reaffirmed the old Act of 1214 regarding the ploughing of land.

Large amounts of grain, meal, malt, butter, cheese, cattle, sheep, swine, etc., rendered as rent, were consumed by the lords and their numerous followers. Thus, Campbell of Glenurchy required 571 bolls of meal and malt, 90 cattle, 20 swine, 200 sheep, 325 stone of cheese and 49 of butter, besides salmon, herring and other fish, and some wheaten loaves and wheaten meal to sustain his household in the year 1590.[37] The weekly consumption of Lord Lovat's household at this period was 7 bolls of malt, 7 of meal, 1 of flour besides meat and fish. The Islay rental in 1542 included 301 marts (cattle) and 301 sheep besides meal, butter, poultry, etc.[38] The Huntly estates received on an average over 12 bolls of meal a day besides much other produce.[39] This custom of rents being rendered largely in kind was a contributory cause of internal

---

[36] *A.P.S.*, VOL. II, pp. 486, 488, 498 ; VOL. III, pp. 225, 426, 577.

[37] Grant, *Social Development*, p. 202.

[38] T. Pennant, *A Tour in Scotland and Voyage to the Hebrides 1772*, henceforth cited as Pennant, *Tour*, 1790 edn. VOL. I, p. 254.

[39] Grant, *Social Development*, p. 202.

strife. To consume produce collected as rent, for little could be sold, the great lords even in times of peace maintained a large retinue of followers. The vast amount of farm produce collected by the Earl of Huntly made him an autocrat. He was fittingly styled " The Cock of the North " and more than once was in open rebellion against his sovereign. The Scottish nobles, as Fynes Moryson, an Englishman, noted in 1598, lived in factions. They were ever ready to find cause for a feud.

Nevertheless, despite the great scarcity of coinage and the difficulty of marketing farm produce, there were signs of a swing away from the old idea of farming for self-sufficiency only. It was evident that the trend of the times was towards division of labour and farming for profit. The establishment of the cottery village of Balgersho by the Coupar Abbey estate was followed by its elevation by James IV to a free burgh of barony, with its own set of weights and measures and its market where surplus meal, wheat, rye, peas, butter, cheese, malt, hides, wool, salt, wine, tools and clothing could be bought and sold. The growing ease with which land products could be converted into cash or otherwise exchanged is suggested by an Act of 1581,[40] which required the nobility to live with their families on their estates. Evidently the Parliament of that time became alarmed at the growing tendency of the nobility to dwell in " burghs, towns, clachans and alehouses " thereby causing " scaithfull and shamefull inconvenientis " such as defrauding the poor of alms.

Agriculture was predominantly the country's chief industry. The relatively small quantity of farm produce available for export or for internal sale bore little relation to the total quantity produced, yet agricultural products formed the greater part of Scotland's exports. Particulars for 1614, a typical year, show that the total value of Scotland's exports was £736,986.[41] Of these, hides and skins, mostly of sheep, goats and cattle, were valued at £238,712, wool at £51,870, grain and its products together with meat at £37,653, and clothing and leather goods and the processed material of the farm at £169,497. Fishery products amounted to £153,354. Incidentally there had been a great increase in hides exported since 1327 when the number was only 8861; by 1378-79 the figure had risen to 44,559.

[40] A.P.S., VOL. III, p. 222.
[41] P. Hume Brown, Scotland in the time of Queen Mary, London 1904, pp. 227-30.

In the sixteenth century the subject of teinds sprang into prominence. So accustomed had the people become to paying teinds that by the time of the Reformation no very great resentment was expressed against paying them in principle, but their collection and allocation was a different matter. In most cases the right of collecting teinds and the obligation of distributing them before the Reformation belonged to great Church institutions like the Abbeys. So grasping had many of these Abbeys become that the religious needs of the parishes were shamefully neglected while teinds in many parishes were farmed out to tacksmen on favourable terms. The new owners and the tacksmen of the teinds often showed little consideration to the people when collecting their dues. At the Reformation there was an undignified scramble for the seizure of all Church property including teinds. The Reformed Church claimed everything, intending to use the income for the upkeep of religious services, education, and the support of the poor. The nobles, doubtless with ulterior motives, turned down the claim. The story of what actually happened is somewhat obscure, but evidently the Crown seized both property and teinds, allocating in theory two-thirds of the income to the old incumbents for their lifetime and reserving the remaining one-third for allocation by commissioners between the Reformed Church and the Crown. When John Knox heard of this he described the arrangement as giving two-thirds to the devil and sharing the remaining third between God and the devil.[42] It had been intended that the arrangement for the distribution of " the thirds of the benefices ", as that third portion was termed, would be temporary until what was conceded to be the proper income of the Reformed Church—the teinds—could be made over to that body. This was never done, nor did the Reformed Church receive any additional income when the old incumbents died. So matters were allowed to drift; flatterers and favourites of the Crown were granted Church property and the right of collecting the teinds. The commissioners appointed to allocate the " thirds of the benefices " dealt with the clergy in a most niggardly manner. The latter were most inadequately paid, often receiving as much from charitable contributions as from the teinds. So much criticism was aroused that Queen Mary, the regents, and latterly King James VI interested themselves in the matter. Moreover, great resentment was expressed as to the manner of collection. To ease the situation laws were passed by the Parliaments of 1567, 1579,

42 W. Chambers, *The Book of Scotland*, Edinburgh 1830, p. 438.

F

1587, 1592, 1606, 1612 and 1617.[43]  But the Lords of Erection, the name given to the recipients of Church property, and those who owned the right of collecting teinds of the parishes, were too strongly entrenched to allow wrongs to be righted.  In 1617 it was decreed that each parish minister should be paid a stipend of at least 5 chalders of meal or 500 merks and not more than 8 chalders or 800 merks, the balance over the latter amounts being kept by the titular holder.[44] This arrangement held good for some years but when Charles I came to the throne he decided to revoke all grants of Church lands and property made by the Crown since the Reformation.  In this resolve he was influenced, in part at least, by a desire to establish the clergy in comfort and security.

Great alarm was felt by the beneficiaries.  There was no outcry, however, from the cultivators who probably felt they had nothing to lose but probably something to gain from being freed from the grip of greedy titular holders.  The clergy favoured the proposed change and Charles, having gained considerable support, appointed a commission of enquiry.  Following its findings all lands and revenues formerly belonging to the Church were made over to the Crown.  A composition on favourable terms for the holders was arranged for the lands and as for the teinds Charles decreed that, to make better provision for kirks and ministers, parish heritors should possess the right of collection on their lands.  Accordingly they were allowed to buy the teinds at nine years' purchase of the tithing which was to be fixed at a fifth of the annual rental less all burdens.[45]  The Parliament of 1633 ratified these decrees and commissioners were appointed to value and ordain the price of the teinds.  Henceforth ministers were to receive their stipends either in money or in victual, conversion equivalents to be used and minimum payments enforced.  Where the stipends were lower than the cash values of the teinds the ministers became entitled to demand a rearrangement every nineteen years.  Incidentally, English farmers had to wait for two hundred years before a similar step was taken and agricultural development was in consequence considerably

[43] *A.P.S.*, VOL. III, pp. 37, 139, 544, 553 ; VOL. IV, pp. 286, 541.

[44] J. Cunningham, *The Church of Scotland*, Edinburgh 1859, VOL. II, p. 54.

[45] The ultimate effect of the teinds being purchasable was that teinds and rents instead of being separated were combined in the rent payable to the landlord. In the parish of Mid and South Yell, Shetland, the stipend at the end of the eighteenth century was as follows : 178 lispunds and 10 merks butter; $70\frac{5}{12}$ lambs and 4 merks wool with every lamb; $211\frac{3}{4}$ ling; $503\frac{1}{2}$ cans of oil; £175. 15s. Scots with £40 Scots for communion expenses. *F.S.A.*, VOL. II, pp. 573-4.

retarded. In passing it may also be mentioned that the Scots Parliament decreed that every parish minister was to have a manse and a glebe of four Scots acres arable ground and where this extent of arable ground could not be found, as in the Highlands and Islands, he should have the equivalent in value of the land in pasture.[46]

While the decline of the Scottish branch of the Church just before the Reformation can be attributed to a number of causes, all stem from a general decay in religious faith. In Rome, which had previously reserved to itself the right of appointing church dignitaries, important livings had been openly bought and sold and even absentee appointments had been made. When the power of making such appointments passed to the Scottish King and his Court the same practice was followed and the appointments made were often most unsuitable, men unfitted by age, training and experience and of loose and dissolute habits were often placed in office. Cunningham, a Church historian, has told how bishoprics, abbacies, priories and appointments to parishes were openly sold by the King and his favourites.[47] This decline in standards was reflected in lower standards of estate administration.

Another factor which influenced the policy on Church estates was that just before the Reformation both the Church and the Crown encountered serious financial difficulties. The causes need not be enlarged upon here, but one result of the shortage of money was a greater recourse by both bodies to the practice of feuing land. This system of feuing was peculiar to Scotland. It was really a development of the feudal system with fixed cash rents, absolute security of tenure, and certain casualties substituted for services, rents in kind, and uncertainty as regards casualties and occupation. Leases had provided a limited measure of security but grassums were demanded when a lease was renewed. The burden of herezelde when a tenant died and other irregular casualties also bore heavily on tenants who, to escape them, were in some instances prepared to give a higher perpetual rent as well as to make a considerable initial payment. Although a rather impure form of feuing had been previously practised in Scotland [48] feu-farming proper was first introduced in the latter part of the fourteenth century, and during the following century the Church gradually extended its use. With its gradual decline the Church was in greater need of hard

[46] *A.P.S.*, VOL. IV, p. 285.
[47] Cunningham, *Church History of Scotland*, VOL. I, p. 200.
[48] See pp. 48, 120.

cash than rents in kind or in services.   Heavy expenses were often incurred in lawsuits between abbeys while Rome also required vast sums of money; so more granges were now leased to tenants. Moreover the Church had much less need of military service from its tenants than the Crown or the lay lords, and could the more readily grant feus from such services.   From the landlord's point of view there were immediate advantages in feuing land.   Ready cash could be raised and higher rents obtained although these advantages were soon wiped out by depreciation of the coinage.

Not until the middle of the fifteenth century was feuing practised by the Crown.   Many estates by that time had come into its possession, largely by confiscation.   Money was scarce and this feuing movement seemed to both King and Government an easy and ready means of raising money.   In 1457 an Act commending the practice implied that the policy was enlightened.   Lucrative it certainly was, as may be seen from examples in Fife where sums of from three to five times the initial rents were sometimes paid as entry fees and where rents were doubled and even trebled.[49]   The Crown, however, did not pursue feuing very vigorously until the sixteenth century when the Church, which by this time was becoming more and more embarrassed financially, intensified the practice. Hitherto the Church had been careful to ensure that its interests were not permanently damaged by feuing.   Accordingly, confirmation of feus had to be referred to Rome.   But as the great climax of the sixteenth century—the Reformation—approached, restrictions on the feuing of Church lands were relaxed.   No confirmation was required from Rome, and Churchmen, apprehensive of the possibility of their properties being confiscated, were not unwilling to feu lands, particularly to their friends.   Indeed some abbots managed to grant feus of the land over which they had control to some of their illegitimate sons.   Bishop Hepburn, " the great dilapidator of the See of Moray," was a notorious example while Abbot Campbell of Coupar Abbey followed suit.[50]

From the royal rental book of 1541 we get a description of what might be termed a model feu farm.   By the conditions attached to the Crown feus the feuar bound himself to erect a commodious house, to lay out a well-furnished, hedged-in garden, to plant trees, to provide other amenities and to grow certain crops. In other cases land reclamation was stipulated in the deed of transfer.   From this angle feuing could be regarded as an enlightened policy, but there is no

[49] Grant, *Social Development*, p. 268.          [50] *op. cit.*, p. 271.

evidence that at this period it was followed by general improvements in farming. Although not exclusively confined to comparatively large areas of land let to individual tenants, it was usually related to such areas, and feuars often took good care to extract the last penny of rent from their tenants. Feuing favoured the richer more than the poorer classes. Much as poor tenants desired greater security of tenure, most of them could not afford to take feus. The movement at this time appears largely to have been confined to Church and Crown lands, for there is little evidence of much feuing on ordinary estates. Feuing, however, provided private owners with opportunities to enlarge or round off their estates or to provide for their younger sons, and considerable areas of former Church and Crown lands were so feued. The Church lands of Lesmahagow, owned by Kelso Abbey, were disposed of in feu to Hamilton of Finnart for £1500. Lord Lovat acquired Church lands near Inverness, the laird of Grant part of the Church lands of Strathspey and the laird of Mackintosh those of the barony of Moy.[51] There were similar transactions throughout Scotland.

The practice of the Church in feuing land varied. Much Church land was feued in large blocks over the heads of the tenants, but the Bishop of Glasgow feued direct to tenants and at Coupar Abbey, where much of the land was feued just before the Reformation, some tenants were able to acquire a feu of their land. Nevertheless, the movement was far from popular and occasioned much uneasiness among sitting tenants who either had had no opportunity of acquiring feus or had been reluctant to become feuars. As tenants of the feuar they feared either being rack-rented or evicted.

Linked up with feuing was the practice of wadsetting. In its case the tenure was for a limited number of years, but the initial purpose of wadsetting land was somewhat similar to that of feuing. On payment of a lump sum a proprietor would arrange for a tenant to occupy a piece of land rent free for a limited number of years. At the end of the period the proprietor was free to rent it to some other party, and should he wish to resume occupancy of the land during the period he could redeem the wadset. But with the feu system the proprietor's right to resume occupancy passed from him.

What with rack rents, threats of eviction, feudal casualties, grassums, lowered standards in Church life, resentment against teinds and their manner of collection, herezelde, mortuaries, unsettled times, recurring famines and the wretched system of agriculture

---

[51] Grant, *Social Development*, pp. 270-4.

practised, the cultivator's lot was not an easy one and there was
much outspoken resentment.   Sir Richard Maitland wrote thus :

> Sum with deir ferme are herriet hail
> That wount to pay but penny maill
> Sum by thar lordis are opprest
> Put fra th land that they possest.

In Lindsay's *Satire of the Three Estates* [52] the woes of the
common people are proclaimed through the complaints of a poor
man, who formerly was stated to have earned his living by carting
coals from Tranent to the ports or to Edinburgh.   He owned a mare
and three cows and supported his father, mother, wife and family of
" six or seven ".   Misfortunes overtook him.   First of all his father
died, and since his name was in the lease, the laird took possession
of the mare for " hire-yield " (herezelde), while the vicar by virtue
of his right to claim the most valuable animal belonging to the
deceased as mortuary, possessed himself in succession of the three
cows on the occasions of the death of the father, the mother and
the wife, the latter being so overcome by their misfortunes that
she sickened and " deit for verie sorrow ".   Even the vicar's clerk
went off with the " corse present ", apparently the coverlet of the
bed.   The poor man, now deprived of his wife, his cows and his
means of livelihood, and with a family to support, goes about
seeking redress but finds none from either Session or Senate.   Other
complaints were voiced in similar vein.   Lords and churchmen
were alleged to oppress the poor so as to live in luxury.   Maitland
of Lethington stated that the commons could keep nothing in their
possession.   Rents were raised so high that the tenants could afford
to drink only water, and, if they were unable to pay their rents, both
cattle and farm were taken from them.[53]   The Church was certainly
badly served by its officers just before the Reformation, and it is
probably true, as was alleged, that it was used as " a club to oppress
the people ".   Yet the Church was a more humane landlord than
the lay lords, many of whom led vicious lives.   Hector Boece,[54]
writing about 1527, deplored the gross vices of high society of the
time.   The medieval forms of diversion were indeed injurious to
public morals.

[52] Sir David Lindsay of the Mount, *The Satire of the Three Estates*, Festival
version by Robert Kemp, London 1951.

[53] *The Complaynt of Scotlande*, ed. J. A. H. Murray, Early English Text Society,
Extra Series VOL. XVII, London 1872, pp. 122-5.

[54] P. Hume Brown, *Scotland before 1700*, Edinburgh 1893, pp. 64 ff.

The close of this period was one of discord and unrest. In the minority of James VI there was a strong pro-Marian party which fomented civil wars and disorders. By 1571 we read of the whole realm being so divided into factions that people could scarcely profess their adherence to either King or Queen without suffering harm.[55] The Reformation, too, had caused much discord even amongst neighbours. The changes in the ownership of Church lands had not improved the lot of the tenants. Moreover the rights of property over old Church lands were very obscure. In 1587 James VI, following in the steps of his predecessors, revoked all alienations made during his minority, and feus of Church lands made just before the Reformation had often to be confirmed.

It would almost seem that agriculture declined during these centuries. No new methods of cultivation had been adopted, no new crops introduced, while continual cropping without cleaning and adequate dunging of the infield and with impoverishment of the outfield had in all probability reduced yields well below their thirteenth-century level. As against this, it seems probable that more land had been brought under at least temporary cultivation and livestock numbers had been increased. This is suggested, as already mentioned, by the great increase in hides exported between 1327 and 1614. These three centuries, so far as material wealth was concerned, had been unfortunate for the Scottish people. Their independence had been bought and maintained at great cost; the humanising effect of the Church on the national life and its beneficial effects on agriculture had declined, and, although serfdom and bondage had disappeared, it is doubtful if the welfare of the common people had been improved. Despite the scarcity of coinage, buying and selling of farm produce was, however, much more common, and the division of labour more pronounced. Fairs were more numerous at the end of the period and cattle were being bought and sold. Considerable numbers were even being brought from the Highlands, " Ergyle ky " being exchanged for " Lawland victuals " [56] and doubtless some, despite the export prohibitions imposed by the

[55] R. Chambers, *Domestic Annals of Scotland from the Reformation to the Revolution*, henceforth cited as *Domestic Annals*, VOLS. I-II, Edinburgh 1858, VOL. I, p. 72.

[56] A. R. B. Haldane, *The Drove Roads of Scotland*, London 1952, p. 14. *Register of the Privy Council of Scotland*, henceforth cited as *R.P.C.S.*, 1st ser. VOL. I, pp. 401, 470-1.

Scottish Parliament, found their way to England. But the bulk of the cattle, to judge from the great export of hides, were undoubtedly killed and eaten at home. Scottish people of these centuries did not live solely on oatmeal. Their partiality for this cereal appears to have grown with the passing of the years and probably reached its height in the eighteenth century.

# CHAPTER VI

# BEFORE THE DAWN

Unsettled conditions...Bad seasons, unusual frosts, wind-
storms and floods...Development and features of tacksman
system...Administration of private estates by the barons'
courts...Private estate regulations...Legislation in agricultural
interests...Development of store cattle trade...Enclosures
...Marking of drove roads...Repair of highways...Develop-
ments of English agriculture...Drainage of fens...Turnips
and red clover...Migrations of Ayrshire and Renfrewshire
farmers to Kintyre.

LIKE THE THREE PRECEDING CENTURIES the seventeenth was one
of turmoil and unrest. While the Union of the Crowns had
put an end to the long strife between Scotland and England, the
northern kingdom was greatly disturbed by civil wars, political
strife, religious persecution and general lawlessness, particularly in
the Highlands where cattle-stealing from the Lowlands had become
more frequent. There was, moreover, little friendly intercourse
between the two nations and knowledge of the better methods of
farming now being introduced in England did not spread to Scotland,
where the time-honoured but reprehensible system of infield and
outfield without fallowing or fallow crops, without liming or adequate
drainage, was still practised on soils largely exhausted of fertility.
Only one exception to this has been noted. Towards the end of
the century John Walker, a farmer at Beanston in East Lothian,
on the advice of an English visitor began to bare-fallow part of his
ground. People wondered what was happening when they saw
him cultivating his ground in midsummer but not sowing a crop;
to them it seemed a foolish waste of land. But when later they
saw his crops, particularly his wheat crop grown on outfield land—
a practice hitherto unknown—they became less critical and some
even copied his methods.[1]

Years of short crop were far too frequent. The year 1634 was
a particularly bad one, especially in Caithness and Orkney.[2] Many

[1] *F.S.A.*, VOL. X, p. 171.
[2] *R.P.C.S.*, 2nd ser. VOL. V, Edinburgh 1904, pp. 284-5.

people died of starvation and the survivors were often too weak to bury their dead. So dire were their straits that seed corn was eaten and in the following spring the customary amount of land could not be seeded down to crop. In some cases little more than a half or two-thirds of the usual acreage was cropped. So badly filled were the oat grains that a boll of oats sometimes did not produce a peck of meal. In 1635 meal was actually changing hands at £10-12 a boll, and to their shame some of the clergy who received their teinds in the form of oatmeal were charging this ransom price. In 1640 the country suffered greatly from a prolonged spell of what was termed a cold drought; dearth years followed; the price of oatmeal rose again from about £2 to the high figure of £10 per boll, and one of the recurring pestilences swept the land. Weakened by privations many people perished. The years 1622-23, 1634-35, 1649-51, and 1655-56, amongst others, were all marked by extreme scarcity, the price of bere rising to the high level of £20 Scots per boll. In such years dogs and sea ware were used as food, suicides were common and people were executed for stealing food. About 1680, according to the minister of Duthil, there was such a severe famine that a formerly well-inhabited large area of that parish was completely cleared of people in the course of a single year.[3]

But bad as these terrible years were they were exceeded in severity by the seven years at the turn of the century—" King William's ill years " as they were called. Their dire results will be described in the following chapter. The century also witnessed other calamities, including some great frosts. Describing the frost of 1614-15 Sir Robert Gordon wrote that " most part of the horse, nolt and sheep of the kingdom did perish ". The spring of 1674 was one of extreme cold: many of the farmers in the Southern Uplands lost all their sheep in the February snowstorm, which was long remembered as the " thirteen drifty days ".[4] Another very cold winter was that of 1683-84, when stretches of the Tay at Dundee and of the Forth at Bo'ness were frozen over and many of the farm animals perished. Towards the end of the century disaster overtook the fertile Moray barony of Culbin. It was completely submerged by sandstorms, the result not of a single night's wind—although the damage done in one particularly devastating night was so over-whelming as to remain fixed in the memories of the people—but of

[3] *F.S.A.*, vol. iv, p. 316.
[4] Chambers, *Domestic Annals*, vol. ii, pp. 365-7.

recurring storms spread over a period of twenty years. Even the manor house of Culbin was obliterated. Disasters followed in quick succession in this century; in 1608 an earthquake so impressed credulous Aberdonians that a special meeting of the Kirk Session was convened to determine the cause of God's wrath. Salmon fishers on the Dee were named as the culprits and were rebuked for the sin of catching fish on Sundays. Comets, regarded as portents of coming disasters, appeared in 1618, 1664, 1665, 1676, 1680 and 1682. In this century of civil war, religious fanaticism, witch-hunting and recurring famines, every phenomenon was held to be a Divine warning and every disaster was ascribed to the effect of God's wrath against a sinful people.

One significant feature of the century was the development in the north of Scotland of the tacksman system, an early example of which is mentioned in the preceding chapter in the lease drawn up between two Hays and the Abbot of Scone. Its development at this particular time was probably associated with the growing practice of rendering rents in money or in readily marketable stock rather than in services or unmarketable produce. Since rents in kind had largely to be consumed on the spot owners of land could not easily leave their domains. But with cash in their pockets the owners were now free to spend at least part of the year elsewhere. This may have been for their own pleasure; on the other hand they may have participated in Government affairs or in the wars of the period, but in their absence arrangements had to be made for rent collections and the administration of their estates. These obligations included the organisation and military training of their followers, the settlement of local disputes, the observance of a reasonable measure of law and order, and the safeguarding of the landlord's own interests. Since younger sons and other relatives of the chief or lord—men who by blood, instincts and training were natural leaders of the people—were often appointed as tacksmen, the system functioned in many, though not in all parts, extremely well.

Usually in return for freeing the landlord from the above duties a tacksman was allowed to lease a block of land, including his own farm, at a rent much about the same as the aggregate of the rents payable by the subtenants, provided these could be all collected. But " Balnespick ", as William Mackintosh, tacksman at Dunachton, Kincraig, Inverness-shire, in the latter part of the eighteenth century was called, was never able to collect all the rents. Indeed, he was often out of pocket as he provided needy subtenants with loans to tide them over difficulties.[5] This William Mackintosh may, however, not have been a typical tacksman of the period after the Forty-Five. Many, indeed most according to some writers, are said to have been greedy and unscrupulous. Their tenants often had no choice but to pay higher rents or leave their holdings; but Balnespick was a friend to his tenants, who turned to him in time of trouble such as illness, death, lean years or loss of stock. He was their organiser and banker; through him seed corn and meal were purchased; he bought their store cattle and would undertake to work their land and lay down their crops when misfortune supervened. A native of the district, he understood the ways, customs and thoughts of the people; his interests and theirs were closely interwoven. Living at a time when the old system of farming was passing away, he was responsible for introducing underground drainage and liming, new crops such as potatoes, new implements and the Linton breed of sheep.[6] Thus the tacksman system had both its good and its bad points. It certainly placed too much power in the hands of greedy individuals in the Highlands and, when abused, disrupted the happy relationship between chief and people. Abused it certainly was in some island districts at the beginning of the eighteenth century. Following complaints by some Argyllshire tenants of victimisation in the matter of rent, services, and tenure, Sheriff Campbell was appointed to investigate. His report brought out a sorry state of affairs. It records the view that the domestic economy of Iona, Mull, Tiree and the peninsula of Morven was worse than it had been for over a period of over a thousand years.[7]

Curiously enough the system was evidently unknown in Aberdeenshire, but in Sutherland two-thirds of the whole of the rental of the Crown lands comprised in the Earldom of Sutherland was between 1508 and 1513 paid by seven tenants.[8] It would seem that the tacksman system developed in the Highlands at about the same time as feuing elsewhere. Most of the criticisms against the system were made after the Forty-Five. Tacksmen were then no longer a necessary part of the military organisation of the clan and it seems probable that many who took tacks were not only unfamiliar

[5] W. R. Scott, preface to I. F. Grant, *Everyday Life on an old Highland Farm 1769-1782*, henceforth cited as Grant, *Highland Farm*, London 1924.
[6] *op. cit.*, pp. 135-47.
[7] Argyll, *Scotland*, pp. 244-50, 387 ff.
[8] *Rotuli Scaccarium regum Scotorum, The Exchequer Rolls of Scotland*, VOL. XIII, edd. G. Burnett and Ae. J. G. Mackay, Edinburgh 1891, p. cxl.

with, and unsympathetic to, the people, but were also determined to extract the maximum from their tenants before their own leases expired. The system had certainly outlived its usefulness.

Chapter II gave a short account of the Baron's Court and its functions. We are fortunate in having records of some of the courts functioning during a large part of this century, and from those of the Baron's Court of Ury we get an interesting picture of farming on that estate near Stonehaven in Kincardineshire. At the beginning of the seventeenth century the Ury or Urie estate belonged to the Erroll family but the improvidence of one of its members led to the sale of the estate. The Earl Marischal, who purchased it, sold it in 1648 to a Scottish soldier of fortune, Colonel David Barclay. This led to complications since the Earl's estates, because of his Royalist leanings, were confiscated about this time and Barclay's right to the property was questioned. It was not until 1666 that he came to reside at Ury and only in 1679 was his right to own the land finally admitted.[9]

The tenants on this estate, according to the editor of the Court Book, were renters in perpetuity and a number of farms seem to have been occupied in severalty. Much of the estate was poor moorland and presumably did not lend itself so readily to joint occupancy as estates where a full ploughland of land could be found in one compact block. When Barclay came to live on the estate he found to his dismay that the prolonged absence of the preceding owner and the disuse of the Baron's Court had made the tenants slack in rendering the stipulated number of services to the landlord. He remedied this fault and for so doing was stigmatised as an oppressor. This naturally perturbed Barclay, who had become a Quaker; to vindicate his rights he revived the Baron's Court at Ury and appeared in the dock self-charged with being an oppressor. The design succeeded and he was acquitted.

From the court records we learn that there were still various grades amongst the people—husbandmen (in this instance all the main tenants), grassmen, and herds, each of the latter with a house and kailyard. Petty thefts seem to have been frequent. The temptation to steal another's peats was sometimes too great to be resisted; pilfering from the laird's garden was common while sheaves blown from the unfenced rig of one man to another's ground gave rise to misunderstandings. Where theft could not be proved, but was strongly suspected, the accused would be suitably warned, while

[9] *Urie Court Book*, pp. xxvi, xxix.

persistent offenders were removed from the estate within three days of conviction. At Ury the Barclays, as befitting a Quaker family, never resorted to very harsh measures and indeed one of them scarcely made use of the court.[10]  Trespass by fowls was frequent, as might well be imagined, and in such cases the Ury Court decreed that the owner must hand over a peck of grain for every trespassing fowl.[11]  Quite a number of poaching offences were dealt with. The right to kill game of any kind was by the Act of Parliament of 1621 confined to the heritable owners of a plough of land. It ordained " that no man hunt nor haulk at anye tyme heirefter quha hes not a pleughe of land in heretage under the payne off ane hunderethe pundis ".[12]  It was also an offence even to kill pigeons, or " doos " as they were called, although they fed on other people's crops. In 1684-92 a number of tenants were convicted of killing " haires, doves, partriges, duke and draike " and their " gunnes " had to be given up.[13]  Although Robert, the third Barclay, was a Quaker he did not hesitate to deal with offences relating to poaching and theft. In the records for 1672 the court dealt with a complaint by the laird's gardener that some people were breaking the dykes surrounding the orchard and stealing " turnepes ", " carrottis " and " uther rootis ".[14]  Turnips were evidently grown then as a garden crop at Ury and it was a century later that they were first extensively grown on this estate as a field crop and were used to fatten sheep and cattle.

Despite the reprehensible system of cropping the land in successive years without cleaning it, people then had some definite ideas about good and bad farming. Estate regulations were drawn up to ensure that land was not being wasted.[15]  At that time land was often ruined by being " skinned ". Broad-bladed spades, " flaughter spades ", would take off a thin paring of turf to put over the wattling in houses before the thatch went on, or for making sod walls. Turf was even mixed with used thatch and the droppings of animals to augment the supply of farmyard manure, and parings were also used as fuel. The skinned land—the land from which the turf was taken—was impoverished by the process and on the Ury estate the taking of turf was limited to specified places. No more than four successive crops could be taken from outfield land and on steep ground special measures were taken to prevent erosion.

[10] *Urie Court Book*, pp. xxxviii-xxxix.          [11] *op. cit.*, p. l.
[12] *A.P.S.*, VOL. IV, p. 629.                      [13] *Urie Court Book*, p. 98.
[14] *op. cit.*, p. 92.                              [15] *op. cit.*, p. 158.

It was enacted that all existing steep land should not be worked for more than three years at a time, after which it had to be rested for nine years. Care was also taken to ensure the orderly cutting of peats, to prevent wastage of the moss. Muirburn regulations were drawn up, while a tenant who was giving up the tenancy of a farm was forbidden, under penalty of a hundred pounds Scots, to overcrop his land before way-go. Wood used for building houses remained the property of the tenant who, on his way-go, was compelled to leave it, but provision was made in 1712 for the incoming tenant to take it over at valuation. This step was taken to prevent the outgoing tenant from pulling down the walls, which he was likely to do in order to remove the wood.[16]

The Acts of 1426 and 1457 decreeing that tenants who were owners of plough teams (seven oxen) must sow at least a firlot of wheat, half a firlot of peas and forty beans, could scarcely be complied with where the land and climate were unsuitable for wheat growing, as was largely the case at Ury; so in this instance the estate forced tenants occupying a " plough " of land to sow a firlot of peas or beans. The smaller tenants sowed these crops in quantities proportionate to the land they occupied.[17] " Birley " men were appointed to settle vexed questions regarding trespass, boundaries and valuation. Although in a sense they were servants of the landlord, their decisions were usually accepted in good spirit.[18] We learn from the records of the Baron's Court that the tenant of Monquich, finding himself domiciled in the old mansion house of that subsidiary estate and being either too poor or too lazy to repair his farm buildings, housed his " hors " in the hall and " chalmeris ".[19]

During the period 1604-72 prices for farm animals did not fluctuate greatly. For the purposes of rent collection the value of each kind of animal was calculated as a fixed proportion of the value of others. Thus about 1620 a fowl was worth 3s. 4d., a capon 6s. 8d., a wether or wedder £3. 6s. 8d., a swine £6. 13s. 4d., a cow £10 and a " mart " from £10 to £13. 6s. 8d. These prices were all in Scots money, now worth only a twelfth of the corresponding English coinage. Meal and bere prices on the contrary fluctuated considerably according to abundance or scarcity.[20] In 1621 bere was priced at £5 per boll and the price of oatmeal was probably about the same.

[16] *Urie Court Book*, pp. xlix, 116.
[17] *op. cit.*, pp. 124-5.
[18] *op. cit.*, p. xlix.
[19] *op. cit.*, p. 24.
[20] *op. cit.*, p. 181.

Its average price about 1600 was only about 40s. but sometimes rose to £10 per boll.

One other feature of this Court administration may be noted. In the reign of James VI provision was made whereby the " deserving " poor were licensed by the Kirk Sessions to beg within the bounds of a parish or, if the parish were very large, within the bounds of a part. Those authorised were required to wear little stamps of lead on their gowns for identification. At Ury the Baron's Court also took steps to support the poor by collecting " vagabond " money, half from the proprietor and half from the tenants.

In England and Scotland the poor in medieval times enjoyed the charity of both Church and individual. The Christian religion enforced almsgiving as a duty, but by the sixteenth century voluntary almsgiving was found in England to be inadequate, and the principle of compulsory relief was applied in Queen Elizabeth's reign through the medium of the newly-introduced Poor Law.[21] In Scotland, too, Parliament permitted the levying of an assessment for the poor and impotent, but advantage was seldom taken of this and in practice provision for the poor consisted of licensed begging, together with the funds under the control of the kirk sessions derived from church collections and occasional fees and fines.

Just before the court at Ury ceased to operate in 1747 there were complaints that too many houses were being built and that the mosses were in danger of being used up too quickly. Steps were accordingly taken to limit the number of houses on the estate. Cottars and grassmen were allowed to keep cattle on payment of a grazing rent which varied with the season : in 1636 the grazing rent for an ox was 16s. 8d. This privilege encouraged overstocking of the pastures and proprietors were thus concerned to limit the numbers of all classes of tenants to the resources of their estates.

Husbandmen on the Ury estate were divided into two classes, the maillories and the fermories, according to whether they paid their rents, exclusive of services, in the form of maillie (money) or ferme (grain).[22] The maillories paid their rents at Whitsunday and Martinmas, the fermories delivered their oats to the landlord's store at Candlemas and their barley or bere on Rood Day. In addition to these grain and corn rents stock rents were payable. In 1604 the tenant of Balnageithe (" ane pleuche ") paid as rent ten bolls of victual, one mart, one wedder, a dozen capons and a dozen

[21] Ernle, *English Farming*, p. 74.
[22] *Urie Court Book*, pp. xliii, lii, liii, liv.

poultry. Another farm, Cairntoune, consisting also of one " pleuch "
evidently either larger in extent or else of better quality soil, had
the same rent as Balnageithe except that the grain rent was twenty
bolls instead of ten and two wedders instead of one.

Besides grain and stock rents many other dues and services
were obligatory.[23] The teind silver had to be rendered, taxes
collected for the upkeep of the schoolmaster, the smithy and the
poor, and at the beginning of a lease the much-resented grassum
had to be paid. The tenants who were " suckeners " of a particular
mill had not only to render every thirteenth peck of meal, but also
to give a certain amount to the miller's servant. Tenants on the
Cowie estate, which was outside the sucken, got their grain ground
on easier terms. The frequent disputes between miller and tenants
recorded in the Urie court book indicate how greatly thirlage and
services connected with the upkeep of the mill were resented.
General services to the estate were of the usual character, digging,
winning and conveying peats, long carriage to Aberdeen, assistance
at the home farm at seed-time and harvest, and maintaining the
mill lade, clearing it of weeds in summer and ice in winter and
bringing home the millstones.

How far the wise and orderly administration of the Ury estate
was typical cannot be determined, but the *Black Book of Taymouth*
provides a record of how an estate in the Highland portion of
Perthshire was run in the seventeenth century.[24] The estate regulations in this case were comprehensive. They regulated muirburn,
which was only to be carried out in March, forbade poaching of
game, provided rules for the upkeep of the head dykes and ensured
that the humbler people had gardens in which they might grow
kale and have facilities for procuring fuel. Dwelling houses at out-
go had to be left in as good condition as they were at in-go. There
was also a regulation, probably the survival of an old superstition,
forbidding the cutting of briars and thorns at the waning of the
moon. Provision was made for land to be irrigated, drained and
supplied with manure. Trees had to be planted and young plants
had to be supplied by the gardener. The keeping of swine was
forbidden and permission was required to cut broom. Woodlands
had to be cared for by the tenants. All horses, cattle and sheep had
to be pastured beyond the head dykes between 1st May and 8th

---

[23] *Urie Court Book*, p. xliv.
[24] *The Black Book of Taymouth*, ed. C. Innes, Bannatyne Club, Edinburgh
1885, pp. 352-6.

G

June; then until 15th July they had to be grazed on the distant
shielings. Every tenant had to make four " crosscattes " of iron
for slaying wolves, which at that time still roamed the Highlands
although in much decreased numbers. War had to be waged on
" rucks, hoodit craws and pyats " (rooks, hooded crows and magpies).
The people had to avoid local disputes. So much white oats, as
opposed to the old grey oats, had to be sown. There were regulations about the sale of ale, the upkeep of the mill, trespass of stock
and its penalties. There had to be enough pounds to accommodate
trespassing animals. Penalties were prescribed for transgressing
the numerous regulations. Some tenants on this estate were, it
appears, on the steelbow system of tenure. A full-time " feal "
(turf) dyker was kept and received as an annual wage in the year
1630 20 merks and 20s. for travelling expenses along with a stone
of cheese, a pair of shoes and meat and drink.[25] One gathers from
these records that agriculture even in the Highlands was not so
backward as it has generally been depicted.

The Restoration of 1660 was an event of paramount importance
to both nations. From this time onwards we may trace a certain
quickening of spirit and action in Scotland and a growing tendency
to question slavish adherence to time-honoured customs, traditions
and practices. The Scots Parliament became more concerned with
the development of the country's resources, its sessions of 1661,
1663, 1669, 1685, 1686 and 1695 being notable for their attention
to agriculture. Thus the enclosure (i.e. fencing) of land was encouraged by Acts passed in 1661, 1669, 1685 and 1695; in 1663
duties were imposed on the importation of Irish grain; in 1672
importation of Irish meal was forbidden when the price was under a
certain figure; in 1669 the considerable duty on the export of grain
was replaced by a nominal charge and in 1695 grain exports were
encouraged by a subsidy. These measures were designed to encourage farmers to put down more land to grain and so even out
the extreme price fluctuations between good and bad years.[26]

In Dunbar's *Social Life in Former Days* mention is made of
the *Penelope of Pittenweim* being chartered in 1679 to convey
800 bolls of " bear " (bere) from " Ferrieoyus ", Sutherland, to a
Norwegian port where the ship would be loaded with timber.[27] On
the return journey the ship would unload its cargo of " daills "

---

[25] *The Black Book of Taymouth*, pp. 421-2.
[26] R. Chambers, *Domestic Annals*, VOL. III, Edinburgh 1861, p. 137.
[27] Dunbar, *Social Life in Moray*, p. 115.

(deals) and take other 800 bolls of bear to Rotterdam. In the next century we read that considerable quantities of grain collected as rent from the Monymusk tenants were shipped at Aberdeen.

In 1641 Parliament decreed that the export of eggs should be stopped, in the hope that the " poore laboureing people and servants who eat only bread and drink water " might, because of the consequential fall in the price, find them sufficiently cheap to use.[28] In the years 1641 and 1686 Acts were passed to encourage flax growing, one unfortunate result being that people retted their flax in inland lochs, so poisoning the fish; preventive measures then had to be taken. Another Act was designed to encourage the making of spirits at home. A statute of 1641 prohibited the importation of spirituous liquor.

An Act passed in 1686—the Winter Herding Act—ordained that " heretors, liferenters, tenents and cotters . . . . . herd their horses, nolt, sheep, suyne and goats the wholl year alse weell in winter as in summer and in night tyme shall cause keep the same in houses, folds or inclosures ". The object was twofold, first to prevent trespass on the unfenced patches of crop during the growing season, and secondly to keep animals from damaging young trees and hedges. Owners of animals found trespassing were liable to pay half a merk for each animal, and the owner of the ground on which the animals were found had power to detain them until the fines and expenses for keep were paid. This Act has never been repealed and was cited recently in cases where sheep from the Lanarkshire hills trespassed in private gardens. On conviction the stipulated fine of half a merk was imposed.

As noted earlier the commons or commonties in Scotland were regarded as the undivided property of proprietors whose land adjoined. By Acts passed in 1669 and 1685 any proprietor with an interest in such land could take steps to compel a division. One Act passed in 1695 enabled owners of lands worked in run-rig to have them disentangled and reallocated; another empowered the Court of Session to divide the commonties among the proprietors claiming rights over them should a request be made. These Acts paved the way for the agricultural revolution of the eighteenth century. Another Act passed in the same year and doubtless inspired by the Culbin disaster, forbade the pulling of bent, juniper and broom on sandhills.

[28] *A.P.S.*, VOL. v, ed. C. Innes, p. 421.

One definite advance made in agriculture besides the introduction of fallowing is to be recorded. Elsewhere, in Chapter XX, it is mentioned how the ill-fated Galloway laird, Sir David Dunbar,[29] established his great park at Baldoon where he kept 1000 head of cattle, selling the surplus animals at four years of age as stores for fattening on the rich pastures of the Norfolk marshes. His example in rearing stores for the English market was followed by a number of Galloway and Ayrshire lairds. The growing trade in store cattle with England led, however, to difficulties associated with wayleave and trespass when the droves of cattle were being driven towards the Border. To overcome these, a well-defined drove road was marked out between New Galloway and Dumfries. The Road Act of 1669 stipulated that a road passing through land on which crops were growing had to be fenced. In Scotland, generally, drovers became expert in discovering drove roads where trespass or passage money was either not demanded or could be easily paid.

In this century Parliament realised the need for the better upkeep of the roads, which were quagmires in wet weather and morasses in winter. Only travellers on foot or on horseback could use them and then only by making constant detours. There were few bridges over the large rivers and goods were transported by pack horses or by sea. In 1617 and again in 1661 the matter was considered in Parliament, proceedings which led to the passing of the Road Act of 1669 referred to above. It made the Sheriffs and Justices of the Peace in the various counties responsible for the upkeep of the highways, the labour being provided by the male inhabitants, every one of whom between the ages of fifteen and sixty had to turn out to repair the roads on so many days of the year—six days for three years after the Act was passed, and four thereafter. Although action was taken in 1670 to avoid calling out men at seed-time and harvest the labour was grudgingly given and ineffectively employed. No one seems to have understood the principles of road-making. Holes and ruts were merely filled up with soft material and the supposed " levelling " merely concealed the more dangerous parts, making the roads, if anything, more treacherous.

In England great advances in agriculture were made during this century. A famous Dutch engineer, Cornelius Vermuyden, was brought over from Holland to drain the fenlands. Catchwater drains were made, and rivers were embanked, to prevent water

---

[29] Chambers, *Domestic Annals*, VOL. III, p. 152.

pouring over the fens. The intercepted waters were conveyed and discharged either into the rivers at points lower downstream or into the sea. The problem of draining the fens was thus largely one of dealing with surface rainwater. Scoop wheels operated by wind power were used to raise the water from low level to higher level ditches and so on to the sea. In 1651 over 1000 Scots prisoners were employed on the work. In Scotland little was done during this century to improve arterial drainage. The Pow of Inchaffray in Perthshire appears, however, to have been twice cleaned, steps being taken in 1641 and 1696 to carry out the maintenance works and to apportion the expense between the different proprietors. In the early years of the century a cutting was made through rocks at Loth in Sutherland to enable the waters of the Loth burn to pass directly into the sea, thus freeing a large area of land for cropping. Other drainage works were carried out in the Saughton-Corstorphine district in 1661.

Royalist squires, forced to fly to the Continent at the close of the Civil War, returned to England at the Restoration and practised the improved methods of cultivation they had seen in Holland and elsewhere. A century earlier an English writer, Barnaby Googe, in his book *Foure Bookes of Husbandrie* (1577) had recommended turnips as a field crop but the practice of growing them had never caught on until Weston and other Royalists returned from the Low Countries. Now turnips and clover were introduced and popularised.[30] But Scotland, too preoccupied with internal struggles and religious strife, and too intensely nationalistic or proud to follow suit, did not adopt these field crops until nearly a century later.

Nevertheless, there were areas where improvements could be and were made as, for example, in Kintyre.[31] Yet despite these advances and the legislative measures taken by Parliament to encourage grain growing, protection of crops from trespass by stock, consolidation of run-rig lands, enclosures and maintenance of roads, this century can be described as the dark period that precedes the dawn. Had he lived longer Cromwell, who was conscious of the backward state of Scottish agriculture, might have expedited developments. Commissioners were appointed in 1650 by the English Parliament to improve lands in Scotland but apparently nothing was done. So long as Scottish farmers were content

[30] Ernle, *English Farming*, p. 107.     [31] See p. 129.

NOTTINGHAM
UNIVERSITY
SCHOOL OF
AGRICULTURE
LIBRARY

to work undrained, unenclosed, weed-ridden, over-acid and exhausted lands with inefficient tools, and so long as they grazed their animals in common, followed no constructive breeding policy, and provided their farm animals with insufficient winter food, progress was out of the question. A radical change in outlook was needed to rouse Scottish agriculture from her centuries-old sleep and to set in motion those forces which ultimately made Scottish farming so famous.

# CHAPTER VII

# THE DAWN : 1700-1749

Dismal dawn of the century...Rural Scotland described...
Customs of the times...Effect of the Union of Parliaments...John Cockburn of Ormiston...New crops and
methods...Barley mill and fanner...Grass and clover seeds
introduced...Planting of Binning Woods...Society of Improvers
founded...Work of John, Earl of Stair, Craik of Arbigland...
Sir Archibald Grant of Monymusk...Liming and burning
land...Potatoes grown on farms...Store cattle trade...The
Levellers, Abolition of heritable jurisdictions.

THE EIGHTEENTH CENTURY, which was to see Scotland initiate
her agricultural and industrial revolution, began in settled
gloom. There had been a run of extremely bad seasons
characterised by blight and famine. Felt as early as 1693 [1] in some
parts, by 1695 in most, the pinch continued until 1702. These
" seven ill years " or " King William's dear years ", as they were
significantly called, brought disaster and death. The summers
were sunless, cold and rainy; grain crops failed to ripen; early
frosts put an end to the maturing process, and fields were being
shorn in December, January and February in a desperate attempt
to salvage part of the ruined crops.[2]

For lack of food many people perished. On the group farm of
Littertie, in Monquitter parish, Aberdeenshire, thirteen of the
sixteen resident families were "extinguished".[3] So ill nourished
were the people that the living could scarcely carry the dead to the
churchyard; on the approach of death people were said to crawl
to the kirkyards to ensure decent burial. The population of many
parishes was reduced, partly by death, partly by exodus, to a half.
Prices of provisions rose to extortionate levels, yet not until the
height of the scarcity did the Privy Council admit foreign grain
free of duty. In Cromarty oats rose to ten times their former price.[4]

---

[1] Alexander, *Notes and Sketches*, p. 42.
[2] Graham, *Social Life*, p. 146.          [3] *F.S.A.*, VOL. VI, p. 132.
[4] Sir John Sinclair, *General View of the Agriculture of the Northern Counties
and Islands of Scotland*, henceforth cited as Sinclair, *Agric. Northern Counties*,
London 1795, p. 9.

People had not the wherewithal to buy food. Fletcher of Saltoun, a fiery republican patriot, reckoned that two hundred thousand of Scotland's population of a million begged their living from door to door.[5] Though probably a wild guess this statement reflected the country's general state of destitution. Thousands of sheep and cattle died and to add to Scotland's misfortunes the Darien Scheme, from which so much had been hoped, proved a miserable fiasco.[6]

There was bitter resentment against England in these years.[7] She was blamed for not helping Scotland in her hour of need. Each country regarded the other with so much distrust that passions engendered by centuries of wars and political strife were fanned into flame at the time of the negotiations for the Treaty of Union. So strong were the feelings against England that the more ardent Scots condemned the then considerable trade in store cattle between the two countries. The significance of this was great since Scottish store cattle, poor as they were and poor as were the prices they fetched, brought money into the country and Scotland was desperately in need of cash, Poverty, tariffs and bad roads hindered commerce; hardly any coin was in circulation and the Scots pound was worth only one-twelfth of the English pound.

It was indeed an unhappy era. Landlords, unable to find tenants with sufficient capital to stock their farms, let them in steelbow, *i.e.* with stock, implements, and seed as well as the land. On the Erroll estate, Aberdeenshire, so many tenants had deserted their farms that the proprietors turned their holdings into sheep walks.[8] For the first thirty years no more than sixteen years' purchase could be obtained for Aberdeenshire land rented at ridiculously low figures.[9] To add to the miseries of the people there was pronounced ill feeling in the spheres of politics and religion. Quarrels on these accounts between the various members of a plough team would sometimes delay ploughing for weeks at a time.

To English travellers, unaccustomed to see vast stretches of treeless landscape, infertile moorlands, wide areas of morass, miserable tracks serving as roads, meagre and weedy crops of oats and bere often growing in irregular-shaped patches on rocky hillsides, ill-bred and half-starved cattle, horses, sheep and pigs, and

[5] G. M. Trevelyan, *English Social History*, henceforth cited as Trevelyan, *Social History*, London 1944, p. 434.

[6] Graham, *Social Life*, pp. 506-07.

[7] Trevelyan, *Social History*, pp. 432-7.

[8] Alexander, *Notes and Sketches*, p. 44.        [9] *op. cit.*, pp. 1-2.

mean thatch-covered houses with walls of turf and unquarried stone, the land presented a desolate prospect. Despite the Act of 1695 little or no attempt was made to consolidate run-rig lands until about 1730. Sloth, ignorance and poverty seemed then to be the dominant characteristics of the Scots.

If to English eyes this was a true picture of the Lowlands the condition of the Highlands beggared description and some uncanny tales were rife about that part of Scotland. Unused as the southerners usually were to wild scenery, the rugged mist-topped mountains, the naked rocks, the narrow valleys and the bleak open moorlands appeared forbidding indeed, while the people in unfamiliar dress and speaking a strange tongue had the appearance of savages. Edward Burt, an Englishman in the service of Marshal Wade, wrote to a friend about 1730 that " the huge naked rocks produce the appearance of a scabbed head " and that the sight of the hills was " most disagreeable of all when the heath is in bloom ".[10] Until the time of Robert Burns with his songs and Sir Walter Scott with his poems and romances, no Scottish poet or writer of eminence had been inspired to sing the praises of this land of brown heath and shaggy wood, to depict the incomparable beauty of its hills and valleys, lochs and rivers, to romanticise on its past or to describe with kindly pen the characteristics of its people.

Throughout Scotland the common food of the people was derived from oats. Porridge, brose, sowans and oatcakes were the daily fare and formed the main article of diet at every meal. Other foods included barley bannocks, peasemeal brose, salt herring, sea fish and shell-fish in maritime areas, kail broth thickened with barley or oat groats, salmon from the rivers, salt meat in the richer households, butter, cheese, or crowdy (a crude form of cheese), and an occasional egg or even a fowl. Home-brewed ale, whey and milk served as drink. At this period scarcely any beef was consumed in households of the common folk. Poor as was the price of cattle, the money they fetched when sold as stores was preferred to their meat.

Inns were the last word in wretchedness and discomfort and were avoided by the landed classes. Instead they chose, when travelling, to stay in each other's houses. The tall, ungainly, corbel-stepped gable-roof buildings which served them as homes, though

---

[10] Edward Burt or Birt, *Letters from a Gentleman in the North of Scotland to his Friend in London*, henceforth cited as Burt, *Letters*, 3rd edn. London 1815, VOL. I, pp. 282-5.

lacking in comfort, were to be preferred to the wretched hostelries. Like the common people the gentry made much use of oatmeal, but in the matter of flesh foods they fared much better than their tenants. They had salt meat all winter and for fresh meat had the " kain " hens, which formed part of the rent paid by the tenants, winged or protected ground game that could be shot or snared on the moorlands, " doos " from the " doo cot "—there were 360 of these " doo cots " in Fife at the end of the century [11]—and fish caught in the rivers. In some of the gardens attached to gentlemen's houses many kinds of vegetables and some fruit, mostly apples and gooseberries and, in favoured spots, pears, were grown. Every cottar had his " kail yaird ". Kail was a specific against scurvy, a disease to which the people were prone, and kail brose and broth were popular articles of diet. Hospitality, rude as it was, was practised by all classes. From far and near people would flock to parish communions and would stay for days at a time. In the houses of the landlords guests would arrive unexpectedly and were welcomed as a matter of course, the groom taking charge of the horses. No questions would be asked, nor information volunteered as to the length of stay.

One such visitor, so the story goes, arrived on horseback at the house of a Fife laird and lingered on. Then came the day when he decided to go. His mare was ordered to be saddled but no mare was forthcoming, the groom explaining that the mare " had deed [died] twa years syne " adding, significantly, " Afore she deed she left a fine horse foal that micht tak ye awa ".

The language spoken by all classes, except in the Highlands, was broad Lowland Scots. Landlords mingled freely with their tenants who conversed with them on terms of intimacy. Both had sat on the same bench at school; both attended the same kirk and each knew a good deal about the other's affairs.[12] In times of distress many landlords were kind to their tenants, but their own poverty limited the assistance they could give, and bad seasons were frequent. If tenants were impoverished the landlords were at least impecunious.

The Union of Parliaments in 1707 was an event of the greatest importance to Scottish agriculture. On their journeys to and from London Scottish members of Parliament were much impressed

---

[11] J. Thomson, *General View of the Agriculture of the County of Fife*, henceforth cited as Thomson, *Agric. Fife*, London 1800, p. 270.

[12] Trevelyan, *Social History*, p. 428.

by improvements in farm practice in England, a country hitherto practically unknown to Scotsmen. Land was being enclosed, farms consolidated and fields shaped and surrounded by hedges; turnips and red clover—crops hitherto unknown—were being introduced from the Continent, new and improved implements were to be seen, and rotational systems of cropping were being devised. The turnip crop, in particular, was now beginning to play a noticeable part in promoting an all-round improvement in English farming.

The land had to be thoroughly cultivated and cleaned before the crop could be laid down, and well fertilised to ensure a good yield. This crop enabled farmers to provide their animals with ample winter food. Larger and better cattle could thus be produced and winter-fattening practised. More dung could be made and the level of soil fertility stepped up. To protect the crop from stock after harvest the turnip land had to be enclosed, a process which led to the abandonment of run-rig and to the consolidation of farms. It was only after turnips had been introduced that rotations were adopted. In these rotations it became customary to lay down the land periodically to a crop of rye-grass and red clover. Profitable temporary pastures could now replace the unprofitable outfield. The inclusion of these crops in the system of husbandry had thus a profound effect in raising the general standard of farming.

So manifest were the improvements that a few Scottish members of Parliament and others, who had travelled in England, resolved to introduce some of the new practices into farming routine in their own areas. One of the first to do so was John Cockburn (1679-1758) who represented the county of Haddington. The eldest son of Adam Cockburn, Lord Justice-Clerk for Scotland and proprietor of the estate of Ormiston in East Lothian, John Cockburn had been a member of the old Scots Parliament and had actively assisted the negotiations leading to Union.[13]

Although his Parliamentary duties involved long absences from home he nevertheless took the greatest interest in the agricultural and social development of the family estate at Ormiston. In 1714 John assumed management of the estate and before long put some of his ideas into practice. He held strong views about the short leases then customary, which he considered effectively debarred tenants from improving land; he thought long leases would provide a much needed incentive. In 1718 on behalf of his father he granted

[13] William Anderson, *The Scottish Nation*, Edinburgh 1860-63, VOL. I, pp. 659-60.

Robert Wight, the sitting tenant of Murrays, or Muirhouse farm, a thirty-eight years' lease. Thereafter, upon payment of £1200 Scots, the equivalent of £100 sterling, the lease was to be renewed for further periods of nineteen years indefinitely. This was Cockburn's plan to encourage tenants to improve land not only for themselves but also, as he expressed it "that their children's children would be advantaged". A contemporary averred that his leases were arranged for three lives.

The immediate result was that Wight, the first of a famous family of East Lothian farmers, began to plan how to lay out and enclose his fields. Boundary ditches were dug; the excavated earth was heaped on one side and on the top of the ridge thus formed hedges of white and black thorn, elder and privet were established. Nor were considerations of beauty ignored in the construction of these hedges. Occasional plants of honeysuckle were put in, while at intervals in the hedges single trees of various kinds were planted, a procedure which evidently did not commend itself to certain tenants.[14] John Cockburn followed these developments with the greatest interest and his correspondence shows that he kept in close touch with Wight and his gardener, Charles Bell. He gave detailed instructions about the preparation of the turnip and potato land, the sowing of grass and clover seeds and how land should be fallowed and laid down to wheat. He was of opinion that East Lothian was a fine but neglected county for barley growing.

Claims to have been the first to grow turnips in the field are not easily settled. The Earl of Rothes is said to have grown them in 1716.[15] Wight, Cockburn's tenant, was probably the first tenant farmer to cultivate them in drills. He was growing them as early as 1724 and his success is proved by the fact that one root which he grew, and which was exhibited as a curiosity in Edinburgh, weighed 34¾ lb. From Cockburn's correspondence with Wight it seems that the turnips were grown in rows and that they were sometimes sown and thinned much too late to yield a full crop. In a letter dated 18th August 1725 Cockburn points out to Wight that

[14] In a letter dated 9th October 1739 Cockburn tells Bell, his gardener, to plant a horse-chestnut tree in a hedge, but to slip it in without the knowledge of David Wight, the tenant. John Cockburn, *Letters to his Gardener 1727-44*, ed. James Colville, henceforth cited as Cockburn, *Letters*, Scottish History Society VOL. XLV, Edinburgh 1904, pp. xxv, 47.

[15] Sir Arthur Grant, "Description of the present state of Monymusk", henceforth cited as Grant, "State of Monymusk", in *Miscellany of the Spalding Club*, ed. J. Stuart, VOL. II, Aberdeen, 1842, p. 96.

they should have been hoed (singled) earlier. Other tenants on the same estate were induced by similar long leases to improve their farms. Meantime Cockburn was doing his best to lay out the policy grounds at Ormiston. Sweet chestnuts, oriental planes, evergreen oaks and silver firs were planted and wall and espalier fruit trees were established in the garden.

After succeeding to the estate in 1734 Cockburn rebuilt the village of Ormiston. Today its wide street and its trees give it a spacious, dignified and attractive appearance which readily distinguishes it from so many of Scotland's ugly and badly planned villages. Feus on advantageous terms were granted to householders but only on condition that the houses built would conform to specified standards. Flax-growing and its processing and weaving into linen were actively encouraged. Skilled workers were obtained from Ireland to familiarise the local people with the best methods of manufacture, and the second bleachfield in Scotland was set up. The erection of a brewery and distillery provided a market for locally grown barley. But the apathy, indolence, conservatism and sometimes even the antagonism of the people severely tried Cockburn's patience. It was no easy matter to awaken them to a sense of the possibility of improving their way of life and standard of living and this reluctance he attributed largely to their low diet. " Delays ", he wrote, " were a great delight to the people in Scotland; being punctual is a great sin in our country."

His passion for agricultural and social improvement induced him in 1736 to form a local constituent society of the Edinburgh Society of Improvers to which reference will be made later. One of the aims of the original society was to establish similar bodies in other parts of Scotland. One was set up in Buchan in Aberdeenshire in 1730, another at Ratho in Midlothian. The flourishing Ormiston society, of which Cockburn was chairman, had at one time 122 members.

But despite his energy, zeal and vision Cockburn died poor in worldly wealth. The long leases which he arranged with Wight and others benefited the tenants but brought only inadequate returns to the landlord during this period of inflation. For his own improvements he borrowed money, and the estate, which was pledged to raise a loan of £10,000, had eventually to be sold. Scottish agriculture, however, owes him an inestimable debt of gratitude for he was its first great improver. He had introduced the system of long leases, made enclosures, reallocated scattered and intermixed lands into compact blocks, encouraged the making of open drains and the planting of hedges, taught the preparation of land for turnips and potatoes, advocated the use of fallows, fattened cattle and sheep, planted trees extensively, promoted horticulture, striven to develop the keeping of better poultry by offers of sittings of eggs, sought the advancement of rural industries, aimed at providing a sound pattern for village planning and helped to foster in the minds of the people a true sense of artistic values. Cockburn was indeed the father of Scottish agriculture.[16]

In these early days the Lothians were in the vanguard of agricultural progress.     Mention is made elsewhere of how James Meikle, an ingenious mechanic, went in 1710 to Holland at the instigation of Fletcher of Saltoun to try to discover the secret of making pearl or decorticated barley.  His quest was successful. On his return to East Lothian he erected the first barley mill and provided Scotland with its first winnowing machine.[17]

Mrs Henry Fletcher, Fletcher's sister-in-law, was the moving spirit in this enterprise of pearl barley making.  For long she was able to guard the secret of its making and so established a monopoly. Another lady instrumental in promoting agriculture and arboriculture was the Countess of Haddington.  For her sake, the sixth Earl (1680-1735) abandoned his beloved field sports to further the interests of farming and of forestry.  He introduced fallowing on the advice of some Dorset farmers, and as early as 1708 is reported to have been sowing rye-grass and clover seeds.  The local people regarded these innovations as a misuse of good land—growing " English weeds " for stock when it might have been growing food for the people.[18]  On the wind-swept sandy lands of Tyninghame the Earl began to plant trees which in time developed into the much-famed Binning Woods.

But the mainspring of the movement to transform Scotland's agriculture came from the city of Edinburgh.  On 8th June 1723 the Honourable the Society of Improvers was founded.  A fuller account of its membership, activities and widespread influence is given elsewhere.[19]  Here it may be noted that Maxwell, its indefatigable secretary, had leased the farm of Cliftonhall near

---

[16] Anon., " John Cockburn of Ormiston ", in *The Farmer's Magazine*, v (1804), pp. 129-47.
[17] Graham, *Social Life*, pp. 173-4.  See pp. 382-3.
[18] John Walker, *An Economical History of the Hebrides*, henceforth cited as Walker, *History Hebrides*, Edinburgh 1808, VOL. I, p. 190 ; Graham, *Social Life*, p. 171.                        [19] See p. 302.

Edinburgh and was vigorously putting some of his precepts into practice.

One person whom the Society inspired was John, Earl of Stair (1679-1747). After a distinguished career as a soldier and diplomat, he settled down at home to practise improved methods of husbandry on his estates in West Lothian and Wigtownshire. He is said to have been the first to grow turnips and cabbages in the field, a claim made for other improvers elsewhere.[20] He reallocated and enclosed land, drained marshes, made roads and limed land. He introduced an improved plough and established the fine woods that adorn Newliston in West Lothian. On his Wigtownshire estate half a million trees were planted.

In Galloway, Craik of Arbigland (1703-98) was a notable improver. Influenced by some of Jethro Tull's writings on drill husbandry, he devised machines for sowing all his crops by drill. He used ploughs drawn by two horses and was the first (about 1745) to make turnip growing in Galloway a practical proposition. He was regarded as the father of agriculture in Dumfries and Galloway,[21] and his work was known and his example followed by progressive farmers in Berwickshire and Cumberland. In Moray the urge to improve was stimulated by Henrietta Mordaunt, daughter of the Earl of Peterborough. In 1706 she married the eldest son of the Duke of Gordon and to her Moray home brought English ploughs and men to work them. These men introduced fallowing and hay-making to Moray. She planted moors and like the Earl of Haddington sowed "foreign" grasses.[22] She introduced a new style of architecture and her skill in planning gardens did much to encourage gardening at mansion houses. Another noted improver at this time was the Earl of Rothes.

Though few in number the pioneers of agricultural improvement in the first half of the eighteenth century were most energetic. Amongst them the fame of Sir Archibald Grant of Monymusk ranks high. In the year 1715 his father, Lord Cullen, purchased the old Forbes and Priory lands of Monymusk in Aberdeenshire. Their condition was then pitiful, so much so that he began to rue

---

[20] Anderson, *Scottish Nation*, VOL. III, p. 505.

[21] W. Singer, *View of the Agriculture, State of the Property and Improvements in the County of Dumfries*, henceforth cited as Singer, *Agric. Dumfries*, Edinburgh 1812, p. 221.

[22] William Mackintosh, *Essay on Ways and Means of inclosing, fallowing planting, &c. Scotland, and that in Sixteen Years at farthest*, Edinburgh 1729, p. xliii.

the bargain. About 1716, however, he entrusted the management of the estate to his son Archibald, then a young man of twenty. Archibald's task was difficult for no part of the estate was enclosed; the farms were badly laid out, the tenants occupying alternate crooked rigs, the fertility of which, through continual cropping and lack of proper tillage, was low; and there was practically no timber on the estate. " The farmehouses, and even the corn millns, mans [manse] and scool were all poor, dirty hutts, pulled in pieces for manure or fell of themselves almost each alternate year ".[23] There was no wheeled vehicle on the estate nor, for that matter, any road on which a carriage could safely be used. One house was described as having " no dor, no windo, no lum ".[24] The condition of the people was equally deplorable: Sir Archibald described them as poor, ignorant, slothful and confirmed opponents to planting, enclosing, improvements or cleanliness.

Determined to improve matters, the young man began with the home farm, enclosing the land and portioning it out into fields. Ditches were dug, boulders cleared, stone dykes erected and crops such as peas, vetches, beans, turnips, the clovers and rye-grass introduced. The " scourging " crops—cereals—were alternated with " meliorating " ones—the legumes and root crops. An English manager was appointed and English horses, harness and ploughs were purchased. Tree planting was started and in due time wide stretches of waste were covered with plantations of beech, alder, oak, elm and fir. At the outset his tenants, who were concerned about the curtailment of the grazing area of the common pasture, bitterly resented the planting of trees. Under cover of night fences were pulled down, young trees wantonly destroyed and the labours of years ruthlessly wasted. Almost in vain, it would seem, Sir Archibald tried to convince his tenants of the folly of their ways. By persistent persuasion, by the insertion of conditions in their leases, and by exercising his rights at the Baron's Court of Monymusk, he eventually overcame their resistance and some millions of trees—some authors mention fifty millions—were planted during his lifetime. His improvements were not confined to land, for he tried to raise the whole standard of social life and living of the people. A striking tribute was paid him by John Wesley who visited Monymusk in 1761. In his Journal he tells how he listened to a choir of thirty or forty people singing " an anthem after sermon with

---

[23] Grant, " State of Monymusk ", p. 97.
[24] *Monymusk Papers*, ed. Hamilton, p. 15.

such voices as well as judgement, that I doubt whether they could have been excelled in any cathedral in England ".[25] This was remarkable praise when it is recalled that at that time church music in Scotland was seriously neglected.

It was well into the century before Sir Archibald began to reap the full rewards of his work as an improver. In the interval, however, a remarkable change had taken place, for Monymusk had been transformed from a bleak, treeless waste into one of the most beautiful estates in the country. A stretch of woodland bordering the river Don, named Paradise, does not belie its name. Other notable tree-planters were John, Duke of Atholl, and Farquharson of Invercauld.

From the manuscripts of John Ramsay, Ochtertyre, in the Perthshire portion of the Carse of Stirling we derive interesting information about improvements in central Scotland at this time, for it was then that liming first came to be extensively practised in that area. The use of lime in agriculture had, however, been known much earlier. Thus about 1633 it was mentioned in connexion with a valuation process for tithe purposes on an estate in the Forth valley.[26] We know, too, that after the Clackmannanshire estate of Tullibody had passed to a new proprietor he arranged with his tenants as to the price payable for lime supplied from a deposit at Cambus. Before the end of the seventeenth century boatloads of lime were being landed at places below Abbey Craig on the Forth. The first to go up river beyond this point was for a Mr Galloway, of Cornton near Bridge of Allan.[27] The lime was conveyed from the landing-place by sledges and tumbrils, for at that time there were no wheeled carts in the area nor roads fit to carry them. The first cart in the Dunblane area only appeared about 1730.[28]

In a wild part of the estate of Sauchie a limestone deposit was discovered, but the stone, though excellent in quality, had to be carried away on the backs of horses. In the absence of proper roads and of bridges over rivers like the Forth no real advance was possible in the liming of land. Moreover, it was then customary to burn lime at the farm, probably because of the difficulties of supplying

[25] John Wesley, *Journal*, Everyman edn. London 1906, VOL. III, p. 54.

[26] John Ramsay, *Scotland and Scotsmen in the Eighteenth Century*, ed. A. Allardyce, henceforth cited as Ramsay, *Scotland and Scotsmen*, Edinburgh 1888, VOL. II, p. 205 *n*.

[27] *op. cit.*, p. 252 *n*.     [28] *op. cit.*, p. 220 *n*.

H

adequate fuel for the kilns at the quarries. Indeed it was only in the latter half of the eighteenth century that burning began at Lord Elgin's quarries at Broomhall near the Forth. After that sales of lime at Broomhall rose spectacularly, the profits rising from £70 a year until after 1771 they exceeded £1000 annually. Great quantities of shell lime were taken by boats to various places on the Forth.

When first applied to acid soils lime gave remarkable results. For example, about the beginning of the eighteenth century a tenant on the Ochtertyre estate limed a single ridge in what had evidently been unenclosed run-rig land. The ridge was longer and broader than the others, but the crop was so luxuriant that the laird offered to take the produce in payment of the rent of the whole farm.[29] Other enterprising tenants followed suit and, with the introduction of better roads, more bridges and proper carts, the practice of liming spread. So popular did the use of lime become in the 1760's that some fifty or sixty horses would often arrive of a morning at the Swallowhaugh lime quarry in the den of Sauchie.

Much time in the early years of this century appears to have been spent in preparing composts for land fertilisation. Turf would be skinned off waste land and mixed with dung and peat ashes and later with lime. To fertilise moss-covered land or indeed any land covered with a thick turf the surface would be dug, dried, gathered into heaps and fired.[30] Much of the fertile Carse of Stirling was originally covered with moss, but at this period, quite apart from the extensive moss reclamations carried out by Lord Kames, the moss area had through the above process shrunk materially. We read of this practice being carried out on the clays of the Beauly Firth area and on the heather-clad moorlands of Caithness.

Another important development in the first half of the century was the growing practice by landlords in the Carse of Stirling of abolishing run-rig and redividing their land into compact holdings of from thirty to fifty or sixty acres, the smaller holdings being on the richer Carse area where the land was mostly infield and was worked on a three years' rotation—beans, barley and oats. The idea of abolishing the distinction between infield and outfield was

[29] Ramsay, *Scotland and Scotsmen*, VOL. II, pp. 205, 254 *n.*
[30] *op. cit.*, pp. 193-4.

a later development and in this area was encouraged by a local landlord, Mr Callendar of Craigforth.[31] So enthusiastic was he that he put aside his beloved music and literary work, assumed a farm labourer's garb and gave his whole time to the improvement of his estate; he was of opinion that by proper cultivation, manuring and liming, the outfield could in time be made to yield about as much as the infield.

The honour of being the foremost improver in central Scotland at that time probably belonged to the Duke of Perth, who was a firm advocate of English farming methods. He introduced English workmen and tools but unfortunately he became involved in the Forty-Five and it was not until after the Rebellion that improvements on the English pattern began to be more generally adopted. Ramsay mentions one rather interesting method of land improvement, viz. enclosing an area and letting it for stance and grazing rights to dealers and to drovers driving cattle to and from the developing cattle markets like Falkirk. It was merely an adaptation of the fold system. The heavy dunging of the land from the droppings of the animals is said to have promoted a rich growth of natural grass and clover. Probably at that time people were so little accustomed to good pastures that even such self-sown pastures would appear luxuriant.[32]

It was in the first half of this century that potatoes were first grown in fields. Introduced to the British Isles from America about the year 1586,[33] potatoes were apparently unknown in Scotland for well nigh a century thereafter, when they were mentioned as a garden crop and a herbal curiosity.[34] In spite of the fact that they were recommended as a food and a field crop,[35] it was not until 1739, when Robert Graham, a Kilsyth man, successfully demonstrated their cultivation in fields,[36] that their possibilities as a field crop came to be recognised.

Yet at first potatoes were regarded with the greatest suspicion. An amusing story is told about their introduction to South Uist and Benbecula. Macdonald of Clanranald, after visiting some of

[31] Ramsay, *Scotland and Scotsmen*, VOL. II, pp. 238-9.

[32] *op. cit.*, p. 224.

[33] T. Whitehead, T. McIntosh *et al.*, *The Potato in Health and Disease*, henceforth cited as Whitehead, *Potato*, Edinburgh 1945, p. 16.

[34] J. Reid, *The Scots Gardener*, 1776 edn. Edinburgh, pp. 123, 137.

[35] James Donaldson, *Husbandry Anatomized*, Edinburgh 1697, p. 117.

[36] *F.S.A.*, VOL. XVIII, pp. 282-3.

his relatives in Ireland, brought back a small quantity in 1743 and ordered his clansmen to plant them. They refused to do so and it was only after some objectors were imprisoned that they acceded to the chief's wish. When autumn came the tenants brought the harvested crop to the chief's house protesting that although he might force them to grow potatoes he could not compel them to eat them.[37] But in course of time the prejudice against potatoes died down. People recognised them to be a wholesome and abundant source of food and a most accommodating crop; they could readily be grown on all classes of soils from virgin peat to sandy land; they were particularly suitable as a first crop in reclaiming waste land. " The nearer the sod the better the crop " was a saying applied to the potato. Soon after the middle of the century the growing of potatoes became widespread in Scotland. In the second half of the century 1756, 1778, 1782, 1796 and 1799 were years of scarcity but, particularly after 1782, despite a great increase in the population, people did not perish from starvation as they had done in King William's " dear " years. That was very largely due to the introduction of the potato.

The beginning of the century saw a marked development in the store cattle trade between Scotland and England. The example of the ill-fated David Dunbar of Baldoon in Galloway in enclosing land to rear stores for the English graziers had been followed by other proprietors in the south west. According to Maxwell of Munshes many Galloway proprietors enclosed their grounds to stock them with " black " cattle. This practice meant some curtailment of the rights of common pasturage and the eviction of tenants whose holdings were enclosed. These unfortunates and their sympathisers used to assemble at night to maim the cattle and overturn the newly erected dykes. On the cry " ower wi' it " down would go the dykes. Those on Barncailzie, Munshes, Netherlaw, Dunrod and Kilwhaneday were pulled down by the rioters, described significantly as " Levellers ".[38] Military forces had to be called out and the aid of the clergy invoked before order could be restored.[39]

Elsewhere in Scotland the trade in store cattle grew in the early years of the century. By 1723 Crieff had become the great rendezvous for the store cattle trade of the Highland area. In that

[37] Walker, *History Hebrides*, VOL. I, pp. 187-8.
[38] John Maxwell, letter quoted in *N.S.A.*, VOL. IV, Kirkcudbrightshire p. 206.
[39] Graham, *Social Life*, pp. 169-70.

year 30,000 cattle [40] were sold there and more than 30,000 guineas in ready money were paid to the sellers. Cattle dealing in those days was considered to be an honourable and esteemed occupation. It is related that when Lord Seafield, who as Chancellor of Scotland had taken an active part in the Union proceedings, remonstrated with his brother on what he considered to be the undignified business of cattle dealing, he received the tart reply : " Better sell nowte [cattle] than sell nations ",[41] a reflection doubtless on the alleged bribing of some of the Scottish noblemen who had negotiated the Act of Union.

Cattle sent to the various fairs were collected about the end of August or the beginning of September when they were in prime condition. Only the more mature animals were chosen for sale, partly because English farmers were averse to buying the less mature Scottish stores and in part because animals under four years of age were unlikely to withstand the perils and hardships of a long trek. A mature animal then was small in comparison with present-day standards. About 1740 the largest oxen in Kincardineshire are said to have weighed only from 25 to 30 stone dead weight.[42] Since at that time the Kincardineshire stone weighed 17.4 imperial lb. it would seem that the largest oxen ranged in live weight from 7 to 9 cwt. This agrees well with other estimates. The reporter for Caithness at the beginning of the nineteenth century estimated that the dead weight of Caithness stores when fattened ranged from 200 to 280 lb., corresponding to a live weight of from $3\frac{1}{2}$ to 5 cwt.,[43] or little more than the weight of a well-suckled six-months-old calf of present-day beef breeds. Lord Ernle gives 370 lb. as the average dead weight of beeves sent to the Smithfield market in 1710. By 1795 the average had risen to 800 lb.[44]

In 1748 an Act of great significance abolished heritable jurisdictions, which for so long had had a cramping effect on tenants. No longer could barons or chieftains try their tenants at their private courts and, knowing full well that there would be no appeal, inflict sentences according to their particular whims. Scots tenants were now free men, except for services to their landlord and thirlage. Feudalism and its evils had received a severe blow. With the

[40] Alexander, *Notes and Sketches*, p. 62.
[41] *ibid.*
[42] Robertson, *Agric. Kincardineshire*, p. 381.
[43] John Henderson, *General View of the Agriculture of the County of Caithness*, henceforth cited as Henderson, *Agric. Caithness*, London 1812, pp. 191-2.
[44] Ernle, *English Farming*, p. 188.

abolition of these powers one may associate the passing of the grinding poverty that had for so long afflicted the Scottish people.

Although the first half of the century saw scarcely any change in the external aspect of the Scottish landscape her agriculture, nevertheless, was undergoing considerable transformation. Farming was now becoming a popular theme; the time-honoured practice of fragmentation farming was being abandoned, for a start had been made with reallocating and consolidating run-rig lands; commonties were being divided and portions turned into arable land, new crops had been introduced and crop rotations adopted; the people were beginning to realise the value of lime, of drainage, of fallows or a fallow crop, of haining fields for hay, and of providing winter keep for animals, while the land itself had come to be regarded as an investment. Progress was on the march; money was beginning to circulate more freely; industrial life was developing, and in the planting of woods and hedges landlords were not unmindful of æsthetic values. The dawn of a better day had begun; the spirit of enterprise was abroad.

CHAPTER VIII

# THE HIGHLANDS AND NORTHERN
# ISLANDS : BEFORE 1745

Early tillage...Church and land ownership...Celtic feudalism
...Land measurements...Merging of Celtic, Anglian and
Norwegian ideas...Norman feudalism introduced into eastern
Highlands ... Charters ... Feuing, leases, raids ... Sixteenth-
century stock and crops in Urquhart...Farming in Strathtay,
Badenoch and Western Isles...Evils of tacksman system...
Unsettled conditions in Western Highlands and islands...
Colonisation of Kintyre...Cattle stealing, Rob Roy...Black-
mail...Store cattle trade...The Forty-Five...Udal system
in Orkney—Misgovernment of northern islands.

THE STORY OF AGRICULTURAL PROGRESS in the Highlands is not
easily told, chiefly because of the lack of reliable information
and the fact that the Highland area as such has no specific geo-
graphically defined boundaries.    Inverness, the capital, lies on the
edge of a firth which, as regards climate and the land in its vicinity,
is lowland in its characteristics.   There is a marked difference, too,
between the inland straths of the eastern watershed, the narrow
rugged glens of the west and the featureless " machairs " or peat-
covered lands of some of the islands.   Travellers and historians have
usually divided Scotland into two parts, the Highlands and the Lowlands, allocating to each different manners, customs and speech.   But
such a clear-cut distinction is somewhat unwarranted, since Lowland
Scotland merges gradually into the Highlands while the eastern
Highlands were subject to different influences from the western or
northern parts.

From what we can learn, there seems to have been little tillage
in the Highlands in the earlier centuries of the Christian era.   Dio
Cassius, writing in the third century, reported the people as living
by pasturage, the chase and by gathering berries, etc.[1]   Yet long
before this, in the late Stone or Bronze Age, bere or bear was
evidently grown in the Shetlands, while the scattered remains of
ancient human settlements in the more fertile parts of northern

[1] Mackay, *Urquhart and Glenmoriston*, p. 438.

and western Scotland indicate that cereals were cultivated and domesticated farm animals kept. Indeed in the Shetlands crofting would appear to have been largely self-supporting as early as the latter part of the second millennium B.C.

In St Columba's time there is evidence that some grain, presumably bere, was grown on the small and scattered settlements, but whether the saint and his followers did much to introduce tillage or merely to extend existing farming practices is not known. In all likelihood they spread the knowledge of practices familiar to them in Ireland. Significantly, however, about this time the term "plough" is first mentioned in historical records of the Highlands. At this time, too, the right of private property was to some extent recognised. Iona was the saint's, or rather the Church's, while gifts of land for church purposes were made to his followers[2] as well as to those of St Ninian, some of whom had ventured into the eastern Highlands. Probably this right of individual ownership was limited to the Church. At that time, and for many centuries thereafter, land was held merely by virtue of occupancy and not by title deeds.

The eastern portion of the northern Highlands first came under the sway of Scotland when in 1078 Malcolm Canmore defeated the Mormaer of Moray and annexed his province. Prior to this Moray (which included the county of Inverness) had had a troubled existence, being threatened by the Norsemen from the one side and by southern Picts from the other. Its annexation to Scotland did not, however, bring settled rule. Rebellions broke out, but in the time of David I the province was brought more or less into subjection. Following the feudal practice of the Norman French David parcelled out the eastern portion of Inverness-shire; the Comyns got Badenoch and Lochaber; the Bissets Aird and Strathglass, and the Durwards Glenurquhart. From the castles which they built and in which they housed their retainers, these families ruled their territory by force of arms.

The first mention of a title deed for the Urquhart district of Inverness-shire was, according to Dr Mackay's *Urquhart and Glenmoriston*, in 1233 when Sir Alan Durward gifted to the Chancellor of Moray one-half of a davoch of land in "pure free and perpetual charity", the other in perpetual feu farm, the feu duty being ten shillings a year.[3]

[2] Mackay, *Urquhart and Glenmoriston*, p. 438.
[3] *op. cit.*, pp. 15-16.

The incident reveals that in this part of the Highlands Norman French feudalism had by then either been substituted for, or had largely been merged into, the earlier Celtic system. The two systems showed wide differences as well as close similarities. The main difference lay in ideas concerning ownership of land, the relations of the chiefs or lords with the people, the stress placed on kinship and the question of primogeniture. Under Celtic feudalism the land was considered to be owned not by the king but by the people themselves, the chief being merely their spokesman and leader, demanding and receiving an obedience fostered by affection rather than by power or fear, and in addition the Celtic dues *Cain* and *Conveth*. *Cain* represented a fixed amount of the produce of the land. *Conveth* was produce earmarked for the entertainment of the chief on his visits to vassals. Those destined to be chiefs were trained in the art of winning the affection of their people, who were regarded, not so much as a lower as distinct from a higher class, but more as relatives in varying degrees of kinship.

With the passage of time some of the Celtic ideas about succession, ownership of land and kinship were considerably modified in the eastern parts of the Highlands, but in general they continued elsewhere in the Highlands to dominate thought and outlook. Full appreciation of the circumstances helps to an understanding of many things peculiar to the Highlands. While Norman feudalism brought the whole of the Lowlands under the sway of the central authority this was far from being the case in the more remote Highlands. There, the authority of the chief, as representing the people, was paramount, so, when the king confiscated land in the Highlands and transferred it to a new owner, the act of transference was often ignored on the plea that the king was giving away what was not his to bestow. Possession of land was maintained by the sword and chieftains referred scathingly to charters as " sheepskin possession ". Moreover the doctrine that the land was owned by the people for the people was expanded to justify the " lifting " of cattle from the Lowlands, on the principle that, in default of voluntary sharing-out of produce of all the land, good and bad, the Highlanders were merely taking forcible possession of some of the produce of better-class land which had been stolen from them. This idea of the people owning the land under a patriarchal form of administration does much to explain their bewilderment on being forcibly ejected from houses and lands at the time of the Highland clearances. They simply could not grasp the idea of one man owning the land, nor could they bring themselves to believe at first that their chiefs or lords would disown those who were in a sense kith and kin.

Yet another feature of the difference between Norman and Celtic feudalism may be noted. Primogeniture and the keeping of estates intact were features of the Norman French type, but division of land was more inherent in the Celtic type. The clans had their subdivisions and when, in the nineteenth century, all the available arable land on holdings was used up, the crofter would subdivide his croft to give each of his sons a portion. Consideration of some of these features places a new light on the behaviour of the Highland people before 1745. Lawless they must have appeared to Lowland eyes; and undoubtedly there was much lawlessness after the clans had become strong; but in many of their allegedly criminal acts they were merely carrying into effect their own customs and code of laws in an area which, because of the poverty of its soil and its climate, was constantly short of food.

To return to this gift of half a davoch of land made by Sir Alan Durward to the Chancellor of Moray, it may be pointed out that the term davoch had in time come to mean a particular locality, capable of supporting a certain number of people and stock.[4] The ten davochs into which Urquhart had originally been divided retained their identity for centuries but varied in extent and importance.[5] In a charter dated 1509 conveying the lands of Urquhart in feu to one of the Strathspey Grants these lands are mentioned by name, some being designated twelve, some six and some three merk lands.[6] Incidentally, the names persist in present-day farms— Kerrogair, Drumbuie, Borlum, etc. The conditions attached to the Grant's feu repay study. The yearly duty was £46. 6s. 8d., but the feuar was bound to provide fifteen horsemen for the King's service and to keep Urquhart Castle and its outhouses in repair. He had to reclaim untilled land, grow flax and hemp, construct an orchard, provide enclosures and improve the King's highway within the barony. For all practical purposes he might have been the feuar of an estate in the Lowlands.

Urquhart at one time had belonged to the Macdonalds and hundreds of years later there were Macdonalds in the glen who, on occasion, refused to recognise Grant as landlord. Furthermore, the newly-elected claimant to the Lordship of the Isles, Sir Donald

---

[4] See p. 30.
[5] Mackay, *Urquhart and Glenmoriston*, p. 440.
[6] *op. cit.*, pp. 78-9.

Macdonald of Lochalsh, took the view that he, as head of the Macdonalds, was still the owner. Accordingly he took forcible possession of Urquhart in 1510, the year after Grant had become the feuar. Macdonald retained it in his own hands until his expulsion three years later, when Grant put in a claim for what had been stolen in the shape of goods and livestock and for the rents of which he had been deprived. The sum awarded was £2000, but in those days it was one thing to award damages against a Highland chief but quite another to make him pay; in fact Grant was never recompensed. The agricultural part of the claim, which totalled 300 cattle, 1000 sheep, 960 bolls of oats and 740 of bere, suggests that large amounts of grain were grown, that more land was under oats than under bere, and that the home farm was heavily stocked. For the purposes of the claim cows were valued at 26s. 8d. each, sheep at 4s. a head, the boll of bere at 8s. and the boll of oats at 4s.[7]

Thirty-five years later, in April 1545, there was another but more sweeping raid, this time by the Camerons, aided by the Macdonalds of Glengarry, Glencoe, Keppoch and Moidart. The booty, according to the claim, comprised 1188 " great " cattle, 392 young cattle, 525 calves, 2 plough oxen, 383 horses and mares, 1978 sheep, 1099 lambs, 2204 goats and kids, 122 swine, 64 geese, 3006 bolls of oats and 1277 bolls of bere.[8] Seldom in the history of the Highlands was a raid so thorough in its execution, although others exceeded it in actual numbers of cattle stolen. Thus in a raid by the Clans Gregor and Chattan on Glenshee and Glen Isla in 1602, 2700 cattle were lifted.[9] From the details of this claim one can trace a rough and ready relationship between the numbers of cattle and sheep, and those of bolls of bere and oats. Evidently most occupiers were generally allowed to keep so many cattle and sheep in proportion to their arable land—an indication that the " souming " system was practised. The sequel to this raid shows how ineffective at this time was the power of the Government in the Highlands. For convenience the claim made by the occupiers for loss of stock, grain, etc., was placed in the hands of the two lairds. As might have been expected neither Lochiel nor Glengarry, the defendants, appeared to contest the claim. A sum of £10,770. 13s. 4d. was awarded as damages against them but, as usually happened in similar cases, was never paid. In consequence, some of the defendants' lands in the west were confiscated and given

[7] Mackay, *Urquhart and Glenmoriston*, pp. 85-6.  [8] *op. cit.*, p. 98.
[9] *R.P.C.S.*, 1st ser. VOL. VI, ed. D. Masson, Edinburgh 1877, pp. 500-01.

to Grant who, however, never managed to collect any rent from them. He never even took possession of them, but his son was afterwards able to dispose of this undesirable property.

The use of plough oxen in Glenurquhart [10] is established by the fact that in a will proven in 1553 mention is made of there being twenty plough oxen (*boves arabiles*) on the home or old grange farm of Kil St Ninian near Temple Pier in Glenurquhart.[11] Besides these oxen there were twenty mature cattle, eight younger cattle and five calves.

The first mention of a written lease in this parish is in 1554, when the Bishop of Moray granted a nineteen years' lease of the Church lands of Achmonie, the rent payable being £3. 3s. 4d. Scots and 2 kids. With the Reformation in the offing, however, the Bishop acted three years later like many other churchmen of the time. He granted the lands in perpetual feu to McGillies, the tenant.[12] The latter had, probably with ulterior intent, donated a lump sum, the amount of which was not disclosed, to the Bishop and agreed to an increase of £2. 4s. 6d. in the yearly rent. In this way he became virtually the owner. The rest of the Church lands in Urquhart at the time of the Reformation were quietly appropriated.[13] The chapels were allowed to fall into neglect, the parish priest, now a Protestant, was allowed to become an exhorter, but after his death no minister was appointed for many years. The teinds were collected but only a small share was passed over to the Church.

On this estate rents in general, down to about the end of the eighteenth century, were paid partly in money and partly in services and in kind. Thereafter they were paid in cash only. The services included casting and conveyance of the laird's peats, tilling his land, shearing his grain crop, spreading the dung on the home farm, etc. Up to the time of Culloden each tenant was expected to answer his

---

[10] Considerable doubt exists as to how far work oxen were used in the Highlands. Sir James Scott Watson, writing in *Scottish Journal of Agriculture*, henceforth cited as *S. J. Agric.*, XIV (1931), p. 114, stated that they were seldom used west of the Highland line. But this is not entirely borne out by the reference to plough oxen in the parish of Urquhart and Glenmoriston, or by Sinclair in *Agric. Northern Counties*, p. 78, or by Dr I. F. Grant's *Highland Farm* (at Kincraig, Inverness-shire), where it is stated that oxen were generally used for ploughing (p. 69) and where the term " oxengate " is used as an area measurement in rentals. Mixed teams of horses and oxen were often used in the Highlands for ploughing, but where light ploughs were used teams of horses alone were employed.

[11] Mackay, *Urquhart and Glenmoriston*, p. 114 *n.*

[12] *op. cit.*, pp. 479-80.          [13] *op. cit.*, p. 117

chief's call to be trained in arms and to mobilise for defence or offence. After the Grants got possession of Urquhart the clan Macdonald tenants on the estate generally ignored calls to mobilise under the Grants. At Culloden they fought under their own chiefs.[14] The crops grown in Urquhart, besides bere and oats, were flax and rye. The place name of one of the farms, Shewglie (Seagalaidh) indicates that rye was once grown there.

From the time of the great raid in 1545 until 1636 the number of tenants and subtenants in Glenurquhart remained more or less constant. Pestilences, recurring years of short crop and a high infant mortality prevented any appreciable increase in population. Including subtenants, the number was 111 in 1548 and 110 in 1636. In 1765 the tenants were reclassified, and these were then 81 tenants, 70 subtenants and 50 cottars. This suggests that latterly the land was being let to tacksmen, as there were fewer tenants but more subtenants.[15]

Such is the picture of a district in the eastern Highlands from early medieval times to the Forty-Five. Here the old Highland and the Lowland style of farming were merged. Land cultivation seems to have been done partly and presumably mainly by the lighter plough drawn by horses, and partly by the heavier wooden plough drawn either by oxen or by mixed teams of oxen and horses. Harrowing was done by wooden pegged harrows. The houses were poor and mean, being built of turf, loose stones and timber, with wicker work on the inside wall to prevent the earth from falling inwards.[16] There was little or no incentive to build better and more permanent houses because of frequent raids and insecurity of tenure. The first house in Glenurquhart to be roofed with slate was one at Corrimony in 1740.[17]

In the glens of the eastern Highlands, remains of head dykes tell of the old custom of keeping stock in early summer and autumn on the adjoining moorlands. This allowed herding to protect

---

[14] Mackay, *Urquhart and Glenmoriston*, p. 447.     [15] *op. cit.*, p. 441.

[16] Samuel Johnson and James Boswell, *Journey to the Western Islands of Scotland and Journal of a Tour to the Hebrides*, ed. R. W. Chapman, Oxford 1930, p. 91. The reason why the remains of houses in the Highlands are so scanty is that many were built almost entirely of turf. In Sutherland these turf huts were scarcely distinguishable from the ground. An Englishman seeing these houses remarked that " the people make their houses of the grass and feed their cattle on the stones ". In other parts of the Highlands the houses were shaped like a beehive and covered with turf. See *F.S.A.*, vol. VIII, p. 6, and Pennant, *Tour*, VOL. I, p. 262 and Plates XV, XVI.

[17] Mackay, *Urquhart and Glenmoriston*, p. 459.

the arable crops to be dispensed with.    In midsummer the animals
were sent to distant shielings.    The grazings of " Cluanie ", on the
road to Kintail, were the common sheilings of Urquhart and Glenmoriston.    In Speyside those of Dunachton and Raits in the Kincraig
district were in the upper Dulnain valley seven or eight miles distant.
The breed of cattle then kept must have been hardy for most of
them, except the cows and work-oxen, were expected to live all
winter out of doors.[18]    Until the end of the eighteenth century the
people throughout the Highlands always lived in groups, which
varied according to the number of families that could be supported
in the vicinity.    In the Highland parish of Crathie and Braemar,
as set out in the list of King's tenants in 1539, four to eight tenants,
with their subtenants or cottars, comprised a group.    Evidently the
size of the group in this latter parish corresponded with the number
of tenants with sufficient draught animals among them to operate
either a heavy or a light plough.

In Strathtay the same considerations applied.    When a survey
of Lochtayside was made in 1769 the average size of a holding was
found to be 21.8 acres (Scots) of infield and 16.3 acres of outfield,
exclusive of pasture land.[19]    Such a holding might have four tenants
and be termed a one-plough holding.    Those of seventy to eighty
acres were worked by two ploughs of the light type drawn by four
horses abreast.    At the end of the eighteenth century it was quite
common to find a light plough being used at the western end of a
Perthshire parish and a heavy one with plough oxen at the eastern
end.    In the eastern Highlands more land was cultivated than is
now the case; there were formerly more cattle, fewer sheep and far
more goats.

The proportion of infield to outfield in the eastern Highlands
varied greatly.    Dr I. F. Grant in *Everyday Life on an old Highland
Farm* has been at pains to determine how the different portions of
her ancestor's farm at Dunachton, Kincraig (in the Badenoch district
of Inverness-shire) were cultivated.    Although her researches refer
to the period just after the Forty-Five they were doubtless true of
earlier times.    The infield was under constant crop and some parts
of it seem to have grown the same crop year after year.    As for the
outfield, which was much larger in area than the infield, no definite
system appears to have been followed.    Some particular outfield

[18] Mackay, *Urquhart and Glenmoriston*, p. 445.
[19] *Survey of Lochtayside 1769*, ed. Margaret McArthur, Scottish History
Society, ser. III, VOL. XXVII, Edinburgh 1936, p. xlvi.

fields, known to have been cropped in 1769, were bearing no crops at all after an interval of at least ten years.[20] Other portions might be cropped two, three or four years in succession before being allowed to remain " out ". Some cropped portions were small and scattered among the woods. For the main part they were in a block, although somewhat intermingled with land occupied by subtenants. In addition to his main farm Mackintosh, her ancestor, held some land in run-rig. Different varieties of oats were used for cropping; some were white, others, termed " small ", were undoubtedly the old grey oat. Both bere and barley were grown but chiefly bere. Balnespick gradually increased the proportion of barley and reduced the amount of bere sown. He is known to have " lymed " land which provided soil conditions more suitable to the growth of barley.[21] The quantities sown at a time were extremely small (sometimes even less than a bushel). For instance in 1774 19 bolls of grain and peas were sown in 17 separate lots. The kinds of seed sown were rye, white oats, small oats, bere, barley, peas and mixed grains. Often more than one kind would be sown on one rig or plot. The average return over the ten-year period 1769-78 for each boll of oat seed sown at Dunachton, where the land was probably more than usually fertile for the area, was rather less than two and a half bolls, and about three and a half in the case of bere.[22] In some years, as in 1770, the returns were probably less than the seed sown. In abundant years such as 1775 the crops may have been fifty per cent. better than average.

Elsewhere in much of the Highlands, where the soil was less fertile than in Upper Speyside, crop yields must have been much poorer. In Glen Etive and Glencoe, for instance, one can assess the poverty of some of the crops from an inspection of formerly cultivated patches on the hill-sides. The soil in these glens is either peaty or consists largely of coarse gravel and stones. Writing about Glencoe, Macaulay stated that " all the science and industry of a peaceful age can extract nothing valuable from that wilderness ".[23] This observation is, however, too sweeping for, poor as the soil was, the Glen was in parts cultivated and supported stock. The formerly cultivated patches still to be seen on the hill-sides may have been cropped for only one year and

---

[20] Grant, *Highland Farm*, p. 51.

[21] *op. cit.*, p. 239.  [22] *op. cit.*, p. 54.

[23] Thomas, Lord Macaulay, *History of England*, 1858-62 edn., VOL. VI, London 1860, pp. 197-8.

therefore are not typical of the cultivated land in the valley bottoms. In Gairloch it was customary for isolated patches up the hill-side to be cropped for a year or two and then abandoned. Before being cropped they were enclosed and used as folds for the cattle.[24] Meal, as a rule, had to be brought in from the Lowlands. A huge boulder in Glenlochay still retains its old name of Herring Stone, and is said to have been the rendezvous of men from the east and the west, meal being bartered for herring. Large quantities of meal were also imported by sea to the Islands from the Lowlands in exchange for cattle.[25] In earlier times the cattle were consumed at home.

Until fairly recently, movable cultivation was the rule in parts of the Outer Hebrides. Fresh land for cultivation was acquired every three years and was divided carefully into portions of equal size and merit as regards quality of soil. Some portions having been set aside for the herdsman and the maintenance of the poor, lots were cast for the remainder.[26] This system of movable cultivation must have persisted for many centuries; it is the most primitive method of agriculture.

In most parts of the Western Isles two types of soil predominate —the sands of the machair and the more inland peats. The lazy-bed system of cultivation applies mainly to peaty soils, the narrow heaped-up ridges, formed by digging with the *càschrom*, aggregating the fertile portions of the soil and making them high and dry. On the machair land the ristle and the single-stilted plough seem to have been used, the *càschrom* being preferred in districts with only small pockets of good soil. At the close of the eighteenth century two of the very large parishes in Lewis—Lochs and Uig—were cultivated entirely by the *càschrom*, and even today some land is so cultivated. Seaweed, disused thatch from the houses, bracken, peat ash and animal droppings were used as manure.

Up to about the year 1500 bere would appear to have been the principal cereal grown in Skye for food. Don Pedro de Ayala, a Spaniard who visited Scotland in 1498, compiled a useful record of his impressions and speaks of the great quantity of barley (bere) raised in the Western Islands.[27] In various forms, along with fish and meat, bere formed the main diet of the people, but in years of scarcity shell-fish and soup made from seaweed were consumed.

[24] Osgood H. Màckenzie, *A Hundred Years in the Highlands*, henceforth cited as Mackenzie, *Hundred Years*, London 1921, p. 188.

[25] *R.P.C.S.*, 1st ser. VOL. I, ed. J. H. Burton, Edinburgh 1877, pp. 201, 470-1.

[26] *Crofters Commission Report*, pp. 466-7.

[27] Nicolson, *History of Skye*, pp. 40, 99.

After 1500, oats, presumably grey oats, seem to have been grown to a greater extent than bere. Even at the beginning of the nineteenth century bere bread was used almost exclusively in Coll, Tiree and the Long Island.[28] The poverty of the land in the poorer and more remote parts of the Highlands, coupled with the growing lawlessness of the chiefs in the troubled centuries after Bannockburn, tended both to hinder any development in the art of agriculture and to promote raids into the Lowlands and strife between opposing clans. We have seen how settlers in Glenurquhart suffered from the Lochaber clans, but matters were even worse in the west and in the Islands.

The powerful Macdonald clan, for instance, had for long resisted the Scottish Crown. Early in the seventeenth century they were defeated and Kintyre passed to the Earl of Argyll, the leader of clans loyal to the Crown. But the effect of inter-clan wars upon the relatively fertile district of Kintyre had been so devastating that of the 353 merklands in the peninsula no fewer than 113 were lying waste.[29] The devastated areas were largely recolonised by farmers from the counties of Ayr and Renfrew. These colonists were united with the few original inhabitants who chose to remain, many of the dispossessed clan leaders and followers having fled to Ireland. This union was fortunate; improved methods of agriculture were introduced; cultivators were granted leases direct from the landlords, while the industry and the law-abiding habits of the newcomers were copied by the former settlers who thereafter gave more attention to farming.

Elsewhere, over much of the western Highlands, the growing powers of the chiefs in the fourteenth, fifteenth and sixteenth centuries did little to advance, but much to retard, peaceful development. Deeds of violence were exalted into feats of bravery and virtue; the practice of religion fell into disuse and marriage was largely replaced by " handfasting ", a contract of union for only a short term of years. The work of tending the crops was left largely to women who, however, by singing made light of the work, every task having its distinctive tune. Whereas in St Columba's time we get a picture of a happy, contented community in which agriculture flourished, a thousand years later unsettled conditions precluded development and agriculture in the interval had probably

---

[28] James Macdonald, *General View of the Agriculture of the Hebrides*, henceforth cited as Macdonald, *Agric. Hebrides*, London 1811, p. 204.

[29] Argyll, *Scotland*, p. 217.

I

deteriorated.[30]  The wasteful custom of holding stalks of grain in the naked flame to prepare grain for grinding was still in vogue although kilns for drying grain were known in St Columba's time. Yet all was not gloom; traditional song and story kept the spirits of the people alive.

The adoption of the custom of letting the land to tacksmen seems, however, to have caused much discontent to the rank and file of occupiers in some of the islands, as happened on some estates in Mull, Iona, Tiree and the peninsula of Morven.[31]  There, tacksmen were reported as exacting high rents, whether in cash, rents or services, while their tenants had no leases and could be removed at will.  The report of Lord President Duncan Forbes of Culloden made in 1737, a copy of which is published in Appendix A to the Crofter's Commission Report 1884, discloses a most unhappy position even before the Forty-Five.  In seven years " above one hundred families had been reduced to beggary and driven out of the island "—evidently Mull.

We have shown how the Celtic idea of the ownership of land, that everyone was entitled to a share, was in course of time extended to justify " lifting " cattle from the more fertile Lowlands.  Usually lifting was done by small bodies of armed men who, in a swift night operation and before any organised force could disturb them, would have the animals safely hidden away in some distant secluded hollow in the hills.  The operation postulated courage, resource and endurance, qualities lauded in song and story in the Highlands as estimable virtues.  Frequently the lifting was accomplished without bloodshed; at other times many men on both sides were wounded or slain.  Despite the law of " claremathan ", attributed to William the Lion, and designed to enable owners of stolen cattle to recover them, and another Act passed against the " Ketherani " in 1385, the lifting of cattle, so far from being regarded by clansmen as an offence, was viewed by them as a praiseworthy feat.[32]  " Steal ane cow, twa cow, dat be common tief, Lift hundred cow that be shentelman drovers ", indignantly rejoined a clansman who had been indicted. To steal, according to Macaulay, was regarded as honourable an occupation as cultivating the soil.[33]

The growing spirit of lawlessness which characterised the

[30] Argyll, *Scotland*, pp. 168-71, 249.
[31] See p. 92.
[32] *A.P.S.*, VOL. I, pp. 372, 550 b.
[33] Macaulay, *History of England*, VOL. VI, p. 198.

development of the clans after 1400 encouraged cattle-stealing.[34]
From all parts of the Highlands, but particularly from Glencoe
and Lochaber the "cateran" would descend on unsuspecting
farmers in the Lowlands and drive away their cattle.   By the seventeenth century, besides lack of food, there was another incentive
to steal cattle; it was possible to market them, for we read of the
beginning of an export trade in cattle from Skye at the end of the
sixteenth century, while as early as 1502 the marts from the Crown
lands of Trotternish in Skye were conveyed to Inverness and from
thence to the Lowlands.[35]

A letter dated 18th October 1645 from Lochiel, the chief of the
clan Cameron, to his "friend", the laird of Grant, is revealing.
The Camerons had tried to lift cattle from the fertile lands of Moray,
but unfortunately had mistaken the lands of Moyness, occupied
by a Grant, for the lands of Moray.   Grant had not taken the theft
lying down, for in Lochiel's letter to the laird of Grant, the former
states that "aught" (eight) of the raiding party had lost their lives,
and other twelve or thirteen were so seriously wounded as to make
their recovery doubtful.   Yet, as Lochiel explains, it was all due
to a mistake in thinking that Grant of Moyness was "ane Murray-
man"; his men went to "Murraylands, where all men taken [can
take] their prey".   Lochiel naïvely concludes the letter by hoping
that the laird of Grant "shall not be offended at my friend's
innocence".[36]

Cattle thefts were frequent and long distances were travelled.
In 1689 a dozen Lochaber men lifted six score black cattle from the
heart of Aberdeenshire.[37]   Proprietors on estates bordering the
Highlands were obliged to pay blackmail money or "watch money"
as protection against cattle-stealing by the cateran.[38]   At a later
date Cluny Macpherson and the Laird of Kyllachy were employed
by East Coast lairds to maintain watches in the upper valleys of the
Spey and the Findhorn.   For a time the strong rule of Cromwell
had deterred cattle-stealing, but after the Restoration the practice

[34] According to the Duke of Argyll (*Scotland*, p. 162), 10,000 cattle besides
sheep and horses were lifted from Arran and the Cumbraes in 1455 ; the numbers
stolen from Glenurquhart and the Glenshee and Glenisla districts have already been
mentioned (see p. 123), but even in smaller raids considerable numbers were lifted.
In 1602 Rose of Kilravock, Nairnshire, lost 240 cattle and 480 sheep : Grant,
*Social Development*, p. 546.

[35] Grant, *Social Development*, p. 545.

[36] Alexander, *Notes and Sketches*, p. 67.

[37] *op. cit.*, p. 63.                    [38] *op. cit.*, p. 65.

once more became rife. " Louss and ydle " men raided the Lowlands, and when complaints were made about certain clansmen
King Charles II, fearing to offend their chiefs, who had been on
the Royalist side, did not allow the law to take its course. A noted
cateran from the clan Maclean was apprehended and hanged by
the Chisholm. In revenge, the Macleans twice raided Chisholm's
lands, stole his cattle and burned barns full of corn. Graham of
Gartmore reckoned that the value of animals stolen in a single year
was in the region of £5000 while another £5000 was levied as
blackmail.[39]

The notorious freebooter, Rob Roy, was at first an honest
cattle drover. Trusted and esteemed, he was employed as an
agent by landlords such as Montrose until misfortune overtook him.
He was cheated by one of his own agents and went bankrupt, and
Montrose, who had lost money through him, turned Rob Roy's wife
out of her home. In revenge Rob saved Montrose the trouble of
collecting some of his rents. Thereafter he lived the life of a freebooter and " protector " of many persons who deemed it wise to
pay him blackmail.[40]

In the reign of William and Mary steps were taken by the
Government to end cattle-stealing by the establishment of an armed
watch, and in 1724 six companies of native soldiers from loyal clans
were raised to assist. From the plain dark-coloured tartan uniform
which they wore they came to be known as the Black Watch. Cattle-
lifting then declined but was resumed during the troubled times
of the Forty-Five. But despite cattle-lifting in the seventeenth
century the Highland store cattle trade increased.[41] By 1723 the
flourishing cattle market at Crieff was able to dispose of from
25,000 to 30,000 head yearly. Crieff was a convenient centre for
most parts of the Highlands, and from there the cattle were driven
by devious ways known to the drovers as unlikely to involve payment
of tolls or fines for trespass to the great English fairs, e.g. St Faith's
at Norwich or Barnet Fair near London.

As more English buyers came north to buy Highland stores
Falkirk became a much more convenient centre than Crieff. Cattle
from the West Highlands and the Islands were saved many weary
miles of travel by coming direct to Falkirk, so as Falkirk Tryst
flourished Crieff Tryst declined. By the end of the eighteenth and
the beginning of the nineteenth century as many as 50-60,000 cattle in

[39] Alexander, *Notes and Sketches*, p. 66.　　　[40] *op. cit.*, p. 63.
[41] Nicolson, *History of Skye*, p. 272.

the aggregate might be present at the "Three Falkirk Trysts", but it would be wrong to conclude that these all came from the Highlands. At that time the north-eastern and the central counties had not developed into the great cattle-fattening areas they eventually became and many stores came to Falkirk from those districts.

The fateful years 1745-46 ended the old clan system, disturbed if not destroyed the old patriarchal relationship between chieftain and people and fostered new ideas concerning land ownership. The effect of these changes will be discussed later, but beyond question the rebellion of 1745 marked the end of an epoch in Highland history—an epoch in which little advance in agriculture could be traced. In many parts in fact there had been no development at all since the time of St Columba.

No account of the system of land tenure in Scotland at this time would be complete without reference to Orkney and Shetland. These two counties came under the dominion of Scotland in the year 1468, and in the transfer it was stipulated that the people should continue to be governed by their own laws and usages. We shall see, however, how grossly this stipulation was evaded and ignored by bad governors. In these islands there had been no such system as feudalism ; there prevailed instead the udal system. The occupiers of the land or at least all the main occupiers—the udallers —were the owners, to whom no man was superior. Although they paid taxes to the central government to defray its expenses, they were vassals to none; they paid no rent and gave no peace-time services, so the udal system might even be described as the negation of feudal principles.[42]

Following the transfer of the islands to Scotland these taxes were remitted to the Crown and the task of collection was allotted to some Scottish nobles and Church dignitaries, who received a commission for their trouble and expense. As can be imagined, this system of farming out the collection of the "skatt tax", as it was called, encouraged the use of unjust and oppressive methods. In 1472 Bishop Tulloch, who had been appointed to collect the tax, used his position to extort what he could from the udallers. Feudal as well as udal payments were demanded and, as the Bishop represented both Church and State, the unfortunate udaller had no court to which he could appeal. The Bishop was followed by others

[42] John Gunn, *The Orkney Book*, London 1909, pp. 110 ff.

equally extortionate in their demands and their activities led to such discontent that in 1529 rebellion broke out. Although it was suppressed the root cause of discontent remained. James V visited the islands and put an end to some but not to all of the abuses. About 1565 Lord Robert Stewart, a half-brother of Mary Queen of Scots, obtained by doubtful means a feu charter of both Orkney and Shetland for the sum of £2000 Scots. From that time onwards his whole energies were devoted to forcing the udallers to accept feus from him. Feudal casualties were exacted ; rents were raised to the limit, and udallers showing resistance were evicted. He is said even to have encouraged piracy to ensure a share of the booty. His son and successor, the wicked Earl Patrick, was an even worse oppressor. Anyone attempting to defy him was subjected in Earl Patrick's own court, to a trumped-up charge of treason. Since the charge, if proved, involved confiscation of the land to the king and guilt in such circumstances was a foregone conclusion, the accused were in a hopeless position. But confiscation of the land for the king was not Earl Patrick's primary motive ; he wanted part of the lands for himself, and the udaller, knowing the alternative should he fail to compound, was usually induced to make over part of his lands to the oppressor. The story of his misgovernment at length reached Edinburgh. He was arrested and put to death, but so disastrous were the results of the long-continued oppression that it was well into the eighteenth century before marked signs of returning prosperity were discernible.

From the time of the absorption of the udal lands by feudal superiors until the eighteenth century the people of Orkney could roughly be divided into five classes : the proprietors, who farmed a good deal of their own land ; the larger tenants ; the " peerie " tenants—men who occupied ten to fifty acres, including heath, in scattered patches ; the " oncas ", a term synonymous with the mainland term " cottar " ; and the " bowmen " or ploughmen.[43] The oncas worked for the larger tenants at busy seasons of the year and were very much at their mercy. Bowmen, however, worked all the year round and were so poorly paid that even as late as 1796, when much more money was in circulation, one man who raised his ploughman's cash wage from 7s. 6d. to 10s. in the half year was soundly berated by his fellows for establishing an undesirable precedent.

In the earlier part of the eighteenth century so little money was

[43] *Crofters Commission Report*, Appendix pp. 270 ff.

in circulation that some Orcadians might be well advanced in years before they either saw or handled a coin. Up to that time housing was most primitive. A steep bank sloping to the south would be chosen as a site so that, when the earth was excavated to provide a level floor, the perpendicular face of the bank formed the back of the house. The walls, 4½-5 ft. high, and the gables were of turf. A " lum " hole in the centre of the roof and a " reek " hole at the end (usually stuffed) allowed the reek to escape ; a straw mat did duty for a door. Until wooden beds were introduced in the latter part of the eighteenth century the people slept on heather or straw. The system of agriculture was equally primitive : the patches of crops were all intermixed and the plough used was the one-stilted type which merely scratched the soil ; wild sheep roamed at large, the cows ate seaweed, and the people themselves subsisted in part on the products of the sea, fish and shellfish ; they were too poor to buy salt and used sea-water to season food.

Kelp appears to have first been made about the year 1719, and the first cargo was shipped from Kirkwall in 1725. Money now began to circulate and before 1750 one proprietor even attempted to carry out improvements but met with strong opposition. The condition of the people right down to the middle of the century was miserable in the extreme. There was no system of education and poverty prevailed. Such surplus grain as was available for export was sent to Norway. Bere and grey oats were the only crops grown. For land near the sea, seaweed was used as manure; so indolent were some of the people that farmyard manure was considered a nuisance and was dumped into the sea. This probably happened when kelp-making became a flourishing industry to the neglect of agriculture. To convey the seaweed to the land the people loaded it into creels on horses' backs, a method which survived until the thirties of the nineteenth century.

# CHAPTER IX

# IMPROVERS, THE LATTER PART OF THE EIGHTEENTH CENTURY

Land reclamation in north-east...Influence of Silver, Barclay and Anderson...Farming Club at Aberdeen and University Professors...Sir John Sinclair...Board of Agriculture established...Forth Valley moss reclamations...Improvements by tenants...Dawson, Frogden...The Middletons, Ross-shire ...West of Scotland pioneers...Ayrshire pastures...Turnip growing in south-west...Improved sheep and cattle...Turnip growing in drills...Abolition of thirlage.

ALTHOUGH COCKBURN OF ORMISTON, Grant of Monymusk, the Earls of Stair, Rothes and Haddington and many other improvers had done notable work in the first half of the eighteenth century, the agricultural revolution began in earnest only in its second half. Two Kincardineshire improvers, Silver of Netherley and Barclay of Ury, merit special attention. Silver owes his fame partly to the formidable nature of the land he sought to reclaim, and in part to the success which attended his work. Barclay attempted tasks which would have daunted the most enterprising of mortals and was responsible for the introduction of new crops and implements and for the methods of cultivation and stock management which are largely in use today.

Silver, like many another young and enterprising Scot, had made his fortune abroad, in this case in Jamaica.[1] In 1751, while still a comparatively young man, he returned to his native district and in the following year purchased the Netherley estate between Stonehaven and Aberdeen. More unpromising territory could scarcely be found, for there the tail of the Grampians, formed of the hard crystalline rocks of one of the oldest and hardest geological formations, dips gradually towards the North Sea. Granite and gneiss boulders were at that time profusely scattered over the uneven glacier-scarred surface. In the hollows were peat bogs and morasses, on the heights outcrops of rock. It was indeed a scene of desolation —a barren, bleak, treeless, roadless, almost uninhabitable waste.

[1] Robertson, *Agric. Kincardineshire*, pp. 316-20.

A thin, acid soil overlay either peat, rock, or an obdurate pan, and
only the hardier heath plants could survive in this boulder-embedded
terrain. Undaunted by these obstacles Silver resolved on his great
task of reclamation. With spade and tramp pick he trenched the
land to a depth of from fifteen to twenty inches. He blasted the
larger and with iron levers displaced the smaller boulders, which
were conveyed by sledge to form stone walls or dykes, to face the
sides of numerous ditches or for use in covered drains. There was no
road at that time from Netherley to the port of Stonehaven, so
essential supplies of lime had to be transported about six miles in
creels and bags on the backs of packhorses. Almost 200 acres of
this wilderness were transformed into arable land, while trees,
judiciously planted in the more rugged portions to form plantations
and shelter belts, in time much enhanced the beauty of the landscape
and provided valuable shelter.

But Robert Barclay (1730-97), the fifth of his family at the
nearby estate of Ury, already referred to in an earlier chapter, did
even better. Barclay, who succeeded to the estate in 1760, had
been trained in agriculture in Norfolk, then agriculturally the most
advanced English county. There he became acquainted with some
of the great Norfolk improvers and so acquired knowledge of the
latest and best agricultural innovations—rotational farming, cultivation of the turnip crop, the sowing of grass and clover seeds, the
fattening of cattle in winter and the use of well-designed implements.
His skill in all manual operations enabled him to perform, instruct
and supervise. Young Barclay, who had inherited the " mens sana
in corpore sano " of his family, applied himself to the task of improving his land. Unreclaimed marshy moors and badly-farmed
fields and farms were transformed into an estate worthy, so a
contemporary reporter noted, of the better parts of England. Nearly
every field was encumbered by pools and quagmires, boulders and
untidy baulks of unploughed land between the ploughed rigs. There
were no enclosures, no wheeled vehicles and no roads, while the
only crops grown, bere and oats, were poor and weedy.[2] On the
expiry of the farm leases Barclay took over the subjects and one of
his first jobs was to blast the large boulders and prise out the smaller
ones with levers. An enormous plough, drawn by six to eight
horses, and taking a furrow sixteen to eighteen inches deep, was
used to turn over the more tractable parts of the land, the less
tractable being trenched. This involved systematic opening of

[2] Robertson, *Agric. Kincardineshire*, pp. 324-5.

trenches all over the land, each trench being filled with the excavated material from the adjoining trench, the larger stones being left on the surface. Usually the trench was 3 ft. wide by 14-15 in. So thick was the crop of stones brought up that sometimes a thousand loads were removed from a single acre, while after their removal the level of the land was in places lowered, so Robertson informs us, by from ten to twelve inches. Being generally unsuitable for building into stone dykes because of their round shape, these stones were used to make drains and roads and to fill up hollows and morasses.[3]

Although turnips had been grown as a field crop at Milton of Mathers in Kincardineshire as early as 1754 it was Barclay who first grew them extensively and demonstrated how they could be used to fatten stock in winter. As many as 130 acres of land would be laid down to this crop in a season. Alternate strips would be pulled, loaded into carts and spread on the grass fields to be eaten by mature cattle, five to seven years old. The remainder were eaten unpulled on the field by much the same class of animals and by sheep. Many of the cattle were actually fattened on turnips carted on to the grass during the winter, but Robertson, the reporter for Kincardineshire, expressed doubts about the universal practicability of this method. He pointed out that the Ury fields, being sheltered from the wind and exposed to the sun, enjoyed more favourable conditions than most. One of Barclay's greatest difficulties was the instruction of his farm staff in the various manual processes connected with farming. A skilled workman himself, he disliked seeing work being done in a dilatory or slovenly manner, so he brought from Norfolk a number of skilled farm workers to teach his men how to handle the wheeled Norfolk plough, to single turnips, etc. At first the local employees were unresponsive to Barclay's teachings, nor were they willing to learn from the English workers. Quaker though he was, his patience sometimes became exhausted and he would strike an offending worker. But in time success attended his efforts and a worker seeking a job on a farm could offer no higher recommendation than having been trained at Ury.[4] He would boast that he had learned through being " beat " by Barclay. As oxen were too sluggish in movement for Barclay's liking he employed about thirty horses and from forty to sixty workers. In all he improved over 900 acres, one half of which had been entirely waste.

[3] Robertson, *Agric. Kincardineshire*, pp. 328-9.　　[4] *op. cit.*, pp. 347-9.

Barclay set a fine example to Scottish landowners. In his lifetime he transformed a niggardly patrimony with an annual value of £200 into a fine estate worth £1650 a year.[5] The steeper slopes and less fertile lands were planted with trees ; the farm land was reclaimed, enclosed by thorn hedges, and improved by liming, drainage and proper cultivation ; new implements were introduced and men taught how to handle them ; the Norfolk four-course rotation, modified to suit Scottish conditions, was adopted; grass and clover seeds were sown, turnips grown and the possibility of fattening stock in winter—a practice hitherto largely unheard of in Scotland—was demonstrated. A real altruist, Barclay took delight in showing visitors round his fields, farms and plantations, and in explaining the various operations involved. His fame spread afar and he helped many a young Scot wishing to extend his knowledge of farming by recommending him to his English or Lothian farming friends.

Inspired by such notable performers as Silver and Barclay the north-east soon produced many other improvers. Among the more notable were the landlords and men of the educated classes. One of the latter was James Anderson, who had been brought north in 1777 from the farm of Hermiston near Edinburgh by Mr Udny of Udny, Aberdeenshire, to be tenant of his 1130-acre farm of Monkshill.[6] The laird hoped that his other tenants would follow Anderson's lead and example. Anderson's career was unusual. At the age of fifteen he was called upon to manage the family farm and from the outset showed signs of great ability. Besides managing the farm he attended Dr Cullen's chemistry lectures at Edinburgh University. These induced him to examine his farming problems from the scientific angle. He invented an improved plough which did not, however, come into use because of Small's production of an even better implement of its kind. His two-volume *Essays in Agriculture and Rural Affairs*, published in 1775, reached a third edition by 1779. Even today some of his ideas are singularly modern.

Anderson's landlord, Udny of Udny, was himself no mean improver. By 1779 he had reclaimed all the land near Udny, enclosed it, planted thorn hedges and built commodious farm offices. To improve the local breed of cattle, he brought north

---

[5] Robertson, *Agric. Kincardineshire*, p. 349.

[6] Alex. J. McCallum, " James Anderson ", in *S. J. Agric.*, XXII (1939), pp. 236-47.

an English " shorthorned " bull and some Berwickshire cows.[7]  He invented the " bobbin john " for sowing turnips and by doing so enabled those who could not afford to buy a turnip-sowing machine to grow that crop.  An amusing incident is told of his fool, Jamie Fleeman.  One of the improving landlords with whom Jamie was then staying was unsuccessful with one field for it failed to produce good crops.  Advice was sought on the spot from the factor who, more adept at collecting rents than managing land, could not give an explanation, whereupon Jamie remarked " Saw [sow] it wi' factors, laird.  Saw it wi' factors.  They aye thrive ! " [8]

Throughout most of the eighteenth century it was the fashion to talk of agricultural improvements.  Robert Walpole, the Prime Minister, is said to have opened his farm steward's letters before breaking the seals of correspondence on State affairs.  King George III, " Farmer George ", was greatly interested in farming.  A striking example of the interest of distinguished University professors in farming is referred to in Chapter XIX in connexion with the Farming Club at Gordon's Mill, Aberdeen.  The noted north-eastern improvers of the time, Barclay of Ury, Sir Archibald Grant of Monymusk, Cummine of Auchry, Douglas of Fechil and others, gave papers and took part in the discussions of this Society.  Information about improved implements and practices was sought, gathered and disseminated in various ways.  The net cast by the society was wide and although it appears to have been wound up in 1765, it had aroused much enthusiasm in the north-east.  Nowhere in Scotland was the spirit of improvement so pronounced as around Aberdeen and nowhere were greater difficulties tackled and surmounted.  To ensure for improvers a proper reward for their labours the landowners within the city boundary began to feu their lands extensively.

Infected by the fever for improvement the feuars of Aberdeen began to reclaim the most unpromising areas.  The original condition of some such land may be gathered from Dr Anderson's description.  " In any other part of the world I have seen it would be reckoned impossible to convert such soils to any valuable use, and the most daring improver I have met anywhere would shrink back from attempting to cultivate a field which an Aberdeen man

---

[7] A. Wight, *Present State of Husbandry in Scotland*, henceforth cited as Wight, *State of Husbandry*, Edinburgh 1778-84, VOL. III, p. 605.

[8] *The Life and Death of Jamie Fleeman, the Laird of Udny's Fool*, Aberdeen 1838, p. 21.

would consider as a trifling labour." [9]   Even at a time when labour
was very cheap the cost of these reclamations might be as high
as £100 per acre, but often enough a quarter of the expenditure
could be recovered by sending the dislodged stones to London for
use in street paving.   Adam Duff, one of Aberdeen's Provosts,
feued 150 acres of land at three shillings an acre and reclaimed
it at a cost of £3750.[10]   Another Provost, Alexander Robertson,
drained Lochhills through which the main way to the north, Loch
Street, now runs.   The fame of an impetuous, fiery-tempered,
improving Aberdeenshire laird was long perpetuated by the saying
" Like Laird Hacket that bann't a' the ouk and del't dockens on
Sunday " (that cursed all the week and dug up docks on Sunday).[11]

Today in the approach to Aberdeen from the south striking
evidence of these formidable tasks of land reclamation may be seen
from the railway in the shape of great cairns of land-gathered stones
and broad " consumption " dykes.   These dykes were erected for
the twin purposes of enclosing the fields and getting rid of the stones.
Visible, too, are portions of land still unreclaimed where large
boulders seem to occupy half the surface area.   Just west of Aberdeen
there is a consumption dyke 440 yards long, 27 feet wide and 6 feet
high, with a path running along the top.   Known as the Kingswell
dyke it is now classed as a national monument.[12]   A similar dyke
in the parish of Strachan in Kincardineshire was ten feet high and
in places broad enough to allow a cart to pass along; it was long
used as a quarry for road metal.

The last quarter of the eighteenth century, particularly after
the disastrous harvest of 1782, saw notable advances in farming.
It would seem that Scotland's energies, for centuries held fast in
the grip of feudalism, superstition, internal and external strife,
religious discord, misrule and fanatical adherence to outmoded
customs and practices, had suddenly been released.   In industry
and trade, in art and literature, in science and medicine, and in
architecture and engineering, striking advances were being recorded.
Scottish philosophers and political economists were achieving
world fame and in the general advance agriculture did not lag.

[9] James Anderson, *Observations on the means of exciting a spirit of National
Industry chiefly intended to promote the Agriculture, Commerce, Manufactures and
Fisheries of Scotland*, Edinburgh 1777, p. 65.
[10] Wight, *State of Husbandry*, VOL. III, pp. 587 ff.
[11] Alexander, *Notes and Sketches*, pp. 108-15.
[12] *Monymusk Papers*, ed. Hamilton, p. lxvii ; *Miscellany of the Third Spalding
Club*, VOL. I, Aberdeen 1935, p. 142.

It was a Caithness landlord, Sir John Sinclair (1754-1835), who, perhaps more than anyone else, exemplified the spirit of the age.[13] He succeeded to his father's estate of Ulbster at the age of sixteen and soon gave signs of his abilities. When he was eighteen he assembled some 1260 workers, convened under the regulations in the Statute Labour Act of 1719, to construct a road of some miles long over the trackless waste of Ben Cheilt. The work was completed in a single day and though by no means perfect this road was as good as many others of the period. On his estate he enclosed land, reallocated the run-rig portions, created self-contained holdings, let them on long leases, fostered liming, introduced new crops and the Cheviot breed of sheep, abolished the reprehensible practice of thirlage, commuted service into money rents and encouraged tenants to erect good houses and farm buildings. He became a Member of Parliament and in 1793 moved an address in the House of Commons for the establishment of a Board of Agriculture. The motion was carried and he became its first President with Arthur Young as the first Secretary. As a member of the General Assembly of the Church of Scotland in 1790 he proposed that each parish minister throughout Scotland should provide a Statistical Account of his parish. The task was enormous and the twenty-first and final volume of the First *Statistical Account of Scotland* was not completed until 1799. He also arranged, on becoming President of the Board of Agriculture, that every county in Great Britain should be surveyed and reported upon by writers conversant with farming affairs and endowed with literary gifts. By such means he hoped to provide information concerning the latest improvements in agriculture, nor was he disappointed in his expectations. He impressed farmers with the need to improve the quality of their wool, and it was to his foresight and zeal that the Highland Society largely owed the success of its first show in December 1822. Indeed his activities were so numerous that the Abbé Grégoire described " the chevalier Sinclair " as " the most indefatigable man in Europe and the man with the most extensive acquaintance ". The utilisation of the Highlands was in Sinclair's time a burning question; in his view the hill pastures could be used to better advantage by sheep than by cattle under the old crofting system.

Another energetic man of great mental stature was Henry Home, afterwards Lord Kames. Born in 1696, the son of a Berwickshire

[13] Anderson, *The Scottish Nation*, VOL. III, pp. 463-7.

landlord, he trained as a lawyer and in 1752 was raised to the bench of the Court of Session. Like many law lords of his time, such as Lords Monboddo and Gardenstone, he was keenly interested in agricultural improvements. At first these were practised only on his Berwickshire estate of Kames where he was one of the first to grow turnips in drills, but when his wife succeeded to her brother's estate at Blair Drummond in the Forth valley, he began to carry out the improvements so intimately associated with his name.[14] Situated on the floor of the Carse of Stirling and belonging to this estate was the extensive Moss of Kincardine which, under a deposit of eight or nine feet of peat, had a subsoil of much the same nature as that of the alluvial clay soils on the adjoining farm lands. The problem was how to get rid of the peat, and Kames conceived the plan of cutting it into pieces and floating it down to the Forth. What he did was to raise part of the waters of the Teith, one of the Forth's tributaries, seventeen feet by means of a water wheel. This water was stored in reservoirs and released at given times, the velocity of the freed waters carrying away the detached pieces of peat into the Forth. The moss was let out in lots of eight Scots acres on improving leases of thirty-eight years, each tenant being supplied with sufficient timber for his house. He was also provided with two bolls of oatmeal while employed in building his house, the walls of which were usually of turf taken from the moss. No rent was paid for the first seven years. During Kames' lifetime about one-third of this 1800-acre moss was reclaimed. This achievement is all the more remarkable since he was a man of seventy before the work began. At Blair Drummond extensive improvements were made, such as enclosing, draining, fallowing, road and bridge-making, the laying down of land to grass and clovers and the planting of trees. A profound thinker, Kames did much to enlighten the people concerning plant nourishment. He strongly advocated the teaching of agricultural science by Edinburgh University.

While initiative in the matter of improvements in the early stages rested with the landlords, tenants were at first reluctant to follow their example. Caution, conservatism and lack of sufficient cash were the main obstacles. Innovations introduced by landlords were criticised on the grounds that they alone had the necessary capital which, if they were foolish enough to spend it unwisely, was their own affair; for their part, tenants were hard put to find cash

[14] Wight, *State of Husbandry*, VOL. I, pp. 382-91 : Alex. McCallum, " A great agricultural improver, Lord Kames ", in *S.J. Agric.*, XVIII (1935), pp. 334-42.

to pay their rents. Nor was this attitude altogether unjustified; some landlords, impressed by happenings in England, or misled by the writings of theorists, introduced crops and methods totally unsuited to the climate and soil of Scotland. Yet so pronounced was the distrust of innovation that as late as 1770-80, when improvements were well advanced, liming was often regarded as a waste of money—" a step towards utter ruin " as one old farmer expressed it when counselling a widow who sought his advice.[15] Not until someone of their own status had succeeded in proving the value of innovations were tenants disposed to follow the lead given by the landlords. Near Coldstream, Pringle, a retired army surgeon, had settled down to farm his own land and by adopting new methods was able to grow crops superior to others in the district.[16] Among the crops grown were turnips but no neighbour would follow his example until William Dawson, a tenant farmer at Frogden several miles away, grew them in drills on an extensive scale. The establishment of banks in country towns after 1760 had a profound effect in promoting improvements by tenants. Credit could be had on good security and paper money became more plentiful.

The great work of Barclay and Silver near Stonehaven was to some extent matched in the same district by such tenants as Alexander Walker, of Auchwearie [17] (now spelt " Aquhirie "), and Francis Logie, of Uras.[18] The former won a prize offered by the Select Society for planting the largest number of trees. He did this on barren knolls and waste corners and for this improvement £500 was paid in 1796 in compensation to his heirs. Enlightened landlords like Barclay realised the value of good tenants. It is said that although offered a rent of £71 for one of his farms he let it to another man for £60 a year, and expressed his willingness to lend him £200 free of interest to facilitate the construction of suitable buildings. Barclay explained that he acted from selfish motives : " I never was more selfish in my life," he declared.[19]

There were many such examples. The case of Dr Anderson, Udny, has been mentioned. Skene, the proprietor of Wester Fintray farm in the Don valley, let this subject, one of the best in the county of Aberdeen, to a promising tenant, George Walker, under a thirty-three years' lease.[20] For the first eleven years the rent was to be

---

[15] Alexander, *Notes and Sketches*, p. 5.
[16] Ernle, *English Farming*, pp. 176-7 *n.*
[17] Robertson, *Agric. Kincardineshire*, pp. 314-15.          [18] *op. cit.*, p. 362.
[19] Keith, *Agric. Aberdeenshire*, p. 620 *n.*          [20] *op. cit.*, p. 135.

£130, for the second £175, and for the third £215. Walker, who had once been a carpenter, was to erect the farm offices, the landlord providing him with wood and £150 in cash. Walker at that time had less than £200 of his own but Skene realised how good a tenant he was likely to become. He became in fact an example to all tenants. His fat cattle grew to an enormous size; some were said to have weighed 14 cwt. when killed, a marked contrast to animals in the earlier part of the century when the largest oxen in Kincardineshire killed at just over 4 cwt. dead weight.[21]

Mention should also be made of how the Earl of Findlater (1716-70), the leading improver in Banffshire, brought his lands into profitable cultivation.[22] Like John Cockburn of Ormiston he believed in long leases which, however, stipulated that so much land should be improved within a specified time. So successful was he in introducing improvements that Wight described his land west of the town of Banff as being cultivated like a garden. The lease of one of his farms, Brangan,[23] was for nineteen years and a life. This meant that some time before the expiry of the first nineteen years, John Wilson, the tenant, had to nominate another person for the lease and so long as the person named was alive the lease would continue at the original rent. At a time of ever-rising prices this was a boon to the tenant who, of course, was careful to nominate a promising young person of his own family. Wilson nominated his second son and, as this lad lived until he was eighty-seven, Brangan was occupied by the two Wilsons for well-nigh a century at a most moderate rent. Long leases were, however, a two-edged weapon. Unless improvements were stipulated, the landlord could not get rid of lazy and incompetent tenants. The fact that such tenants had begun their lease at a time when rents were low and that prices had risen in the interval enabled them to pursue a leisurely farming course.

In his zeal for the advancement of farming methods the Earl of Findlater exercised great care in the choice of a factor, and in training him in the most up-to-date methods of land management. He chose a promising young man, John Wilson, the son of a tenant. Wilson was paid by the Earl, who was then none too affluent, to do what might be termed the agricultural grand tour of Britain and his reports show that he was a lad of unusual ability. Among

[21] Robertson, *Agric. Kincardineshire*, p. 381.
[22] Wight, *State of Husbandry*, VOL. III, p. 721.
[23] A. A. Brown, *The Wilsons*, privately printed 1936, pp. 14-37.

K

the people he visited was Arthur Young, the talented agricultural writer. Wilson's observations about Young were far from flattering, for despite Young's ability as a writer on farming he was not a successful farmer. For forty-two years Wilson managed the Earl's estate. Trusted by his master and esteemed by the tenantry, he did much to improve agriculture in lower Banffshire. On his home farm the Earl was the first in the area to grow turnips. Out of curiosity people came to see this strange crop and many unauthorised samples were taken. On a report by the farm manager that the people were stealing turnips the Earl exclaimed: " That precisely answers my purpose. Having learned their value in this way they will not fail to sow them for themselves ". But besides being a great agricultural improver the Earl was also a great planter of trees and in his lifetime planted eleven million. He was also greatly interested in the development of rural industries, particularly the manufacture of linen, and the lead which he gave was widely followed.

In Ross-shire, where land improvement was being developed by noted generals and admirals, by men who had made fortunes in business, and by parish ministers, the work done by two brothers of the tenant-farming class merits special mention. These two men, of the name of Middleton, had been induced to come north from the famous farming area of the Tyne valley.[24] Leasing land near Cromarty they practised the system of farming to which they had been accustomed. Wheat, said to have been grown for the first time in the county—although this is doubtful if applied to the combined counties of Ross and of Cromarty[25]—and on land which had been fallowed, yielded extraordinarily well and commanded the highest price in the London market. Eight quarters of oats to the acre—presumably the Scots acre—are said to have been grown. Two varieties were sown—the Potato oat and the Polish oat. George Middleton, one of the brothers, was employed by Sir John Sinclair in an advisory capacity to report upon farming in Caithness. The descendants of the Middletons for long set the pace in Ross-shire farming and made Easter Ross and the Black Isle famous for their agriculture. In the latter part of the nineteenth century one of them, Jonathan, was growing wonderful crops of hay on his farm at Clay of Allan; others were sending cargoes of seed and ware

[24] *The Aberdeen Press and Journal*, 24th January 1939.
[25] Burt reported, in his letters written about 1730, wheat as having been grown in Ross-shire. Burt, *Letters*, VOL. I, letter xiii, p. 261.

potatoes to England. Another Middleton, Thomas, who was later knighted, was one of Edinburgh's early graduates in agriculture. His name will always be linked with those of Somerville and Gilchrist at Cockle Park. He it was who gave shape to the national agricultural policy of the 1914-18 war and who later was to guide, encourage and supervise the early stages and struggles of agricultural research in Britain.

A similar story of agricultural progress could be told of all counties. In Angus, the Earl of Strathmore did great work.[26] The level of the Loch of Forfar was lowered by sixteen feet to reach the valuable beds of shell marl at its bottom. Large ditches dug to lead off the water were used as canals to enable the marl to be water-borne to convenient points for use on farms on his own estate and elsewhere. Shell marl was, indeed, a valuable commodity in the inland Howe of Strathmore where there were no conveniently situated deposits of limestone. Some Forfarshire landlords even dredged the bottoms of the central chain of Forfarshire lochs to get at the marl. It was men like Dalgairns, Ingliston, one of the Earl's tenants,[27] who doubled the agricultural output of their lands, making the Howe of Strathmore famed for its fertility.

Gradually the system of agriculture in Scotland was being moulded to a suitable pattern. At Roseneath on the Firth of Clyde, the Duke of Argyll carried out extensive improvements, while at Ardincaple Lord Frederick Campbell converted a large extent of dangerous morass into highly fertile land.[28] In Ayrshire, part of which was described by Bishop Leslie in 1578 in the following terms: " The pastorall is plesand, as afor I spak, of quhilke we haue cheis nane fyner and buttir in gret quantitie," [29] that noted improver, Sir Adam Ferguson, realised that the soil and climate were better suited for grass than for cereals. Accordingly he did his utmost to convert moorland into productive and profitable pasture fields.[30] Other notable Ayrshire improvers were Alexander, Earl of Eglinton, and John, Earl of Loudoun. In Galloway, Craik of Arbigland, mentioned in Chapter VII, for long set a notable example. Ayrshire cattle and their owners were, towards the end of the century, penetrating into Wigtownshire and Dumfriesshire. The milk was

[26] Wight, *State of Husbandry*, VOL. I, p. 275.
[27] *op. cit.*, VOL. I, pp. 288-9.
[28] *op. cit.*, VOL. III, pp. 297-300.
[29] P. Hume Brown, *Scotland before 1700*, p. 118.
[30] Wight, *State of Husbandry*, VOL. III, pp. 157-64.

made into Dunlop cheese. At Ingleston Lodge in Kirkcudbrightshire, a noted partnership was set up between a tenant farmer,
James Rome, and his landlord, Heron of Heron.[31] Here from 130
to 180 acres of land might be sown to turnips in a single season.
While Scotland's great poet Robert Burns, who farmed Ellisland,
six miles from Dumfries, and kept Ayrshire cows, could not rank
as an improver, his landlord Miller of Dalswinton,[32] certainly
could. He took farms into his own hands, improved them according
to the best known methods of the time and then relet them. One
farm of 985 acres, which had formerly been rented for £50, was
reported as being expected to let for £1000. On this estate no fewer
than 5000 acres were improved. On all well-managed estates in
the area the same plan was followed. Diligent search was made
for marl deposits, enterprising tenants were in demand and farms
were let to them on long lease, a valuable instrument in good farming.
Farmers would be under obligation to adhere to some modification
or other of the four-course Norfolk system and special injunctions
were sometimes added that the land should remain for four years
in pasture after the first or second year's clover hay crop had been
taken.

Chapter XX describes the considerable progress with stock
made at this period in the southern counties. Now that farms had
been consolidated and laid off into fields surrounded by stock-proof
stone dykes and hedges, it was relatively easy to pursue a progressive
livestock improvement policy. The fame of the Lancaster and the
Teeswater breeds of cattle had reached Scotland, and Scottish
landlords and farmers were taking breeding animals north with
them to improve the native breeds. On the Border hills efforts were
being made to improve the breed of sheep. In Chapter XX mention
is made of Robson, a young Northumbrian, who had taken the farm
of Belford at the top of the Bowmont Water in Roxburghshire [33]
and got great praise from Wight for effecting significant improvements in the Cheviot breed of sheep. Farmers on the Border hills
sometimes forgot, however, that size, conformation and wool
qualities were not always associated with hardiness.[34] But although
the progeny of superior sheep acquired from noted English breeders
might not do well on poor hill land, they did well on good land. The

---

[31] Wight, *State of Husbandry*, VOL. III, pp. 53-66.
[32] Singer, *Agric. Dumfries*, pp. 549 ff.
[33] Wight, *State of Husbandry*, VOL. II, pp. 364-7.
[34] *op. cit.*, VOL. II, pp. 401-03.

noted Leicester breed of sheep had been brought north and was being developed at Harden for conformation, prepotency and prolificacy. In time it became a distinct breed, the noted Border Leicester.

The Border area produced many land improvers. Some were landlords, such as Lord Kames, or the Lord Justice-Clerk, Sir Gilbert Elliot of Minto, who after seeing the good effects of marling in Angus introduced it to the Borders. Tenants like William Dawson of Frogden, already mentioned in connexion with turnip growing, and George Logan of Fishwick,[35] near Berwick-on-Tweed, did notable work. Dawson solved the difficulty of underground drainage in an area where land-gathered stones were scarce, by making faggot drains. Another difficulty which he surmounted was the forming of ridges on which to grow turnips and determining their optimum distance apart. His ridges were made by single ploughs drawn by two horses. Two furrows were laid together and other two furrows were placed on top. Thus each ridge or drill consisted of four 9-in. furrows thrown together, the distance between being later reduced to 27 in. He personally taught his workmen how to form the ridges and those trained by him readily found posts. Another improvement of Dawson's was the change-over from marling to liming even though the lime had to be carted some twenty miles. On the farm of Harperton, which he took over from his father, he would sometimes apply four hundred cartloads of clay marl per acre. Much of the material reckoned in those days to be marl contained little lime and Dawson latterly found it more convenient to buy shell lime and slake it. He applied it to fallow land and harrowed it in thoroughly, a process that gave a better result than that obtained from ploughing down the lime, as appears to have been the general practice at that time. Finding that the soil of Frogden,[36] another of his farms, was insufficiently fertile to stand up to the four-course Norfolk system he decided to lay the land down to grass for periods of from two to four years. He also folded sheep in summer on the first year's grass to build up fertility. In his cattle courts, each equipped with a broad footway in the centre to enable the turnips and straw to be easily fed, he fattened cattle in winter and marketed them either in Edinburgh or in Morpeth. In time, however, he became convinced that the

---

[35] Wight, *State of Husbandry*, VOL. II, pp. 326-31.

[36] J. S. L. Waldie, " William Dawson, 1734-1815 ", in *Agricultural Progress*, XXVI (1951), PT. II, pp. 94-8.

land benefited more from the turnips being eaten off by sheep and so fewer cattle were fattened. So successful was he in his farming that he bought the estate of Graden adjoining Frogden. From Marshall, the English agricultural writer of the time, who generally was rather critical, he received great praise. So pronounced was his influence that before he died in 1815, in his eighty-first year, he was regarded as the Father of Agriculture in that part of Scotland. This title was also given to other improvers, Cockburn of Ormiston, Barclay of Ury and Craik of Arbigland. Each had played a significant part in the introduction and cultivation of new crops and in the regeneration of unproductive Scottish soils.

In 1784 there occurred an event of the greatest significance to Scottish agriculture. That year saw the birth of the Highland Society. In a sense it was the posthumous child of the Society of Improvers. Despite the untimely end of this latter society in 1745 the spirit which it had engendered for improvement and development in Scotland's cultural life and natural resources found expression in 1754 in the establishment of the " Select Society " by Allan Ramsay, the noted painter and son of the poet.[37] Out of this Society, which was concerned mainly with Scotland's cultural advancement, there was founded in 1755 the Edinburgh Society with the more practical aim of capturing interest in and advancing the progress of the arts, sciences and manufacturers of the country, including Scottish agriculture. Prizes were offered for essays on vegetation and the principles of agriculture. The Society encouraged the enclosing of land and the planting of thorn hedges by offering a reward to the farmer who reared the largest number of young thorn trees. It was the first body of its kind in Scotland to hold livestock competitions.[38] These appear to have been judged largely at the farms themselves, not at agricultural shows as stated by some writers.

Unfortunately for these societies the times were unpropitious. Britain was then at war with France and British forces were engaged on many fronts; money was scarce and in 1764 there was a financial crisis in the affairs of both societies. For lack of support the Edinburgh Society had to close down, but the setback was only temporary. Later, after peace had been signed with America, the

[37] A. Ramsay, *History of the Highland and Agricultural Society of Scotland*, henceforth cited as Ramsay, *History H.A.S.*, Edinburgh 1879, pp. 28-9.

[38] J. A. S. Watson and M. E. Hobbs, *Great Farmers*, 2nd edn. London 1951, p. 260.

Highland Society was founded on 9th February 1784 at a meeting in Edinburgh attended by about fifty gentlemen, the Duke of Argyll being appointed the first President.[39]

The founders of the Highland Society were concerned purely with the Highlands, which after the Forty-Five were in a sorry plight. The old Highland way of life had gone; frustration and despair had driven or were driving men to forsake the glens and islands of the north-west of Scotland; greedy landlords and selfishly ambitious sheep farmers were replacing the former patriarchal chiefs and their tacksmen, so the clansmen and their cattle had to make way for a few shepherds and their flocks of sheep. The founders of the Highland Society were pledged to promote the prosperity of the Highlands and to preserve its language, music, poetry, and general culture. As was to be expected the Society devoted much attention to agricultural developments, but this project was much too wide to be limited to the Highlands. Gradually the Society's activities in farming, forestry and general rural development were extended to cover the whole of Scotland. All possible means of improvement were encouraged. Premiums were given for land reclamation, the best-managed farms, the production of grain of the highest bushel weight, the finest performances at ploughing matches, the best-kept cottages, the greatest length of sheep drains, etc.[40] Handsome awards were offered for essays describing reclamations and other farming improvements. Through their publications a wide reading public was reached and valuable information imparted. The Society encouraged inventions in farm machinery, promoted better methods of drainage and stimulated the improvement of livestock, but as these activities can be dealt with more appropriately in other chapters they need not be discussed here in detail.

One important result of the Society's efforts was the virtual abolition of the reprehensible and outmoded system of thirlage. An Act passed in 1799 made it competent for the proprietor of the mill or of the thirled lands to apply for a valuation, either in kind or in money, to indemnify millers for loss through the abolition of this outmoded custom.[41] Thirlage lingered on to some extent, for we find that Keith in his report on the agriculture of Aberdeenshire of 1811 mentions it as still being a cause of grievance in that county.[42] Robertson, the Kincardineshire reporter, in 1810 also admits that

[39] Ramsay, *History H.A.S.*, pp. 45-8.  [40] *op. cit.*, pp. 103, 139, 156.
[41] 39 Geo. III, c. 55.  [42] Keith, *Agric. Aberdeenshire*, p. 617.

it was still to some extent prevalent in the county, but points out that all complaints had died down, the thirled customers of the miller being unwilling to pay extra rents to free them from the bondage, for that was what the valuation would in effect amount to.[43] Curiously enough even as late as 1935 an Aberdeenshire miller successfully sued a farmer who was thirled to his mill for sending oats to another mill to be ground.[44] Although feudalism had virtually been abolished after the Forty-Five traces still remained in the form of the game laws and carriage servitudes, but these latter were by now much less onerous.

In the last half of the century measures were taken by Parliament to facilitate land improvement and reclamation. For instance the restrictions imposed on owners of entailed estates were considerably relaxed by an Act passed in 1770. This allowed them to contract leases with improving tenants up to a limit of nineteen years where land was cultivated, and up to thirty-one years where it was unreclaimed. Another Act providing further freedom from restrictions was passed in 1836.[45]

Lack of roads, bridges and good harbours had been great drawbacks to developments in farming. The naturally acid soils of Scotland could not be made fertile unless they were limed and, in the absence of these facilities, lime could not be brought to the farm, nor could farmers get an easy outlet for their grain. For want of a bridge over the Tweed at Coldstream, many Berwickshire and Roxburghshire farmers were denied easy access to lime deposits in Northumberland. Others in the northern parts of the same counties could not obtain lime from the Midlothian quarries since there was no proper access road.[46] Farmers in the fertile Howe of the Mearns had to use the long and treacherous North Esk ford at

---

[43] Robertson, *Agric. Kincardineshire*, p. 460.

[44] Findlay, *Oats*, p. 182.

[45] The purpose of entailing an estate was to ensure that it should pass down to successive heirs, the motive being the proprietor's desire to found a family. An Act of 1685 recognised the principle. Certain conditions had to be observed : estates could not be alienated ; debts on the estate could not be contracted—if an owner contracted a debt the creditor could not claim it from the estate ; and there could be no alteration in the order of succession. These measures proved to be so detrimental to good estate management and were so productive of injustices that in time they were considerably modified. Thus it became legal to borrow money for improvements to an estate, to make provision for younger children, to grant feus and leases for certain definite periods, to excamb portions of the estate and even to break the entail.

[46] G. Robertson, *General View of the Agriculture of the County of Midlothian*, henceforth cited as Robertson, *Agric. Midlothian*, Edinburgh 1793, pp. 25, 142.

Marykirk to reach the market town and harbour of Montrose.[47]
The state of the roads is indicated by the fact that Hepburn, in
reporting on the agriculture of East Lothian, mentioned that before
1750 a horse's " load " in Haddington in winter was reckoned to be
about 2 cwt. or what it could carry on its back.[48]  General Wade's
military roads, built in the generation before 1745, had little direct
effect on Scottish agriculture at that time.  But indirectly they had;
they brought Lowland influence to bear on the Highlands, and made
people everywhere conscious of the benefits derived from good
roads and bridges and also helped to develop the store cattle
trade.

Steps were taken in 1751 to make turnpike roads; in 1770 grants
were given for making bridges and roads in the Highlands and in
1792 measures were taken to have statute labour commuted into
money payments.  From this time onwards there was great activity
in the construction of feeder or side roads.  Since this subject is
more related to the first part of the nineteenth century it will be more
fully dealt with in the next chapter.

Scotland had undergone an extraordinary transformation during
the eighteenth century.  In mentality and in manners, in dress
and in the bearing of the people, in housing and in shipping, in
commerce, industry and in agriculture surprising changes had taken
place.  In the latter years of the century, especially after the
disastrous harvest of 1782, the rate of advance in farming had
been particularly rapid.  More turnips were grown to provide
animal food, more potatoes to provide human food.  At the beginning
of the period Scotland had lagged behind England, but so quickly
had she made use of and developed the methods practised by her
southern neighbour that by its end, despite quick progress in
England after 1760, Scottish-trained agriculturists were in demand
to manage English farms and estates.  The pupil was now in process
of outshining his teacher.

Largely because Scottish farming methods had been much more
primitive than those in England and because tenants had no legal
rights in the common grazings, the changes effected in the northern
kingdom were more sweeping, ruthless and thorough.  Run-rig, save
in the Highlands and Islands, had been largely abandoned; the
enclosure of land, the consolidation of scattered patches occupied

---

[47] Robertson, *Agric. Kincardineshire*, p. 450.
[48] G. Hepburn, *General View of the Agriculture and Rural Economy of the
County of East Lothian*, Edinburgh 1794, p. 151.

by tenants, the sweeping away of old ferme-touns and buildings, the formation of straight-sided fields, the adoption of new crops and rotations, and implements such as two-horse swing ploughs, harrows, carts, fanners, threshing mills and turnip-sowers—all designed on mechanical principles—the increased attention given to stock-breeding and fattening, the erection of substantial stone-built farm-houses and steadings, the reclamation of moor and marshlands, and the planting of woods and shelter-belts, all testified to the sweeping nature of Scotland's agricultural revolution.

From the struggle and chaos of the revolution two new rural classes had emerged, the tenant-farmer with capital and the landless farm worker, who replaced the former small tenant, subtenant or cottar. The married farm worker could, however, still keep a cow, and in many counties could get sufficient land on which to grow his lint and potatoes; in all cases he was entitled to specified amounts of oatmeal as part wages. No longer was he haunted, as his grand-father had so often been, by the spectre of famine, nor was his spirit crushed by dire poverty. The better-off ploughman could now afford an elaborate Sunday attire—a blue cloth coat, velvet vest, corduroy breeches, calf-skin shoes, shirt with ruffles, white muslin cravat, hat and watch, while young women would appear in church with fine cotton and sometimes silk dresses, bonnets, white stockings and cloth shoes,[49] the latter probably carried in the hand and not put on till somewhere near the church. A reporter contrasted the briskness of the Scottish farm worker with the languor of the English ploughman.[50] The former was reckoned to do twice as much work as his forebears.

The diet of the people was changing. Potatoes, cabbages, carrots and turnips were extensively grown and used for food; tea drinking, to the dismay of those who regarded it as an extravagance and a vice, was now becoming popular.[51] Town Councils, lairds, ministers and farmers denounced tea drinking. Solemn bonds not to drink " so demoralising a drug " were entered into. The people who drank tea were considered weak, indolent and useless. In the fiirst *Statistical Account* the reporter for the parish of Ayton in Berwickshire mentions that " tradesmen and labourers are addicted to the pernicious habit of using tea ".[52] The sweeping changes in food production that had occurred during the century may be instanced by the fact that at its beginning Scotland's population

[49] Graham, *Social Life*, p. 215.            [50] *F.S.A.*, VOL. IV, p. 509.
[51] Graham, *Social Life*, p. 217.            [52] *F.S.A.*, VOL. I, p. 87.

was estimated to be about a million, many of whom were under-nourished, while at its end the number had increased to 1,652,000, most of whom were supported by the land.   While it would be wrong to claim that there were no food shortages at the end of the period, death from starvation was now unknown.   Superstitions lingered on, however, particularly in the glens.   Above some of the byre doors crosses made of rowan wood might be seen.

> Rowan trees and reid threed (thread)
> Keep the witches fae their speed.

The old belief that " elf ill " in plough teams could be avoided by making the team plough a somewhat crooked furrow, so preventing the elves from shooting straight, was being ended by the adoption of straight furrows.   Yet ills in cattle were still attributed to people with the evil eye or uncanny eyes.[53]   Farm workers changing situations would not do so on Fridays.   But gradually beliefs in elves and brownies disappeared, and they and the fairies survived only in tales told to the children.   Much progress had still to be made but much of the dirt, disease, sloth, and narrowness of outlook, formerly so characteristic of the country, had disappeared and a spirit of optimism pervaded the people.

[53] Graham, *Social Life*, pp. 192-4.

# CHAPTER X

# PROSPERITY AND DEPRESSION: 1800-1836

Continued prosperity...Rising costs of agricultural products, land values, rents and wages...Housing of farm workers... Effect of yearly or half-yearly engagements...Post-war extravagances...Utilitarian spirit in agriculture...Road and canal making...Wheat exports to England...Slumps after 1813...Peace and the cattle trade...The great depression...The Corn Laws...Protection...Slow recovery...Low price of sheep and wool...Cobbett on East Lothian...Depression on clay farms...Corn rents...Sutherland farming...Underground drainage...Fixed equipment...Plans for farm buildings... Agricultural societies...Promotion of Live Stock Shows... Ploughing matches...Farming contrasts.

THE MARKED PROGRESS IN SCOTTISH AGRICULTURE recorded in the closing quarter of the eighteenth century continued unabated into the nineteenth. It could scarcely have been otherwise since the times were most propitious for farmers. Britain was at war with France and her European allies now under the leadership of Napoleon. The war years brought rising prices for produce yet there was little disturbance of the even tenor of farm life—no call-up of men, no requisitioning of horses. From 1793 to 1815, save for two short periods, Britain and France were engaged in a deadly struggle. Britain's naval supremacy gave her command of the sea and so at no time were food supplies from overseas entirely cut off. Nevertheless, the fear that imports might cease created almost panic conditions in years of poor harvests. If Napoleon could not prevent British ships from bringing in corn from other European countries, he could at least by his decrees exert pressure to deter those countries from exporting grain to Britain. The United States and Canada at that time had not much surplus grain to dispose of. An additional factor in raising grain prices was the unprecedented rise in the cost of freights and insurance. During the years 1810-12 the transport charge of foreign wheat to this country rose to 50s. a quarter.[1]

The situation was aggravated by the growing needs of an ever-increasing population and an unusual number of poor harvests.

[1] Ernle, *English Farming*, p. 270.

Britain's population during the war years was mounting rapidly; new towns were being built and new industries established. While it was true that the improved system of rotational farming, more thorough cultivations, the use of better implements, the consolidation of scattered patches of land into self-contained farms, the reclamation of land from moorland and marsh and the adoption of the potato as a food crop, had increased the amount of home-grown food, the supply seldom exceeded and often was short of the requirements of

CLACKMANNAN FIARS' PRICES

| | | Wheat per boll of 4 bushels, 1½ pecks | | Carse oats per boll of 6 bushels, 1½ pecks | |
|---|---|---|---|---|---|
| | | Fiars' Price | Preceding 20 years' Average | Fiars' Price | Preceding 20 years' Average |
| Remarks | Year | s.   d. | s.   d. | s.   d. | s.   d. |
| Scarcity   .   . | 1795 | 45   0 | 19   6½ | 20   0 | 13   2½ |
| Normal .   .   . | 1797 | 19   6 | 21   5 | 14   0 | 13   7¼ |
| „   .   .   . | 1798 | 21   6 | 21   4¾ | 15   0 | 13   9¼ |
| Scarcity   .   . | 1799 | 35   0 | 21   7¼ | 24   0 | 14   4 |
| „   .   . | 1800 | 60   0 | 22   7¼ | 38   0 | 15   0¼ |
| „   .   . | 1801 | 36   0 | 25   8¾ | 17   6 | 16   4½ |
| „   .   . | 1804 | 40   0 | 25   11 | 20   0 | 16   10½ |
| „   .   . | 1808 | 43   6 | 29   0¾ | 24   3 | 18   5¾ |
| „   .   . | 1809 | 43   0 | 30   3 | 27   0 | 19   1 |
| Normal   .   . | 1810 | 34   6 | 31   3 | 21   0 | 19   9¼ |
| Scarcity   .   . | 1811 | 46   0 | 31   10¼ | 24   0 | 20   1 |
| „   .   . | 1812 | 58   0 | 33   1¾ | 30   0 | 20   6¼ |

the people. Against this background the fear of famine conditions was the chief cause of high prices and violent price fluctuations. Of the twenty-two war harvests in Britain seven were deficient, seven more very deficient and only two really abundant.[2] The greatest fluctuations took place in the price of wheat, the principal cereal grown and used in England. Considerable amounts of wheat were grown at that time in Scotland for sale to England. How great these price fluctuations were is manifest from an examination of the Clackmannanshire fiars' prices for certain selected years.[3]

The outstanding years of crop deficiencies were 1795, 1799,

[2] Ernle, *English Farming*, p. 269.

[3] Sir John Sinclair, *General Report of the Agricultural State and Political Circumstances of Scotland*, henceforth cited as Sinclair, *General Report*, Edinburgh 1814, VOL. V, pp. 355 ff. See also Appendix III, p. 457.

1800, 1808, 1811 and 1812. In 1800 the price of wheat in Scotland was nearly three times that of the preceding twenty-year average, while the price of oats had risen two and a half times, but except for that year and the years 1795, 1799, 1808, 1809 and 1812 the price of oats tended more than that of wheat to approximate to the average level. So bad were the harvests of 1799 and 1800 that in Scotland they were known as the " dear years ". Oatmeal at one stage was being sold at 10s. a stone and Thomas Carlyle's father noticed the labourers " retire each separately to a brook and there drink, instead of dining, without complaint, anxious only to hide it " (their want).[4] In 1812 English wheat was actually selling at 155s. a quarter.[5] Cattle prices rose correspondingly. There was a heavy demand for salt beef for the Navy. Partly because of their increase in size and partly because of an advance in the price of meat, cattle often made three times their former price.

Napoleon, feared and hated by British people, conferred an inestimable boon on Britain's farming. Rises in prices of farm produce promoted rises in rents and land values and prospective tenants sometimes offered five to seven times the old rental. In 1748 Scotland's rental was estimated to be £822,857; in 1813 the figure had risen to £6,285,500. So anxious were men to rent land that auctioneers sometimes warned clients that they were not buyers but merely the prospective renters of land. Buyers wishing to profit from the higher rentals and to enjoy the social prestige of land ownership offered fabulous prices. Extravagance was rife and the money earned and spent seemed to suggest that the wartime prosperity would last indefinitely.

In the latter half of the eighteenth and the earlier part of the nineteenth century Scottish architecture had made striking progress. The New Town of Edinburgh, planned on spacious and dignified lines, was being built. In the country the tall, grim-looking house of the laird, with its small windows and crow-stepped gables, was being replaced by a cheerful and well-lit Georgian or classical mansion whose extensive policies were enclosed by walls of stone and lime and adorned by ornamental trees. Money was spent lavishly on interior furnishings and skilled artists were employed to paint the family portraits. The rents ruling for agricultural land seemed to warrant these extravagances. Little did the lairds of that time realise that some of these gorgeous mansion houses would in the next century be sold at demolition prices. Little, too, did many

---

[4] Trevelyan, *Social History*, p. 462.        [5] Ernle, *English Farming*, p. 270.

landowners who borrowed money to embellish their estates, or farmers who had equipped their farms largely by means of loans, realise that this wartime prosperity rested on a shaky foundation.

The war created a demand for labour. Wages rose, possibly not in proportion to food prices, although Sinclair in the *Appendix to the General Report on the Agriculture of Scotland* estimated that in many districts during the reign of George III wages had soared to three or four times their former levels.[6] There was, however, no pronounced scarcity of farm workers. The chief difficulty experienced by Scottish farmers of the time was in regard to accommodation for labour. Unlike his English neighbour the Scottish farmer had no nearby village from which to draw labour, for at that time Scotland had few villages. The newly-created farms usually occupied the site of the demolished ferme-touns. The former mean dwelling houses of the people had disappeared or were in process of so doing. To provide accommodation for workers, either the tenant-farmer or his landlord had to build " cottar " houses. To ensure that the worker would not quit, his system of payment had to be one best suited to reconcile the old way of life on the ferme-touns, where self-sufficiency in food and clothing for each family had been the aim, with the new one of producing food on farms where the worker was but an employee. And so wages were largely if not wholly paid in kind. For married workers a tied cottage was usually supplied; in the south-eastern districts it was often a one-roomed house.[7] In Kincardineshire two apartments were created by a special end-to-end arrangement of the boxed-in beds.[8] Single workers were variously accommodated. In the eastern arable areas a bothy was provided where the men could cook, dine, sit and sleep. In other areas they were given food and often sleeping quarters in the farmer's house; or sleeping quarters were provided in lofts called " chaumers " (Fr. *chambre*) sometimes located above the stable.

In East Lothian typical yearly wages for married men about the beginning of the century were the provision of a house, which was not always rent-free, the keep of a cow, ten bolls of oats, three of barley and two of pease, and so much land on which to grow lint

---

[6] Sinclair, *General Report*, vol. v, p. 187.

[7] Robert Somerville, *General View of the Agriculture of East Lothian*, henceforth cited as Somerville, *Agric. E. Lothian*, London 1805, p. 49 ; J. Wilson, " Half a century as a Border farmer ", henceforth cited as Wilson, " Border farmer ", in *T.H.A.S.*, 5th ser. xiv (1902), p. 38.

[8] Robertson, *Agric. Kincardineshire*, p. 426.

and potatoes, but no cash.[9] At a later date cash was given in addition to perquisites. Free carriage for fuel and for the sale of grain not required in the household would be given. Usually the worker was obliged to supply extra help, generally his wife, who might have to give eighteen days' work in harvest without wages but with victuals for herself and her husband in lieu of house rent.[10] In this way the change-over from the old way of run-rig farming with its self-sufficiency and independence to the new one of employer and employee, was effected without undue hardship. In the dear years of the war workers actually benefited for they had butter, eggs and grain or meal to sell. Hens and a pig could be kept. Extra allowances, too, might be given for stacking in harvest. The cash value of these wages averaged about £25 a year in 1810. Single workers who lodged with the farmer got £10 to £14 a year.

Such a system seems to have lasted until the 1850's, when rent-free houses were given and the worker was not always required to provide a " bondager "[11] as the female outworker was called. But the custom of supplying a bondager lasted well into the twentieth century. In Kincardineshire, where south of Stonehaven the bothy system prevailed, unmarried men were given two pecks of oatmeal a week, the milk of a cow or its equivalent amongst three men, accommodation in the bothy and fuel, and from £16. 16s. 0d. to £21 a year.[12] Married men got less cash wages but were allowed to keep a cow and were given potato and lint ground in addition to a rent-free house and fuel. They got the same amount of meal as the bothy men. In most counties the yearly amount of meal allowed to married men was six and a half bolls. Single workers in Aberdeenshire might get as much as £20 a year in addition to their board and lodging,[13] the tendency being for wages to be highest in the industrial areas and lowest in the extreme north. In Ross-shire unmarried workers might get only £12 a year in cash wages, while in Caithness only £6 or £7 might be paid. This latter figure was, of course, exclusive of the value of the perquisites which were reckoned to be worth about £14. 14s. 0d. a year. Men hired for harvest got the equivalent of £3 and women of £2.[14]

The bothy system was largely confined to the area of the eastern counties from north of the Forth to the Howe of the Mearns in

[9] Somerville, *Agric. E. Lothian*, p. 207.
[10] Wilson, " Border farmer ", p. 38.          [11] *op. cit.*, pp. 37-8.
[12] Robertson, *Agric. Kincardineshire*, p. 429.
[13] Keith, *Agric. Aberdeenshire*, p. 514.
[14] Henderson, *Agric. Caithness*, pp. 228-9.

Kincardineshire, but was also in use on some of the larger Aberdeenshire and Moray farms. In the eastern counties farms were usually
large and the wives of the larger farmers no doubt found it burdensome to cook, wash dishes, make beds, clean premises, etc. for some
four, six or even eight single men. When the bothy system was
evolved, the basis and indeed the greater part of the food eaten in
Scottish country districts was, apart from potatoes, oatmeal, which
could be quickly made into porridge or brose. It seemed no great
hardship at that time, therefore, to leave single men to cook their
own meals. The system was, however, unworthy of the country or
its agriculture. Cobbett was stirred to indignation when he saw
the treatment meted out to farm workers in bothies. One which he
visited near Dunfermline had an earthen floor and accommodated
three wooden beds. There were no cooking utensils except possibly
the pot or kettle; spoons were evidently the only table utensil
required. The workers were allowed $6\frac{1}{2}$ bolls of oatmeal each a
year and so much milk. Three sacks of oatmeal were stacked inside
the bothy very much in the same way as sacks of feed would be
stacked inside the store of a piggery. Evidently the meals were
mainly of brose. Cobbett, in whose view the workers were treated
worse than horses or dogs, scathingly described the bothy as a mere
shed and, as was his custom, inveighed against " grasping landowners ". The tenant-farmer, he alleged, got cheap labour by this
system, and so was enabled to pay a high rent.[15]

Though somewhat more refined, the system of providing single
men with sleeping accommodation outside the farmhouse and with
food in the farm kitchen was nevertheless rather crude. There
was little or no privacy for the worker and, as the social distinction
between worker and farmer tended to widen on farms where the
farmer and his family did not dine and sit in the kitchen, the worker
lacked the refining influence and intercourse of normal family life.
Most chaumers were without fire-places, the only fire available
being in the farm kitchen. There the worker might not feel at ease
and, if a friend called and privacy was desired, the only comfortable
place available was the farm stable, the lid of the corn chest providing
the necessary seating accommodation. Horses, ploughing matches
and the gossip of the countryside were normal topics of conversation.

In these formative years at the beginning of the nineteenth
century the pattern of life on Scottish farms that was to prevail

[15] William Cobbett, *A Tour in Scotland and in the Four Northern Counties of
England*, London 1833, pp. 130-2.

L

throughout the next hundred years or more was evolved.   Hard work, long hours, rigid discipline, zeal and efficiency rewarded by low cash wages, poor accommodation, little leisure and still less encouragement of the cultivation of the finer graces of life character- ised the labour situation.   With little respite maidservants, earning from £5 to £6 in cash in the year,[16] worked alongside their mistresses on farms from 5 a.m. until 9 p.m.   Yet with all its austerity farm life at that period was an excellent training for the hardships of pioneer life in the new countries of the world.

Not in vain had Barclay of Ury or Dawson of Frogden taught and disciplined their workers.[17]   Wherever they went men and women trained on Scottish farms earned fame for their skill and capacity for hard work.   But there was little repose in the home life of the workers.   At the Whitsunday and Martinmas terms single workers shifted from farm to farm, some to better their positions, but most with no real objective.   Even married workers showed the same tendency to " flit " at the end of their yearly engagements. A slight misunderstanding with their master or fellow-workers, or between one worker's wife and another's, might be the excuse; often there was none.   But it could scarcely be said that tied houses were conducive to a long stay; they were more in the nature of shelters from the elements than homes; they often consisted of one or at most two rooms; their gardens lacked flowers, ornamental shrubs and fruit bushes and trees.   The masters for their part acquiesced in the constant change of workers and did little towards ending the system.   So short was the supply of houses for married workers that engagements were, as has been pointed out, often conditional on providing a woman outworker.[18]   This scarcity of cottar houses was too often a prime cause of immorality and of emigration.

These early years of the century saw considerable developments in agriculture.   As already mentioned the war hardly affected the even trend of farming; no great expeditionary force had been sent overseas and fewer than forty thousand British soldiers died in the Peninsular War.[19]   Landlords and tenant-farmers prospered and rents rose.   Byron inveighed against the prosperous landlords— " They roar'd, they dined, they drank, they swore, they meant to

[16] Robertson, *Agric. Kincardineshire*, p. 430.
[17] *op. cit.*, pp. 347, 427.
[18] Wilson, " Border farmer ", p. 38.
[19] Trevelyan, *Social History*, p. 467.

die for England—Why then live ? For rent ! " [20] It was the time
of the Regency extravagances, but Byron's castigations could not
fairly be applied to Scottish landlords in general or to many Highland landlords in particular.

The times, however, saw the widening of the gulf between
landlord and tenant and between tenant and worker. In dress and
deportment, in politics and religion, a noticeable social distinction
between landlord and tenant evolved. Landlords' children sent to
English public schools acquired a different accent and mode of life.
Only in the Highlands was the old-time social intercourse between
high and low, rich and poor, preserved. Cadets of Highland landlords' families, after serving as officers in the Army or in some
occupation abroad would return to one of the estate farms and
mingle freely with all classes. They were equally at home in castle
or cottage and at one with peer and peasant.

In general the period was utilitarian, the aim being to produce
as much food as possible. The former small occupiers were displaced
and their scattered patches consolidated into square or rectangular
fields of a farm with centrally placed steading and cottages. Adam
Smith, philosopher and economist, declared that the reduction in
the number of cottagers and small occupiers had in every part of
Europe been the forerunner of improvement and better cultivation.
There could be no comparison between the output per acre of the
independent occupier of a small area of unfenced land, who spent
much of his time tending his few stock and walking to and from
his small scattered patches of cultivated land, and that of his opposite
number working a full day on a well-organised farm with conveniently situated fields.

This utilitarian spirit stimulated Sir John Sinclair to advocate
that the Highlands should be stocked with sheep instead of cattle.
Double, and even treble, the amount of meat, apart altogether from
wool, could, he pointed out, be got from the same area of land.[21]
Everywhere the spirit of enterprise was manifest. The problem
of the slow dissemination of knowledge, formerly the great obstacle
to improvement in farming, was now being vigorously tackled by
Sinclair and his colleagues in the newly-formed Board of Agriculture.
As pointed out in Chapter XIX, writers chosen for their literary
skill and knowledge of farming were engaged to describe the general
state of agriculture in each county in Great Britain. Two different

---

[20] George Gordon, Lord Byron, *The Age of Bronze*, London 1823.
[21] Sinclair, *Agric. Northern Counties*, p. 110.

accounts were furnished, the first from 1793, the second largely from 1801 to 1814. Sinclair himself wrote the first account for the northern counties of Scotland. The performances of many Scottish reporters such as Skene Keith for Aberdeenshire, the Robertsons for Perth, Kincardine and Midlothian, Fullerton for Ayr, Singer for Dumfries, Somerville for East Lothian and Thomson for Fife, were highly creditable. These publications and others, such as the *Farmers' Magazine* (first produced in January 1800) and the essays published by the Highland Society, helped in the quick diffusion of knowledge.

The great development in road-making did much to foster progress by promoting frequency of travel and convenience of transport. As has already been pointed out the deplorable state of the Scottish roads had forced Parliament in the seventeenth century to pass various Acts relating to roads and their maintenance. Statute labour, whereby able-bodied men had to provide so many days' labour in the year, had been customary; but the results were so unsatisfactory that a strengthening Act embodying the same principle was passed in 1719. But while this Act improved matters, knowledge of road-making and maintenance was still lacking, supervision lax, labour grudgingly given and inadequately applied. This, however, led to the passing of the Turnpike Road Act in 1751, after which marked developments took place. The money for the turnpike roads could be raised by subscription or loan by specially appointed trustees and maintenance was secured by tolls. Between 1796 and 1811 over 300 miles of these roads were reported by Skene Keith as having been made in Aberdeenshire.[22] In 1792 an Act was passed whereby statute labour could be commuted into money payments. This led to a great development in the making and improving of the cross-country and feeder roads. The same reporter speaks of great activity in Aberdeenshire in the making of non-turnpike or commutation roads, as they were called,[23] over 1000 miles having been made by 1811. In the Highlands special measures had to be taken ; trustees were appointed to make roads, the expense being borne equally by local subscriptions and Parliamentary grants. Telford was engaged and made 900 miles of roads.[24] He it was who made the Glasgow-Carlisle road about the year 1814. Another engineer responsible for making many Scottish roads at this time was Charles Abercrombie, while McAdam,

[22] Keith, *Agric. Aberdeenshire*, p. 535.        [23] *op. cit.*, p. 539.
[24] Ernle, *English Farming*, p. 286.

a native of Moffat, perpetuated his name in the system of road-metalling he evolved. In 1827 he was appointed Surveyor-General of roads in Great Britain.

This great development in road-making speeded up liming. Instead of being carried on horseback lime was conveyed in carts from harbours and lime works.[25] Very long distances, sometimes as many as fifty miles, were travelled to obtain lime, a *sine qua non* for promoting fertility in Scotland's acid soils. A striking picture was given by Wilson, a Berwickshire farmer, of veritable cavalcades of carts making for the lime kilns in the summer twilight. Following a short rest at the kilns the carts would be filled and the long journey home completed after an absence of from sixteen to eighteen hours.[26] The erection of a bridge over the Tweed at Coldstream was a great boon to many Berwickshire farmers who could now get their lime from Northumberland. So too was the Aberdeenshire canal to farmers in that area. It was opened for traffic in 1806 and in the three years 1808-10 over 70,000 bolls of lime were carried to inland farms. The sight of such strings of carts, bearing wheat to the port of Dunbar for export to England, amazed Cobbett on his visit to Scotland in 1832[27] and provided him with more material with which to attack the landlord class. Here, he alleged, was an instance of Scotland's wealth being misused for the benefit of absentee landlords.

The false prosperity of the war years reached its zenith in the years 1812 and 1813. The average price per quarter for British wheat in England and Wales in the former year was 126s. 6d. and in the latter 109s. 9d.: in the following year it was only 74s. 4d. The bountiful harvest of 1813 was one of the best in memory so, despite the war, the price of wheat per quarter sank well below, and during the rest of the nineteenth century never regained, the three-figure level. Except for one or two years between 1814 and 1820 the wheat price remained fairly steady at between 65s. and 90s. a quarter; even at these prices wheat should have paid well, but high rents, poor crops—the results of slovenly farming and over-cropping and of wheat sown being on wet, acid, or unsuitable land—made its production a losing proposition on many farms. Until the end of the war the price of cattle remained high, but the news of the great victory of Waterloo markedly reduced prices. As George Williamson,

[25] Robertson, *Agric. Kincardineshire*, p. 319.
[26] Wilson, " Border Farmer ", p. 41.
[27] Cobbett, *Tour in Scotland*, p. 90.

a famous Aberdeenshire cattle dealer, was passing through the streets of Perth with a great drove of cattle, the church bells were ringing a merry peal for the peace. But, as he pithily observed, it was a sorrowful peal for him, for he lost £4000 by the fall in prices.[28]

From the twenty-two years' struggle with Napoleon, Britain emerged victorious but exhausted. The National Debt was enormous and taxation was at a high level. The prosperity of the war years quickly vanished and industries such as agriculture, which had enjoyed protection during the war, began to languish. As has been pointed out high rents combined with poor yields and the fall in the price of grain or beef made farming a ruinous proposition. Credit was disturbed and confidence shaken : the currency was disordered and unemployment was rife. At home discharged soldiers and sailors could not find jobs and abroad there was no sufficient market for British goods. Many farmers who had leased farms at high rents, or had borrowed money to stock them, found themselves in such dire straits that they went bankrupt. The depression was felt to a greater extent in England, where much of the land had been given over to wheat growing. There thousands of acres even in restricted areas were without tenants. The price of wheat, England's main cereal crop, had fallen to proportionally lower levels than that of oats, Scotland's major crop. Partly for this reason, partly because farming was more mixed in character in Scotland, and in part because the Scottish farmer had been more disposed to invest his wartime profits in land improvements, the depression was felt much less acutely in Scotland ; but in the wheat-growing Lothians many of the younger generation had, according to one writer, lost their heads. They aped the manners and extravagant habits of the wealthier classes, kept greyhounds, and joined coursing clubs.[29] After 1815 they had either to settle down to hard work and a simpler mode of life or go bankrupt.

In another respect the Scottish farmer was more fortunate than his English contemporary, who was often compelled to bear the heavy burden of high poor rates. In some English counties a foolish, short-sighted system of supporting the poor had been adopted. Every poor person was entitled to receive a sum to supplement his wages, if below a certain variable level, to bring them up to prescribed standards. These standards were worked on

[28] W. McCombie, *Cattle and Cattle-Breeders*, 4th edn. Edinburgh 1886, p. 34.
[29] Watson and Hobbs, *Great Farmers*, p. 98.

a sliding scale according to the size of the family and the price of bread.[30] Thus no matter how little a labourer might be paid, he was entitled under the Speenhamland Act to have his wages made up to " appropriate " levels. The general wave of unemployment threw many men out of work in the villages and towns, and they were glad to get work on any terms, knowing that their wages would be made up to a certain standard. Labour in consequence became cheap. Farmers, hit by the hard times and besieged by workers willing to accept low rates, were often tempted to lower the wages of their regular workers to levels which enabled them to qualify for assistance. This meant, of course, an additional burden for the ratepayers.

Labourers who had saved money or had purchased a cottage were ineligible for assistance, but stripped of their savings or of the ownership of their cottages they qualified for help. It thus paid men to become penniless; there was no incentive for the labourer to save money and the less the farmer paid the worker, the more the latter got by way of assistance. Cobbett, obsessed by his ideas on landlordism, saw in this foolish system the means whereby rents would remain at high and wages at low levels. In Scotland, however, comparatively few parishes had a legal assessment, the poor being supported almost entirely by the Church. Little wonder then that Scottish and Irish beggars found England a country much more to their liking than their own and were at pains to get there. A Northumbrian contractor, we learn, received so much per head for returning Scottish beggars to their own country. They were conveyed to Kelso and there handed over to the authorities. Patrick Sellar, the progressive and enlightened tenant of three Sutherland farms, observed in 1830 that in the parish of Golspie there were no poor rates, no drunkards, and no beggars except the Irish and a few squalid ruined men from the south who wandered occasionally into the county.[31] Possibly the Irish in question were Highland tinkers who only used English when begging, but who customarily spoke Gaelic or, as it was sometimes termed, Erse.

From about the end of the seventeenth century until 1815 the operation of the Corn Laws had been administered on recognised principles. In normal years imports of foreign grain were practically prohibited while exports, which for centuries had been

---

[30] Ernle, *English Farming*, pp. 327-8.
[31] Patrick Sellar in *Reports of Select Farms*, henceforth cited as *Farm Reports*, Library of Useful Knowledge, London 1831, p. 86.

subject to customs duty, and which on occasion were prohibited, were usually encouraged by bounties. This induced farmers to expand their grain acreages so that, in the event of a poor harvest, the country might still be able to provide most of its own food. In years of poor harvests, when prices rose above a certain level, exports were prohibited and imports permitted either duty free or at reduced rates. The scales were often revised but the principle remained the same. The system tended to stabilise acreages and prices except during the Napoleonic Wars when imports from foreign countries fell to a mere trickle. It could scarcely be claimed, therefore, that the Corn Laws up till 1814 had prejudiced consumers' interests or had unduly benefited farmers and landowners; they were based solely on moral principles.

After 1815, the bounty on exports was abolished but freedom to export was continued. The needs of Britain's population had, however, by now left no exportable surplus of grain. Although imports were allowed, heavy duties had to be paid so long as the average price of wheat, rye, barley, oats, peas and beans remained below certain high levels. From 1815 to 1822 the price level for wheat was 80s., for barley it was 40s., and for oats 27s. per quarter.[32] The Corn Laws at this time were frankly protective and were intended to shut out imports. British colonies were, however, allowed preferential rates. These new measures helped in some degree to ease the post-war depression and its worst effects were gradually overcome. But improvident or bad farmers, or those who had borrowed money too lavishly, went bankrupt and their farms were let at lower rents. Lower rents, too, were arranged when leases were renewed.

The expedient of " corn rents " was often resorted to when the inflated cash rent, imposed under a lease begun shortly before the fall in prices, became too onerous. This was a much more equitable system. If grain rose in price up went the rent; if the price went down the rent fell correspondingly. Many Lothian landlords and farmers adopted this system. The landlord, knowing that insistence on a high rent contracted for during the war might at a later date force a good tenant into the Bankruptcy Court, and leave the owner with a farm which could be let only at a much lower rent, usually agreed to a corn rent.

Six years after the close of the war the commercial depression throughout the country lightened and credit and confidence revived.

[32] 55 Geo. III, c. 26.

This welcome turn towards prosperity was reflected in the price of wheat, which became steady at about 60s. a quarter. Unfortunately after 1818 mutton and wool declined in price and reached low levels in 1821-24, when hill lambs were fetching only from 4s. to 7s. a head, Blackface wool 2½d. per lb. and Cheviot wool from 4d. to 5d. per lb., or little over a quarter of their 1818 prices.[33] But expenses on sheep farms were low and by the 1830's farm prices had reached reasonably profitable levels and farming on dry land was again prosperous.

Entering East Lothian at Cockburnspath one October day in 1832 Cobbett saw stretched out before him a wonderfully prosperous and fertile countryside. He described it as the most fertile and finest farming land he had ever seen.[34] "Such cornfields, such fields of turnips, such turnips in those fields, such stackyards—as never surely were seen in any country upon earth." There were often more than a hundred stacks in a single stackyard, all neatly built and thatched and, on his reckoning, containing on an average from fifteen to twenty quarters of wheat or oats. Many farms had steam engines to drive their threshing mills, others employed horses. But the absence of houses appalled Cobbett, in whose view the people had been removed from the land to make way for a capitalistic though an efficient kind of farming. To him smoke stacks on the farms were emblematic of Satanic mills which had robbed the lower classes of their independence and imperilled their livelihood. Lord Ernle, however, provides a doleful picture of the post-war depression in England which lasted for nearly a quarter of a century.[35] To the southern farmers, peace in many cases meant beggary, some clay farms being entirely abandoned. Landlords, tenants and labourers alike suffered but, since the landed interests were strongly represented in Parliament, attention was ever being called to the prevailing distress. Prices for agricultural products were stated to be unremunerative and higher prices were demanded. Evidence before Select Committees in 1820, 1821, 1822 and 1833 supported the general view that many farmers were in a bad way. In spite of rent reductions amounting in many instances to about one half the former rent there was, according to Lord Ernle, scarcely one solvent tenant in the Weald lands of Sussex and Kent.

Watson and Hobbs [36] also paint a vivid picture of the post-war

[33] " Prices of wool since 1818 " in *T.H.A.S.*, 5th ser. xxxiv (1922), pp. 289-91.
[34] Cobbett, *Tour in Scotland*, pp. 89-90.     [35] Ernle, *English Farming*, pp. 316 ff.
[36] Watson and Hobbs, *Gerat Farmers*, pp. 97 ff.

struggle of the Hope family on Fenton Barns, an East Lothian farm, later to attain European fame for its excellent crops and management.   Faced with bankruptcy and having to pay a stiff cash rent, Robert Hope, the tenant, thought of going to America, but a frank talk with the factor led to the latter agreeing to a corn instead of a cash rent.   This decided Hope to stay on, but for years he was hard put to it to make ends meet.   The cold and as yet undrained, sticky soil of much of the farm precluded full yields and there was no surplus cash available to drain the wet land.   George Hope, the tenant's son, who later became famous, was chagrined on his journey to market to see much better crops grown on other farms.   The remedy lay in under-drainage, but until money became more plentiful that was out of the question.   When, however, income became adjusted to expenditure and the Hopes became more prosperous many miles of drains were laid on this farm and better crops were grown.   In the four years immediately preceding 1836 the then satisfactory average yield of 28 bushels of wheat per acre was being reaped on the 175 acres under that crop.   Drainage and good management coupled with more prosperous times for farming had effected a wonderful change on this potentially fertile farm.

It would be wrong to suppose that in the two decades following the close of the Napoleonic Wars there was little or no progress. So great was the land hunger in Scotland that even then reclamations were being carried out.   Sutherland, because of its isolation, had been one of the last of the Scottish counties to be influenced either by improvements in arable cultivation or by the revolutionary changes in pastoral farming exemplified by the Highland clearances.

It was to this backward county that Patrick Sellar, a Moray farmer, came to settle about 1809.   There were then no roads, no harbours and no evidence whatever of the practice of improved methods of agriculture.[37]   Yet by 1820, despite the setbacks experienced at the close of the wars, great improvements had been effected. Many farm steadings had been built, much land enclosed, roads made and harbours formed.   As many as twenty vessels could sometimes be seen at one time loading or unloading cargoes at the different ports.   The value of the fish, wool and mutton exported

[37] Sellar in *Farm Reports*, pp. 65 ff.; J. Macdonald, " On the agriculture of the county of Sutherland ", henceforth cited as Macdonald, " Agriculture of Sutherland ", in *T.H.A.S.*, 4th ser. XII (1880), p. 26.

annually was thought to be about £70,000. Sinclair, writing twenty-five years earlier, had estimated the whole yearly valuation of the county to be about £2200. Of the 650 acres arable on Sellar's arable farms, Culmaily, entered in 1810, and Morvich, in 1818, about 250 acres had by 1820 been reclaimed from moorland by Sellar and all the land had been limed. He was even growing wheat, the result doubtless of the protective effects of the Corn Laws. At the time Sellar wrote, in 1830, wheat was selling at 60s. a quarter and oats at 24s. Given a good yield wheat was undoubtedly the more profitable crop. His rotational system was the five- or six-course one with either two or three years' temporary ley. For the whole 650 acres only six full-time pairs of horses were employed. Dung, supplemented by sea ware, was used to manure the fallow crop and when the supply was exhausted bone dust, now being used as a fertiliser, was applied. Turnip crops of between twenty and thirty tons per acre were sometimes grown. Sellar's picture of the working of these farms indicates that, apart from the use of artificial manures and the coming of the reaper and binder, there were few improvements on his system during the next eighty years. The system of rotation, the methods of cropping and the organisation of labour remained much the same. Even in the manner of grazing his pastures he was singularly modern. Three cattle would be put on for every acre and shifted to another grass field when the grass had been eaten down. On some hirsels of his large sheep farm in Strathnaver " pine " was known to exist. His remedy was to move sheep to his arable farm of Culmaily. Braxy was countered by taking the wether lambs off the hills about the middle of September, feeding them on rape and turnips on the low ground farm of Culmaily for a limited number of hours during the day and there-after putting them on the heather for the afternoon and night. The ewe lambs were wintered in the grass fields at Morvich and Culmaily. By such means Sellar was able to halve the death rate, bringing it down to seven or eight per cent. His lambing rate varied from eighty-five to ninety per cent. Sellar's work, as recorded, was largely done in those post-war years when depression was so marked a feature of many parts of the country. In the adjoining county of Ross land was also reclaimed during the years of depression. Land previously covered with scrub wood was enclosed, trenched, limed with Sunderland lime at the rate of five tons of shell lime per acre and drained where springs were encountered.[38] Farming

[38] J. Baigrie in *Farm Reports*, pp. 88-96.

Societies offered premiums to owners of Clydesdale stallions in the south-west to send their horses to Ross-shire. But so many Ross-shire farmers were prepared to use Clydesdales that owners were induced to send them north without a premium.

The high prices for wheat ruling during the war had tempted many Scottish farmers to grow it in counties where neither the soil nor the climate was suitable. In Ayrshire, for example, wheat-growing had now become largely unprofitable and land was laid down to grass to produce milk for making into cheese. One reporter for Ayr county, who was evidently far ahead of his time, recommended sowing the seeds of cocksfoot, timothy and rib-grass in addition to the customary rye-grass and clover seeds. He advocated a very fine seed bed and rolling both before and after sowing the seed. He pointed out that perennial rye-grass alone in a seed mixture gave undesirable results, and cautioned farmers against grazing the young pastures in bad weather.[39]

Several reasons, apart from lower rents, explain the quick recovery of Scottish agriculture from the post-war depression. One was the adherence to the practice of temporary leys. On the relatively poor soils of Scotland the laying down of grass for a period of two, three or more years had become a necessity if the fertility of the soil was to be maintained. High prices for grain during the war had tempted farmers to overcrop, with consequent poor yields, but Scottish farmers quickly found the remedy in the use of the temporary ley. Another reason for the quick recovery was the growing popularity of under-drainage. As described in Chapter XXV, Smith of Deanston was a vigorous advocate of systematic under-drainage. He had shown that on stiff wet lands, and wherever a hard impenetrable pan impeded the passage of water downwards, under-drainage, often coupled with subsoiling, could produce wonderful results. Thus on some farms in the Stirlingshire parish of St Ninian's, yields had risen by about sixty per cent.[40] Many tile works were set up, landlords and even tenants sometimes having works of their own; horseshoe tiles were made before the cylindrical tile was evolved.[41]

In the latter part of the previous century it had been customary for tenants to erect both farm-houses and steadings. The landlord might advance the money at prevailing rates of interest, but scarcity

[39] Anon. in *Farm Reports*, p. 38.
[40] *N.S.A.*, VOL. VIII, Stirlingshire p. 327.
[41] Watson and Hobbs, *Great Farmers*, p. 21.

of capital and a general aversion to heavy borrowing tempted many tenants to construct rather mean and badly-planned buildings. Landlords now began to realise that if their farms were to attract satisfactory tenants and command good rents they themselves would have to provide dwelling-houses and steadings. Those who had acted with discretion during the war years were generally able to supply the capital and so, when new leases were being arranged and the tenant complained about the poor state of buildings which he had either built himself or had taken over at valuation, the landlord would usually agree to provide new ones. In consequence, poor scattered buildings on farms were replaced by well-built, well-designed steadings. They were designed in the form of a square, with buildings on three or all four of its sides and the open dung midden in the centre; the threshing mill, barn with straw house and granary, and cart sheds, might occupy one wing, the byres, stable and other houses the other two or three. Wherever possible water power was used to drive the threshing mills, but this often led to steadings being inconveniently situated from the point of view of working the land. On flat land steam engines or horses provided power for the machinery. Unfortunately, many steadings of those days, though good to look at, were not planned with a view to economy in labour. Labour was then cheap and rents, even when reduced, remained relatively high. A century later, when this position was reversed, the construction of a well-planned steading designed to reduce labour costs to a minimum became vitally important to the farmer.

This post-war period saw considerable development in the activities of agricultural societies. Ranking high in importance among their activities was the holding of livestock shows and ploughing matches. In a backyard off the Canongate in Edinburgh the Highland Society held its first general show of stock on 26th December 1822.[42] This was not the first show of its kind, but the Society's prestige undoubtedly stimulated the promotion of stock shows everywhere. It is largely because of these shows—parish, district, county and national—that Scotland has attained her pre-eminence in livestock breeding. Ploughing matches, too, came to be regarded as outstanding events and the contest held in the early spring of 1839, under the auspices of the Clackmannan Union Agricultural Society, attracted 107 competitors. Incidentally it was in this county in 1784 that the first really great ploughing

⁴² Ramsay, *History H.A.S.*, p. 161.

match ever to be held in Scotland took place.  It may be mentioned, too, that an Alloa ploughman was selected to give an exhibition of ploughing before " Farmer George ".[43]

Agricultural historians are disposed to end this period of post-war depression with the close of William IV's reign and to date the beginning of a new era of prosperity from the accession of Queen Victoria.  There is, however, in point of time no sharp division between the periods.  Rents in the post-war depression became gradually related to prices.  Bountiful seasons from 1831 to 1836, despite the demands of Britain's growing population, caused wheat to slump in 1835 below 40s. per quarter, the lowest figure for over half a century.  The fiars' price of oats in East Lothian in 1833 was 19s. 1d.; in 1812 it had been £2. 10s. 9¾d.  But despite this, agriculture was undoubtedly showing signs of progress.  The long period of depression, though hard to endure, had a salutary effect.  Incompetent farmers had been weeded out; overcropping—so much the vogue during the Napoleonic wars—had been stopped, while thrift and hard work replaced the follies and extravagances of the preceding boom.  More attention was being paid to drainage and liming than hitherto.  New and better implements had been invented and thought had been given to the proper organisation of labour.

There were great advances to record in the breeding and feeding of stock, for the foundations of the Aberdeen-Angus and the Scottish Shorthorn breeds had already been laid.  Ayrshire breeders for their part were busy improving the characteristics of their breed.  In all breeds of farm animals the tendency was to use male animals bred either by the very best specialised breeders, or from stock bred by such breeders.  The blood of the very best animals soon began to be concentrated in élite, and to be infused into most commercial herds.

Before the first forty years of the nineteenth century had expired there had been a wonderful transformation in Scottish agriculture.  More farms had been laid out in orderly fashion; bogs and morasses had been drained and the whin and heather-clad lower hills were fast being converted into arable fields.  On the relatively abundant rotation pastures contented and well-bred animals could eat their fill.  The crops were cleaner and much more abundant.  Bare though the countryside may have appeared to a traveller from south of the Border, it was the bareness of good, and in some parts, of intensive

[43] N.S.A., VOL. VIII, Clackmannanshire p. 47.

farming. Alexander, in his Aberdeenshire classic *Johnny Gibb of Gushetneuk*, fittingly summed up the situation in Gibb's words (suitably translated) on his retirement from farming: " When we [that is, Mrs Gibb and Johnny] began to farm with three young cattle and a brindled cow the one side of Gushetneuk was taken up with broom bushes and heather knolls and the other was mostly bogs growing little but sprets and rushes. It looks like yesterday when we had the new houses all built and the land all under the plough and yet it's more than thirty years since." [44] Gibb's achievements were equalled on many Scottish farms about that time.

[44] William Alexander, *Johnny Gibb o' Gushetneuk*, Aberdeen 1871, Chapter XLIV.

# CHAPTER XI

## YEARS OF PROSPERITY : 1837-1874

Beginning of Industrial Age ... Railways ... Bone meal ...
Drainage...Turnips...Progress in cattle breeding...Pattern of
Scottish agriculture moulded...Sheltering effects of Corn
Laws...Growing reaction against Protection...Poor harvests
and high prices...Repeal of Corn Laws...Effect on prices...
Golden Age of farming in sixties...Use of artificial fertilisers...
Improving landlords and tenants...High farming in Lothians
...Resentment against Game Laws...Social status of
landlords and farmers.

IN 1837 QUEEN VICTORIA began her long momentous reign. For
agriculture and industry its opening was a time of transition.
The country was recovering from the depression which followed
the Napoleonic Wars and industry and commerce were progressing.
The era of coal, iron and railways had begun. The impact of the
railways and of steam boats was to have far-reaching effects on
our commerce, industry and agriculture. Through their agency
communications were developed and knowledge was advanced. In
the transport of lime, seeds, fertilisers, feeding stuffs, implements,
grain, fat animals and store stock, railways were to exercise a profound
influence on British farming. At first transport developments
brought prosperity to farmers, but later they were the chief cause
of the great depression which began about 1875. Queen Victoria's
reign can indeed, with respect to agriculture, be divided into two
distinct periods; the first one of great prosperity, the second, one
of profound depression. But for the country as a whole the reign
throughout was marked by great progress as befitted the efforts of
a vigorous, self-reliant and self-disciplined nation.

Railways were at first of interest to farmers only in easing horse
haulage to and from ports and markets. No fewer than 146 pages of
the 1824 *Transactions of the Highland Society* discussed " railroads "
from that angle. Such railways had long been in use in mines,
with horses drawing trucks first on wooden rails then on flanged
iron rails, and finally on smooth rails which took flanged wheels.
Such problems as braking, curves, gradients, etc. gave rise to much

discussion. But with the development of the steam railway engine treatises on these problems disappeared from agricultural literature and were replaced by others to which the railways themselves had largely given rise.

The two decades 1815-34 of post-war depression had had a salutary influence on farming. They had seen the weeding out of bad, careless and extravagant farmers, the adjustment of rents to some semblance of realism, the abandonment of overcropping and a return to rotations designed to maintain, if not to enhance, the fertility and cleanliness of arable land. Liming was better understood; by 1837 Smith's system of thorough underground drainage was being extensively practised, while the application of bone meal or dust to turnip land had enabled enterprising farmers to extend their acreages of turnips with great advantage to supplies of winter keep. In the agricultural literature of the time there are references to the results of trials to determine whether bones, introduced as a fertiliser about 1800, were as good a fertiliser as dung, and some surprisingly good crops were grown. Thus in the 1820's Patrick Sellar, the enterprising Sutherland farmer previously mentioned, found that he got even heavier crops of turnips by using bone dust instead of dung.[1] He does not disclose, however, how his trials were carried out. In other instances the crops grown with the aid of bone dust weighed three tons per acre less. English farmers might grumble that wheat was fetching little over 50s. a quarter, but on well-managed land in some Scottish counties wheat was a good paying crop. As has already been mentioned, it was being grown as far north as Sutherland. No Scottish farmer with a climate and soil suitable for wheat-growing could afford, so long as oats commanded less than half the price, to have all his grain acreage under oats.[2] Farmers still sheltered under the umbrella of the Corn Laws which specially favoured wheat.

Great progress was being made in livestock breeding, feeding and management. Livestock shows, many of which had been instituted a little earlier, encouraged farmers to select breeding animals with more care. The great wealth of flesh and the early maturity of the Shorthorn fostered a demand for bulls of that breed to cross with native cows. Scottish farmers like Watson, McCombie, Walker, Fullerton and Bowie, realising what had been done by English breeders such as Bakewell, the Collings and the Culleys to improve certain breeds of cattle and sheep, sought to do likewise

[1] Sellar in *Farm Reports*, p. 74.          [2] *op. cit.*, p. 75.

M

for their native Angus and Aberdeenshire black cattle, and found that by this time they had good material to work with. Ayrshire breeders were doing well with their cattle. Breed societies were formed and herd-books compiled.[3] Far-sighted landlords who had improved the stock on their home farms, encouraged their tenants by supplying them with good bulls. At livestock shows bulls were sometimes given away as prizes instead of medals or money.[4] Now that ample supplies of turnips and oat straw could be provided as winter food for cattle much greater care was bestowed on the feeding and management of the animals. With a supplement of oil cake and oats, winter-fattening could be carried out much more quickly and with younger animals, *i.e.* animals no more than two and a half to three years old. Russian linseed was being imported for crushing and the by-product was available for fattening sheep and cattle. The disappearance of the ox teams, formerly such a burden on food resources, meant a considerable increase in cattle output. While it was true that the pairs of horses which replaced the oxen had to be well fed, the quantity of food consumed was small by comparison with that eaten by the eight to twelve oxen of the old plough team. Rising prices for meat induced farmers to grow more winter feed for fattening cattle instead of selling them as stores.

Throughout Scotland, save in the West Highlands and Islands, the Lanarkshire breed of horses was gaining in popularity. They were strong, docile, hardy and extremely active. The sight of a well-matched, well-groomed, spirited pair of Clydesdales in shining harness at a ploughing match was most pleasing to the eye. Bradley,[5] an Englishman, greatly admired them, as had his countryman, Abraham Jones, seventy-five years before.[6] Travelling stallions were sent from the Clyde valley to all parts of Scotland. The brisk ploughmen who worked them took immense pride in keeping them well fed and groomed, and in caring for their harness.

Farmers of the period were at pains to arrange their cropping programmes to ensure that winter would be balanced with summer keep, that the fertility and cleanliness of their land would at least be

[3] The date of *Coates's Herd Book* (Shorthorn) was 1822 ; the first volume of the *Aberdeen-Angus Herd Book* was issued in 1862 ; the *Galloway Herd Book* was established in 1877, the *Ayrshire Herd Book* in 1878, and the *Highland Herd Book* in 1885.

[4] Watson and Hobbs, *Great Farmers*, p. 160.

[5] A. G. Bradley, *When Squires and Farmers Thrived*, henceforth cited as Bradley, *Squires and Farmers*, London 1927, p. 78.

[6] Robertson, *Agric. Midlothian*, App. II, p. 15.

maintained if not improved, that wet land would be made dry and sour land sweet, that labour requirements would be so adjusted that, so far as could be foreseen, every hour of the working day and every possible working day of the year would be profitably employed. At hay-time and harvest extra help was needed in the arable areas, but such help was readily obtained locally or was provided by harvest hands from the Highlands and Islands. In byre and stable, in field and stackyard, in the routine of the day's work and in the larger sphere of co-ordinated planning for the farm, order, efficiency and perfectionism were characteristic of the period. " A man ", wrote McCombie about fattening cattle, " may take care of, and pull turnips for, thirty cattle very well, but when the day gets short twenty to twenty-five are as many as a man can feed to do them justice if tied up ".[7] Judged by present-day standards the use of labour was extravagant, but in those days labour was cheap and excellence in fattening cattle was the main objective.

In one respect progress was disappointing—a reflection doubtless on the cheapness and abundance of part-time labour for farm work at busy seasons of the year. Bell's revolutionary invention of the reaper in 1828 appears to have been ignored. While his machine continued to be used year after year on his brother's farm, farmers elsewhere were content to cut their crops with the scythe. Not until the 1850's, when reapers began to be manufactured in this country, did our farmers awaken to the fact that Bell in Britain and McCormick in America had provided them with an outstanding invention.

Scottish farmers allocated a pair of work horses to every 50 to 100 acres of arable land according to the rotation practised and the slope and character of the land. Thus on arable farms in the Lothians where the land was sown down to grass for only one year, a pair of horses would work fifty acres, whereas on a longer grass rotation on light, level and dry farms in Sutherland Patrick Sellar employed one full-time pair of horses for $108\frac{1}{2}$ acres arable—a very fine performance.[8] His was partly the five-course rotation, three crops followed by two years' grass, and in part the six-course, three crops followed by three years' grass.

So sound were these rotation systems that they enabled most Scottish farmers to weather the long depression which lasted with but one short interruption from about 1879 to 1939. Yet they had

[7] McCombie, *Cattle and Cattle-Breeders*, p. 26.
[8] Sellar in *Farm Reports*, p. 68.

their weak features. In late June and early July the turnip and the hay crop often demanded simultaneous attention and delay usually meant some measure of loss in one or other of these crops. Similarly, the clearing of the ground of turnips in spring frequently held up the completion of the sowing of the cereal crop with consequential lower yields. But in general the system of farming practised in the fifties and sixties of the nineteenth century was admirable.

In 1815, the Government's fiscal policy in regard to homegrown grain was protective. No duty-free imports were allowed so long as the current prices of wheat, barley and oats were below certain high levels, *e.g.* 80*s.* per quarter for wheat and 27*s.* per quarter for oats from foreign countries, and 67*s.* and 22*s.* respectively for cereals from the colonies.[9] As may be imagined this policy of the " dear loaf ", as it was called, was greatly resented by the growing industrial population. By the thirties the doctrine of Free Trade was widely embraced, but even advanced Free Traders like Porter were apprehensive lest a repeal of the Corn Laws should induce farmers to cut down their wheat acreages. They favoured a policy which would allow agriculture to develop in line with industrial production. Despite an increase in population of 5.7 millions between 1811 and 1841 the number of people which Great Britain was unable to feed had risen only by some 300,000.[10] Thus agricultural output, through more extensive cultivation and better farming methods, had almost kept pace with the rise in population and Porter, author of *The Progress of the Nation*, regarded this rate of expansion as ideal. Yet despite the protective influences of the Corn Laws the price of wheat in some years of the 1830's was lower than it had been for about half a century, and so long as the price remained relatively low there seemed little prospect of the Corn Laws being repealed.

But repealed they were. Poor harvests in the period 1837-41 caused the price of grain to rise and with it the opposition to the Corn Laws. Manufacturers, anxious to sell their goods in the world market, were converted to the policy of Free Trade. In their view it implied cheap food, and in turn low costs of living, low wages and low costs of production. The movement was strengthened as the years passed. In 1845 there was a poor grain harvest while blight ruined the potato crop. The following year was to

⁹ Ernle, *English Farming*, p. 494.
¹⁰ G. R. Porter, *The Progress of the Nation*, 2nd edn. London 1847, p. 136.

see yet another disaster to the potato crop. In Ireland the sufferings of the people were indescribable: over a quarter of a million are stated too have died from starvation during a dreadful winter.[11] The rains of these years " washed away " the Corn Laws. So in 1846 the duties were modified; in 1849 all kinds of foreign grain were admitted at a nominal duty of 1s. a quarter [12] and even that impost was removed in 1869. The victory of the Free Trade campaigners was complete.

But the virtual removal of protective duties did not at first greatly affect the price of wheat. After remaining for two or three years at about 40s. a quarter it rose to over 50s. in 1852 and to over 70s. in 1854 and 1855. From then onwards it remained for twenty years at highly remunerative levels for, although prices were considerably below those which ruled in the Napoleonic Wars, farmers had become much more skilful in growing wheat and rents were now more reasonable. Thus there was still a considerable margin between costs of production and market prices. The price of oats also remained fairly steady. In the fifties and sixties of the century Scottish farmers were borne on a generally rising tide of prosperity. Their yearly cash wage bill still remained relatively low. With agriculture prosperous both landlords and tenants were nothing loth to embark on reclaiming land from moor and moss, on rebuilding outmoded farm-houses and steadings and on liming and draining land. Investing money in land was popular and remunerative and prospects for the future seemed to promise well.

On the Ross-shire estate of Ardross no fewer than 2600 acres were reclaimed by trenching, draining and liming in nine years from about 1850. New steadings were erected; $67\frac{1}{2}$ miles of stone dykes were built and 3000 acres were enclosed for planting. All these operations were carried out by the proprietor.[13] More spectacular, if less fruitful in their results, were the reclamations carried out by the Duke of Sutherland in that county. In the Lairg area on the farms of Shiness and Dalchork and elsewhere huge stretches of land were won from heather and bog. In four seasons from the year 1873, 1829 acres were turned over by huge ploughs.[14] When the operations were in full swing fourteen steam engines could be seen puffing in unison.

[11] Arthur Bryant, *English Saga 1840-1940*, London 1940, p. 104.
[12] Ernle, *English Farming*, p. 274.
[13] W. Mackenzie, " Report on improvements at Ardross ", in *T.H.A.S.*, 3rd ser. VIII (1857-59), pp. 131 ff.
[14] Macdonald, " Agriculture of Sutherland ", p. 33.

But not content with this work the Duke began more reclamation work in 1877 in the Badenloch area where he planned to reclaim nearly 1000 acres. A special plough was designed. By October 1879 the amount spent, exclusive of the cost of the working plant, was about £130,000. These reclamations represented only part of the total amount of land reclaimed on the estate, for some of the tenants of the large sheep farms reclaimed upwards of a hundred acres on their individual holdings. Such land was an invaluable adjunct to their farms.[15] Hay and turnips could be grown to tide stock over a snowstorm; grass wintering could be had at home for a proportion of the ewe hoggs and sheltered lambing fields for the hill ewes. In Macdonald's statistics for Sutherland, the arable acreage in 1853 was 22,000; by 1879 it had risen to 29,400 acres.[16]

Much of the reclamation elsewhere in these years of agricultural prosperity was carried out by tenant-farmers. At Drumore of Clava, in the vicinity of Inverness, there were only fifty acres of arable land when Macpherson became tenant about 1857. Thirteen years later upwards of three hundred acres had been reclaimed. The drainage cost the tenant £2000, the ploughing £1100 and the lime £1000. The landlord built the dykes but the tenant quarried and carted the material. So prosperous was agriculture in these years that much of the initial outlay had been recovered within five years.[17]

The times were indeed propitious. Industry was progressing and railways had opened up the country. Farmers could get their artificial manures, lime, feeding stuffs and other requirements delivered at a nearby station, where they could also load their grain, fat and store cattle, and sheep. Sutherland sheep farmers could winter their ewe hoggs in the shires of Moray and Banff and bring hay from the Lowlands to feed their ewes during periods of snowstorm. Argyllshire sheep farmers could send their sheep to wintering grounds in Aberdeenshire. Wars in other countries tended to prolong prosperity in home agriculture. Thus the Crimean War closed the Baltic to grain ships. In the sixties, with war in Europe and in America, Britain enjoyed peace, as again she did during the Franco-Prussian war of 1870-71. In 1864 " laid " Cheviot wool was making about 1s. 6d. a pound, about double the

---

[15] Macdonald, " Agriculture of Sutherland ", p. 48.

[16] op. cit., p. 49.

[17] William Macdonald, " On the agriculture of the county of Inverness ", henceforth cited as Macdonald, " Agriculture of Inverness ", in T.H.A.S., 4th ser. IV (1872), pp. 23-4.

average price for previous years.[18]   In most of the seasons at this time abundant harvests were reaped.

Artificial fertilisers began to be used soon after Queen Victoria ascended the throne.   Up to this time dung, lime and bones were the principal fertilising agencies used by farmers.   Near towns use had been made of soot and waste material like shoddy and horn parings.   In the fourteen years before 1837 the value of imported bones (figures for the whole of Great Britian) rose from £14,395 to £254,600.   In 1835 nitrate of soda and guano were introduced, but so little was known about these manures that it was not until 1847 or thereabouts that the latter was imported on any appreciable scale, while as late as 1850 nitrate was still a novelty.[19]   Guano, which according to Alexander gave phenomenal increases in crops,[20] might be described as a natural manure, but soon the true artificials were to arrive and play their part in offsetting in some degree the effects of the repeal of the Corn Laws.   In 1840 Leibig suggested the treatment of bones with sulphuric acid and in 1843 Lawes began to manufacture superphosphate.[21]   Turnips in Scotland could now, with the aid of these fertilisers, be successfully grown on the whole instead of only part of the fallow land break.

An illustration of the development of the cattle fattening enterprise based on the turnip crop is the fact that in the early part of the century the county of Aberdeen exported annually 9,000 to 10,000 stores in addition to supplying itself with beef, whereas by 1865 about 9,000 fat cattle were being sent annually to southern markets by rail from Aberdeen in addition to the 4,000 or 5,000 despatched by sea and well over 10,000 tons of dead meat [22] or the equivalent of nearly 35,000 cattle.   In the aggregate nearly 50,000 fat cattle were being exported from an area probably a third larger than Aberdeenshire.   This revolution in the cattle trade had been brought about by the use of fertilisers through extending the acreage of turnips, by the development of rail and steamboat transport and by great improvements in stock and crop management. Bradley, the author of *When Squires and Farmers Thrived*, commented that Aberdeenshire farmers talked about cattle and little else;[23] cattle were indeed their farming mainstay.

18   " Prices of sheep since 1818 ", in *T.H.A.S.*, 5th ser. xv (1904), pp. 373-4.
19   Ernle, *English Farming*, p. 369.
20   W. Alexander, *Johnny Gibb o' Gushetneuk*, Chapter xi.
21   Ernle, *English Farming*, p. 370.
22   McCombie, *Cattle and Cattle-Breeders*, p. 82.
23   Bradley, *Squires and Farmers*, p. 180.

Although progress in livestock was marked, the period saw some disastrous visitations of cattle disease. From 1839 onwards there had been outbreaks of foot-and-mouth disease. Pleuropneumonia developed in 1840 and rinderpest in 1865. So dire were the effects of the latter that energetic action had to be taken. Early in 1866 the slaughter of diseased animals was made compulsory and for a time over ten thousand cattle were being killed each week.[24] But this drastic measure was justified, for the incidence of disease dropped rapidly. Many farmers were nearly ruined by these outbreaks; the author's great-grandfather twice lost practically the whole of his stock but so prosperous were the times that the losses were soon made good.

During this period no Government or quasi-governmental body dictated the kind of crop to be grown, or how land should be utilised or managed. But the landlords saw to it that there was no misuse of land. Great care was taken in drawing up leases to ensure that tenants abode by the rules of good husbandry. Certain rotations had to be observed and in many instances, to prevent the impoverishment of land by the sale of cash crops, only limited acreages of potatoes were allowed. Neither straw nor dung could be sold off the farm. At changes of tenancy an outgoing tenant usually had to hand over unused crops and farmyard manure to the incoming tenant at valuation. Weeds such as thistles had to be cut by a certain date to prevent the dispersal of seed by the wind. Thus, partly by restrictive measures and in part by adherence to the tradition of good farming, a uniformly creditable standard of farming was maintained. In the Lothians the whole countryside was impressive to the eye. The straight-sided, rectangular fields were trim and clean; there were no waste lands, no odd corners, no straggling hedges; even in winter the rich brown earth gave promise of great fertility—so Bradley described the East Lothian of the seventies.

It was, indeed, an era when it paid to farm well. Scottish farmers sought to increase output and profits by better farming. This involved draining wet land, liming, liberal applications of artificial manures particularly to turnip crops, clean farming, timeous cultivation and the breeding and keeping of good stock. On Fenton Barns the wheat crops in the seventies yielded from six to seven quarters per acre and sometimes were as high as eight.[25] This was

---

[24] Ernle, *English Farming*, p. 375 *n.*
[25] Bradley, *Squires and Farmers*, p. 78.

a marked advance on the 1832-36 average of rather less than three and a half quarters, which at that time was considered satisfactory.[26]

Prosperous times, increasing rents and higher standards of farming, induced both landlords and tenants to spend money lavishly on land. The splendid farm-houses to be seen in the Lothians, in Strathmore, the Laigh of Moray and Easter Ross were erected largely during this period. In other instances the old plain-fronted farm-house with its small rooms and windows was enlarged by building a new wing with oriel windows to the front, thus giving the house a somewhat T- or L-shaped appearance. The rebuilt steadings, designed on what were then considered to be up-to-date principles, were intended to economise labour and to be comfortable for the animals. Gradually, in the eastern cropping districts and in Moray the straw yards and open dung middens were converted into covered courts. Incidentally McCombie disliked buying store cattle wintered in such courts: he preferred those wintered in open yards.[27] In the Kincardineshire parish of Durris the landlord, a noted improver, chanced upon a workman, who had been ordered to pave a ditch with stones to prevent erosion, doing slipshod work and found fault with him. The man answered the laird that the ditch " would last your time and mine ". " But I want it to last for all eternity", rejoined the landlord. In this spirit were improvements projected and carried out. Bad landlords there were, but most Scottish lairds were deeply land-conscious and anxious to leave their estates more productive than they found them. There was something very wholesome in this pride on the part of landlords, and it was matched by the tenants' pride in good farming and by the workers' in farm craftsmanship.

In country districts society was based on an aristocratic social system. At the top were the lairds, their wives and their families. An exclusive class, this county aristocracy mixed on terms of social equality only with other landlords. Towards their tenants they were friendly within limits. Their accents, manner of speech and conversation differed; they drove in a carriage and pair and they were interested, in a philanthropic but rather condescending way, in social welfare movements such as stock or flower shows, charity bazaars, social gatherings, Girls' Friendly Societies, etc. Only in the excitement of a good curling match did lairds thaw sufficiently to address their tenants or their workmen, or allow themselves to be

[26] Watson and Hobbs, *Great Farmers*, p. 100.
[27] McCombie, *Cattle and Cattle-Breeders*, p. 19.

addressed, in familiar terms. The largest tenants for their part drove to kirk and market in their gigs; the smaller either walked or rode in farm carts. All raised their caps to the laird but to no one else. Few, however, expressed a very close personal attachment to the landowners;[28] only in the Highlands did the old-time intimate relationship between landlord and tenant linger.

The landlord for his part was well aware of the value of good tenants in enhancing his prestige and the value of his estate. Many of these good landlords regarded their land not as a profit-making concern but as a trust to be maintained and developed in good commercial partnership with tenants and workers. When a farm became vacant great care was taken to choose a desirable tenant. The young man of push and character, particularly if he were public-spirited and of satisfactory social standing, was not always handicapped by lack of means in leasing a farm.

But in these halcyon times there were causes of friction even on the best estates. Feudalism was supposed to have been eradicated by legislation after the Forty-Five but some of its roots still remained. The right to kill game, for instance, was vested solely in the landlord. The old Act of 1621 decreed that only owners of ploughgates of land, *i.e.* about 130 imperial acres, could kill game of any kind—rabbits, hares, partridges, duck, etc., but no tenant farmer could view without misgiving rabbits destroying his crops. He usually had the privilege of killing them on his own land but that privilege did not embrace killing hares; if he set out to kill rabbits on his farm at night time he was guilty of an offence; moreover some landlords, who wanted the right of killing rabbits exclusively for themselves, would not accept tenants who wished to kill rabbits.

Landlords resident in the country were proud of their game preserves which enabled them to entertain their many guests lavishly during the shooting season. Their love of sport often blinded them to other considerations. In evidence led before Mr Bright in 1846 a Mr Landale from near Kirkcaldy stated that on land extending to 1300 acres he had assessed the yearly damage done by rabbits over a period of years as anything from £320 to about £1000. In 1839 it was £428, in 1841 it was £655 and in 1844 it was practically £1000.[29]

---

[28] Bradley, *Squires and Farmers*, pp. 121 ff.

[29] David Bruce, " Game Laws ", in *The Standard Cyclopaedia of Modern Agriculture and Rural Economy*, ed. Sir R. P. Wright, London 1908-11, VOL. VI. pp. 86-90.

The labouring classes, too, had strong feelings in the matter. Some of them wondered who gave the landlords the right to own game which might at one moment be on one estate, and in a matter of minutes be on the public road or on someone else's estate. Domestic animals were different; they were privately owned: no one contemplated taking them for that ranked as theft; but they argued that the creatures of the wild were either no man's or every man's property. Accordingly they arranged poaching parties and defied both laird and keeper. Parliament, in which the landed interests were firmly entrenched, passed ever stricter laws, e.g. the Night Poaching Act of 1829, the Game Act of 1832. After this feeling against landlords sometimes ran high. The effigy of one, otherwise highly esteemed, was burned in a county town with rabbits hanging on to his coat tails. John Bright wrote a trenchant article on the need for reform of the game laws, but it was not until 1880 that they were amended to allow tenant-farmers the right to kill rabbits and hares on their own land.[30] The landlord could no longer reserve to himself, as he sometimes had, the exclusive right to do this. Nevertheless one English landlord in 1924 advertised for a tenant who would not interfere with the landlord's shooting.

In parenthesis it may be pointed out that until about 1820 wild rabbits are scarcely mentioned in Scottish agricultural books. They were probably introduced by the Normans and in the Middle Ages were kept in warrens. But even as late as 1810 Robertson, the reporter for Kincardineshire, mentioned that he saw no wild rabbits during the course of his survey of that county. Elsewhere in the surveys they are mentioned as being prevalent in certain coastal areas. In 1688 Davenant estimated that there were a million rabbits in England and Wales and that the value of each was five pence, i.e. about the hundredth part of a cattle beast at that time. The

[30] John Bright, " Game Preservation " (reprint from article in Morton's *Cyclopaedia of Agriculture*) in *Standard Cyclopaedia of Modern Agriculture*, VOL. VI, pp., 90-3.

[31] In the Fragmentary Collection of old laws it was decreed that the creatures of the wild, being by nature wild, belonged to no man before capture ; but it was also decreed that if a man were found on another man's ground he was guilty of trespass (*A.P.S.*, VOL. I, pp. 749-51). In the time of Alexander I the hunting of hares in forests was prohibited, but apart from the question of trespass it was legal to kill them elsewhere (*op. cit.*, p. 652). The Night Poaching Act 1828 made it a crime for a tenant-farmer to set out at night to kill rabbits on the land he farmed. If bees swarmed and the swarm left the premises of the owner they remained his property as long as he could keep them in sight. If he lost sight of them and they lodged on the property of another they became the property of that other.

spread of rabbits in Scotland during the nineteenth century is thought to have been associated with agricultural improvements.

There were other reasons for tension between some landlords and their tenants. The disruption of the Church of Scotland in 1843 had been in the nature of a rebellion against the powers and privileges of the landlords. The Free Kirk adherents had openly defied patronage. Tenants, particularly those who had left the "Auld Kirk", became so bold as to speak publicly against such grievances as insecurity of tenure, and to advocate better housing for workers, compensation for unexhausted improvements, the extension of the franchise, the amendment of the game laws and the abolition of hypothec or the law whereby rent was secured on a tenant's goods. Hypothec was made illegal by an Act passed in 1880. Some landlords even regarded those who voted Liberal as fomenters of strife and discontent, threatening the ideal society which the charity of landlords, and their interest in their tenants and workers had done so much to promote. The unfailing remedy adopted by some landlords was to turn such tenants out of their farms at the end of the lease. The tenant might have converted heather and bog into smiling cornfields; he might have spent much money, time and labour in liming and draining his farm or erecting buildings, but out he had to go.

With remarkable energy three generations of Hopes had transformed the East Lothian farm of Fenton Barns from a wet, sour and unproductive subject, that refused to grow crops in a wet year and good crops in any year, into one whose fame, for its excellent crops and the masterly organisation of its labour, was not confined to Britain. It had become one of Britain's model farms. But George Hope, the third of his generation, had advanced political views and was emboldened to stand as Liberal candidate for the county. He was unsuccessful but the incident was not forgotten; eight years later, when the lease of Fenton Barns was due to expire, Hope was informed that his application for the renewal of the lease would not be entertained.[32] The affair caused a sensation. The Liberal Press stormed and even the Conservatives were uneasy. Such things had been done before, but the name and fame of George Hope and Fenton Barns were known everywhere. "Save us from our friends", was the silent prayer of other landlords. George Hope was too magnanimous to pose as a martyr, but the indignation aroused caused his landlord much anxiety, for he had injured his

[32] Bradley, *Squires and Farmers*, pp. 196-7.

class and his party. But happily few landlords were of that mould.
It is told how Dr Farquharson, the laird of Finzean in Aberdeenshire, answered a small tenant who complained that his rent was
too high. " How could that be, John ? " said the worthy doctor,
" you've paid no rent at all for some time past."

So long as prices for horn and corn remained high tenant-farmers
prospered and landlords strove to maintain their social prestige.
Whenever possible the larger landlords added to their possessions
and there were then few owner-occupiers in Scotland. But by the
" sixties " there were signs that the period of great prosperity was
coming to an end, though wars in Europe and America helped to
continue the illusion that the farming prosperity of the period
would last, a belief encouraged by the great industrial and commercial developments then in progress. Men who had made fortunes
in trade were keen to invest money in land, regarding it as a safe
investment as well as a means of advancing social prestige. Rents
continued to rise until the mid-seventies and landed proprietors
were not reluctant to spend money on developments in farming
and forestry.

It was a period of great developments in stock farming. As
has been mentioned herd books appeared and pedigree breeding
became fashionable. In 1856 the number of cattle in Scotland was
returned at 967,000; by 1876 it had risen to 1,131,087. In symmetry
and quality great progress was being made with such breeds as the
Shorthorn and the Aberdeen-Angus, while the milk-producing
Ayrshire breed was being greatly improved. The 1860's have been
aptly termed the Golden Age of Agriculture. The era 1837-74
was certainly one of great prosperity and development in agriculture but the latter year marked the beginning of the end of
that prosperity. For the next forty years farmers were to suffer
adversity and in many cases great hardship.

# CHAPTER XII

# FORTY BLEAK YEARS: 1875-1914

Free Trade and prices...Food imports...Bad seasons...The
disasters of 1879...Heavy fall in grain yields...No compensation through rising prices...The depression in England...
Elasticity of Scottish farming...Loss of land to cultivation...
Migrations...Decline in hill sheep farming...Conversion of
sheep farms into deer forests...Passing of fairs and establishment of live stock auction marts...Richmond Commission,
1879-82...Royal Commission, 1893...Government aids...
Legislation...Low prices in early nineties, gradual improvement...The landlord system...Crop yields...Progress in dairy
farming ... John Speir ... Farm implements ... Establishment
of agricultural colleges.

THE 1860'S HAD SEEN BRITISH AGRICULTURE reach its zenith of
prosperity. Little, however, did either landlords or farmers
realise that, but for the American Civil War and its after effects,
adversity would already have set in. These events hindered the
normal development of the great corn and cattle areas of the as yet
undeveloped Middle West of America. Moreover, an aggressive
Germany was arising to disturb the peace of Europe. Under these
circumstances the expansion in the flow of imports to this country
was slower than it would otherwise have been. In 1867, when our
grain harvest was poor, the average price of wheat actually reached
64s. 5d. a quarter.[1] At that time not even the worst pessimist would
have forecast that in less than twenty years' time this figure would
be halved, and that in the nineties it would have fallen still further to
23s., the lowest for more than two centuries. The temporary with-
drawal of France and Germany from commercial competition in
1870-71 helped to continue this illusion of prosperity. So keen
were farmers to lease land that high rents were offered and long
leases arranged on high terms. Not until 1875 was there any very
significant break in values of farm produce, and even then the price
fall was not continuous, being interrupted by the Russo-Turkish
war. By the early eighties, however, most farmers realised that
they were in for a prolonged period of depression.

[1] Ernle, *English Farming*, p. 489.

At the time of the repeal of the Corn Laws in 1846 the popular cry was for cheap food which in turn meant low costs of living, low wages and cheap manufactured goods, particularly for export. As Britain was then enjoying a virtual monopoly in industry it was argued that it was in the best interests of the country to allow free imports of food. Under this policy we would be paid for the goods we exported, while food prices would be prevented from rising to very high levels. Home agriculture, it was expected, would continue to flourish, but "rapacious landlords" would be denied outrageously high rents. Disraeli, however, saw through these fallacies.[2] He foresaw that foreigners would not for ever accept our monopoly of industry and might build up tariff walls to exclude our goods, that they might undersell us in the world markets, and even dump on our home markets foods and feeding-stuffs in such large quantities and at such low prices as to ruin British agriculture. In Disraeli's younger days agriculture was our most important industry and, in his view, the Free Trade policy was too doctrinaire and inelastic to suit all circumstances. Not for nearly a century, however, were his views accepted, and in the interval we were nearly defeated in a major war for, in April 1917, we found ourselves on the brink of starvation. In retrospect it would seem that there was a lack of vision in the conduct of national affairs and that too much emphasis was laid on factors of a purely economic and temporary kind.

After the American Civil War industry in the United States was in a bad way and unemployment was widespread particularly in towns. Discharged soldiers, fresh from the perils of the battlefield, were willing to seek adventure in the as yet undeveloped parts of the Middle West where work could be found, food grown and independence secured. The fertile lands of the West were indeed crying out for settlers. Accordingly, townsmen and ex-soldiers bought horses and waggons on which they loaded their household goods, ploughs and harrows, and set off for the great open spaces, while Irishmen bidding adieu to poverty and distress at home, Germans fleeing from despotic rulers, Scandinavians and other emigrants, joined them in the journey westward to Illinois, Iowa, Minnesota, etc. The settlers lived like true pioneers but the cattle and grain they produced helped materially to swell American food exports to Britain. The tide of immigrants to the prairie provinces of the United States was further swollen by the American industrial

[2] Bryant, *English Saga*, pp. 92-6.

crisis of 1873-74 which drove more people from the eastern towns and
cities to seek their fortunes by farming in the Middle West. They
in turn increased agricultural production while the development of
Canada, Argentina and Australasia raised still further the volume
of Britain's imported food and feeding stuffs.

The aggregate annual value of such imported foods, including
live animals, for the five years 1866-70 was £77 million. The
figure rose during the next five years to £108 million and by 1877
to £140 million.[3]  So rapid an expansion greatly disturbed the
price levels of home-produced food, particularly grain. Wheat,
which in 1871-74 had remained fairly steady at about 57s. a quarter,
fell in 1875 to 45s. Wool, a very important source of income to
many Scottish farmers, dropped in price by a third after 1880.
The fall in fat cattle prices was not very pronounced until 1885,
and those for sheep remained fairly steady until 1890, but the
eventual fall in price of all farm produce was most significant.
Moreover the price fall was only one of several misfortunes that
befell farmers in the late seventies. Pleuro-pneumonia and foot-and-
mouth disease had again broken out among cattle and liver rot was
rampant amongst sheep. There were three successive seasons of
bleak springs and wet, cold and inclement summers;[4] the land could
not be properly cleaned and the crops were poor, but the steady
flow of imports prevented any compensating rise in prices. Indeed,
in some cases, there was a downward trend. Farmers had therefore
to fight low prices as well as adverse seasons.

In the late seventies the country was involved in a world-wide
depression and the city streets were thronged with unemployed.
In 1878 the City of Glasgow Bank failed, along with some others.
Many people were ruined and confidence was undermined. The
following winter was one of almost unparalleled severity and for five
months the land was in the grip of frost and snow. Heavy snowfalls
of 14 to 36 in. in February ruined many of the fir woods [5] and prevented sheep from grazing on the hills. On the higher mossy
tablelands of Sutherland two to three feet of closely packed frost-
bound snow lay for three months and sheep had to be moved to the
low grounds of Caithness so that they could be fed with hay and oats.
Special trains, laden with hay, had to be sent north every two days

  [3] Ernle, *English Farming*, p. 510.
  [4] *op. cit.*, p. 379.
  [5] R. Hutchinson, " On the effects of the severe frost and winter of 1878-79
on trees and shrubs ", in *T.H.A.S.*, 4th ser. XII (1880), p. 182.

to keep the starving animals alive.[6] So intense and prolonged was the frost that in May a fox, an animal which rarely trusts itself on ice after Candlemas, was seen to cross frozen Loch Callater in Aberdeenshire.[7]

Hill sheep losses everywhere were colossal. Of one flock of five hundred only forty survived; from another of the same size only fifty lambs were reared, while one Sutherland sheep farmer was a thousand lambs short. As can be imagined, the lambs of the 1879 crop were poor and prices were low compared with those of previous years. While Sutherland probably suffered most, other parts of Scotland were badly hit. The lamb crop in Selkirkshire was poor in numbers and quality, thirty to forty per cent. of the ewes often being unable to nurse their lambs.[8] Seed-time came unusually late and crops were handicapped from the start. A cold, sunless summer followed, the average temperature from April to August being 3.2° below normal.[9] A lowering of the average summer temperature by even 2.5° always affects grain-growing in Scotland adversely since ripening is unduly retarded and proper filling prevented. The grain harvest on the eastern seaboard was from twenty to forty days late in starting. Fortunately the weather in this part was fairly good in October but on the western seaboard the grain harvest, though earlier, was deplorable. Yields were lamentably low. Thus wheat yielded a half to a third below average and the returns from oats were down; potatoes were a miserable crop and turnips in some parts a failure. In England the average wheat yield was scarcely $15\frac{1}{2}$ bushels per acre.[10] There was, moreover, no compensatory rise in price for in that year, as it happened, American crops were good. What with losses in stock, poor crops and poor prices for produce the year 1879 was unique in its tale of disaster: it marked the beginning of a prolonged period of agricultural depression. Farmers sitting on long leases, contracted in times of prosperity, were in despair. In its passing the year had one last orgy of destruction. On the night of 28th December 1879 a fierce gale raged over Scotland, the wind at times reaching 110-120 miles an hour; it was the night of the Tay Bridge disaster;[11] very serious

---

[6] J. Macdonald, " Agriculture of Sutherland ", p. 81.

[7] Hutchinson, in *T.H.A.S.*, 4th ser. XII (1880), p. 188.

[8] Crop reports for 1879 in *T.H.A.S.*, 4th ser. XII (1880), p. 306.

[9] Meteorological reports for 1879 in *T.H.A.S.*, 4th ser. XII (1880), p. 317.

[10] Ernle, *English Farming*, p. 379.

[11] *Journal of the Scottish Meteorological Society*, New Ser., Nos. LXIV-LXIX (1879), p. 110.

N

damage was done to woodlands and farm property of all kinds and
once again the winter was severe.

The depression was felt most severely in the great wheat-growing
areas of England. Scottish farming, being more elastic, again
withstood the shock better, for wheat was grown on only a relatively
small scale. The other Scottish cash crops—oats, barley and
potatoes—together with the stock activities, dairying, stock raising
and fattening—although very much down in output, were not so
badly affected in price. In England, on many of the clay lands of
the Midlands and East Anglia wheat was the farmer's main crop.
On the less fertile clays it could not henceforth be grown at a profit.
Many farms were in consequence allowed to tumble down to grass,
and many tenants, unable to pay their rents, had to abandon their
holdings. Some landlords, despairing either of being able to let
their farms or to work them without loss, allowed them to go derelict.
Disraeli's prophecies had come true, yet although he had now
become Prime Minister he did nothing to save agriculture.[12]
Immersed in oriental policies he had allowed himself to become
indifferent to its fate. The drift of workers from the land, following
the decline in the arable acreage, involved no national problem of
unemployment since the general development in industry absorbed
all who left the land, and statesmen, no matter to what party they
belonged, were content to leave it at that.

The opening up of the great Middle West of America, with
the consequent fall in grain prices, affected other European countries.
Denmark, for instance, was hard hit, but its resourceful farmers
turned the fall in grain prices to good purpose. Taking advantage
of the low world price of cereals and other feeding stuffs they bought
them for conversion into pig meat, eggs and butter—breakfast-table
commodities—for which a ready market was to be found in Britain.
While in Denmark the spirit of enterprise, mutual help and co-
operation was fostered and developed, in Britain individual farming
was still the order of the day, our farmers being either too conser-
vative or too independent to copy the example of the Danes.

As has been already suggested the elasticity of Scottish farming
saved it from ruin. In general half or nearly half of the ploughable
land on a Scottish farm, except in the cropping areas of the east, was
under temporary grass leys. These leys provided the cheapest of
food for farm animals, restored fertility to the land, kept it relatively
clean and favoured the rearing of stock or the production of milk.

[12] Trevelyan, *Social History*, p. 553.

In the arable areas of eastern Scotland less wheat had been grown than during the Napoleonic Wars. Wheat was merely one of the three cereal crops grown and its acreage by this time was largely regulated by that of potatoes, which in some parts might have been described as a complementary crop. Wheat straw was used to cover the potato pits before they were earthed up, and wheat was usually sown on the potato land after the crop had been harvested. Potato growing was, on the average, still profitable. The only competition which potato-growing farmers had to meet was from each other. A large acreage and a good season might mean low prices, but high prices prevailed when crops were short, and in general, given good management, the crop yielded a profit.

On the cropping farms of the Lothians, Fife, Angus and Perthshire high farming and associated high yields per acre were regarded as the best weapons with which to combat low prices. Dung from the towns was railed to stations or railway sidings in these areas. It was used to supplement home supplies from cake-fed animals fattened during winter, while artificial manures were applied liberally. Great attention was paid to the organisation of labour. Skilful farming, good organisation and cuts in household expenses enabled farmers in the best arable areas to survive. Rents were in course of time reduced. The few farmers who were unable to adapt themselves to their new circumstances were forced to quit, but so keen was the demand for farms in the best areas that landlords could still afford to be selective in their choice of tenants.

In the west and south-west farming was largely associated with dairying, often carried on by the farmer and his family. Dairying in its various forms—liquid milk production, cheese or buttermaking—involved living a hard and disciplined life. But the hard labour associated with this kind of farming, combined with the thrift that is characteristic of Scottish farmers in areas of small or medium-sized farms, were sound weapons with which to meet depression. Cheese indeed had slumped in price when the market became glutted with American produce,[13] but south-western farmers had determined, like their brethren in the east, to achieve success. In their case high average quality of cheese and good stockmanship were twin objectives. A dairy school, replacing the itinerant instruction previously given, was in course of time established to provide proper training for cheese-makers. From this western area came the bulk of those Scotsmen who showed Essex farmers how

[13] Ernle, *English Farming*, p. 379.

even derelict clay holdings might be transformed into prosperous dairy farms and how advantage could be taken of the low price of imported feeding stuffs to produce milk.    The disciplined and thorough training which these migrants had received in the west of Scotland stood them in good stead when they took farms elsewhere, not only in Essex and the adjacent counties but also in the Lothians, Berwickshire, Fife, Perthshire and Angus.    " Go east for a farm, go west for a wife " was a saying of the time.    It is not without significance that in Britain milk recording began in the west of Scotland, a testimony to the determination of the west country farmer to become more proficient at his job.

The north and north-east of Scotland had by the late sixties achieved fame for fat cattle.    No beef was in higher esteem than that produced in Aberdeenshire and the adjacent counties.    Thanks to the skill and enterprise of Aberdeenshire farmers and butchers a high class trade in beef had been developed with London.    The greatest care was given to the breeding and fattening of cattle. No self-respecting north-eastern farmer, half a century before bull licensing was introduced in 1931, would have dreamt of using a non-pedigree bull.    To produce sufficient winter feed much thought was given to the growing of good turnip crops.    In the belief that like produces like, farmers selected with the utmost care the turnip bulbs from which they grew their seed so as to combine size, resistance to disease and frost, and feeding quality;  in this way they evolved superior strains.    Manuring, too, was a subject of intensive study.    John Hart, a Kincardineshire factor and farmer, told how, in the summer of 1889, no fewer than forty-one farmers in that county conducted trials to determine the type of phosphate best suited to the turnip crop.[14]    Another farmer, John Milne of Turriff, conducted a number of cattle-fattening trials and published the results.[15]    At the ports agricultural companies had set up oil mills where linseed and other oil seeds could be crushed and oil cake made.    Large quantities of feeding-stuffs, imported at low prices, were used by Scottish farmers to hasten the fattening of their animals.    Everywhere local associations did their best to promote the production of good stock and to encourage the proficiency of workers.    The breeding of good draught horses for town lorries

---

[14] John Hart, " Report of experiments with turnip manure in Kincardineshire ", in *T.H.A.S.*, 5th ser. II (1890), pp. 267 ff.

[15] John Milne, " Cattle-feeding experiments ", in *T.H.A.S.*, 5th ser. IV (1892), pp. 154 ff. and v (1893), pp. 339 ff.

became a profitable sideline on many a farm.  Just as high yields
were saving the eastern arable areas from ruin and high-class dairy
farming coupled with hard work was enabling western farmers
to remain prosperous, so good stock and crop husbandry linked
with industry and thrift kept agriculture from languishing in the
north and north-east.  There the two famous beef breeds, the
Aberdeen-Angus and the Beef Shorthorn were being developed,
but the main industry was not the breeding of pure-bred animals
but the production of high-class commercial stock.

It is significant that in the comparatively large county of Aberdeen
the grain acreage remained much the same during the whole period
of 1879-1914, while that of turnips fell by only seven per cent.  But
this was by no means representative of the rest of Scotland, particularly in counties where a higher proportion of the arable land
fringed the hills, and where ripening and harvesting were often
difficult.  In such instances the higher fields and farms were sown
out to grass and the land grazed by sheep.  Such was the fate of
much of the land in that cold, infertile plateau which stretches from
Midlothian in the east through West Lothian, Stirlingshire and
Lanarkshire to Dunbartonshire in the west.  Scotland's acreage of
permanent grass rose during this period from 1,160,000 to 1,490,000
while the grain acreage declined from 1,390,000 to 1,186,000 or by
nearly 15 per cent.  In England, between 1871 and 1914 the percentage decline in grain acreage was double this amount, although
the fertility of English soils was higher.

Thus was adversity countered by industry, thrift, an excellent
rotation system, attention to the breeding and management of
livestock, sound labour organisation, skill and pride in farm craft,
and the combination of agricultural science, so far as was then
known, with practice.  Rents under new leases were invariably
lowered; wages were reduced, but not significantly, and by the nineties
had practically returned to their former level which was, however,
as always, well below that of industrial workers.  The depression
was probably felt worst on the uneconomically small units of the
eastern glens.  There the land is often steep, the soil thin, acid and
stony, and the climate not too well suited to crop growing.  Seed-
time is often delayed and the harvesting of the poor, often badly-
filled and sometimes frosted grain crops is in most years a precarious
undertaking.  Since arable crops in these areas were deemed indispensable for providing winter keep for the cattle—the main source
of income—farmers found themselves tied to a system which,

with its poor prices and inadequate returns, involved them in dire losses. The less productive holdings and those that could not be economically worked were the first to suffer and there was much depopulation in the eastern glens.

The landlord-tenant system, then almost universal in Scotland, did not tie occupiers to the land as an owner-occupier system would have done, and young, enterprising glen farmers were nothing loth to better themselves by leasing farms in kindlier areas. It became customary for farmers from the upper reaches of the rivers Tay, Dee, Don and Spey to lease farms in their lower and more fertile valleys. Their sons in turn might take farms in the still more fertile lands of Strathmore, Kincardineshire and Moray. The years of depression saw this type of migration in all areas. Men from the south-west came to the richer Lothians, to Berwickshire and to Fife. Banffshire and Aberdeenshire men invaded Moray, Kincardineshire and Angus, while men from Caithness went to Ross-shire. The harder upbringing experienced on stock-rearing or dairying farms stood the migrants in good stead. There was thus an internal migration in Scotland as well as an external one to England. In the Highlands and Islands, where crop-growing had always been subordinated to stock husbandry, the fall in the price of cattle and sheep was neither so sudden nor so drastic as that of grain. But even though delayed, the fall seriously affected the economics of hill sheep-farming. But the price of sheep and wool is not the sole factor in determining the profitability of hill farming; the output of stock and wool is of equal, if not of more importance, and costs cannot be ignored. A severe winter tells most heavily on hill sheep farms. The lambing rate may be lowered by one half and the death-rate increased by a similar amount; wintering expenses may rise quickly and the quality of the whole flock may be reduced since the less desirable ewe lambs, that ordinarily would be sold, may have to be kept for replacements. Moreover, the wether lambs sold are usually stunted in growth after a bad winter and a large proportion must rank as " seconds ".

Early in the century, when sheep-farming was introduced to the northern Highlands, the pioneers had faced many difficulties, such as the fall in prices at the close of the Napoleonic Wars, the hostility of the displaced crofters, and sheep stealing. Thus in 1815 raiders are said to have made off with 1,591 sheep from eleven farms in Sutherland.[16] But these bad times came to an end. From

16 J. Macdonald, " Agriculture of Sutherland ", p. 64.

1830 to 1874 the story of hill sheep-farming is one of continuing prosperity apart from such bad seasons as 1838 and 1860, when the winters were stormy. By 1874, however, there were definite signs of decline. The grazings in the Highlands could no longer support satisfactorily the numbers of sheep they had once carried.[17] The younger sheep, formerly wintered on the sweet grass of the old crofting lands, had to be sent away for wintering since this vegetation had reverted to heather and coarse grass. Moreover prices were on the down grade—not markedly perhaps, but the implications were clear, while wages and sheep-farming accessories were costing more. Thus sheep farmers were faced with falling returns and rising costs. In time prices declined still further. Unwashed Cheviot wool, which in the sixties had sold freely at 1s. 0½d. per lb., was by the nineties commanding only 6½d. The average three-year-old Cheviot wether, which in the seventies sold at 45s., was, by the end of the century, changing hands at 28s., a reflection partly of the lowered price of mutton and in part of a change in fashion, the small joint of the young animal having become in greater demand. The higher, more exposed and poorer grazings which had been stocked with wethers, suffered first. But all classes of hill sheep farms were affected and rents had to be appreciably lowered to provide tenants with even a bare living.

Concurrently with this decline came a rising demand for moors for sporting purposes. No class of sport was held in higher esteem, or was so costly, as grouse-shooting or deer-stalking on Scottish moors. The industrial age had brought great wealth to Britain but this was unequally distributed. Wealthy industrial magnates were eager to rent for themselves and for the entertainment of their friends the sporting right of a grouse moor or some large expanse of wild moorland where deer could be stalked and shot. For long sheep-farming and sport of the type described co-existed. In theory, provided that the numbers of deer were limited, no very cogent reason could be advanced against this, but in practice it was otherwise. The sheep farmer, knowing the beneficial effects of heather-burning, naturally wished to set fire to wide stretches of moorland; the sportsman, who wanted protective cover for his young grouse, wished to limit heather-burning to narrow strips. In consequence, too little burning was done. The man stalking a " Royal " objected to interruption by a nervous sheep and, for the privilege of a clear field to shoot deer, was prepared to pay both the grazing and the

---

[17] J. Macdonald, "Agriculture of Sutherland", p. 83.

sporting rent.  Sheep interests were thus on many grazings ruthlessly
ignored and for the second time in a century there was another
clearance in the Highlands—this time of the sheep, the shepherds
and their dogs.  The area of deer forest rose from 1,975,209 acres
in 1883 to 3,584,966 acres in 1912.[18]  In the three Highland counties
of Argyll, Inverness and Ross, sheep numbers declined from
2,187,000 in 1879 to 1,609,000 in 1914.  Even this reduction of
578,000 did not tell the whole story, since on the low ground of
two of these counties many more sheep were being kept towards
the end of the period.

In all areas adjustments were made to meet the altered circumstances.  Marginal lands that could not be worked in rotation
at a profit were gradually laid down to grass.  Labour-saving devices,
particularly hay-making and corn-harvesting machinery, came into
use.  With the development in hay-making appliances farmers in
the south-west, where turnips were often an uncertain crop, turned
more and more to hay as winter feed for their stock.  On the heavy
carse lands of the Forth Valley timothy meadows were laid down,
and farmers there became experts at raising great crops of timothy
for hay.  Three to three and a half tons per acre was a common crop
and one of five tons was occasionally grown.[19]  Over the whole of
Scotland the turnip acreage declined from 492,000 acres in 1879
to 431,000 in 1914, but it was in Stirling and some of the south-
western counties that the decline was most marked.  Ensilage,
previously practised in England in Stuart times, was warmly
advocated about 1888 [20] but failed to make headway.  Zealous
exponents of the system even tried to make it from bracken.  One
significant feature was the marked drop in the bare fallow acreage,
which fell from 21,000 to 7,000 acres.  This indicated that whatever
the advantages of bare fallowing in the past, in these harder times
it was viewed as an expensive luxury.

One regrettable feature was the growing reluctance of farmers
to lime their land.  Before artificial manures were extensively used
liming was linked with good farming.  When artificials were applied,
however, the results in the crops were more spectacular.  Moreover,
the crops commonly grown in Scotland—oats, potatoes, and turnips
—are relatively acid-tolerant and, as most land in the times of

[18] *Report of the Departmental Committee . . . on Lands in Scotland used as
Deer Forests*, Cmd. 1636, 1922, p. 1.
[19] John Drysdale, " Timothy meadows ", in *T.H.A.S.*, 5th ser. XVIII (1906),
p. 22.
[20] Ernle, *English Farming*, p. 131.

prosperity had been liberally supplied with lime, the bad effects of withholding it were not readily felt except by two crops, barley and grass. It was probably largely because of this that the barley acreage went down by a third. The fall in the price of barley was not outstanding but it is significant that although towards the end of the period the crop was only grown on the more suitable soils, the average yields per acre, about 36 bushels, had remained more or less stationary. The bad effects of withholding lime were not so readily noticed on grass land, since the deterioration in rotation pastures was gradual. Red clover, however, did not grow so well as formerly, while rye-grass by the third year largely disappeared and sorrel, bent, Yorkshire fog and other volunteer plants became more widespread.

A significant change during the period in the marketing of livestock was the virtual disappearance of livestock fairs and their replacement by auction marts. Private bargaining of stock at farms became less common for, when selling his stock, the farmer was often at a disadvantage with butchers and dealers who with more experienced eyes could better assess the value of a beast. Moreover, there was always the risk that some buyers might become insolvent before payment was made. So much loss was incurred through bills being dishonoured that the matter was considered by a Parliamentary Committee. These auction marts with their covered-in ranges of buildings and comfortably seated sale rings became a feature of Scottish agriculture. They were particularly common in cattle-fattening areas and were so dispersed that, except in the more sparsely populated districts, fat cattle could readily be walked to the mart. The owners of the mart, sometimes joint stock companies of farmers, sometimes private individuals, undertook all risks in the collection of money. Weighbridges were installed and all fat cattle exposed for sale were weighed. From the comfort of his ringside seat the owner could watch the sale of stock and his ready reckoner enabled him to determine the animal making the top price per live cwt. The sales received an excellent press, and the fortunate owners realised that their success in obtaining high prices would be widely known on the following day. It was indeed a public tribute to their stockmanship. Events like these, the gaining of prizes at the summer stock shows or at the winter root and seed shows, or for the workers the award of the Highland and Agricultural Society's medal for the best ploughed rig at the parish match, had a wonderfully stimulating effect in these times of depression. The determination to persevere,

and wherever possible to excel, was maintained. Times may have
been hard, but if a farmer went to the wall his fate was usually due
to personal extravagance, inefficiency, or over-borrowing.

As a whole, the agricultural industry was certainly passing through
a bad time. A Commission under the chairmanship of the Duke
of Richmond and Gordon, which sat from 1879 to 1882, established
that fact beyond doubt and recorded its opinion that the depression
was due in part to bad seasons and in part to the competition of
food imports from abroad. The view was held, however, that rent
reductions would ease the situation sufficiently. Measures were
taken to stamp out stock diseases, and grants were made to ease the
burden of local taxation. But these measures did little to help
farmers and in the nineties prices for stock and grain fell to still
lower levels. Except in 1888 the seasons were fairly good, but that
particular year was wet and sunless. The corn harvest was a month
to five weeks late and no sooner had it begun in north-east Scotland
than a considerable fall of snow laid low the ripe or ripening corn.[21]
Fortunately the weather thereafter remained fairly good generally
and the crop was secured by the third week of November. Yields
of all crops were down but not so badly as in 1879. The winter of
1894-95 was also exceptionally cold but March was a fairly good
month and outdoor stock did not suffer too severely.

In September 1893 a Royal Commission was appointed to report
on agriculture. Its report was gloomy in the extreme. It found
that since the date of the Duke of Richmond's Commission the
value of farm produce had fallen by nearly one half, while the cost
of production had, if anything, risen; and that large areas of cropped
land had gone out of cultivation.[22] It pointed out, however, that
where high farming was practised, labour-saving devices employed,
good stock reared and industry observed, a living could be gained
from the land. It showed, too, that family farms had weathered
the storm best; as if afraid to broach the subject of agricultural
education it recommended that something should be done to improve
" rural " education; it seemed to give the impression, however,
that the only remedy for low prices was industry and cheap family
labour.

Against the great loss incurred by farmers since the fateful year
1879, remedial measures taken by Government seemed most trivial.
Cheap food, even though it meant the ruin of British agriculture,

[21] Cereal reports, in *T.H.A.S.*, 5th ser. 1 (1889), p. 177.
[22] Ernle, *English Farming*, pp. 383-4.

was considered essential to the nation's well-being. One or two useful Acts were passed. One, the Fertilisers and Feeding Stuffs Act (1893) gave protection against the adulteration of cakes and fertilisers, while in 1896 the passing of the amendment to the Contagious Diseases of Animals Act (1896), requiring all imported farm animals to be slaughtered at the ports, was a valuable aid towards preventing infection. Measures were also taken to ease the burden of local rates on agricultural land by the passing of the Rating Act in 1896.

Compensation for unexhausted improvements had long been a burning question amongst Scottish tenant-farmers. No one was likely to spend money on long-term improvements such as reclamation, buildings, drainage or liming unless he had a fair chance of a reasonable return. Recognition of this principle had led to the institution of the long lease in Scotland—usually one of nineteen years; but farmers felt that this was not enough. They wanted freedom to undertake long-term improvements not merely at the beginning of but during their leases, and to be recompensed on way-go for the unexhausted part of these improvements. With the development in the fattening of cattle with rich cakes, the manurial effects of which were reckoned to be very considerable and to persist for some time, and the use of slow-acting fertilisers like lime and bone meal, this view was considerably strengthened. But no official action was taken until 1875 when the permissive Agricultural Holdings Act was passed.[23] Facetiously described as a " homily to landlords ", this Act did little to remedy matters and more stringent measures followed in 1883. Then came the Agricultural Holdings Amendment Act of 1900 to be followed by another in 1906. Market gardeners had previously benefited by the passing of the Market Gardeners Compensation Act of 1895. Another feature of the times was the setting up in 1889 of the second Board of Agriculture. It applied to the whole of Great Britain, Ireland being separately provided for.

As has already been noted the killing of rabbits on the land had long been a grievance with tenants. So great was the outcry against the restrictions imposed that Parliament was forced to take action. In 1880 the Ground Game Acts were passed: they permitted occupiers resident on rented land to kill hares and rabbits concurrently with any other person who should enjoy the right. The Acts did not apply to land of less than a yearly tenancy, and tenants

[23] Ernle, *English Farming*, p. 382.

of grass parks which ordinarily were not let for the whole season were not eligible to kill the ground game. In 1906 these privileges were extended to occupiers of moorlands. While these Acts were of considerable help they did not protect the farmer from rabbits coming from adjoining land. Much damage to crops was caused and the income derived from snared, trapped, netted, or shot rabbits at no time provided adequate compensation.

By the end of the nineties the worst of the depression was over. Wheat in 1894-95 commanded only 23s. per quarter. Oats in the Edinburgh market averaged 18s. 5d. per quarter in 1896, but this figure was above the average for the whole country. After that year prices began slowly to improve. The worst year for owners of hill sheep was 1892. Blackface lambs then ranged in price from 3s. to 10s. and ewes sold for from 6s. to 17s.[24] At Aboyne in Aberdeenshire the highest bid for some Blackface cast ewes was 2s. 6d. a head. But by this time rents had been adjusted to meet the change in prices. First-class land in the good cropping areas commanded anything from 30s. to 40s. an acre. The good arable stock-rearing and fattening farm was let at about 20s. an acre and second-rate farms of this description might be leased at 15s. or 16s. per acre. But so slowly did prices rise that after the turn of the century farmers were still in financial straits. The harvest of 1903 was deplorable and much of the grain crop was badly damaged. In January 1904 a quantity of barley was sold in the Edinburgh Corn Market at 13s. a quarter and a consignment of oats fetched only 11s. a quarter.[25] As a result bankruptcies amongst farmers were higher than usual. There was another late harvest in 1907, but conditions by that time were definitely on the mend and by 1912, before the outbreak of the First World War, agriculture could be deemed to be mildly prosperous.

In its landlords Scotland was generally more fortunate than England. Much of its land was owned in very large blocks by landlords whose families had long been connected with their estates. The entail system had enabled many estates to be handed down intact to successive owners. When the depression began some of the wealthier landlords did not, as so often happened in England, press for rents when the tenant, through force of circumstances, was unable to pay. Instead they often helped to ease a tenant's burden either by part remission of rent or by delaying collection.

[24] Prices of sheep, in *T.H.A.S.*, 5th ser. XXVII (1915), p. 377.
[25] The Edinburgh corn market, in *T.H.A.S.*, 5th ser. XVII (1905), pp. 397-9.

One remission of rent made by the Marquis of Aberdeen is said to have cost him £20,000. They also took pride in maintaining the permanent equipment of their farms in good condition, and in replacing old, dilapidated and outmoded buildings by new ones. Ownership of land at this period, despite the low rate of interest yielded on the capital involved, was nevertheless prized, for it provided sport and social prestige at a time when local rates, income tax and death duties were much less burdensome than they were to become later. Most landlords could afford to live well, keep their estates in good order, run their home farms in model fashion and take a kindly and helpful interest in local affairs.

It might be supposed that one result of putting down 10 per cent. of the poorest arable land to permanent pasture would have been to increase the average yields of arable crops. The whole period 1879 to 1910 was, however, disappointing in this respect. Figures meticulously recorded by Norrie, an Aberdeenshire farmer, and reported in the *Scottish Journal of Agriculture*,[26] show that, while the grain yields per acre on his farm rose in the sixties and continued to rise till the early eighties they then remained practically stationary until almost the outbreak of the First World War. Norrie's experience was not unusual although official statistics do record a slight rise in the yield of wheat per acre, but barley and oat yields remained much about the same until about 1910, when the introduction of improved varieties of oats led to increased yields. Turnip yields rose slightly but hay yields remained practically stationary. The publicity given to numerous turnip manurial trials had the effect of educating farmers in knowing more how to reduce fertiliser costs rather than to raise yields. The introduction of new varieties of potatoes, amongst them Findlay's Up-to-Date, had, however, a marked influence in increasing potato yields. Thus from 1891 to 1910 the ten-year average yield per acre rose from 5.57 to 6.39 tons. In Ayrshire " boxing " (sprouting) of the seed, introduced about 1881, had become a recognised practice in early potato growing.[27] But in general progress in cropping performances was disappointing, little advance in production being noticeable. Cattle numbers, however, rose appreciably until the nineties when they became stationary. The sheep population, despite the clearances

[26] J. A. Symon, " Cairnhill, Turriff 1861-1926 ", in *Scottish Agriculture*, henceforth cited as *Scot. Agric.*, XXXI (1951-52), p. 26.
[27] John Speir, " Boxing seed potatoes " in *T.H.A.S.*, 5th ser. XIV (1902), p. 149.

for deer forests, continued to rise owing to their increasing popularity on low ground farms. But overall progress in farm output during the period left much to be desired.

In industry the period was one of great activity in manufacturing and engineering, and farmers benefited from the introduction of labour-saving appliances. Binders, reaping machines and mowers displaced scythes and reduced hand work in the hay and harvest fields. Light " Yankee " ploughs and factory-made short-boarded ploughs with bar-pointed socks and chilled steel replaceable wearing parts, gradually ousted the blacksmith-made swing plough. These new ploughs took broader furrows, broke up the land and buried the turf better. Disc and spring-toothed harrows became popular; potato diggers were constantly being improved and new potato dressing machines were designed. Cream separators, improved churns, incubators and foster mothers came into use. By the end of the period there were many oil engines on farms, the smaller ones operating turnip cutters and potato sorters and the larger, threshing mills. Grain and artificial fertilisers were sown largely by machine. But in general, if we exclude the above implements, there was at this time no very outstanding development in the production of agricultural machinery. Most farm implements were similar to those used sixty to eighty years earlier. The numbers of permanent workers on farms, despite high emigration, particularly to Canada, were not greatly lowered, the main difference being that fewer people were employed at the grain harvest.

In milk production considerable developments were in the making. Premises in which milk was produced for sale had to conform to specific standards. The adoption of a presumptive standard for whole milk, viz., 3 per cent. butter fat and 8·5 per cent. solids not fat, discouraged producer-retailers from selling their morning milk to customers while it was still warm, the morning milk often being distinctly poorer in butter fat than the evening milk. As the demand for liquid milk grew with the rise in population, producer-retailers tended to diminish in number and milk, now drawn from wider areas, was increasingly consigned to firms who specialised in retailing. To prevent milk souring coolers were installed on farms and the railways became popular for transporting it to the consuming centres.

John Speir, of Newton, near Glasgow, did much to introduce improved methods to dairy farmers. He dispelled the popular idea that close, warm and unventilated byres were necessary for the maximum output of milk. He largely exploded the theory that food for cows was improved by cooking. He introduced milk recording by association recorders. He tested the milking machine invented by Murchland, experimented with new varieties of oats, assessed the merits of the practice of sprouting potatoes, publicised the results of his work and in many ways was indefatigable in promoting improvements in machinery and furthering agricultural education. Scottish dairy farmers were later to reap a rich reward from his labours.[28]

It was when times were at their worst that leading agriculturalists came to realise the need for additional facilities for agricultural education, and the closer union of science with practice. The excellent work done by the Highland and Agricultural Society had shown that too little was known about animal and plant nutrition, diseases and pests, the production of more prolific strains of different crops, the management of pastures, etc. Obsessed by industrial development, Great Britain had apparently forgotten that such an important industry as farming existed. For over sixty years until 1889 it had no Agricultural Department, for the first Board of Agriculture had come to an untimely end in 1828. Rothamsted, which had done much useful work in revealing the secrets of plant nutrition, was for long run as a private enterprise. The teaching facilities in agriculture at Edinburgh, Glasgow and Aberdeen were meagre. Excellent performers as many of the Scottish farmers were, their systems had been based on experience without an understanding of the principles involved. There was great need for establishing the relationship between cause and effect, for substituting certainty for surmise and for examining all farming practices critically. Poultry yards were polluted with disease and accommodated too many old age pensioners; in winter there were few eggs, and few producers knew the remedy; braxy and louping-ill took heavy toll of hill sheep flocks; potato varieties were constantly deteriorating; no one quite knew when land needed lime or why rye-grass ceased to grow in many pastures after the second year. John Speir by his researches on cow byre temperatures had cast doubt on the theory that warmth under all circumstances meant a saving in food for animals and had shown the need for further investigations. Practices such as giving a large amount of protein-rich cakes to fattening cattle were seldom questioned, being assumed to be right because they were associated with high farming. Thus,

[28] J. A. Symon, " John Speir ", in *Scot. Agric.*, xxx (1950-51), pp. 35-9.

while protein-rich feeding stuffs were given wastefully to fattening animals, adequate amounts were withheld from milking cows and laying hens, animals whose function it is to produce protein-rich human food.    At the turn of the century there was much need for a better understanding of the principles of animal and plant nutrition, of the control of diseases and pests and of how to breed more prolific and disease-resistant strains of plants.

To meet these clamant needs the Colleges of Agriculture were set up.    Their story and that of the diffusion of agricultural knowledge is told in Chapter XIX.    Suffice it here to say that the twentieth century saw the dawn of another era in agriculture, one in which the importance of agricultural education and research came to be recognised not merely by farmers but by the country as a whole.    Even before the outbreak of war in 1914 the first beneficial effects of the marriage between science and practice were apparent. More prolific varieties of oats were being used by farmers; the principles of manuring were better understood; milk recording had become firmly established; pastures were becoming distinctly better and farmers were realising that poultry flocks could by good management be made to pay.    Older farmers might scoff at the " book learned " college men who set out to advise people with a lifetime's experience in farming, but in due time the results of agricultural education became apparent and would have been realised more quickly but for the outbreak of the First World War which, incidentally, brought to an end the first phase of the long period of depression.    The industry had suffered grievous hurt but had survived and by 1914 it was in a reasonably sound condition.

# CHAPTER XIII

## THE FIRST WORLD WAR: 1914-1918

The country at war...Effect of national commercial policy...
Contrast with Germany...Shipping losses, 1915...Appoint-
ment of Wason Committee for Scotland (1915)...Unpro-
ductive harvest in 1916...Growing need of a directed policy...
Compulsory cropping and guaranteed prices...Agricultural
Executive Committees in Scotland...Labour and supply
difficulties...Price control...Effect on milk and hay production
...Gratifying results of 1918 campaign...Scotland and
England compared.

WHEN ON 4TH AUGUST 1914 WAR was declared between Britain
and Germany the ninety-nine years' lease of peace enjoyed
by farmers in Britain from the end of the Napoleonic
Wars ended abruptly. Wars there had been in the interval but none
serious enough to disturb the even tenor of our home agriculture.
Never during this period had British farmers been deprived of men
and horses, or directed by their rulers to plough up and crop more
land and in doing so to transgress accepted rules of good husbandry.
Even before the Napoleonic era, wars waged abroad had always
brought prosperity to agriculture and stimulated developments in
farming. Food imports had been slowed down; the demands of
the Forces for provisions had tended to raise prices and so encouraged
farmers to plough more land and produce more food. This policy
of individual choice of action for farmers had been universally
accepted as most suitable in war as in peace.

But since the Napoleonic Wars circumstances in the United
Kingdom had changed materially. The population in 1815 was
eighteen millions. In years of bountiful harvests like 1813 there
was food enough to feed the nation and to provide a carry-over.[1]
Only in years when crops were poor and imports of food restricted
were the people likely to go short. We have noted the fear of starvation in years of poor crops such as 1800, 1810 and 1812. But in
general home production of food was nearly equal to the nation's

---

[1] Ernle, *English Farming*, p. 399.

needs and continued to be so until the end of the 1830's.[2] The relatively high prices of grain at that time had encouraged individual farmers to develop their land. Production was then stimulated by the Corn Laws.

The policy of Free Trade, unrestricted food imports and allowing the farmer freedom of choice in farming his land had, as we have seen, resulted during the forty years 1875-1914 in much arable land being laid down to grass. The tillage acreage in England and Wales had fallen by about two and a half million acres. Although the proportion of land lost to arable crops in Scotland had been relatively less, it was sufficiently pronounced to affect adversely her total agricultural output expressed in terms of food. The explanation is, of course, that land under grass and devoted to meat production produces much less human food than land growing cereals and potatoes.[3] Average crops of wheat produce per acre, in units of energy, about twenty times as much food as an average acre of grass land devoted to stock rearing. An acre of potatoes produces forty times as much, and an acre of pasture used for milk production about four to five times, the dairy cow being a much more efficient converter of herbage into human food than the animal intended purely for meat.[4] The decline in the acreage of tilled land and the increasing consumption of meat meant that by 1914 the United Kingdom was supporting, on a theoretical calculation, something like eight million people fewer than it did in the 1870's. In 1840 enough home-grown food was produced to maintain

[2] T. H. Middleton, *Food Production in War*, henceforth cited as Middleton, *Food Production*, Carnegie Endowment for International Peace, Economic and Social History of the World War, British series, Oxford 1923, p. 97.

[3] The number of persons who could be maintained for a year on the average produce of 100 acres of land growing the principal crops of the United Kingdom as before 1914, was during the First World War as follows :

| Crop | Edible products | Persons maintained per 100 acres of land |
|---|---|---|
| Wheat | Bread, beef, pork | 208 |
| Oats | Meat, beef, pork | 172 |
| Potatoes | Vegetable, pork | 418 |
| Swedes and turnips | Beef, mutton | 20 |
| ,,          ,, | Milk | 85 |
| Rotation hay | Beef, mutton | 13 |
| Average pastures | ,,          ,, | 9 |
| ,,          ,, | Milk | 41 |

(Middleton, *Food Production*, Table IX).   Since the table was published yields of certain crops have risen considerably.

[4] Middleton, *Food Production*, p. 83.

24,000,000 people, while by 1914 only between 15 and 16,000,000 could live on such food.[5] Putting it crudely, we were only able to supply the meals for the weekend; meals for the other days had to be imported. Despite these facts the possible effects on food supplies of a great European war had received small attention. Even were war to break out Britain would still, it was fondly imagined, be mistress of the seas and an enemy could do little or nothing to check the inflow of food from abroad. In any case rising prices would provide incentives to farmers to break up more land and so to relieve shortages. One writer, who ventured to call attention to the possible dire effects of the submarine in interrupting the flow of imports, was dubbed a scaremonger. No action was taken for we were wedded to the policy of Free Trade and freedom of action for our farmers and all considerations had to be subordinated to that policy.

Germany's policy was in marked contrast; her statesmen had been quick to realise that in the event of war she must be able to feed herself practically from her own resources. Britain's policy of Free Trade, particularly in allowing free imports of food, would, it was deemed, have put much land out of cultivation if it had been applied in Germany. Germany's policy therefore was Protection not Free Trade, the plough at home not on overseas farms, and stock related to crop and not to grass-growing. As T. H. Middleton (later Sir Thomas Middleton) pointed out in a Parliamentary Paper in the summer of 1916,[6] the part played by the German farmer was in marked contrast to that played by the British farmer. A unit of arable land in Germany was supporting 50 per cent. more persons than its equivalent in Britain. In Germany twice as much grain, five times the quantity of potatoes and half as much milk again were being produced on each unit of a hundred acres. In addition German farms were producing sugar beet, a crop scarcely known at that time in this country. Startling as these facts were, nearly two years of war had elapsed before they were brought to light and appreciated. In the first five months of the war Britain was lulled into comparative complacency so far as the food situation was concerned. Shipping had certainly been lost. Enemy cruisers, mines and submarines had cost us over a quarter of a million gross tons of shipping, but the submarine alone had by that time done comparatively little damage. Shipping losses had, however, been

[5] Middleton, *Food Production*, pp. 94-7.
[6] *The Recent Development of German Agriculture*, Cmd. paper 8305, 1916.

made good by the gain of war prizes [7] and imports—meat, wheat,
flour and feeding stuffs—continued to arrive more or less normally.
On the farms at home labour losses occasioned by the call-up of
the Territorials and reservists, and the voluntary enlistment of men
for Kitchener's Army had been made good. Many farm horses
had been bought for army transport but their loss did not seriously
incommode Scottish farmers who in 1915 raised the acreage of
cereals, largely at the expense of roots, by 33,000. The extra
contribution that year from England and Wales was 174,000 acres.

But rising shipping losses in May and June 1915 caused alarm.
Double the earlier tonnage was now being put out of action each
month without compensatory gain from the capture of enemy ships
which by now had been cleared from the high seas. It became
apparent that the war might be prolonged well beyond the harvest
of 1916 and that it might therefore be necessary to organise and
harness agriculture to the nation's needs if defeat through starvation
were to be averted. Committees for each country [8] were appointed
to consider the situation and to report on the steps to be taken by
legislation or otherwise to maintain, and if possible to increase,
production on the assumption that the war would continue beyond
the harvest of 1916. The Scottish Committee, under the chairmanship of Mr Eugene Wason, M.P., did not recommend legislation or
compulsion, and regarded a proposal to guarantee a price for cereals
as impracticable. The considerable rise in prices of farm produce
since the outbreak of the war was thought to provide a sufficient
incentive for farmers to produce all the home-grown food required.
Some doubt was even expressed as to whether the prices then
prevailing could be maintained at existing levels. One witness
thought that they would soon be lowered. The whole tone of the
report was extremely cautious. No effective action was recommended, though the Government were advised that if any more
workers were taken from the land food production might suffer.
The Committee pointed out, however, that altered circumstances
might later make it necessary to reconsider the matter; they recommended that they should not be disbanded but should remain
as a Committee to be summoned if and when required. They also
advocated the creation of District Agricultural Committees to
stimulate local effort.[9] In retrospect it is difficult to appreciate why

---

[7] Ernle, *English Farming*, p. 395.

[8] Charles Douglas, " Scottish agriculture during the war ", henceforth cited
as Douglas, " Agric. during the war ", in *T.H.A.S.*, 5th ser. XXXI (1919), p. 5.

[9] *op. cit.*, pp. 5-7.

so unrealistic a view should have been taken of the situation a year after the outbreak of war, but this mood of complacency appears to have pervaded the whole country at that time. The English Committee under the chairmanship of Lord Milner were, however, bolder in their proposals. In their interim report they recommended the guarantee of a minimum price for wheat for a period of four years. The appointment of district committees to assess the cropping acreage capacity of each farm was also recommended, but immediate compulsion in cultivation was not advised. Consideration of such a policy could be deferred until reports were forthcoming from the district committees showing possible increases in the cropping acreage.[10]

Beyond asking county councils to form agricultural committees the Government took no definite action and meantime the situation deteriorated. In 1916 shipping losses mounted rapidly, those for the last three months of the year being particularly heavy. Much of our shipping was required to supply the needs of the Forces. The Battle of the Somme, from which so much had been expected, proved to be a holocaust with no appreciable gain to set against the immense sacrifice. There was no indication that the enemy were beaten; everything indeed pointed to the war being prolonged. The position on the Western Front established two years earlier was one of stalemate and advances were reckoned in terms of yards instead of miles. The harvest of 1916 had been bad, and despite the larger acreage of oats in Scotland the total production of grain was below the 1914 level. But if the total production of oats had gone down slightly that of potatoes had slumped alarmingly. The acreage in 1916 was 9 per cent. down on the previous year's figures and the crop was poor. The estimated total yield, instead of being over 1,000,000 tons as in 1914, was reckoned to be only 531,000 tons.[11] Taking into consideration the fact that seed for the 1917 crop year had to be retained for planting, the tonnage available for sale as ware was much less than half the normal amount. Labour difficulties too had by this time become apparent on Scottish farms and it now became evident that food production was likely to be hampered if more men joined the Forces.

In August 1916 a committee, or rather a sub-committee of the Reconstruction Committee, under the chairmanship of Lord Selborne, had been appointed to consider agricultural reconstruction after the

[10] Ernle, *English Farming*, pp. 395-6.
[11] Douglas, " Agric. during the war ", p. 48.

war. At a very early stage this committee had to take into account
the serious results of blind adherence to the policy of free imports of
food, coupled with lack of direction, control or assistance of home
agriculture. Its report, presented in January 1917, contained far-
reaching recommendations. The Committee found that the
management and utilisation of the land should be a matter of
concern, not only to individual owners and occupiers but also to
the State, and that in the State's interests the land must gradually
be made to yield the maximum production of foodstuffs and timber.[12]
They recommended that producers should be secured against the
evil effects of continued low prices, that State guarantees should be
given for wheat and oats, that in return effecent occupancy of the
land should be insisted upon, and that the principle of a guaranteed
agricultural minimum wage should be brought into being.

Meantime the prospect of a speedy and victorious end to the
war seemed to grow more remote. The submarine campaign had
become more acute; the acreage of autumn-sown wheat was down;
Italy and France were showing signs of war weariness, for besides
the strain of war both countries were handicapped by serious losses
of valuable territory. At home discontent against Asquith's leadership was becoming pronounced and more vigorous prosecution of
war measures was urged. In December a new Coalition Government with Lloyd George as Prime Minister took office and at once
announced a new agricultural policy. The outlook in agriculture
at that time was not hopeful. There was an acute shortage of
potatoes; labour had been allowed to drift from the farms; farm
workers who had enlisted or had been called up could not be spared
from the Forces; horses had been commandeered; implement
factories had switched over to the making of munitions; the country
districts had been largely depleted of their tradesmen—horses might
remain unshod and broken implements and harness unmended
because the blacksmiths, saddlers, etc. had enlisted; fertilisers
were scarce and potash could not be had; lime works were closed
for lack of labour; the transport of munitions was given priority over
that of feeding-stuffs, fertilisers and farm implements, while the
late, poor and prolonged harvest of 1916 had discouraged farmers.[13]

In the light of the Government's decision to use compulsory
powers, the Wason Committee were consulted about the action to

[12] Reconstruction Committee, *Report of the Agricultural Subcommittee*, PT. I,
Jan. 1917.
[13] Ernle, *English Farming*, pp. 397-8.

be taken. They recommended the appointment of District Agricultural Executive Committees to advise the Board of Agriculture for Scotland in all matters relating to increased food production,[14] viz., to survey farms, to determine the acreage of land that could be devoted to crop-growing, and to advise on labour, fertiliser and general supply problems. The Committee also recommended that the Board should provide facilities for training women in agriculture and that they should undertake to supply labour-saving implements and agricultural machinery, particularly tractors. Recommendations were also made regarding the killing of deer and rabbits. The Board were warned of a probable serious shortage in the supply of milk because of growing labour difficulties and the prevailing scarcity and high price of feeding-stuffs coupled with price control. Regarding the call-up of farm workers the Committee recommended that no one working on a farm should be called up for military service without the sanction of the Board of Agriculture for Scotland.

Early in 1917 the Prime Minister announced that in order to encourage farmers to break up grassland and to devote a larger acreage to grain production the Government would guarantee a minimum price for wheat and oats. A new regulation made by Order in Council in January[15] empowered the Boards of Agriculture in England and Scotland to make orders for better and more extended cultivation of agricultural land. In England these powers were delegated to the Agricultural Executive Committees;[16] in Scotland they remained in the hands of the Scottish Board of Agriculture who were advised by the Executive Committees. It was too late in the season to expect these newly-appointed local committees to do much to secure any great increases for the cropping year 1917. The winter was unusually severe and prolonged; spring came late and spring work had to be done with a rush to get the crops down in time. Nevertheless the cropping results were most gratifying. Compared with the 1914 figures the grain crop acreage was up by 86,000, while compared with 1916 that of potatoes had gone up by 17,600. Lloyd George's vigorous leadership, coupled with a growing realisation of the country's increasing dependence on home-grown food, was having beneficial results. In England permanent pasture in 1917 was down by 650,000 acres on the 1914

---

[14] Douglas, " Agric. during the war ", p. 9.
[15] Middleton, *Food Production*, p. 167.
[16] *op. cit.*, pp. 169-76.

figure. By 1918 nearly 3,000,000 more acres (U.K. figures) were being cropped as compared with the pre-war average.[17]

In April 1917 a Bill was introduced authorising guaranteed prices for wheat and oats. The prices named, 60s. for wheat for the 1918 and 1919 crops and 38s. 6d. for oats, bore little relationship to the prevailing prices. These were very much higher (about 80s. a quarter for wheat and over 60s. for oats), but as prices were to be guaranteed until 1922 it was apparent that the Government fully appreciated the English farmer's reluctance to break up grassland unless he had an assurance that over a series of years prices, particularly for wheat, would be maintained at profitable levels. Potatoes were also to be guaranteed for one year at £6 per ton.[18] The Corn Production Act 1917 was duly passed. Machinery was set up to secure minimum wage rates for farm workers, and no effort was spared to secure a maximum tillage acreage for the cropping season 1918. The relationship between the local Scottish Agricultural Executive Committees and the Board of Agriculture led, however, to some misunderstandings.[19] Recommendations by the Committees for the use of compulsory powers might not always be accepted by the Board. The task of the Committees was at no time easy; they had to administer regulations which were unpopular, explain certain decisions which were taken against their own recommendations, point out perhaps to life-long friends and neighbours the error of their ways in farming and do their utmost, despite serious difficulties with labour and supplies of all kinds, to get production stepped up for the 1918 crop. Local farmers alleged that in adhering closely to the policy of getting more acres ploughed the Committees overlooked the need to make fuller use of land already ploughed, and contended that some of the land scheduled for ploughing would not yield a profitable crop.

By the winter of 1917-18 labour difficulties had apparently reached their peak. Scottish agriculture had by this time supplied a considerable number of experienced farm workers to the Forces; other workers had left, attracted by higher wages elsewhere, while the Services were demanding still more men. It was arranged that wherever possible substitute labour should be provided, but the machinery for doing this was slow and cumbersome, and the Army evidently took little care to ensure that soldiers released for farm

---

[17] At that time the whole of Ireland was included in the U.K. Middleton, *Food Production*, p. 312.

[18] *op. cit.*, p. 204.     [19] Douglas, " Agric. during the war ", pp. 17-18.

work had had previous farming experience or were likely to make good. When farm workers were called up the Committees were given the difficult task of adjudicating between the needs of the Army and the claims of agriculture. The military authorities were often disposed to think that the farm's exigencies were being used to shelter the farmer's family, for in many instances the farmer's son seemed always to be the key man of the farm and as such indispensable. "What does he do?" would be the question put to the exasperated father who was wont to reply: "What disna' he do?" There were other snags. While soldier or prisoner labour was controlled by the War Office, alien labour came under the wing of another Government Department and volunteer labour under yet another. The Ministry of Food dealt with feeding-stuffs and the Ministry of Munitions with fertilisers and machinery.[20] These arrangements seemed at the time needlessly complicated and the Committees had constantly to exercise patience and persistence. They often had to make arrangements to accommodate stock displaced from ploughed-up grass land: in the Highlands deer forests were made available for grazing sheep and cattle.

Despite the late and cold spring 1917 was, in marked contrast to its predecessor, a good cropping year. The oat crop yielded about 4 bushels per acre over the average and the potato crop a ton more.[21] Because of the great extension of the allotment movement that year the demand for potatoes was slow at first and the exceptionally large crop made farmers apprehensive that many would be left unsold. The Government had guaranteed a price of £6 per ton but took no steps towards fulfilling this obligation until late in the potato season.[22] In the meantime many growers, anxious to be rid of their crop, had sold their potatoes at lower prices. The bumper crop did much, however, to allay anxiety about the food position.

In view of the food shortages in the spring of 1917 it had been deemed expedient to control producers' prices for potatoes and grain. Milk prices had been controlled as early as November 1916. The control of wholesale meat prices followed in the early autumn of 1917 when maximum prices were fixed. The intention underlying these controls was to protect the consumers' interest by preventing the shortage of supplies from forcing up prices to too high levels. The Wason Committee had, however, pointed out one of the dangers of control. They considered that the prevailing maximum price of

[20] Ernle, *English Farming*, p. 403.
[21] Douglas, "Agric. during the war", p. 48.     [22] *op. cit.*, p. 26.

milk was not related to the costs of labour and feeding-stuffs and that these and other difficulties associated with dairying might lead to shortages in production. So unworkable was the first part of the 1916 measure that part was at once abandoned, while later in 1917 [23] a new range of milk prices had to be substituted for those in being. Cheese prices were controlled at levels bearing some relationship to the price of milk, but the maximum price of butter in relation to cheese and milk was so low that many butter makers gave up production and turned either to cheese-making or to liquid milk production.

In the early stages of the war a considerable amount of hay was required by the Army for foraging transport horses. Increasing difficulties in obtaining it led to part of the 1915 crop being commandeered at prices relatively lower than those of other feeding materials. The result was that, because of its scarcity, such hay as was not commandeered could be sold in the open market at much higher prices. The high prices (which reached £12 to £14 per ton during a snowstorm in 1916) bore heavily on sheep farmers and dairymen in towns who had to buy all their feed at high competitive prices and yet were restricted in the price they could charge for their milk. Early in 1917, therefore, controls were placed on the sale of hay, oat straw and wheat straw. In course of time the Army Council controlled the distribution of forage, but they fixed the price so low that farmers reduced their acreage of hay.[24] Producers were allowed, however, to retain hay required for their own use.

With the increasing shortage of feeding-stuffs, and the high prices demanded for them, both milk and meat producers were greatly hampered. Labour too was now becoming so scarce on dairy farms that many milk producers, despite the offer of very high wages, could scarcely get milkers. On smaller dairy farms, where most of the work was done by family labour, difficulties were less acute than on the larger holdings,[25] some of which were obliged to switch over to beef production. Lack of concentrated feeding-stuffs forced beef-producing farmers to alter their methods of fattening. Oats could be used in place of cake, but oats had risen proportionately more in price than cattle and farmers were consequently reluctant to use this or any other cereal, so instead of fattening animals at just over two years of age they allowed them to remain on for another year. As more mature animals they

[23] Douglas, " Agric. during the war ", pp. 65-6.
[24] op. cit., p. 46.        [25] op. cit., pp. 37-8.

could be fattened mainly on turnips, oat straw and hay, but the turnover was of course very much less and, as in the case of milk, the output of beef from farms was greatly reduced.

In December 1917 an elaborate system of grading fat cattle was introduced. Producers could either dispose of the animals at recognised markets, where their live weight was ascertained and their killing-out percentage estimated by graders representing farmers and butchers, or they could have their animals slaughtered and the carcasses weighed. Standard graded prices per cwt. live weight relating to the killing percentages were fixed, the payment for slaughtered animals being adjusted to the live weight prices. For sheep a somewhat similar system was used, but in their case the live weight was estimated. As may be imagined a system which, apart from the killing-out percentage, ignored the superior quality of Scottish-bred and fattened animals, was none too popular;[26] but as it was recognised that in the interest of consumers prices could not be allowed to find their natural level, and that each citizen was entitled to a proportionate share of essential foods, the controls were generally accepted with good grace.

The story of the latter stages of the war, so far as farming is concerned, was one of continued recourse to expedients of every kind. Substitute labour had to be employed; to satisfy Executive Committees pastures had to be broken up before their time, and cross-cropping, regarded as bad farming, had to be practised. Government tractors were used to break up land and slower methods of fattening animals were adopted. But farmers rose to the occasion; the serious military reverses in the spring of 1918 urged them to fresh endeavours and when the June agricultural statistics came to be published the results were seen to be most gratifying. The Scottish acreage under grain crops had risen from 1,235,184 in 1916 to 1,494,414 in 1918,[27] an increase of more than 21 per cent. in two years, despite shortages of men, horses and artificial fertilisers. Agriculturists had certainly begun to realise that they had a vital part to play, not only in staving off defeat but also in helping to attain victory. The increased acreage of potatoes, attained largely at the expense of turnips, underlined the view that in time of war human food was more important than food for animals. The significant reduction in the acreage of temporary and permanent grass, coupled with the reduction in turnips, the acreage of which had steadily declined from 431,000 in 1914 to 396,000 in 1918,

[26] Douglas, "Agric. during the war", p. 64.          [27] op. cit., p. 46.

might have been expected to result in a considerable reduction in the cattle population. This, however, was not the case, for cattle numbers remained very steady throughout the war. Sheep numbers declined somewhat and those of pigs, because of the growing shortage of feeding-stuffs, fell by 16 per cent.

The year 1918 was, however, an anxious one for everyone. The major disasters in March of that year led to general despondency. The casualties were so great that a further 5,500 men were called for from agriculture in Scotland.[28] The food situation was most acute and an ever-increasing volume of shipping had to be diverted to ferrying American troops and their supplies across the Atlantic. Although much more land had been put down to crop anxiety was felt about the harvest. The summer was rather sunless and wet, and although crops in general were good farmers were apprehensive, because of the lateness of the harvest and the general scarcity of labour, that they would not all be secured. Fortunately these fears were groundless and a record crop of grain and potatoes was eventually harvested.

Meantime plans had been drawn up for extending the food production campaign to 1919, but on 11th November came the glad news of the Armistice. The last two years had been particularly trying for the Agricultural Executive Committees, farmers and farm workers, whose courage, determination and patriotism had played a major part in saving the country from defeat. Their performance was all the more remarkable when it is considered that at a rather late stage in the war everyone had to be converted from a policy of freedom in agriculture to one of direction, from individualism to State control, and that before control was assumed the industry had been somewhat crippled. But once the principle of State control had been accepted and applied, it was loyally observed. Without it the country would have been in extreme peril; because of it the danger to our food supplies was considerably reduced. It should be recorded that our comparative elasticity in farming methods enabled the food production campaign to be carried on in Scotland with much less trouble and expense to the nation than in England. Much of the pasture ploughed up in Scotland was temporary grass which would have been ploughed up in any case, possibly a year later, while many of the permanent grass fields broken up had been such inferior pasture that ploughing-up would have been the first step towards improvement. In some

[28] Middleton, *Food Production*, p. 265.

cases where ploughing was enforced the work was done too late and too badly to ensure the production of maximum crops. Most Scottish farmers, however, owned their own ploughs and were given a considerable amount of freedom in selecting the land to be ploughed. As a rule, good and profitable crops were grown and little resentment at control was expressed. The routine of the farm was not greatly disturbed, and Scottish farmers generally took their imposed tasks in their stride. They cut down on low ground sheep, but kept much the same number of cattle, and by working longer hours stepped up production.

In England the circumstances were in large measure different. There many of the farms were given over entirely to grass; horses had been sold and ploughs allowed to dissolve into rust, while many of the workers had never been trained to operate a plough. Compliance with the English Committee's orders was not always easy for it often meant starting an unfamiliar branch of agriculture. Proudly esteemed permanent pastures had to be destroyed and resentment against this policy was freely expressed. Letters in the Press would point out that thousands of acres of the finest old pasture had been transformed as a result of enforced, untimely and indifferent methods of tillage, shortage of skilled labour, insect pests, etc., into wretched wastes, bearing abundant crops of weeds but certainly not the crops the Committees had hoped to see.[29] Many English farmers firmly believed that it would take at least ten years before the reseeded pastures would regain their former productivity. These forebodings notwithstanding, England's achievements, mainly because her scope for improvement was much greater, were relatively higher than Scotland's. The total yield of wheat and potatoes in England was up by well over 40 per cent., from which it may be gathered that much had been done to tap latent sources of food supplies.

[29] Middleton, *Food Production*, p. 238.

## CHAPTER XIV

# ANOTHER DEPRESSION : 1921-1939

From war to peace...Difficulties in agriculture...War lessons
...Seed testing and plant registration stations...Rise in prices
...Effects of decontrol on price of fat stock...The Agriculture
Act, 1920...Price falls...Repeal of 1920 Act...Land values...
Wild white clover...Intense depression of early thirties...
Marketing Acts, 1931 and 1933...Free Trade abandoned...
Wheat Act, 1932...Marketing Boards...Assistance—barley,
oats and meat...Sugar beet...Land fertility schemes...Farming
organisations...Wages Boards...Seed potatoes...Mechanisa-
tion...Scientific discoveries...Women's Rural Institutes...
Young Farmers' Clubs.

WHEN THE ARMISTICE WAS SIGNED on 11th November 1918
Great Britain had already steeled herself for another year
of war, but the magnitude and severity of the struggle had
told heavily on her resources. The nation and all its main industries
had been organised for war and so the transformation to a peace-
time footing was bound to be difficult and painful. It was not merely
a problem of reabsorbing some millions of ex-service men into
industry and commerce but also of transferring hundreds of thousands
of workers and numerous industries from munition-making and
other forms of war production to their normal functions. It was
not easy to perform this task quickly. Service men clamoured for
early release, but their former employers were not always able to
take them on again at once because their business circumstances
were being readjusted. The problem in agriculture was, fortunately,
not so formidable. Under the stress of war conditions arrears of
work had accumulated on most farms: in any case increased cultivation meant that more work had to be done and, before service men
could be released in large numbers, the slack winter was giving way
to the busy spring season. Thus as the wartime substitute labour
was released from farms no difficulty was experienced by ex-service
farm workers in finding work or by employers in accommodating
them. The change-over was gradual, smooth and effective.

The world scarcity of food and the shortage of shipping at the
close of the war were so great, however, that although the tension

of war had gone the need for the utmost production at home continued. Cereal prices remained high, so much higher than the guaranteed prices for wheat and oats that the need for Government assistance seemed remote. It was otherwise with the potato crop. Throughout Great Britain the 1918 crop had been a bumper one. Its estimated tonnage was above that of 1914—itself a bountiful year.[1] In the spring of 1919 it became evident that much of the Scottish crop would remain unsold. A price guarantee had been given for the 1917 and the 1918 [2] crops, but there were great delays in taking effective action: eventually the Government did take over the unsold portion of the 1918 crop and no great loss was incurred by farmers. Meat was still controlled in price. The slump in cattle prices which occurred just after Waterloo was not repeated. Indeed, it was fully expected that when meat control was removed prices for livestock would advance, and at first this was the case.

The war had taught many valuable lessons. Agriculture's important role in preserving the nation's well-being even in normal times had apparently been realised. The Prime Minister went so far as to promise that never again would the industry be left to sink or swim. The Agricultural Executive Committees continued to supervise in a general way the farming activities of their areas. The principle that the State should exercise supreme control over agricultural land and its use had found acceptance, but now that the war was over freedom of cropping was restored.[3] It was confidently expected that the guaranteed prices for wheat and oats would maintain production at a sufficiently high level. Optimism was unbounded in those days; rosy views were held concerning smallholdings and the benefits of co-operation, organisation, education and research: altogether a promising future for agriculture was envisaged.

The benefits of agricultural education and research had been emphasised during the war. High production, then the objective, can be achieved either by bringing more land under the plough, or by higher production per acre or per animal. Visiting members of agricultural executive committees realised that their efforts to produce more food had often been greatly hampered by failure on the part of many farmers to take full advantage of scientific knowledge. For instance, instead of growing the more prolific grain-producing varieties of oats, some farmers persisted in using the less prolific kinds favoured by their fathers: their fertiliser

---

[1] Douglas, " Agric. during the war ", p. 49.
[2] *op. cit.*, pp. 27, 63.    [3] Ernle, *English Farming*, p. 408.

programmes, too, were designed on too frugal lines, their grass seed mixtures were faulty and in consequence their temporary pastures were relatively unproductive and short-lived. Confidence in the advice of college-trained men was still lacking.

But apart from errors in individual management by farmers there were other grave defects which concerned the industry. Such livestock diseases as contagious abortion in cattle and braxy and louping-ill in sheep were exacting a heavy toll. Significant progress made in the treatment of human ailments suggested that equally great, if not greater, advances could be made in animal diseases, given adequate facilities for research. Many undesirable features in the marketing of grass seeds and seed potatoes had also been disclosed. While most Scottish seedsmen dealt only in high-class seeds, unscrupulous or ignorant merchants were not deterred from selling seeds of low vitality and purity, some even containing many weed seeds. The seed-potato trade in particular was in an unsatisfactory state. Sellers might deceive buyers seeking a new variety of superior merit into purchasing an existing standard variety which had simply been renamed. The breeder of a genuine new potato variety might, by giving it fulsome but unmerited praise, market it at a very high price, and buyers might be chagrined to find such bad faults that it had to be discarded. Obviously there was a clamant need for the dissemination of knowledge on the scientific side of farming, for more research on soil, crop and animal problems, for increased facilities to test the purity and germination of seeds, for legislation to make seed testing compulsory and for reliable information on the purity and agricultural value of new plant varieties offered for sale to farmers.

The newly-formed Scottish Board of Agriculture had set up a seed-testing station as early as 1913 but not until 1917 was seed testing made compulsory and sellers obliged to declare the germination and purity of their seeds. The Board met the need for a registration station, where the merits and distinctiveness of any new variety of oats and potatoes could be properly determined by exhaustive tests, by establishing one at East Craigs near Edinburgh soon after the close of the war. At this centre a new seed-testing station designed and equipped on the most modern lines, and the research station of the Scottish Society for the Promotion of Plant-Breeding were also established. In the promotion of this latter project the Highland and Agricultural Society lent valuable aid.[4]

[4] Douglas, " Agric. during the war ", p. 34.

But despite these and other measures Scottish agriculture was to undergo a profound period of depression when, after 1920, world production of food had overtaken demand and prices dropped catastrophically. In 1919 and for part of 1920 supplies of home-grown and imported foods were generally short of demand and prices soared. In a year's time oats rose in price from 50s. to 65s. a quarter, barley from 70s. to 125s. and wheat from 76s. to 95s.[5] In 1919 the price of fat cattle in Edinburgh was 74s. 8d. a cwt. live weight; in 1920, after decontrol, it averaged 96s. 3d.; in Perth the corresponding figure was 101s. 7d.[6] Until late in 1920 everything seemed to point to further rises and during most of these two years optimism was unbounded.

Had farmers studied the food imports situation they might have had profound misgivings. In 1919 wheat imports totalled 71.4 million cwt. and in 1920 108.3 million cwt.; in the same period the amount of imported dairy produce rose by more than a quarter and maize imports were more than doubled. Only meat, barley and oat imports were down on the year and then not appreciably.[7] By 1921 the food supply situation had entirely changed. World production had overtaken demand. Imports of dairy products were more than doubled, oat imports up by a third; more rice and maize were coming in and meat imports had risen appreciably. The writing was on the wall but few chose to read it.

The slump was sudden and drastic. Between 1920 and 1921 wool sank almost to a quarter of its former value; between 1920 and 1922 the price of wheat was halved, while oats by the latter year were making only about a third of their 1919 price. Stock prices alone remained relatively steady but even so there was a serious fall in the price of sheep in the autumn of 1921. Taking 1911-13 as 100 the agricultural index figure stood at 292 in 1920; by 1921 it had slumped to 219 and by 1922 to 169. Farm produce as a whole in the latter year was little over half its 1920 value.[8]

At first these price falls were not viewed too seriously. It was inevitable, farmers argued, that prices should fall from post-war

[5] Prices of grain, Edinburgh market, in *T.H.A.S.*, 5th ser. XXXII (1920), pp. 272 ff. and XXXIII (1921), pp. 309-12.
[6] Prices of grain, Edinburgh market, in *T.H.A.S.*, 5th ser. XXXIV (1922), p. 283.
[7] "Trade and Navigation Returns 1919-21", in *T.H.A.S.*, 5th ser. XXXIV (1922), p. 278.
[8] Ernle, *English Farming*, p. 450, quoting Ministry of Agriculture and Fisheries Index of Prices of Agricultural Produce (1911-13 = 100).

P

high levels when supplies became abundant. They found comfort in the assurance that, if cereal prices continued to fall, the guarantees promised under the Agriculture Act 1920 would operate so that arable farming would continue to be relatively profitable. This Act, the main purpose of which was to secure farmers against possible losses in wheat and oat growing, had replaced the Corn Production Act 1917, a wartime emergency measure which guaranteed prices only up to 1922. In the 1920 Act the guaranteed prices for wheat and oats were to be based on the average price of 1919, viz. 68s. a quarter for wheat and 46s. for oats, and were subject to an annual revision by Commissioners in accordance with the costs of production. This Act made one very significant change in the law concerning landlord and tenant. No landlord could henceforth displace a tenant against his will on the expiry of his lease without payment of compensation, usually amounting to a year's rent, unless it were proved that the tenant was not cultivating the holding according to the rules of good husbandry. Where the rent was in dispute provision was made for settling the matter by arbitration. The 1920 Act thus gave effect to the following principles: guaranteed prices for wheat and oats; minimum wages; increased security of tenure and some measure of State control over the utilisation of farm land.

After the passing of the Act prosperity seemed assured, but disillusionment came quickly. Prices for grain, as has been shown, dropped rapidly. The prospect of having to face a huge bill to implement their farming guarantees alarmed the Government and in a few months the Act was repealed by the Corn Production Acts (Repeal) Act, 1921. The guarantees for wheat and oats were removed; gone also were the provisions relating to good husbandry and minimum wages; only the clauses relating to tenure and to the destruction of specified injurious weeds remained. At one blow the structure of agricultural protection had been demolished with only some odd bits of salvage. Farmers were compensated to some extent for the loss of the wheat and oats guarantee by an acreage payment, of which Scotland's share amounted to £4.4 million, while for Britain as a whole there was a solatium of £1 million devoted to further education and research.[9]

And so the tragic story of the sacrifice of British agriculture to cheap food and Free Trade was repeated. Without restriction meat, butter, cheese, eggs, vegetables and cereals poured into the country. To add to farmers' difficulties the summers of 1922, '23

[9] Ernle, *English Farming*, p. 417.

and '24 were cold and sunless and the harvests late. The good crop of potatoes in 1923 inflicted losses on many farmers. The price fell so low that potatoes could not be sold in districts remote from markets and there was no benign government, as there had been in 1919, to take over the unopened pits and pay a guaranteed price. For many farmers the sum realised was the price of feeding them to cattle. Farmers who had been prudent enough to bank wartime profits or to invest them in easily realisable securities had perforce to draw upon capital.

But it must be admitted that during the fleeting wartime prosperity not all farmers had been wise or provident. In many instances prosperity had, like strong wine, gone to their heads. Instead of visualising that bad times would probably come, as after the Napoleonic Wars, too many thought that a new and permanent era of prosperity for farming had dawned. Many farmers—the younger generation in particular—instead of attending to business at the farm drove from market to market in their new motor cars and indulged too freely in the delights of town life. Mr A. G. Street, in *Farmer's Glory*, paints a true and vivid picture of the thoughtless extravagances of some of the younger farmers of the period.

Few had suffered more from the war than the landlords. To them it meant increased taxation and heavier upkeep burdens on permanent equipment. Farms rendered vacant by death or by voluntary surrender had indeed commanded higher rents and, in a good locality, might attract upwards of a hundred prospective tenants. But most farmers were sitting on long leases and even when leases were due for renewal the rents were not greatly raised. It was usually only when the landlord was free to advertise his farm to let or for sale that a high rent or a high sale price could be negotiated. Some far-seeing landlords, realising that ownership was unlikely in future to return much net income, and that prosperous times for tenants had swollen their bank balances, now offered their farms for sale. Sitting tenants were often able to buy at from twenty to twenty-five years' purchase, depending on the rent or the number of years that the lease had to run. But farms with immediate entry often commanded fantastic prices in 1919 and 1920.

For many farmers who had borrowed heavily to purchase or stock their farms the slump meant disaster. While live and dead stock values might have fallen by nearly one half within a year, loans and interest charges were not reduced. Such farmers lost all their money and bankruptcies became all too common. Nevertheless, prudent and thrifty farmers were able to adjust themselves to their circumstances. Not for nothing had the older generation endured the privations of the lean years before 1914; the practice of disciplined thrift and hard work had not been forgotten and careful management ensured a bare living. Annual grants for land drainage were offered by the Board of Agriculture for Scotland, and relief was afforded by the passing of the Agriculture Rates Act in 1923. Even greater relief was given later, in 1926 and in 1929, when agricultural land and buildings were freed of all rates, which were charged only on farm dwelling-houses. To farmers who had purchased their farms the Agricultural Credits (Scotland) Acts of 1925 and 1929 were also of considerable assistance.

Prices in the twenties gradually steadied; those of fertilisers and feeding-stuffs came down to levels commensurate with the value of farm products and less productive land was once more laid down to pasture. The discovery of the merits of wild white clover as a pasture plant and a soil fertiliser was a potent factor in easing difficulties. The productive capacity of temporary pastures could be greatly increased—doubled and even trebled in some cases; animals could often be fattened on land formerly used to graze stores, and much better and cleaner crops could be grown after such pastures had been ploughed up. Low prices were thus, in part, offset by increased output of grain and stock. But new problems attended the introduction of this beneficial plant. The relative luxuriance of the pastures intensified the problem of parasitic control of intestinal worms in sheep, and until phenothiazine was discovered to be effective in dislodging such worms there were considerable losses. The fertilising effects of wild white clover were so great on better quality land that lea oat crops often became badly lodged.

Poultry-keeping was now gaining in popularity. The lessons taught by the college instructresses were beginning to bear fruit. Flocks were healthier and better managed. Egg production had been stepped up, thanks to the use of settings of eggs from prolific strains, earlier hatching, better-balanced foods and the discarding of hens at an earlier age, while more eggs were being laid in autumn and winter when egg prices were highest. Farmers began to realise that by converting their grain into eggs and poultry meat, it could be disposed of to better advantage than by sale to a grain merchant.

Once prices had settled down they remained fairly steady until 1929 when, unhappily, another and more severe slump occurred. Between 1930 and 1931 the price of store sheep fell by 40 per cent.

and by 1932 even the low 1931 price had been much reduced.  Black-face ewe lambs were sometimes bought for 7s. a head while the top price was only 14s. 6d.[10]  At an auction sale in Sutherland the only bid for one lot of small lambs was 6d. a head.  During most of December 1933 the highest price for wheat in the Edinburgh market was only 20s. 6d. per quarter and for oats 15s. 9d.[11]  In provincial markets prices were still lower.  Seldom had depression been so pronounced.  Not only were prices for cereals, milk, livestock and wool extremely low, but Scottish potato-growers were sometimes unable to dispose of their crops and those who did so often sold at ruinous prices.  Thus much of the fine crop of 1929, apart from what was eaten by stock or used for seed, was either disposed of for stock feed at very low prices or left to rot in the pits,  nor could all the bountiful 1931 crop be marketed.  Farms in more remote areas such as Ross-shire, where costs of carriage to market were highest, suffered most.  The early years of the thirties saw agriculture at a very low ebb.  Good land in the stock-rearing and cattle-fattening areas of the north-east was sometimes being rented at 10s. or being sold for about £10 an acre.  Estates bought during the post-war boom could sometimes command only one-third of their purchase price. The result was inevitable; everywhere land was laid down to, or kept longer in grass.  The oats acreage of 1,240,000 in 1918 had fallen by 1932 to 867,000 and that of barley from 152,853 to 66,672. Temporary grass rose by 160,000 acres and permanent by over 260,000 acres.

It was indeed a critical time for farmers.  While the main cause of their troubles lay in the Free Trade and cheap food policy adopted eighty-five years earlier, there were many other contributory causes. For instance, when he sold or bought the farmer was often at the mercy of strongly organised groups of traders, while in the sale of perishable commodities he was often his own worst enemy.  Prospects of a glut caused cut-throat competition under which such commodities could be disposed of only at ruinously low prices, if indeed they could be sold at all.  In their desperate situation farmers were willing to consider almost any possible measure that promised relief.  The events leading up to the formation of producer-marketing boards for milk, potatoes and bacon pigs are discussed later [12] and need not be dealt with here except to point out that by

[10] Prices of sheep, in *T.H.A.S.*, 5th ser. XLV (1933), p. 245.

[11] Prices of grain, Edinburgh corn market, in *T.H.A.S.*, 5th ser. XLVI (1934), p. 349.                                    [12] See Chapter XXVII.

the formation of these boards, which did much to improve the situation for producers, farmers largely sacrificed their cherished individual freedom of sale. The Boards did not, however, assist the producers of cereals, cattle, sheep or wool who had to face fierce competition from abroad. Other measures were taken, rather piecemeal in character.

The great trade depression of 1931 forced Britain to abandon her Free Trade policy. Prices by this time had dropped to levels so low that wheat-growing in Britain seemed doomed. As a measure of assistance, and to provide employment for farm workers, who might otherwise augment the already swollen ranks of the un-employed, the Government passed the Wheat Act of 1932 [13] which guaranteed prices for millable wheat, irrespective of the price the individual farmer might get for that commodity; the difference between the ascertained average yearly price and the standard price of 45s. per quarter was paid to the farmer on all that he sold. The requisite funds were raised by a levy on imported wheat. As wheat imports at that time exceeded home production by about five to one, only a relatively small levy was required and, although in the end the consumer paid, the price of bread was then so low that there was no complaint by the public. Since no guarantees were given for barley and oats there was resentment in Scotland. The Wheat Act favoured arable districts in the east, centre and south of England but did little to assist Scottish farmers, relatively few of whom grew wheat.

The Scottish Farmers' Union, however, exerted persistent pressure on the Government and eventually under the Agriculture Act of 1937 price guarantees were extended to oats and barley.[14] These were, however, calculated on a different basis from that for wheat. Any money paid to the farmer came direct from Exche-quer funds, the payment being on an acreage basis. The principle applied to wheat—of making a deficiency payment on the actual amount of millable grain sold—was scarcely applicable to either oats or barley, both of which were, to a considerable extent, retained on farms as stock feed. The method adopted was to determine approx-imately the average amount per acre that would normally be sold, and to base the deficiency payment on that amount. For oats this

[13] " Wheat Act ", in *Journal of the Ministry of Agriculture*, XXXIX (1932-33), pp. 308, 450, 509.

[14] 26th Report of the Department of Agriculture for Scotland, henceforth cited as D.O.A.S. and report no., 1938, p. 9.

was reckoned to be 6 cwt. per acre, an amount then considered to be much too low. Thus if the standard price of oats under the 1937 Act was 8s. per cwt. and the average selling price was 6s. per cwt. the farmer was paid the difference of 2s. per cwt. in respect of 6 cwt. per acre or 12s. in all, irrespective of whether he sold any oats at all or had disposed of as much as 20 cwt. per acre.

The slump of 1930-31 had caused a fall in the price of meat, and it was not surprising that, in the interest of organised marketing, proposals should be mooted for a Meat Marketing Board. Before the days of motor transport fat cattle were sold mainly in auction marts in small towns within walking distance of the farms. There they were bought by dealers and butchers to be conveyed to the larger towns and slaughtering centres. It was realised that with the development of motor transport time and expense could be saved by conveying them direct from the farms to slaughtering centres. But proposals for a Board to undertake the collection and slaughtering of fat animals and the grading and disposal of carcasses did not find acceptance at that time. Beef prices had fallen so severely by the autumn of 1932 that special measures were taken to restrict meat imports.[15] Thus, by agreement, imports from South America were cut by 10 per cent. But although this helped to avert disaster, it did not restore prosperity to beef producers. In 1934 a subsidy policy for beef was introduced as a temporary expedient [16] and, by the passing of the Livestock Industry Act in 1937, a long-term subsidy policy came into operation. The subsidy under this Act amounted to 5s. per cwt. on live home-bred cattle of the ordinary grade and 7s. 6d. per cwt. for cattle of quality grade, with lower rates of subsidy for imported Irish cattle.[17] This policy was adopted partly to assist beef producers, partly to save the British housewife from having to pay more for her meat and in part to avoid further restrictions of imports from the Argentine. Provision was made in the Act for the appointment of a Livestock Commission to develop livestock interests. To stabilise the home market for meat the Board of Trade were empowered to control the importation of livestock and meat. An earlier step to promote improvement in livestock had been taken in 1931 when the Licensing of Bulls Act was passed.

Although in 1921 the nation had abandoned agriculture to its

---

[15] Waldorf, Viscount Astor and B. Seebohm Rowntree, *British Agriculture*, London 1938, p. 193.

[16] *op. cit.*, p. 194.                  [17] D.O.A.S., 26th report, pp. 7-8.

fate a step of great significance was taken in 1924. The Government of that time decided to follow the example of other European countries which had subsidised the establishment of a sugar beet industry. France, for instance had resorted to such an expedient when deprived of her normal amounts of sugar from the West Indies by the British blockade during the Napoleonic Wars. There were sound reasons why Britain should do likewise. In the 1914-18 war there was grave danger of sugar supplies being cut off, so that for reasons of security and finance the advantage of a home-grown supply was obvious. From the farming aspect cogent reasons favoured the growing of sugar beet at home. Many parts of the country had suitable soils and enjoyed a favourable climate for growing it. It provided the farmer with a cash crop and one which also gave him valuable stock feed in the form of leaves, crowns and sugar beet pulp. In demanding early and thorough cultivation and adequate liming and manuring beet was a good crop for the land and it provided considerable employment to people in rural areas.

But to establish such an industry in the face of foreign competition was no easy task. Factories would have to be built to process the beet and financiers were unwilling to provide the money unless there was a guarantee that enough beet could be grown within reach to keep the factory running over a period of years at nearly full capacity. Clearly therefore the industry could be established only by the aid of a subsidy. The Government agreed, the subsidy being allocated on a descending scale in the hope that in ten years the industry could be sufficiently well established to be self-supporting.[18] In 1925 the Beet Sugar (Subsidy) Act was passed and a number of factories were built. A few years later British farmers were growing 300,000 acres of beet. In Scotland the crop had to compete with potatoes, particularly seed potatoes, now a prominent feature of her agriculture. In Scotland, too, most soils were unsuitable for sugar beet, which demands a deep, dry, rich and fertile loam, while a relatively sunny climate is necessary for the growth and harvesting of full crops. Only on the more fertile soils of the eastern counties could it be successfully grown and so Fife became the centre of the industry in Scotland. A factory was erected at Cupar and many farmers in the counties of Angus, Perth, Fife, the Lothians and to a less extent in Moray, Ross, Berwick and Roxburgh began to grow sugar beet.

[18] Astor and Rowntree, *British Agriculture*, p. 95.

In Scotland sugar beet yields were in general smaller than in England. Whether this was because the technique of growing it was less well understood, or because conditions of soil and climate were less favourable was not fully determined. One undoubted drawback was the relatively high degree of acidity of most Scottish soils. Furthermore, sugar beet requires a long period of growth and early sowing is of prime importance for maximum yields. Many Scottish farmers at first treated the crop as they would have treated swedes or turnips; they sowed it too late and ploughed the leaves and crowns in instead of using them to feed to stock. Not until the 1939-45 war, when farmers with suitable land were compelled to grow the crop and when the technique of its cultivation had become better understood, was it realised that in financial returns, and having regard to the stock feed yielded, sugar beet could be quite as profitable as potatoes. Soon after the end of the war yields rose significantly and the acreage, which had declined after compulsory powers were abandoned, also increased. Hopes that ten years after its inception the industry would be able to stand on its own feet were not, however, realised. While the amount of subsidy allocated has been considerable the crop has provided a great deal of employment at home, has promoted better farming and has saved the country a large amount of foreign exchange in the purchase of sugar.

By 1937 shadows of another European war were darkening the international horizon. The prospect made the nation more conscious of the state of its agriculture, which despite the measures already taken to alleviate its condition was still far from flourishing. Fresh legislation to aid the industry was felt to be necessary. Accordingly the Agriculture Act 1937 was passed, which contained price guarantees for barley and oats, and embodied a Land Fertility Scheme, under which a subsidy of 50 per cent. for lime and 25 per cent. for slag applied to the land could be paid.[19] Since 1880 liming had largely been neglected. Much land, particularly in Scotland, had become so lime-deficient that crops such as barley, sugar beet and red clover were often difficult to grow, while the growth of other crops was often restricted. Many poorer soils also suffered from a pronounced shortage of phosphate. Indeed in Scotland practically all land returned as permanent grass betrayed a marked deficiency of these two elements. In England Sir George Stapledon had shown that many of the poorer permanent pastures, when broken

[19] D.O.A.S., 26th report, 1938, pp. 8-9.

up, supplied with adequate amounts of lime and phosphates and properly reseeded, could be made to carry up to four times their former numbers of stock and still feed them better. He and his Welsh grassland enthusiasts saw the key to a more prosperous system of agriculture in the grading-up of the productivity of grasslands by liming, manuring, making use of good grass seed mixtures, and periodical breaking-up and renewal. More stock could be grazed on fewer acres of grass; more land could then be released for cropping and better crops could be grown through progressively raising the fertility of the land by means of temporary pastures, in which clovers would play their part. Should home food production ever become of vital national importance this policy of ley farming would create a bank of fertility in the land which could be drawn upon in time of need.

But so far as reseeding of worn-out pastures—one of the main objects of the Land Fertility Scheme—was concerned there was, for various reasons, little response in Scotland. For a century and a half Scottish farmers had been practising ley farming, while the improvement of poor permanent pastures by reseeding did not appeal to them at that time, partly by reason of the expense involved in reseeding, but also for lack of knowledge of how to do it without putting the land through a costly course of cropping. There was also the fact that, apart from the costly and often difficult and rather wasteful process of hay-making, there was then no practical means of converting the surplus of summer into feed for stock in winter. The making of grass silage and dried grass was then in the experimental stage, and there seemed little purpose in adding to the abundance of summer grass and so widening the imbalance between summer and winter keep. In other respects the Land Fertility Scheme was a success. Farmers showed confidence in soil-testing facilities and, as a result of the aid offered for applying lime and of the disclosure that most Scottish soils suffered from lime deficiency, there was a great revival in the practice of liming. An additional incentive to the breaking-up of old pastures was given at a later stage by the passing of the Agricultural Development Act of 1939. The Act authorised, *inter alia*, a grant of £2 per acre for the ploughing up of grass land seven or more years old if ploughed and reseeded or sown to an approved crop before a certain date in that year. It also provided a price insurance scheme for fat sheep.

During the inter-war period there were considerable developments in the national organisation of farmers and their workers.

Some years before the 1914-18 war progressive farmers in England had recognised the weakness of unorganised opinion in expressing views on farming policy. In 1908 a Scottish farmer, Colin Campbell, who had migrated to England, persuaded his neighbours to form a Farmers' Union.[20] A few years later this body had developed into the National Farmers' Union of England and had established its claim to be the only body representing farmers which the Government could consult on matters of policy and prospective legislation. The success of the English venture did not escape notice in Scotland; in 1913 a group of Scottish farmers, following a meeting held in the show yard of the Highland and Agricultural Society's show at Paisley, formed the National Farmers' Union of Scotland. Its policy was then rather vague; all were agreed that union meant strength but the problem was how best to apply that strength. At first the newly formed Union related its activities to collective bargaining and some useful work was done in connexion with milk marketing in the west of Scotland. Progress, however, was slow; many farmers were apathetic towards the new movement; most enjoyed haggling over a deal and felt that collective bargaining would deny them this pleasure. But as time went on and the Union assumed wider responsibilities, particularly in regard to national planning, the movement grew. By 1915 forty-six branches had been formed with 2000 members. The Union was further strengthened by the circumstances of the 1914-18 war, but its membership was built up largely between the wars, particularly in the early thirties, through the efforts of energetic presidents and as a result of the general reaction to the treatment meted out to Scottish farmers through the decision of the Government to confine aid for cereal production to wheat-growing. By 1938, when it amalgamated with the Scottish Chamber of Agriculture, a body representative of the landlord and larger tenant class, it had a membership of 12,500. During the 1939-45 war and the post-war years its numbers were greatly increased and at the time of writing the Scottish National Farmers' Union is the major voice in Scottish farming affairs.

Although the Union's object was to gain all the advantage of a Trade Union its policy was gradually shaped towards assisting agricultural development in every possible way. Thus the Union gave valuable aid at the time of the passing of the Marketing Acts and the formation of the producer-marketing boards, while during the 1939-45 war its policy was consistently helpful to the food

[20] Orwin, *English Farming*, p. 119.

production campaign. Difficulties about wages, machinery, fertilisers and feeding-stuffs were largely overcome through its ready
assistance and its evidence at the annual price reviews was at
all times carefully considered and the price decisions were loyally
accepted. The Union also submitted constructive views on such
development projects as the Department of Agriculture's Potato
and Oat Certification schemes.

For farm workers the body corresponding to the Farmers'
Union in Scotland is the Scottish Farm Servants' Union, now a
branch of the Transport and General Workers' Union. Until 1912
the workers had never succeeded in giving expression to their views
in a properly organised way; they suffered from being rather
inarticulate and individualistic. Compared with the vast majority of
industrial employees they worked longer hours, got fewer holidays
and certainly no weekly half-holiday—indeed many attended to
animals on Sundays—and most usually got much less pay even
when allowance was made for perquisites. Their relatively
low rates of pay were largely associated with the low level of agricultural prices. Up till 1912 the attempt to form unions of farm
workers seemed doomed to failure.[21] About this time, however,
the newly-formed union was fortunate in securing as secretary the
services of a gifted man, Joseph Duncan. Reared on a farm and
having Trade Union experience he was well qualified to understand
the mentality and needs of the Scottish farm servant and to nurse
the newly-born union through the perils of infancy. Newly-formed
branches were, however, often impatient of the delays which arose
in considering their views and of the difficulties encountered
during negotiations. Not until the latter stages of the 1914-18 war
was headway made, although a weekly half-holiday had previously
been granted in certain counties, notably in the Lothians, while in
Roxburgh the working day on many farms was reduced from ten
to nine hours. After the war, however, the Saturday half-holiday
was generally agreed in negotiation with the Farmers' Union.[22]

By the passing of the Corn Production Act 1917, minimum
wages for farm workers were enforced as the complement to guaranteed prices for wheat and oats. When the Agriculture Act 1920
was repealed in 1921 and prices for wheat and oats were no longer

[21] Joseph Duncan, " The Scottish Agricultural Labourer ", in D. J. Jones,
J. F. Duncan, H. M. Conacher and W. R. Scott, *Rural Scotland during the War*,
Carnegie Endowment for International Peace, Economic and Social History of the
World War, British series, London 1926, p. 201.

[22] *op. cit.*, p. 216.

guaranteed, the principle of minimum wages also ceased to apply. But the Union was still able to safeguard the interests of its members in the matter of wages, hours of work and holidays, and was of considerable assistance to the Government in discussing matters of major policy. One of the first acts of the Labour Government in 1924 was to set up a Wages Board in England. No such Board was thought to be necessary in Scotland at that time, but with the passing of the Agricultural Wages (Regulations) Scotland Act 1937, minimum wages, hours of work, overtime rates and holidays were all regulated by a Scottish Wages Board.

From the property-owning point of view the corresponding body to the Farmers' and Farm Workers' Unions is the Scottish Land Owners' Federation, a body which, like the other two, has always played a helpful part in developing the agricultural interests of Scotland. Founded in 1906, its aim is to represent the views of the landowners and to give free advice and assistance to its members.

The fascinating story of the development of the potato industry in Scotland is dealt with in another chapter. In the meantime it may be said that great developments in the growing of seed potatoes took place during the inter-war period. By 1939 it was reckoned that 100,000 tons of seed were sent annually to England and in 1943-44 the figure rose to the peak one of 473,000 tons.[23] A trade in the export of seed potatoes to foreign countries was also developed.

During the First World War farm tractors were imported in considerable numbers. These enabled more land to be ploughed and cultivated and farmers were brought to realise the advantages of tractors over horses. They were more powerful, could greatly economise man-power, and unlike horses could be used at any hour during the day. They were thus invaluable in overtaking arrears of work, enabling crops to be sown in optimum season and, where desirable, stirring the soil more deeply. They were particularly useful in harvest as they saved time in cutting ripe crops. Unfortunately the tractors introduced during the First World War were imperfect, and since both farmers and tractor drivers had had little or no experience in handling them, breakdowns were frequent. These reasons, coupled with the depression in agriculture, the lack of money, and the low prices of horse feed, which ruled after 1921, explain the temporary setback in the use of tractors after the 1914-18 war. But better tractors were in time manufactured and, as more experience in handling them was acquired, they became increasingly

[23] D.O.A.S., *Agriculture in Scotland*, Report 1951, p. 12.

popular.  Valuable instructional aid was given by the agricultural colleges.

Another feature of the period was the development of the combine harvester.  It first affected British agriculture by lowering the world price of grain, since its adoption by overseas farmers enabled them to produce grain very cheaply and in greater volume.  In Scotland, the "combine", as the machine was called, made little progress before 1939, but its obvious economy both in labour and in minimising the loss of grain by shedding during cutting, stooking, leading and stacking were carefully noted.  The first machines imported were unsuitable for British conditions, our crops being too heavy and too long in the straw.  This fact, combined with their high initial cost and the desire of farmers to make full use of the straw, at first hindered development; but with improvements in the machines and the altered circumstances enforced by war conditions they became more widely used.  Greater use was also made of milking machines, coolers and other dairy equipment, while the extended use of electricity for power and lighting on farms eased indoor work.

The story of this inter-war period would be incomplete without mention of two movements which did much to foster and develop a community spirit amongst farmers and their workers.  Before the 1914-18 war little had been done to meet the aspirations of womenfolk on farms for greater social and educational facilities.  For them farming was a hard way of life, often one of drudgery and monotony.  To meet this situation Women's Rural Institutes were inaugurated in 1917 and an organiser was appointed.[24]  Their aim was to enable rural womenfolk to meet for social and recreational purposes, to raise the status of rural life and to make it easier, more sociable and colourful.  The movement gathered strength; and by 1938 there were 1017 Institutes with an approximate membership of 55,000.[25]

Almost parallel with this movement was the development of Young Farmers' Clubs, which were started in America about the beginning of the century and were introduced to Scotland in 1923.  Their aim, in Scotland, is stated in the motto " Better Farmers, Better countrymen, Better citizens ".  The development of social intercourse and of activities such as speech-making, stock-judging and excursions to farms has tended to make the lives of the growing

[24] 6th Report of the Board of Agriculture for Scotland, henceforth cited as B.O.A.S. and report no., 1918, p. vii.

[25] D.O.A.S., 27th report, 1939, p. 79.

generation of farmers fuller and richer and widened their outlook.[26] At first clubs simply sprang into being, in many cases after a successful evening continuation class held by the agricultural college county organiser. In 1937 joint action by the Carnegie United Kingdom Trust, the Scottish Agricultural Colleges, and the Scottish Departments of Agriculture and Education led to the creation of a central organisation, the Scottish Association of Young Farmers' Clubs.[27]

For British agriculture the inter-war period was one of shadow. The policy of setting cheap imported food and high profit above the needs and security of a continuing society had created a feeling of profound depression in the industry. Only the impact of science and education on production, organised methods of marketing, the co-ordinated expression of views, and a yearning of those who gained their living from the land for the development of a healthy and happy community life gave some promise of brighter days. Nor were indications lacking that the nation was beginning to realise that the land was a precious heritage which it could afford to neglect only at its peril. But the damage done to the industry had been immense and often, in the poorer areas, irreparable. There the permanent equipment of the marginal land farms had been allowed to fall into gross decay; so impoverished had much of this land become that it had degenerated into an agricultural slum, occupied in the main by old and infirm persons. These, by pursuing the least productive form of farming—the rearing of store sheep—managed somehow, and often with outside aid, to maintain themselves on a low standard of living. Impoverished farms with many derelict fields were to be seen everywhere in the poorer areas, silent but eloquent testimonies to the depression in agriculture.

[26] W. J. Grant, " Young Farmers' Clubs ", in *T.H.A.S.*, 5th ser. XLV (1933), pp. 88 ff.
[27] D.O.A.S., 26th report, 1938, p. 45.

# CHAPTER XV

# THE SECOND WORLD WAR: 1939-1945

War plans...Gathering clouds...The ploughing-up scheme
of 1939...Appointment of Agricultural Executive Committees
...Cultivation targets, Price controls, Rationing and co-ordinated Programmes...The first year's Campaign...Coalition
Government's agricultural programme...Guaranteed markets
and prices...New scale of minimum wages...Success of food
production programme...Crop subsidies...Sugar beet and
potatoes...Labour problems...Standstill Order...Women's
Land Army...Feeding-stuffs scarcity...Animal rationing...
Fertilisers...Lime facilities...Machinery and implements...
Maintenance of fertility...Marginal land scheme, Hill sheep
and cattle, Deer forests, Allotments...Victory...Progress
reviewed.

FOR SOME YEARS BEFORE 1939 the clouds of war were massing
over Europe and in Britain the hard lessons of the previous
war were being recalled. It was realised that in the event of war
Britain would become a beleaguered island and that supplies of
imported foods and feeding-stuffs would be drastically reduced. Her
ability to endure would depend largely on the population being
supplied with enough food to maintain health and vigour ; failure in
this respect would invite defeat and disaster. Yet with respect to
home-produced foods and feeding-stuffs the country was much worse
off in 1939 than in 1914. Since 1914 the area of crops and grass in
Great Britain had fallen by 2·7 million acres. Large areas had been
acquired for building and industrial development, sport and re-
creation, aerodromes and other uses; much land formerly classified
as permanent pasture was now " rough grazing ", while a large
proportion of the land previously returned as under crops and
rotation grass had been laid down to permanent pasture. Since 1918
Scotland's cropped area had shrunk from 2,099,000 to 1,480,000
acres [1] and her permanent grassland had increased by 315,000 acres.
Various measures, largely piecemeal, had been taken to arrest
the decline in tillage. Yet despite the creation of Marketing
Boards, the provision of varied subsidies and grants, the Land

[1] *S. J. Agric.*, XXIII (1940-42), p. 107.

Fertility Scheme and the abandonment of Free Trade, this decline was far from being halted. It was evident that, while the Government wanted to appease farming discontent, they were unwilling, under peacetime conditions, to adopt a policy calculated to win back the lost tillage acres. The Prime Minister, Mr Chamberlain, made it clear at Kettering in July 1938 that manufacturing and industrial interests must have priority over those of agriculture. Unless, he said, we were prepared to import food from those overseas countries which had been supplying us, we should be unable to trade with them. Their exports of food enabled them to pay for British manufactured goods. Any substantial change in the direction of self-sufficiency in home-grown foods would, in his opinion, be ruinous. The old policy of cheap food, despite the imposition of some tariffs, was still broadly right. Some of the consequences of this policy had led to the adoption of various expedients, but no plan had been devised to eradicate the deep-rooted cause of the agricultural malaise. But as the international situation worsened some steps were taken to ensure that in the event of a conflict agricultural production would be so organised and controlled as to avert food shortages.

The fourfold task of agriculture in war was to produce more wheat and potatoes for home consumption, so easing the burden on shipping, to maintain the fertility of the land so far as possible, to produce sufficient health-promoting foods and so to plan, as far as circumstances might permit, that the year of supreme effort in food production might be synchronised with the time when our shipping difficulties might be expected to be at their greatest. Much of the country's grassland would have to be converted into arable, and livestock would have to take second place to crops, a change that must imply a smaller consumption of livestock products other than milk. Major adjustments and considerable sacrifices would have to be made by farmers and the process of adjustment must needs be gradual. In the inter-war period both men and horses had decreased in numbers as a consequence of laying down more land to grass. Hard put to it, farmers might achieve a good deal, as they had done in the 1914-18 war, but there was a limit to what the available manpower could do. Steps must therefore be taken to restrict the call-up and possibly the movement of farm workers, to augment the existing supply of farm labour, and to supply more tractors and farm implements; again farm surveys would be required to assess the cropping potentialities of individual farms. The need to provide

Q

sufficient health-promoting foods—proteins and vitamins—was recognised; the question was how best these could be obtained and distributed. The problem had been referred to a committee under the direction of Sir John Boyd Orr (later Lord Boyd Orr) [2] and, on the basis of its report, an admirable rationing system was devised. The respective roles of the various classes of livestock in providing food for the people were thus broadly allocated. Where livestock and human beings were in competition for food the latter must take precedence.

In May 1939 preparatory steps were taken. The Agricultural Development Act was passed, empowering the Government to buy and store farm machinery and to induce farmers to increase the tillage acreage for the 1940 harvest. Under the terms of the Ploughing Grant Scheme land which had been in grass for seven years or more, if ploughed up between 4th May and 31st October 1939, qualified for an acreage grant of £2. The object was twofold—to ensure that more grassland would be ploughed up for wheat, and to encourage the breaking-up and reseeding of poorer grassland. This latter procedure would enable as many, or perhaps more livestock to be grazed on fewer acres and would thus release more grassland for tillage. As designed, the scheme was better suited to English than to Scottish conditions. Wheat, the traditional English bread corn, is usually sown in autumn, so that October as the closing date of the qualifying period for the grant was appropriate for wheat sowing but not for oats, the major cereal crop in Scotland. To meet this difficulty the closing date was subsequently extended to the spring of 1940. It had also been decided that should war break out, committees similar to the agricultural executive committees of the First World War would be appointed, and that, in the interests of increasing food production, they would have power to survey all agricultural land and to issue directions regarding its use. These committees, whose members had been nominated in 1938 and 1939, would advise and assist the Government on the various aspects of the production problems—labour, fertilisers, feeding-stuffs, seeds, livestock, drainage, pests, implements and farm accessories.[3] Under the Emergency Powers (Defence) Act, passed in August 1939, wide powers were given to the Government to make the necessary regulations.

[2] David Marshall, " Scottish agriculture during the war ", henceforth cited as Marshall, " Agric. during the war ", in *T.H.A.S.*, 5th ser. LVIII (1956), p. 6.

[3] D.O.A.S. report, *Agriculture in Scotland 1939-48*, Cmd. 7717, 1949, p. 3.

Accordingly, the day after the declaration of war, forty Scottish Agricultural Executive Committees were called into being. So enthusiastic were these bodies that within a few days of their appointment they had divided their respective areas into districts and had prepared skeleton plans to survey every farm and to assess its potential cropping capability for the harvest of 1940. For that harvest a target of 260,000 additional acres had been deemed appropriate for Scotland [4] and this had been allocated amongst the various committee areas. The object of this ploughing-up campaign was, of course, to make the country more self-sufficient in food and feeding stuffs. Insufficient thought, however, had been given to such consequential problems as labour, prices and other incentives to increase production of particular commodities at the expense of decreasing that of others. In the event, there was at first a good deal of confused thinking with some uncoordinated planning and direction.

On marketing swift action had been taken. The Ministry of Food was created and absorbed the staffs of the Agricultural Marketing Boards. Profiting by the experience of the previous World War, the Government had determined on the early institution of rationing of those main basic foods which were likely to be scarce.[5] They had also decided on price control, although little guidance was to be derived from the experience of the First World War on price fixing. In a prolonged war scarcity of food at some stage would be inevitable Without price control and rationing food prices would soar, and bad distribution and social discontent would follow. There would be queues, black markets, and imperative demands for higher wages leading to inflation. Rationing and control were complementary, and before rationing could be introduced a register of all consumers must be made. That would take time and in the interval it was deemed advisable to control prices. At the outbreak of war, stocks of imported meat, sugar, tea, fats, flour, butter and cheese were plentiful, and it was thought that the pegging of retail prices at pre-war levels, until such time as rationing could be introduced, would meet the situation for some time. Unfortunately the rationing scheme was held up; it came into operation only in January 1940. Meantime prices of imported foods and feeding-stuffs had risen, partly by reason of higher rates

[4] D.O.A.S. report, *Agriculture in Scotland 1939-48*, p. 3.

[5] E. H. Whetham, *British Farming, 1939-49*, henceforth cited as Whetham, *British Farming*, London 1952, pp. 22-3.

of insurance and freight and in part because of depreciation in the value of the pound. Milk producers, who had to pay more for their cow feed, oil and transport, and also higher wages, were dissatisfied with the controlled prices. Their increased costs would normally have been passed on to the consumer, but the retail price of milk had been pegged; hence there was a risk that supplies of milk, now a priority food, would decline. To prevent this a subsidy was provided by the Government to increase prices paid to producers.

At the outbreak of war maximum prices at current levels had been fixed for meat but a few weeks later control had to be abandoned, and before rationing could be introduced meat prices had risen markedly. A rise of about 14 per cent. had been permitted for the standard price of wheat to induce farmers to sow more for the harvest of 1940, but, when in December of that year oats and barley prices soared to almost twice their pre-war levels, while the price of wheat still remained pegged, it became obvious that, unless prices were more closely related to the type of production desired, farmers would concentrate on producing foods less essential than wheat, potatoes and milk. Potato prices in December were actually lower than at the outbreak of war, and considerably lower than the average prices for the period 1936-38.[6]

To stimulate expansion in meat production small increases in mutton prices were at first allowed. It was envisaged that this step would encourage the keeping of more ewes and that the lambs they produced would be ready for killing about a year later. Mistakenly, it was thought that meat and crop expansion would go hand in hand and one Government spokesman in a broadcast even urged the keeping of more ewes. In Scotland the announcement caused much perturbation. On the Scottish low-ground farm the ewe was the first animal that would have to go if more land was to be released for cropping. She was in fact the main obstacle in that first year to the ploughing-up campaign. Before any very clear guidance could be given in the matter, however, the low-ground flocks were mated and no further action could be taken for that season.

Still another example of the lack of a properly co-ordinated wartime policy for agricultural production may be instanced. Hens and pigs were the two main competitors with human beings for food. They were fed largely on milling offals derived from wheat, but

[6] Whetham, *British Farming*, p. 37.

PLATE I

Speed the plough: Horses and tractor

in case of need the percentage of offal pared off the grain of wheat could be lowered with benefit to the human food supply. Moreover, much of the food they ate was imported and absorbed shipping space. Yet the price of eggs and of bacon had risen relatively more than that of milk or of any other stock product, and very much more than wheat and potato prices.

Early in 1940 rationing for butter, bacon, meat and sugar was introduced [7] and to ensure effective distribution the Ministry of Food became the buyer. Government policy was still to peg retail prices of all basic foods. To achieve this in face of rising wholesale prices a food subsidy was necessary, It had also to be determined how the prices of home-grown foods could best be fixed. The drawback of fixing prices for any particular commodity unrelated to others was now becoming obvious. Price-fixing, to be effective in time of war, must be done in a manner to encourage farmers to produce those commodities which the nation most needs. Other means might also have to be employed, such as rationing feeding-stuffs to give priority to animals deemed to be the most important.

The difficulties of adjusting peace-time agricultural production to war conditions, the lack of a clear and co-ordinated policy on the part of the Government, the muddle about prices, the requisitioning of land for service purposes—aerodromes, emergency landing sites, camps, training grounds, etc.—the prolonged and severe winter of 1939-40 and the failure of all classes of the nation to appreciate fully the gravity of the struggle, go far to explain why the first year's ploughing-up campaign in Scotland produced only an additional 183,000 acres instead of the 260,000 desired. There was, moreover, a loss of 31,000 acres in the total area under crops and grass.[8] But the disappointing results were largely offset by a favourable cropping season. May was a warm month and warmth continued throughout the summer. On the lighter lands some crops suffered a good deal from drought, but happily abundant rains fell before much damage was done. When in August our airmen were fighting the Battle of Britain in the clearest of skies, harvesting had begun in Scotland under the most favourable conditions. The magnificent victory in the air was repeated in a minor degree in the harvest field. The actual acreage ploughed may have been rather disappointing but the aggregate production was most encouraging.

[7] Whetham, *British Farming*, p. 58.
[8] D.O.A.S., *Agricultural Statistics 1939-44, Scotland*, 1944, PT. I, pp. 8-9.

Thus grain production in Scotland was up on the year by 22 per cent., while the figures for potatoes and turnips were 17 and 13 per cent. respectively.[9]

National complacency during the first few months of war had been rudely disturbed by the disasters of April, May and June 1940. Germany had occupied Denmark and Norway, her aeroplanes had destroyed the commercial part of Rotterdam and her soldiers had advanced across the plains of the Low Countries. At Dunkirk the bulk of our army had escaped capture but all equipment had been lost; France had capitulated; Italy had entered the war against us and the Mediterranean was virtually closed. We stood alone.

If, however, our material losses were great, compensating influences were at hand. A new Coalition Government had been formed with Winston Churchill as its courageous and inspiring leader, and in memorable phrase he roused the nation to action. Agriculture was assuming a new significance. With the harbours of southern Ireland denied us for naval operations, with German submarines operating from Atlantic bases, with many ports closed, with longer and slower voyages for food ships, with heavier demands on shipping by the Services and an expectation of serious tonnage losses through U-boat activities, it was clear that the nation would have to become as nearly self-sufficient as possible in food and feeding-stuffs.

On 2nd June 1940 the Government broadcast its agricultural policy. Prices and markets were to be guaranteed and price-fixing would be on the basis of the costs of production. Minimum rates of wages were announced, on a scale designed largely to reduce the gap between industry and agriculture. Sacrifices would have to be made in certain classes of stock. These pronouncements enabled the farmer to plan for long-term production, for he knew what he would get in future years for his beef, mutton, milk and potatoes, while grain prices were also assured. Bold the policy certainly was, but it matched the needs of the hour and had a most heartening effect. All connected with the land were resolved to give of their best.

Later in June the Government's detailed programme for Scottish agriculture was announced. An additional 260,000 acres of tillage was required for the crop year 1941. To facilitate this the numbers of low-ground sheep would have to be reduced and, generally speaking, the numbers of all stock would have to be adjusted to the

[9] Marshall, " Agric. during the war ", p. 61.

needs of the national food policy. It was hoped that this early announcement would give farmers ample time to make stock adjustments. It was also suggested that the reductions in larger stock numbers should take place in the following order: firstly, low-ground flocks of commercial breeding ewes; secondly, commercial cattle; and thirdly, pedigree cattle and sheep; dairy cattle were left to the last.[10] To ensure that members of agricultural executive committees adopted uniform principles in securing the right proportion of tillage land from the various types and grades of farms, the Department of Agriculture put forward a number of proposals. On farms on the six-course rotation (three years' crop followed by three years' grass) it was suggested that one-half of what would have been the third year's grass should be cropped in 1941. It was intended that by another year, on farms adhering to this rotation, the pasture would be broken up at the end of its second full season in grass. Proportionate increases would be asked in other cases according to the rotation observed, the inherent fertility of the farm and the class of stock kept. On dairy farms the tillage percentage required would be less than on stock-raising or fattening farms. But so far as practicable the cultivation requirements of all farms would be assessed on a percentage basis according to their categories. Should the war continue beyond 1942 it was hoped that the tillage acreage would become stabilised. It was expected that by that year the 1918 figure for crops would be attained despite the loss in the interval of 300,000 acres to agriculture. These expectations were practically realised, the 1942 tillage acreage, 2,098,000, being short of the 1918 figure by only 2000 acres.[11] Beyond this it was felt that only slight tillage increases could be justified. On most farms the aim would be to maintain the crop acreage rather than increase it. In 1943 the peak figure of 2,121,000 acres of crop was reached. The 1944 figure showed a slight drop but by 1945, when there was an appreciable fall, it had gone down to 2,011,000 acres.

Throughout these years the wheat, rye, sugar beet and potato acreages were being carefully watched. On an acreage basis these crops contribute most to the supply of human food and to ensure a sufficient acreage the Government resorted to the old expedient of the carrot and the stick. The carrot was a special acreage payment for wheat, rye and potatoes, while the stick was a compulsory

---

[10] D.O.A.S., *Revised Memorandum for Increased Cultivation*, 1940.
[11] D.O.A.S., *Agricultural Statistics, 1939-44, Scotland*, PT. I, p. 9.

cropping notice. The Government also allocated through the Agricultural Executive Committees quotas for acreages of sugar beet and potatoes to individual farms according to their suitability for these crops. The result was markedly successful. Directions to grow these crops were loyally, if not always willingly, observed, especially in the case of sugar beet. The potato acreage rose until in 1943 and 1944 it was up by over 70 per cent., while sugar beet went up by nearly 60 per cent. over pre-war figures. Potatoes were so plentiful that, although consumption per head increased by two-thirds, potato rationing was not required during the war years. The measures noted led to some surprising results. Many Scottish farmers, growing potatoes for sale for the first time, found that their farms were particularly suitable for growing seed potatoes, and continued to grow them after the war. Much the same happened in the case of sugar beet. Many farmers new to the crop found that it responded well to good management, and that as well as being a profitable cash crop it supplied much of the stock feed generally provided by turnips, the crop it usually displaced. After the war, when voluntary cropping had been resumed, the aggregate acreage of sugar beet was considerably higher than in pre-war days.

The accomplishment of this task in spite of shortages of implements and manpower provides an interesting story. In essence it is one of the notable parts played by farmer and farm worker alike in rising to a memorable occasion. " Give us the tools and we will finish the job," was the appeal of the Prime Minister to the United States at a critical period ; in this same spirit the task of growing a vastly increased amount of food was tackled by farmers.

In the 1914-18 war over one-third of the agricultural workers joined the Forces and, but for a notable influx of country-bred young men to agriculture at that time, the effect on cropping might have been disastrous. What happened then was that for every two men who left to join the Forces, the place of at least one was taken by a younger man trained to agricultural work. But it was not until the fourth year of the war that the tillage acreage was greatly expanded, and although the labour situation was then acute, the critical period was comparatively short. When the Second World War broke out the agricultural situation was different. Families in the country were smaller, there was no surplus of young men entering the industry, and increased food production was required at once instead of three years after the outbreak of war. Furthermore the possibility of farm workers leaving the land to earn higher wages in war industries had to be faced. The labour situation had therefore to be most carefully examined and action had to be prompt. On many farms key men had gone when the Territorial Army was mobilised. Some farms, particularly in the Orkneys, were left without any men at all. It was essential, therefore, that all men in key managerial positions should be released and immediate steps to this end were taken. It was also realised that the war might be prolonged and that, relatively speaking, many more demands would be made on agriculture over possibly a longer period than in 1914-18. So from the outset the question of farm labour received high priority. A low age of reservation was fixed and a generous policy of deferment was adopted in calling up men. In June 1940 an order, The Undertakings (Restriction on Engagement) Order, was passed to prevent workers, attracted by higher earnings, from leaving the industry. No employer could engage an agricultural worker except for similar work.[12]

The corollary to this and to the promise of guaranteed prices was to bring agricultural wages as far as possible into line with those paid in other industries. The procedure adopted in Scotland differed somewhat from that in England. In both countries it was agreed that Wages Boards should, to begin with, fix 48s. a week as the minimum rate for a male worker of twenty or more and that other rates should be regulated on that basis. By such measures most of the regular farm workers were retained on farms; only 2200 male workers were lost to Scottish agriculture between 1939 and 1940. After 1940 total numbers rose slightly but remained very much on the 1939 level until the end of the war. The Restriction of Engagement Order of 1940 was followed in 1941 by the Essential Work (Agriculture) (Scotland) Order, which prevented workers or employers terminating engagements without the consent of the National Service Officer, cases of misconduct being excepted.[13] The effect of this Order was salutary for it was a step towards bringing to an end an unhappy feature of Scottish country life—workers leaving their employment after six or twelve months to work at another farm. This practice had unsettled farmers and workers alike for in an emergency some farms might be left without workers. One large isolated farm in the north of Scotland had lost nearly all its workers by 1940. Another result of the order was that workers asked for a general revision of wage rates on the ground that they

[12] D.O.A.S., *Agriculture in Scotland 1939-48*, pp. 13-14.
[13] *op. cit.*, p. 19.

were no longer free to sell their labour to the highest bidder. The Scottish Agricultural Wages Board decreed that a 60s. minimum per week was to be paid from January 1942. With later revisions the weekly minimum for male workers reached 90s. by October 1947.

While the number of regular male farm workers remained at much the same level throughout the war, the number of regularly employed women and girls rose significantly. In 1939 their numbers were 14,379; by 1940 they had fallen to 13,612, but they then rose to the peak figure of 27,261 in 1943. This increase was mainly due to the establishment of the Women's Land Army. This body was founded just before the outbreak of war, but did not at first attract many members. Outdoor work on farms involved heavy physical labour and sometimes much discomfort, while the available accommodation was often poor. Recruits at first were slow to come forward but, in due time, as farmers realised that a woman might do certain jobs even better than a man, and as wages and conditions of employment improved, the numbers grew correspondingly. In January 1940 little more than 100 members were in regular employment but in August 1943 a peak enrolment figure of 10,388 was reached. The wastage was always high but the force rendered valuable aid to farmers at a time when the need was very great.[14]

Early in the war the need for organised teams of workers to provide supplementary casual labour became apparent. Grain and potatoes called for special consideration for both crops had to be harvested within the relatively short period of good autumn weather, while picking time for soft fruit crops was limited. Casual labour was made available from many sources, from schools, colleges, universities, offices, factories, etc. Roadmen were released to assist at harvest; soldiers were given leave to work on farms—in fact, every available source was tapped. In the latter stages of the war prisoners-of-war rendered valuable aid, while much maintenance work, such as draining or ditching, was done by Irishmen working individually or in gangs. But this additional labour would have proved inadequate but for the farm tractor. Between 1919 and 1938 the number of horses used for agricultural purposes had fallen from 136,000 to 105,000. The horse is a slow-breeding animal, and its numbers could not have been expanded in time to provide for wartime needs. The horse, too, can work only a restricted number of hours per day, and its pulling powers are limited. Tractors, on

---

[14] D.O.A.S., *Agriculture in Scotland 1939-48*, pp. 15-16.

the other hand, could be greatly augmented in number by imports and could perform very much more work. Although they ran on imported oil they saved stock feed, and the replacement of horses by tractors enabled larger numbers of other farm animals to be kept. Furthermore, their extra power, speed and tirelessness were invaluable in allowing farmers to cultivate their land more thoroughly and to sow and harvest their crops under the best conditions possible. The number of privately owned tractors in Scotland rose from 6,250 in 1939 to 19,000 in 1945. In addition, a fleet of Government-owned tractors, complete with appropriate cultivating and harvesting implements, was employed and in each of the two years 1942-43 nearly 120,000 acres were ploughed and about 120,000 acres of grain harvested by this service.[15]

The Government's broadcast of 2nd June 1940 mentioned the increasing scarcity of feeding-stuffs. Up to the outbreak of war imported stock feed had been plentiful and cheap, so cheap in fact that it was often more economical for many dairy, pig and poultry farmers to buy imported concentrates than to grow them. Considerable stocks had been accumulated, and for the first two months of the war there was no serious shortage. But before the end of 1939 farmers found difficulty in obtaining concentrates for feeding to animals. The obvious remedy was to introduce a livestock rationing scheme designed to give priority to the class of animals producing those foods which were considered to be most important in maintaining the health and vigour of the nation in time of war. Since milk was the most important food the dairy cow received first priority. Pig and poultry keepers were told that supplies of feed would be drastically cut, partly to meet the needs of the dairy cow, and partly to allow a larger proportion of the wheat berry to go into the loaf. Certain supplies would be available for pregnant and young animals, but none would be released for fattening cattle. Cases of hardship would be met by the issue of supplementary rations.

On 1st February 1941, following the report of the committee appointed to examine this issue, an Animal Rationing Scheme was brought into being. The Ministry of Food now controlled all rationed feeding-stuffs. In Scotland animal rationing was operated directly by the Department of Agriculture for Scotland, but the Agricultural Executive Committees were asked to consider and recommend on individual applications for supplementary rations.

[15] D.O.A.S., *Agriculture in Scotland 1939-48*, p. 23.

From the outset the scheme was a marked success.  Without penalis-
ing producers unduly, it stimulated farmers to rely more and more
on their own resources.  Specialised pig and poultry farmers, as
was anticipated, were the worst sufferers.  Even the meagre allowance of one-third on the basis of their pre-war numbers had at a
later date to be reduced.  But since most Scottish farms keeping
pigs and poultry were of a general character the overall effect of the
rationing scheme on the numbers kept was less than expected.  The
pig population fell from 252,000 in 1939 to 168,000 in 1944—the
lowest level—poultry from 7,711,000 in 1939 to 6,178,000 in 1943.[16]
These figures relate, however, only to holdings of one acre or more,
and therefore do not disclose reductions in the numbers of cottagers'
poultry or pigs.  The results were surprising considering the drastic
reduction of imports of feeding-stuffs, the pre-war United Kingdom
figure of $8\frac{3}{4}$ million tons of imports falling to $1\frac{3}{4}$ million.

The fertiliser position at the outbreak of war was most satisfactory but, following the experience of the 1914-18 war, it was
expected that supplies of potash manures might be greatly reduced.
Accumulated stocks of potash were, however, so abundant that there
was no shortage during the first year.  But with the German occupation of France and Belgium in 1940 and the cutting off of continental
supplies steps were taken to limit its use.  Maximum allocations
per acre were allowed for potatoes, flax, sugar beet and some
vegetable crops.  Other crops were not allowed potash unless the
soil showed, on analysis, marked deficiency in this mineral.  Despite
the cutting off of supplies from North Africa the phosphate position
remained fairly satisfactory until 1941.  Supplies of sulphate of
ammonia, being home-produced, were adequate except for a short
period between 1943 and 1944.[17]  The increased tillage area, the
greater demands made on the soil by intensive cropping, enhanced
profits from the application of higher rates of fertiliser per acre and
the persuasive efforts of committee members and officials, led to a
rapid rise in the use of artificial fertilisers, and this stretched the
resources of manufacturers who had to process, store and despatch
them.  Farmers were therefore encouraged to take early delivery and
distribution was accomplished without serious hitch.  In only a
few cases when timeous delivery could not be arranged had the crops
to be grown without fertilisers.

Lime was a different story.  Nearly all Scottish soils are by

---

[16] D.O.A.S., *Agricultural Statistics 1939-44, Scotland*, PT. I, p. 11.
[17] D.O.S·A., *Agriculture in Scotland 1939-48*, pp. 33-4.

PLATE II

Sowing the seed by hand: both hands are used

nature very acid. They had originally been reclaimed or improved by high applications of lime in the eighteenth and nineteenth centuries. But the practice of liming land had largely fallen into disuse before 1900, with the result that the reserves had fallen seriously through leaching and removal by crops and animals. The dire need for lime was to a large extent obscured by the fact that crops like oats, potatoes, turnips and even the all-important wild white clover plant in pastures, were fairly tolerant of acid conditions. Indeed, the effect of applying lime to oats on soils not too acid had on occasion appeared to depress yields. Symptoms of lime shortage in soils were therefore not always apparent. Soil sampling in the thirties disclosed, however, that most Scottish soils were in need of lime, and this led to a revival in liming, a movement encouraged by the Land Fertility Scheme of 1937 which provided a substantial subsidy for lime. At the outbreak of war farmers had become markedly lime-conscious, a feeeling subsequently strengthened by the fact that much of the poorer land brought into tillage was found to be seriously lacking in lime. Lime deficiency, too, was the main reason why committees classified farms as only moderately well or badly managed. To ensure higher productivity was now a national responsibility and the experienced and able members of the committees, aided by technically qualified officers, could often associate low production with lime deficiency. Furthermore, now that farming was prosperous many farmers limed their farms, lack of ready cash having previously been a serious deterrent. The demand for lime rose spectacularly and total deliveries, calculated on a Ca O content basis, increased from 147,000 tons in 1939-40 to 339,000 tons in 1943-44.[18] To meet the growing demand new lime works were opened and improved means of distribution were devised, but even so the demands were never fully met and at the end of the war much of Scotland's soil was still lime-hungry. Further difficulties were occasioned in the early spring months through lack of transport, a factor which often deterred Agricultural Executive Committees from giving directions as to the use of lime.

The Agricultural Executive Committees undertook the task of advising on the distribution of supplies of machinery, implements, building and fencing materials, binder twine, etc. to ensure their use to maximum advantage. So many implement makers were engaged on armaments production that large numbers of tractors, combine harvesters, and other agricultural machinery had to be

[18] Marshall, " Agric. during the war ", p. 77.

imported ; this was arranged through the Ministry of Agriculture and Fisheries, facilities being made available under Lend-Lease. Labour and machinery, fertilisers, lime and drainage were the farmers' tools to enable the soil to yield its increase and to ensure that, with the help of such food as could be imported, the nation would be fed. The weather was always an unpredictable factor, but much was achieved by intelligent planning, by the use of adequate machinery, and by having an ample supply of labour available when weather conditions were favourable. Then there was the question of incentive, another important factor. The Government provided price incentive but this alone was not enough—there had to be a moral incentive as well. Dunkirk provided that spur, for after that event the nation was keyed to give of its best.

What of the achievement ? The fourth year of the war saw the Scottish tillage figures stepped up by 639,000 acres. But acreage increase is not the sole criterion of output: production per acre is also extremely important. Throughout the war, crop yields per acre were not merely maintained but in most instances were increased. Since it was mainly poorer land that had been restored to cultivation this result was rather surprising. The weather—the war years being good cropping years—and the higher level of manuring practised, had much to do with it. Total output figures for the various crops, as estimated by the Department of Agriculture for Scotland, disclosed very satisfactory returns. Compared with 1939, wheat and barley production in 1943 had been more than doubled, oats had been increased by about two-fifths, potatoes were up by about 70 per cent. and sugar beet production had been nearly doubled.[19] In Kincardineshire, of the total area under crops and grass, 96 per cent. came under the plough, the highest county percentage in the United Kingdom. Milk production suffered inevitably from the drastic reduction in feeding-stuffs. In the winter of 1941-42, when the full effect of this reduction was first recorded, production went down by over 12 per cent. but thereafter it rose and by 1943-44 was ahead of the 1939-40 figure. This recovery was most gratifying in showing that farmers had become more self-sufficient in home-grown feeding-stuffs and in getting rid of their poorer yielding cows. Some beef farms, which had switched over to dairying, also helped milk production. The production of poultry meat and eggs was considerably down but this was only to be expected. With the low-ground ewe having to give way to the plough there was

[19] Marshall, " Agric. during the war ", p. 61.

in the aggregate a 15 per cent. reduction in the number of sheep, and beef cattle numbers were slightly down. Pig numbers had dropped considerably and the gross output of fat cattle had dropped appreciably. Instead of fattening cattle with the aid of concentrates at the age of slightly over two years farmers now retained home-bred animals on the farm for another six to twelve months. Furthermore, whereas in arable cropping areas Irish bullocks were formerly quickly fattened on liberal rations of cake, turnips and straw, now only well-grown heavy animals were bought since only animals with sufficient flesh and maturity could be turned out reasonably fat after six or seven months' winter keep on home-grown foods alone. Farms which had previously fattened at least two lots of Irish cattle during the winter period often found difficulty in fattening even one lot.

The Government's policy in determining prices for farm produce was to fix them at levels which would just reimburse farmers with reasonably fertile cropping land. As a corollary it seemed equitable that farmers with land unlikely to give a sufficient return for their outlay should be subsidised to encourage them in the interests of increasing production, to break it up and continue cropping it. When considering this matter the Government had in mind the effects of the wheat, rye and potato subsidies and of the ploughing-up grant on the poorer classes of land. On such land the crop subsidies provided little or no benefit; wheat could not be successfully grown; most farmers did not choose to grow rye, while the potatoes normally grown were intended only for the farmer's own household. The ploughing-up grant had, however, a different effect. It induced farmers to break up poor grassland but did not encourage them to continue cropping it, or to put it through a full rotation to get it properly cleaned and into the best condition to receive a grass seed mixture. In such circumstances farmers could not be expected to continue cropping at a loss and there was a risk that the land would be sown back to grass while the soil remained relatively unimproved.

In 1942 the Secretary of State for Scotland announced special measures for marginal land farmers. Assistance up to 50 per cent. of the costs of such operations as cultivation, seeding, manuring, etc. were foreshadowed, but it was not until the spring of 1943 that the Marginal Production Scheme could be publicised, and it was then too late in the season to induce the breaking-up of fresh land for cultivation. The scheme had a considerable effect in maintaining marginal land cultivation and in raising its output. The task of administration was entrusted to the Agricultural Executive Committees, the general principle being to grade marginal land farms in each area into varying categories of marginality. A particular grant percentage based on approved expenditure incurred on artificial fertilisers and other items was applied to each category. While the expenditure on fertilisers served generally to determine the amount of grant, some committees allowed expenditure on the purchase of seed oats, grass seed mixtures, vaccines and sera to rank for grant. Carefully drawn up directions had to be complied with before grants were paid. Marginal land farmers were obliged in most instances, in order to qualify for assistance, to fertilise their land more generously than they usually did. The operation of the scheme disclosed many potentialities in marginal land. Cereal crops, as a result of more artificials being applied, ripened earlier and yielded better. Even in districts where the land was too high above sea level to justify cropping, the scheme was effective in inducing farmers to reseed old pastures. Where these measures were linked with the keeping of a balanced stock of sheep and cattle, and where care was exercised in pasture management, excellent results usually followed. The M.A.P. Scheme, as it was called, was thus most fruitful in disclosing the latent possibilities of Scottish agriculture in the poorer areas.

The principle of selective subsidies was also applied to some livestock enterprises. The production of fat cattle and sheep ranked amongst the lowest priorities of wartime farming. Prices for these commodities were accordingly fixed at relatively lower levels than those ruling for cereals, potatoes, sugar beet and milk. So low were they for mutton that, while keeping sheep on low ground yielded little profit to the farmer, keeping them on the less productive hills meant certain loss. Hill sheep, like hill cattle, were, however, very important for food production. Along with cattle they were able to convert the rough vegetation of hill lands into useful products. It was on the hills that many of the store sheep and cattle required by the low ground farmers for breeding or fattening were reared and so, under conditions when food production was a major objective, adequate stocking of the hill lands was imperative. But no hill sheep farmer could be expected to run his enterprise at a loss and for many years before the war hill sheep farming had been depressed. Low prices for sheep and wool, coupled with the ever-increasing costs of, and difficulty in obtaining grass wintering, since more low ground farmers were themselves keeping sheep, had made the hill farming industry largely unremunerative. There were instances of landlords being unable to let hill sheep farms, and as they could not be run except at a loss the landlords were obliged to dispose of the sheep. In consequence such farms were left ungrazed. The war worsened the position. The ploughing-up campaign reduced the area available for the grass wintering of younger sheep. Prices of labour and wintering went up without any commensurate rise in the price of sheep. Moreover, the demand for hill sheep was affected by stock adjustments on low ground farms to release more grassland for cropping. Thus the farmer accustomed to buy cast ewes off the hill to cross with Border Leicester rams either no longer required them, or did not need so many. Many low ground flocks were also being disposed of and thus markets for store sheep became depressed as supplies exceeded demand. It was obvious that if the hill sheep industry was to survive or, as was hoped, to expand, special assistance would be required. On 12th December 1940 the Government announced a subsidy for hill ewes in regular age groups. No subsidy was to be paid for lowland flocks, whether or not they belonged to mountain breeds. This subsidy was paid during the war and the immediate post-war years, the rates of payment varying annually according to the ascertained profitability of hill sheep farming for the year under review. For the year 1941, the first year of the hill sheep subsidy, the rate was 2s. 6d. a head on the ewe population; in 1942 it was 7s. 6d., in 1943 8s., in 1944 6s., and in 1945 7s. 6d. a head. Scotland's claim was for about 2¼ million female sheep and in 1943 the total amount paid in subsidy was £916,844.[20]

On the recommendation of the Scottish Agricultural Advisory Council another scheme—the Hill Cattle Subsidy Scheme—was introduced in May 1941. Its object was to increase the productivity and fertility of hill grazings by keeping cattle on them. At first the scheme was intended, like the Hill Sheep Subsidy, to be a Hill-Cattle Subsidy and not a Cattle-on-the-Hill subsidy. A grant of £2 per head was paid for every cow kept on hill grazings, but in later years the scheme was widened to include bullocks and heifers, while animals kept on upland farms also became eligible for subsidy. This widening of the scheme had the effect of releasing more low ground pastures for cropping. After the war the scheme reverted to its original purpose.

[20] D.O.A.S., *Agriculture in Scotland 1939-48*, p. 37.

R

Early in the war the question of the full utilisation of deer forests for food production was considered. While these forests contributed a certain amount of food to the national larder, the amount was small in relation to the potential of the land when fully grazed by cattle or sheep. Agricultural Executive Committees were accordingly instructed to take all possible steps towards stocking deer forests with cattle or sheep. If the owners were unwilling to comply the Committees were empowered to recommend the Secretary of State to take possession of the forests with a view to stocking them. In most cases the owners acquiesced but there were some exceptions. The June 1944 agricultural returns showed that the numbers of sheep grazed on the forests had risen only by 98,000, a figure seemingly small in relation to the three-quarters of a million sheep displaced earlier to make room for deer. But allowance has to made for restocking difficulties. Often enough there were no houses to accommodate shepherds and no buchts, pens, dippers, wool sheds, parks or fences. Moreover, fresh sheep driven on to strange ground were apt to wander and get lost or to perish from diseases to which they had not been immunised; "black loss," the term employed when sheep are permanently lost without trace, for instance, was always high when a forest was being restocked. Foxes were blamed for taking lambs; deer were always liable to trespass on to the inbye land, while on many forests muirburn and draining had been grossly neglected.

No account of the food production campaign would be complete without mention of the important part played by allotment holders. When war broke out there were 25,503 allotments in Scotland; four years later the number had risen to 83,746.[21] Most allotment holders, regarding their plots as part of their war effort, did their utmost to make them highly productive, and found in them a new source of pleasure when their evening's toil was so handsomely rewarded; it was equally gratifying for the housewife to be able to cook and eat vegetables fresh from the family allotment. After the war many allotments continued in being although, as was to be expected, the number fell substantially. As pointed out elsewhere it was estimated that 141,000 tons of potatoes were produced in Scottish allotments during the war years.

In a variety of ways the Second World War was a stimulus to Scottish agriculture. Never before had our farmers been called upon to make such immense efforts and in the result possibilities

[21] D.O.A.S., *Agriculture in Scotland 1939-48*, p. 10.

hitherto undreamt of were realised. Considerable areas of derelict, wet and acid lands were made productive while land long noted for the poverty of its crops became fertile. On the formerly rush-infested pastures of Ayrshire the rush disappeared; on the "riggin" of Fife, the "beggar's mantle" of James VI, good crops of grain replaced worthless pastures; in Aberdeenshire the Loch of Auchlossan was reclaimed, while elsewhere serviceable arterial drainage schemes were carried out. The introduction of new prolific varieties of barley, coupled with heavier manurial dressings and the revived practice of liming, enabled land formerly yielding five quarters to return as many as nine. In a motor journey through the fertile lands of Strathmore or East Lothian nothing but first-class crops were to be seen. "After what I have seen today," remarked an eminent statesman to the writer as he returned from a visit to East Lothian, "I cannot bring myself to believe that this country will ever starve".

American visitors fresh to Scotland were puzzled one November day in 1943 by the tall round cone-topped erections—the grain stacks—that ran lengthwise along the sides of some Fife stubble fields. They could hardly believe that the stacks were produced from the fields they were seeing. To them it was incredible that land could be made to yield such large crops. Features of this kind gave practical expression to the response of farmers and their workers to a vital challenge. The number of evictions and dispossessions were relatively small : only 73 tenancies were terminated under Defence Regulation 62, while the number of farms in the Department's possession was 85. Mistakes were inevitable but surprisingly few occurred. Thus reseeding wet land often resulted in overwhelming infestation of the land with rushes. In most cases of bad farming, however, the land was nursed back to fertility under the sympathetic guidance of the committees and their technical officers. The rehabilitation of poor farms opened the eyes of many to the potentialities of Scottish agriculture.

The end of the war in 1945 saw the industry sound and prosperous. True, in marginal areas the evil effects of the long years of depression, consequent on the nation's neglect of agriculture, were still all too manifest in dilapidated buildings, dykes and fences and inferior pastures, but elsewhere signs of prosperity were evident in the abundance of clean crops and the well-stocked pastures. On the hills herds of cattle, grazing alongside sheep, suggested that, if the wintering problem could be solved, the output of hill lands could be still further increased. Over Scotland as a whole the net agricultural output had increased by over a quarter.

The impact of the war had changed the attitude of the nation towards agriculture. It was felt that in the future the industry could, and must, play a much more important part in the State's welfare, but to do so agriculture must be wisely directed and adequately supported. Continued positive action was called for; this might take the form of some sort of control but it would certainly have to provide the farming community with confidence in the future, for only then would farmers be prepared to undertake programmes of work which, backed by science, would more fully reveal the hidden resources of the land.

# CHAPTER XVI

# POST-WAR PRODUCTION : 1946-1954

Need to continue the food production campaign...Planning
post-war policy...New legislation...Difficulties of transition
period...Hill Farming Act...Agriculture Act, 1947...The expansion programme...Agriculture (Scotland) Act, 1948...
New Committees established...Labour problems...Prices
and wages...Land utilisation...Marketing boards...Progress
report.

IF THE END OF THE WAR brought general relief to the people of
Britain it did little to ease the food situation. While the fear
that the U-boat campaign might starve us into submission no
longer existed, not every farmer was convinced of the need to maintain production at its highest level. Many were disposed to think
that after their supreme efforts both they and the land needed a
rest, and there was something to be said for this viewpoint. But
the need for more food was acute; a hungry Europe had to be fed;
much land had been devastated and draught animals and milking
cows had been taken from the occupied countries. Almost everywhere in Europe there was a shortage of foods and feeding-stuffs,
of seeds, fertilisers and implements, of machinery and manpower.
In the summer of 1945 much of its land was left uncropped and its
wheat production that year barely reached half the pre-war level.[1]
Beyond Europe there was Asia whose food problems could only be
vaguely conjectured. All that was known was that its huge population
had increased vastly during the six years of war and that many of
its people had for long suffered from malnutrition and undernutrition.

There were other aggravating circumstances. Britain, so long
a creditor, was now a debtor nation. When the war ended so would
the sheltering effects of Lend-Lease. But even had there been the
money to buy food from abroad to anything like the same extent
as in pre-war days, the food for purchase simply was not available
in sufficient quantity. The home food requirements of former

[1] Whetham, *British Farming*, p. 138.

exporting countries had grown. America in particular had increased her livestock, which meant that the supply of saleable feeding-stuffs for the world at large had been much reduced. Many of these difficulties had been foreseen, for as early as 1942 much thought had been given to post-war agriculture.[2] Different bodies had examined the matter and had agreed that after the war agriculture could not be abandoned, as in 1921, and that in the national interest it would need support by guaranteed markets and prices. Some measure of control over the use of land had also been decided upon. There was a growing feeling, too, that more land should be devoted to crops than in pre-war days, and that more intensive use should be made of grasslands, to release more land for cropping.

Another item of common agreement was that farmers should be supplied with, and encouraged to take fuller advantage of, knowledge gained from scientific research in agriculture. The war had shown how production from much of the land could be greatly increased by the application of such knowledge. When limed and properly fertilised, the poorer classes of land had often doubled their yields. Notable discoveries had been made by research workers regarding more prolific varieties of cereals and more effective fungicides, insecticides and herbicides. Many an otherwise skilful farmer unaccustomed to growing sugar beet before the outbreak of war had been able to increase his initial yields of that crop by two or three tons per acre through following the advice of a factory fieldsman or a technical adviser from the agricultural colleges. In milk production the seemingly impossible had happened. By 1944-45, despite a drastic reduction in imported feeding-stuffs, more milk was being produced than in pre-war days.[3] The rationing of dairy cows was now better understood, the practice of milk recording had spread, " passenger " cows had been replaced by higher yielding animals and artificial insemination had been proved to be practicable. In the technique of grassland management and grass conservation great developments were foreshadowed. But to ensure the projection of these developments into future practice, fresh legislation to inspire confidence would be necessary and, pending this, it was considered desirable to maintain in being the Agricultural Executive Committees.

The Labour Government which took office in July 1945 did little to change the policy of the wartime coalition. There was

[2] Whetham, *British Farming*, p. 134.
[3] D.O.A.S., *Agriculture in Scotland 1939-48*, p. 10.

some slight relaxation in cropping and the planned revival of live-stock, which was part of the policy of Mr Churchill's Government, was continued. Efforts were made to keep sugar beet and potato acreages at high levels but the wheat acreage had already dropped markedly, declining in Scotland from 152,000 in 1944 to 91,000 acres in 1945.[4] For the United Kingdom as a whole there was a fall of nearly one million acres and a still further decline was to take place in the following year. By 1946 it was evident that the world food situation was so grave that the shift of emphasis from crop to stock production could not be continued. Stocks of food and feeding-stuffs had sunk to perilously low levels and prolonged droughts in India and South Africa had caused these countries to buy extensively in world markets. Steps had to be taken to safe-guard the food needs of the people at home. Bread and flour were rationed,[5] the wheat extraction rate was raised first to 85 and then to 90 per cent.; poultry and pig rations went back to the lowest levels of the war years, and the ploughing-up subsidy of £2 per acre was extended to all grassland of three years of age and upwards ploughed up after 5th February 1946.[6] The winter of 1946-47 was the worst for many years. Vast numbers of hill sheep perished and the lamb crop on the hills was one of the poorest ever known. Sheep numbers fell by over 13 per cent. The farmers were so late in getting on to their land in the spring of 1947 that they were sometimes unable to carry out their full cropping programmes. The potato acreage was considerably reduced and the crop was so light—under six tons per acre—that in the spring of 1948 rationing had to be resorted to for, as it happened, the only season after the outbreak of war.

During these immediate post-war years the Government were faced with a difficult problem. The necessity for restricting purchases of meat, which came mainly from the dollar countries, emphasised the need to produce as much as possible at home, while the need for the highest possible acreage under cereals, potatoes and sugar beet was no less imperative.[7] In the period 1946-48 a number of Acts relating to agriculture were passed. The first of these, the Hill Farming Act 1946, gave effect to many of the recom-mendations of the English and the Scottish Committees appointed in 1942 to investigate the depressed state of hill farming. In

[4] D.O.A.S., *Agriculture in Scotland 1939-48*, p. 9.
[5] Whetham, *British Farming*, p. 139.
[6] D.O.A.S., *Agriculture in Scotland 1939-48*, p. 42.      [7] *ibid.*

Scotland great use was made of the provisions of this Act. Under its terms hill sheep farms, rehabilitated according to an ordered and approved programme, involving improvement of the fertility of the soil and permanent equipment of the farms and the adoption of measures designed to benefit the health and output of the stock, could qualify for aid amounting to half of the approved cost.[8] The period for which such assistance could be given was five years, but in 1951 the benefits were continued and extended to upland stock-rearing farms by the passing of the Livestock Rearing Act of that year. Scottish farmers were not slow to take advantage of the facilities offered.

Statutory effect was also given to the principle that the future of British agriculture should rest upon the twin foundations of stability and efficiency. Part I of the Agriculture Act 1947, which applied to the whole country, guaranteed prices and markets for the main agricultural products—fat stock, the four cereal crops, potatoes, sugar beet, milk and eggs. In order to fix prices the duty was laid upon the Ministers of Agriculture, Scotland being represented by its Secretary of State, to consult producers annually and review the general economic condition and prospects of the industry. In the 1920 Agriculture Act prices for the guaranteed commodities— wheat and oats—were to be fixed according to the costs of production, but the 1947 Act contained no such stipulation. Indeed there was nothing in the Act to preclude the Government from fixing the price of a guaranteed farm commodity at any level.[9] Furthermore, the price guarantee and the assured market applied only to the amount of production deemed to be in accordance with the national interest. In order to enable farmers to plan ahead it was stipulated that the guaranteed minimum prices for crops would be announced eighteen months and for stock products two to four years in advance. The complement to the stability thus provided was embodied, so far as Scotland is concerned, in the Agriculture (Scotland) Act 1948, which requires efficiency in land management and utilisation.[10] The landlord is obliged to equip his land for proper use; the fixed equipment, *e.g.* drainage, buildings, etc. must be in such a condition as not to impede full production. The efficient tenant, for his part, enjoys security of tenure for his lifetime.[11] All land, in fact, whether occupier-owned or not, must

---

[8] D.O.A.S., *Agriculture in Scotland 1939-48*, p. 64.
[9] Whetham, *British Farming*, pp. 143-4.
[10] D.O.A.S., *Agriculture in Scotland 1939-48*, pp. 44-5.
[11] So far as Scotland was concerned this security of tenure was heritable.

be put to efficient use, and land may be compulsorily acquired or managed where circumstances so warrant. To meet objections to the wartime practice of terminating a tenancy with no right of appeal, the Act appoints the Land Court as the appeal tribunal. Under this Act Area Agricultural Executive Committees were set up, Scotland being divided into eleven areas. Agricultural Advisory Committees were also established to advise on matters relating to technical education and development in agriculture.

On the outbreak of war the Pig and Potato Marketing Boards had been suspended while the Milk Marketing Boards had been allowed to carry on as wholesale distributive agents of the Ministry of Food. The purpose of these Boards when set up was virtually to obtain higher prices for farmers. This they achieved by various means but by 1939 they had been subjected to criticism because they were alleged to be too monopolistic.[12] To prevent gluts the Potato Marketing Board had power to restrict supplies and although there was no cause to suspect the justice of its operation it could, if it desired, make consumers pay more than might be considered a fair price. The Milk Marketing Boards had power to fix the retail price of milk. The question arose, therefore, whether, when the Ministry of Food ceased to control the sale and distribution of food, the powers of the Boards should be modified. A committee under the chairmanship of Lord Lucas was set up in 1946 to investigate, in the light of the passing of the 1947 Agriculture Act, the pre-war workings of the Boards with monopoly rights over the marketing of produce. It suggested that Commodity Commissions responsible to the taxpayer should be given the task of supervising the marketing of agricultural products from the time they left the marketing boards until they reached the retailer. The Labour Government, committed to the nationalisation of the more important industries and the establishment of Boards to market coal, gas, etc., did not accept these findings. Instead, they passed the 1949 Marketing Act which considerably modified the powers of the Boards and empowered the Minister of Agriculture to issue directions as to their policy and appoint consumer representatives. In 1950 a Wool Marketing Board was set up and wool was included as one of the farm commodities eligible under statute for a guaranteed price.[13]

In August 1947 farmers were asked, in the interests of national economy, to expand their output, particularly their livestock

---

[12] Whetham, *British Farming*, p. 18.
[13] *op. cit.*, pp. 152-4.

products,[14] within the period of a five-year programme which the Government outlined. It was hoped that net agricultural output would be increased by one-fifth above the level then current, or half as much again as in 1938-39. Attractive price levels for certain commodities would, it was hoped, stimulate farmers who were further encouraged by the offer of grants for calf-rearing, ploughing up grassland not less than three years old, and other activities helpful to agriculture. This policy did much to achieve the results desired. The numbers of livestock rose as did the amount of milk produced. By 1950 pigs and poultry were showing a welcome increase in numbers. Some crops by that year were well ahead of the target figure; others fell behind but the general result apart from the tillage acreages was not unsatisfactory.

These post-war demands on production had their impact on the labour situation. During the war the number of regular male employees had been stabilised at about 75,000 in Scotland, the extra manual work entailed by the food production campaign being largely undertaken, as has been shown, by the Women's Land Army, prisoners of war, Irish labour and organised labour groups of casual workers. But when the war ended much of this extra help was lost although some aid was afforded by European displaced persons. After the war the number of regular male workers remained at about the same level but despite several increases in the wages rate for farm workers the expected inflow from other industries did not materialise. Between 1940 and 1945 farm wages had nearly doubled and the working week had been reduced. In the post-war period other rises in wages were granted, but the gap between the wages of farm workers and other industrial workers remained. So long as the policy of relating fixed prices for farm commodities to costs of production remained, farmers did not resist the pressure for higher wages too strongly. Not only had they to retain their workers but it was in their interests to be on good terms with them; moreover under the price-fixing policy they expected to be compensated for any rise that took place. But the whole post-war period was one of inflation—wages, prices and the cost of living continued to rise. Production meantime was being stepped up largely by the extended use of labour-saving devices and by higher technical efficiency. Output per acre, per dairy cow, per hen, was gradually rising while marked progress was made in the elimination and control of such animal diseases as bovine tuberculosis, contagious

[14] D.O.A.S., *Agriculture in Scotland 1939-48*, p. 42.

abortion, mastitis, braxy, louping-ill and lamb dysentery; great advances had been made in grassland husbandry; and the greater control of potato virus diseases was reflected in appreciably heavier yields.[15] Combine harvesters helped to ease the harvest labour problem and enabled the farmers to reap more grain per acre, while the use of new herbicides by reducing the competition of annual weeds in cereal crops helped to raise average grain yields.

But some anxiety was felt about the ever-rising increase in farm prices and wages, and critics were ready to point out that farmers were getting too generous a deal. Prices for farm produce under the fixed price system were, they alleged, so high that the low-grade farmer was being generously rewarded. The good intentions underlying the Agriculture Act 1947 and the Agriculture (Scotland) Act 1948 in regard to efficient farming and land ownership were not, they asserted, working out in practice for only hopelessly inefficient farmers were being dispossessed. It must also be admitted that the security of tenure for which farmers had striven for seventy years was having some unfortunate repercussions. Farms with vacant possession were commanding double the price of those without that asset and relatively few desirable farms to rent were coming into the market. The result was that the young, enterprising farmer could not find a farm to let and few had the wherewithal to purchase one with possession. There was a feeling too that increased production was being achieved at too high a price, and when in 1953 world prices for a number of farm commodities sank to levels lower than the prices paid to British farmers the feeling became more pronounced.

During the war the right of the State to decide the use of land had not been questioned, and the Agricultural Executive Committees had been given powers to deal with the cultivation, management or use of agricultural land. In 1942 the Government's intention was stated to be " to secure the most appropriate development and use of the land" involving " the general promotion of rural development in the light of a positive policy for the maintenance of a healthy and well-balanced agriculture." [16] Accordingly an organisation was established in the Department of Agriculture to advise the Secretary of State on how best to safeguard, and if possible to develop agricultural interests when proposals were made by other Government departments to purchase land. In pre-war years and until 1945 the

---

[15] D.O.A.S., *Agriculture in Scotland 1951*, p. 11.
[16] D.O.A.S., *Agriculture in Scotland 1939-48*, p. 45.

agricultural industry and the Forestry Commission had sometimes been at variance concerning the use of land acquired for afforestation. Although the Department of Agriculture for Scotland had the right by statute to be consulted in this matter before purchase the Forestry Commission was not bound to accept the Department's views. Under the Forestry Act of 1945 the powers of the Commission to acquire land in Scotland were transferred to the Secretary of State and all lands previously held by the Forestry Commissioners became vested in him although still remaining at the disposal of the Commissioners. This step was designed to lead to a closer integration of the work of the two Departments.[17] In some respects there was considerable need for closer integration. Both the Commission and the Department were interested in the utilisation of hill land. When the Commission acquired such land, formerly used for grazing, it was concerned primarily with the planting of all suitable land below what might be termed the effective timber line, but if all the land were planted without preserving the downfalls, the pastures above the planting line would be sterilised. Moreover the primary concern of the Commission was not with the replanting of shelter belts or small woods, which provided invaluable shelter to farm land in exposed places, but with planting in large blocks. The cutting down of many shelter belts and small woods during the two wars was causing much anxiety to farmers, for little replanting had been done. It was hoped that closer co-operation between the two bodies would result in cut-over shelter belts and sheltering woods being replanted. The Department of Agriculture also advised other authorities concerning the use of land for house building, industrial sites, etc. Land used by the Service Departments for training and other purposes was the subject of useful discussions and by 1948 agreement had been reached regarding the use of some 57,000 acres, mainly rough grazings.

In January 1953 the Government announced its intention to remove the controls on all cereals and feeding-stuffs.[18] Controls for cereals would end with the 1953 harvest crop and feeding-stuffs would be derationed. This meant that the fixed prices for certain commodities would be withdrawn, that farmers would be free to sell their cereals to whom they chose and that, if the average prices were below the standard prices as determined under the 1947 Act, the promises in respect of deficiency payments would be honoured.

[17] D.O.A.S., *Agriculture in Scotland 1939-48*, p. 46.
[18] *Decontrol of Cereals and Feeding-stuffs*, Cmd. 8745, 1953.

The announcements suggested the approach to decontrol in other commodities, milk and meat. The future of the Potato, Pigs and Bacon Marketing Boards, which had been suspended at the beginning of the war, was not then disclosed, nor was there any announcement about the Milk Marketing Boards. It was realised, however, that agriculture would soon pass from a wartime emergency basis to a peacetime status. The announcement was received with mixed feelings by farmers. So accustomed had they become to control restrictions that, although they welcomed a greater measure of freedom, they were somewhat apprehensive concerning the future. But the ending of controls, the derationing of feeding-stuffs and the resumption of free marketing formed only part of the transition from wartime to peacetime conditions. Many wartime expedients to increase production were continued as, for instance, the grants for ploughing, fertilisers and marginal land, and the hill cattle and hill sheep subsidy schemes.

In the aggregate a great increase in agricultural output had been achieved. By 1957 the gain over the pre-war figure stood at about 60 per cent., and this with the employment of less labour and a marked reduction in imported feeding-stuffs. Considering the war and post-war difficulties farmers had to encounter—shortage of labour, lack of sufficient working capital to begin with, the neglected state of the fixed equipment of many farms, the inherent poverty of the soil on which much of the expansion in Scotland took place, and the drastic reduction in imported feeding-stuffs—the results were most gratifying. In no other period in the history of Scottish agriculture, not even during the agricultural revolution, had such great and sustained efforts produced so meritorious a result.

The history of farming is one of long periods of stagnation interspersed with periods of marked progress. Future historians may well record the 1939-45 war period and the post-war era as one of the greatest progress. In those years science had become increasingly linked with practice. Probably the outstanding feature was the advance in mechanisation, but in nearly every sphere of agricultural activity and enterprise striking advances had been made. Agriculture, long the Cinderella of British industries, had assumed an importance which no government could ignore. Our farm lands, the nation's mainstay in war, were now under peace conditions playing their part in providing economic stability while a spirit of enthusiasm pervaded the men who were producing the food. Output was constantly rising and it was most desirable to maintain the upward trend.

Many problems awaited solution, such as those associated with winter keep, hill sheep farming, marginal land production, arterial and underground drainage, soil acidity, the better utilisation of grassland, particularly the poorer permanent pastures, bracken control and many stock diseases. The industry needed to be re-tooled and equipped with modern buildings, etc. The advances made during the years of stress and strain gave promise that some or all of these problems would in due time be solved. Unforeseen difficulties had attended the administration of the 1948 Agriculture Act and at the beginning of 1958 Parliament was discussing amending legislative measures. But to farmers who had seen the dawn of the century, had farmed through two World Wars, had endured the hardships of two depressions and who were now seeing their farms yielding a bountiful increase, the most interesting part of their careers had been the latter years. " I'm glad I've lived to see what has happened to farming," said one who had devoted much of his life to agricultural development in its many phases. He felt he had not lived in vain for his dreams had in large measure come true. A partnership of State and agriculture had been effected; the barrier between science and practice had been broken down; orderly methods of marketing had been adopted; the clouds of depression had been rolled away and although most farm prices were by 1957 on the down grade this decline was largely being offset by the increased technical efficiency of the farmer.

# CHAPTER XVII

# THE HIGHLANDS AND NORTHERN ISLANDS : 1745-1955

Emigration...Pre-disposing causes...Sheep come to the Highlands...Developments in sheep farming...Evictions in Sutherland, Skye and Inverness-shire mainland...Establishment of crofts on seashore...Cheviots introduced into Caithness...Sheep farming in Sutherland...Decline in productivity of Highland grazings...Effects of agricultural depression of eighties...Deer replace sheep...Impact of agricultural revolution on Highland tillage methods...Gradual abandonment of run-rig...Formation of crofts...Effect of introduction of the potato...Failure of crop in 1845-46...Renewal of clearances ...Dissatisfaction and riots...Napier Commission Report, 1884 ...Remedial measures...Developments in Orkney and Shetland.

THE COMMONLY ACCEPTED VIEW that the introduction of sheep farming in the early sixties of the eighteenth century was both the initial and the main cause of the great emigration movement from the Highlands is to some extent erroneous. Emigration on a considerable scale had taken place before the invasion of sheep and shepherds. It had begun even before 1745 and was at first encouraged by the proprietors. There were many causes for this movement. Scarcity of food and the possibility of famine were ever-present and potent factors in the Highlands. While the breaking-up of the clans and the abolition of heritable jurisdiction after the Forty-Five had put an end both to the lifting of cattle and to disorder, it had not removed the root causes of these evils. The more settled conditions which the Highlands enjoyed after the Forty-Five were conducive to an increase in population, which increased the difficulty of providing sufficient food for the people.

The harsh measures taken by the Government after the rebellion were greatly resented, and America came to be regarded as a land of opportunity. At home there was a marked deterioration in the relations between the chief and his clansmen. Many of the old chiefs were now in exile; many of those who remained became more land- and money-conscious, greedy and less scrupulous. Their detractors alleged that they were no longer patriarchs but had become

parasites. The old idea that the land belonged to the people, that
the chief was merely the chief of the clan, and not the owner of the
land, had gone. Now that there was a boom in store cattle, tenants
and tacksmen were asked to pay higher rents. Many of the older
race of tacksmen—men of good education who understood the
people—decided to emigrate and took hundreds with them.[1] Their
farms were let, either to the smaller tenants—thus establishing the
crofting system—or to tacksmen from other areas whose sole aim,
far too often, was to extract what they could before their leases
expired by rack-renting their subtenants. At a later stage the
tacksman's own holding often became the nucleus of the sheep farm
and was enlarged by displacing the subtenants. Sir John Sinclair
in his account of the agriculture of the northern counties, while
favouring the good tacksmen, readily admitted that there were
many bad ones and concluded that the system was on the whole
evil. Dr Johnson, who evidently had met only the good ones,
deplored their going. Many of them, he pointed out, were well
educated, and from birth had mixed with the people and were
familiar with their customs, ways of life and general outlook. They
therefore occupied a very important place in the social structure of
the Highlands.

So strongly, however, did the tide of emigration run that the
Government became alarmed. In the year 1773 a thousand people
left the mainland of Inverness-shire to go overseas, while between
1771 and 1790 two thousand are said to have emigrated from Skye.[2]
Gaelic-speaking communities were formed across the Atlantic.
Some of the negroes of North Carolina, where there were such
settlements, had learned to speak Gaelic. This much surprised some
of the later Highland immigrants who, on hearing them speak,
concluded that the warmer climate had caused some of the older
settlers from the Highlands to turn black !

But strongly as the tide of emigration may have run towards
the end of the century, sheep-farming provided the main impetus.
Its full effect was not felt all at once. It had first to be proved to
be worth while and before this could happen in many areas the
Napoleonic Wars had broken out, and the surplus manpower of
the Highlands was in demand to fight the Corsican tyrant and his
allies. In a period of some forty years from 1797, Skye is said to

---

[1] J. Cameron Lees, *A History of the County of Inverness—mainland*, henceforth cited as Lees, *County of Inverness*, Edinburgh 1897, pp. 248-9.

[2] Nicolson, *History of Skye*, p. 295.

have contributed to the army 21 generals, 45 colonels, 600 commissioned officers, and 10,000 other ranks.[3] The total population of the island during this period varied from about 16,000 to 20,000. Such an achievement was a testimony to the outstanding qualities of the Highlander as a soldier.

It was in 1762 that sheep-farming began in the Highlands. Farmers from Annandale came north to the counties of Perth and Dunbarton, bringing with them flocks of hardy, horned, blackfaced sheep of the Linton (Blackface) breed. On the wide moorlands of those counties they settled down to graze their sheep very much according to the methods used in the Southern Uplands. These methods differed radically from those of the clansmen who kept their few sheep for the sake of their wool, their droppings (which were valued as manure), their milk, which was made into cheese, and their mutton.

In the Highlands it had hitherto been customary, instead of allowing the limited numbers of sheep then kept to graze at will over the wide moorland spaces, to herd or tether them during the day, to keep them in folds at night and to house them in winter.[4] Up to the beginning of the eighteenth century wolves had roamed the wilder parts so that enclosure at night in wolf-proof houses had long been imperative. Furthermore, the need to keep both cattle and sheep near at hand for milking and folding had prevented their being grazed evenly over the vast expanse of hill. The numbers of stock kept—particularly cattle—were limited by the supply of winter food. Little or no hay was made and the reprehensible practice of holding the unthreshed stalks of grain in the fire, so that the grain might be the more easily separated from the stalks and ground into meal, resulted in much of the straw being scorched and burned. For these reasons Highland moorlands were by present-day standards inadequately stocked.

The sheep farmers from the south were agreeably surprised to find how well their flocks survived the Highland winter. Nature, even in relatively barren regions like the Highlands, has provided animals with a certain, if limited, amount of edible and digestible

---

[3] Nicolson, *History of Skye*, p. 410.

[4] According to John Ramsay (*Scotland and Scotsmen*, VOL. II, pp. 517-18), John Campbell, a Tyndrum innkeeper who had fallen on evil days and could ill afford to winter his sheep indoors, was responsible for the discovery that wintering on the Highland hills was possible for sheep. To his astonishment he found that at the end of the winter his sheep were in better condition than the indoor-wintered sheep of his neighbours.

S

food throughout the year. Heather is one example; its young, tender shoots provide food of sorts for sheep at all times of the year but particularly in time of snow, and it is in its complementary aspect as a food that heather is so valuable. Certain other plants such as drawmoss, disliked by animals in summer, may then build up stores of nourishment in their roots. This enables the plant to produce digestible and palatable leaves and stems in the early spring before most pasture plants have begun to grow.

Sheep, because of their close grazing habits, their ability to forage on snow-covered land, their relative mobility in negotiating flow lands and the protection they get from their wool, are much better adapted to withstand the storms and privations of a Highland winter than cattle. Cattle, for the most part, cannot exist without hand feeding whereas adult sheep survive an ordinary winter without it. They can thus be scattered throughout the grazing instead of being confined to portions adjacent to the houses. These considerations seemed to suggest that much fuller use could be made of the Highland grazings by sheep than by cattle. Indeed under the old system practised by the clansmen large areas were never grazed at all.[5] In meat output the new system was therefore greatly superior; Sir John Sinclair estimated that it would be doubled, or even trebled, while the income from wool would be very considerable.[6] It was argued, too, that by settling crofters from the interior near the sea no particular hardship would be incurred since they would be able to provide much of their food from that element. Viewed from the standpoint of the fuller utilisation of the agricultural and fishing resources of the Highlands there was much to be said for sheep-farming and resettlement of the people. What was overlooked was the very important psychological aspect of any compulsory change. The affection of human beings for their homes and the places where they had been born and nurtured, and their natural resentment against flagrant injustice and unfair treatment were factors which ought not to have been ignored.

Extensive sheep farming and crofting did not mix well. Crops could not be grown where sheep grazed at will, nor could the sheep farmer tolerate crofters' dogs disturbing and possibly damaging his sheep. Ambitious sheep farmers had other reasons, too, for seeking to get rid of the crofters. The arable land of the townships, poor as it was, would be invaluable as shelter and food for sheep in winter.

[5] Argyll, *Scotland*, p. 198.
[6] Sinclair, *Agric. Northern Counties*, pp. 110, 154.

For undisturbed occupancy of wide stretches of land sheep farmers were prepared to offer very much higher rents than the crofters, and the temptation thus offered to the landlords often proved irresistible. But in many cases the clearance process was gradual. The shielings were the first to go; next the small tenants, who had no security of tenure, were put out of houses and lands. If they did not leave when requested they were forcibly ejected. The furniture would be thrown outside, the roofs stripped and in many instances the houses burned. The hardships endured were often heart-rending. It was estimated that in Sutherland between 1811 and 1820 15,000 people had to leave their homes.[7] There were evictions in other areas, too. After the famine caused by the failure of the potato crops of 1845 and 1846, proprietors elsewhere, influenced doubtless by fears of over-population and its unhappy repercussions, cleared huge areas. Deer forests, too, soon after this latter date, were becoming fashionable and provided an additional reason for the clearances. In Skye whole communities were cleared, some tenants being forced to leave their homes in mid-winter. On the MacLeod estates 2000 people were dispossessed; Borreraig and Suisnish, two townships on the Macdonald property, were ruthlessly cleared in 1852.[8] In one year, 1849, more than 500 people left the parish of Glenelg.[9] Whole districts in Glengarry, Glen Dessary and Loch Arkaigside were cleared. The poor inhabitants were stunned at these happenings; even children and bedridden folk were deprived of shelter from the elements and deaths from exposure were not unknown.

It is not the purpose of this book to dwell on these tragic events. But whatever the advantages of sheep farming from the point of view of production, the mode of introducing it was in far too many instances both unjustifiable and extremely cruel. At one stroke, through the action of men formerly regarded as guardians of their interests, the people had been deprived of land, houses and livelihood. Many evicted families emigrated; others found their way to the towns, where rapidly expanding industries absorbed them, while others again sought to gain a living from the sea and from the land. On the narrow selvedges of flattish land that fringed the shores they built new houses, reclaimed land from the moor, established crofts or pursued the old system of run-rig and, largely because that

---

[7] Alexander Mackenzie, *A History of the Highland Clearances*, Inverness 1883, p. 178.

[8] Nicolson, *History of Skye*, p. 384.      [9] Lees, *County of Inverness*, p. 261.

newly-introduced crop, the potato, yielded so much food and was so accommodating in respect of soil and climate, they continued somehow to exist.

The spread of sheep-farming in the Highlands was a gradual process. Sheep of the Blackface breed were found to be best adapted to the moorlands of the counties of Perth, Argyll, Inverness and a large part of Ross. In the large Inverness-shire parish of Kilmonivaig there were said to be no fewer than 60,000 sheep at one time.[10] In Morven in Argyllshire, 17 tacksmen owned 14,000 Blackfaces.[11] Further north, in 1792, Sir John Sinclair introduced 500 ewes of the Cheviot breed as an experiment on the moorland farm of Langwell in Caithness. His main objective was to produce a finer wool than that yielded by Blackfaces. So well did this Cheviot flock thrive that, despite depredations by foxes, dearth in winter, etc., the total numbers eight years later amounted to 3,000.[12] Later the Cheviot breed invaded the adjoining county of Sutherland; in 1806 two Northumbrians, Marshall and Atkinson, who had rented a huge grazing in the centre of the county, brought north with them an excellent stock of Cheviots. At one time this firm occupied no fewer than 100,000 acres.[13] The results in Sutherland were so satisfactory that the Cheviots supplanted the Blackfaces which had earlier been brought to the county by pioneers in the industry.

Yet sheep farming in the Highlands had its drawbacks. The opposition of the natives, and serious losses through raiding hindered development: thus in 1815 eleven farmers are said to have lost no fewer than 1591 sheep by raiding; in the following year[14] they lost 1596. After the Napoleonic Wars the prices of wool and sheep fell sharply : between 1818 and 1823 wool dropped to a quarter of its former value while the price of sheep fell by more than half. But with the revival in trade in the early thirties the industry recovered and remained reasonably prosperous until the midseventies. After that, in common with the prices of other agricultural products those of wool and mutton declined and hill sheep farming entered a period of profound depression.

The decline began about 1874. Prices were still high but a series of bad seasons set in. Lamb crops were poor, but there was another disquieting factor. The Sutherland grazings, in common with those other Highland counties, were unable to keep as many

[10] *F.S.A.*, VOL. XVII, p. 544.          [11] *F.S.A.*, VOL. X, pp. 262, 270.
[12] Sinclair, *General Report, Appendix*, VOL. V, p. 177.
[13] J. Macdonald, " Agriculture of Sutherland ", pp. 63 ff.
[14] *op. cit.*, p. 64.

PLATE III

Former arable land in run-rig—Mingulay

sheep as in former years or to feed them as well. Some farmers reckoned that in the late seventies only two-thirds of the numbers maintained about 1840 could be supported. The chief cause was the deterioration of the grazings, particularly on the green or old crofting lands which, after the clearances, had become covered with green herbage invaluable to sheep in winter. But they had become fogged and useless,[15] partly because of the gradual abstraction of their fertility through sheep grazing them by day and lying on the higher moorland areas at night. Other causes were at work. The absence of cattle from the grazings had allowed more aggressive plants to get out of hand; there was also a natural tendency of land reclaimed from heather to revert to its original herbage, while the restrictions imposed by landlords and gamekeepers on muirburn prevented as much burning of heather being done as was desirable in the interests of the sheep. To maintain the former numbers now that railways had facilitated the transport of animals, farmers used to send their young breeding stock to be wintered on grasslands on the eastern seaboard. This practice incidentally reduced the number of deaths by braxy— a disease which caused heavy mortality among sheep in their first year; but the cost of wintering was high and wages and other expenses had been rising considerably since the middle of the century. It was reckoned that in the four or five years preceding 1880 most sheep farmers in Sutherland had lost money. Even then prices for sheep and mutton stood at nearly twice the levels to which they were to sink in the nineties when the depression in hill sheep-farming was at its worst. Another factor which accentuated the depression was that after the seventies public taste in meat began to change; people were asking for smaller joints of meat from younger animals than three- or four-year-old wethers—a class of sheep particularly suitable for grazing on the higher, more exposed and poorer sheep runs. It was on such grazings that the depression was worst felt. This depression in sheep-farming was accompanied by a rising demand for moors for sporting purposes. Rich industrialists were prepared to pay high rents for land grazed exclusively by deer. In stalking they wished to be free from all interruptions and alarms occasioned by shepherds and their dogs, or by nervous sheep. Landlords, faced with considerable rent reductions for their sheep farms, and with the possibility in certain cases of not being able to find new tenants, could not resist the offers of sporting tenants, who demanded exclusive use of the moors. Accordingly the land

[15] J. Macdonald, " Agriculture of Sutherland ", pp. 83-4.

was cleared of sheep. It was the poorer grazings—those formerly grazed by wethers—that were the first to be cleared, but where the interests of sport predominated the ewe grazings also had to go.

The latter part of the nineteenth century thus saw history repeating itself in the Highlands, but this time it was the sheep and not the people that were cleared off the grazings. This movement continued right up to 1914. It was reckoned that the area of deer forests rose from just under 2,000,000 to almost 3,600,000 acres between 1883 and 1912.[16] While this expansion was not wholly attributable to compulsory sheep clearances these were undoubtedly the chief cause. Between 1871-75 and 1938-42 the total number of sheep of all kinds in the five main Highland counties declined by nearly 800,000 or 25 per cent., while in the rest of Scotland there was a rise of just over a million or 27 per cent.[17]

Despite the wholesale clearances of the people from former township lands in the earlier part of the century and the migration of Highlanders, the population of the Highlands rose gradually during most of the first half of the nineteenth century. In Chapter XXIII it is noted how during this period the population of Skye rose by nearly a half and thereafter declined until in 1951 it was little over a third of its peak figure.[18] This rise in population was associated largely with the decline in the death rate from smallpox (owing to the growing practice of vaccination), the demand for kelp (the ashes of seaweed), and the introduction of the potato. Accepted at first with reluctance, the potato was soon regarded in the Highlands as a rich blessing. It was tolerant of soil and climate, suitable to the " lazy-bed " system of cultivation, and by providing an abundant supply of appetising and health-promoting food, seemed to offer a solution to the chronic problem of the Highlands—lack of sufficient food. It also provided the means by which people driven from their homes and deprived of their normal livelihood could subsist on the small pieces of land allotted to them, and enabled an increasing population to be supported on the land. The growing dependence of Highlanders on this crop may be illustrated by figures relating to a Skye parish:

| Year | Produce of oats and bere (bolls) | Produce Potatoes (barrels) | Population |
|------|----------------------------------|----------------------------|------------|
| 1801 | 1,600 | 5,000 | 2,555 |
| 1841 | 1,618 | 32,000 | 3,625 |

[16] *Report of the Departmental Committee on Deer Forests*, 1922, p. 1.
[17] *Report of the Committee on Hill Farming in Scotland*, Cmd. 6494, 1944, p. 9.
[18] Nicolson, *History of Skye*, pp. 401-02.

But this dependence led to disaster after blight had largely destroyed the potato crops of 1845 and 1846. Famine conditions prevailed, and but for relief measures instituted in the larger Scottish cities many people would have died from starvation which was the fate of so many in Ireland. The effects of this disaster were to widen the area of the clearances and to induce much voluntary migration to towns and emigration, largely to North America. But despite a large exodus the population did not show as great a fall relatively as did that of Ireland.

The development of sheep farming in the Highlands is, however, apt to obscure some significant changes that took place about the same time. On many enlightened estates run-rig was finally abandoned in favour of consolidated crofts, although it continued elsewhere until well into the twentieth century. A chauffeur in the Ross-shire parish of Torridon held his land in thirty-six different patches as late as about 1920.[19] Another change that took place was that the crofters copied the methods of the sheep farmer. They acquired sheep of both the Cheviot and the Blackface breeds, keeping them much as the large sheep farmer did. The sheep of the township were sometimes run as a flock, the wool, cast ewes and lambs being disposed of as combined lots and the proceeds, less expenses, being divided in proportion to the number and class of sheep owned by the individual crofter.

On land suitable for ploughing the introduction of light iron ploughs, designed on the pattern invented by James Small, proved a great boon since they could be drawn by a pair of Highland garrons. The old and ineffective wooden ristle and the one-stilted ploughs soon disappeared while the wooden harrow gave place to the iron one and traces of hemp or hair or twisted fir root were replaced by leathern ones or by chains. In the Highlands the barbarous custom of harnessing horses to harrows by their tails gradually declined and finally disappeared. On many crofts, where the extent of arable ground was too small to justify the use of a plough, the càschrom continued, however, to be used. With the making of roads light carts came into use, but on the smaller crofts crops, peat and dung continued to be transported by creels slung one on either side of the pony, or in default of ponies on the backs of the people.

The restricted area of arable land on crofts, coupled with the high cost of fencing small fields, largely prevented the adoption of those full rotational practices which had proved so beneficial in

19 Mackenzie, *Hundred Years*, p. 184.

better-class arable areas. The custom of allowing all arable land in
the townships to become common grazing after the grain harvest
also ruled out the adoption of turnips as a crop, and did much to
restrict the sowing of grass seed. But so long as the population
remained large in relation to the land resources and the people
continued to subsist on the produce of their crofts, cultivation was
carried out very carefully. Seaweed, for instance, was often transported by boat—sometimes as far as ten miles—and carried for two
miles in creels on the backs of ponies or even by human beings to
manure the land. Green-cut bracken was valued as a fertiliser;
potato patches were carefully weeded, and uprooted plants of
chickweed were collected, washed and fed to the cows. Small green
pockets of fertile land in the hills were enclosed for perhaps two
years to grow a potato crop in the first year and grey oats in the
second, a practice indicative of the keen desire of the people to
cultivate all possible land.[20]   At a later date Osgood Mackenzie
deplored the growing carelessness of the people in regard to cultivation, a form of neglect which became all too prevalent at the
approach of the twentieth century.

The prominence given in historical books on the Highlands to
sheep-farming and to the clearances in the eighteenth and nineteenth
centuries is also apt to obscure the fact that cattle still continued
to be reared in large numbers throughout these centuries. In early
summer dealers and drovers from the Lowlands would visit the
Highlands, make their presence known, sometimes by having the
church bell rung, purchase the cattle, assemble them in droves
varying in size from a hundred to three or more hundred animals
and make for the Tryst at Falkirk, then the great cattle market for
Scotland. Writing in 1795 Sir John Sinclair estimated the annual
value of the cattle sold from the Highlands at between £200,000
and £300,000. This probably represented the price of 60,000
animals. The droving trade appeared to reach its peak about 1835;
thereafter it declined. Modern means of transport—the railroad and
steamboat—replaced it and the auction sale displaced the tryst
which, however, lingered on in certain parts such as Muir of
Ord.

As will be noted later there was widespread dissatisfaction
concerning the crofting system in all its aspects. Conscious that
there was something far wrong in the Highlands the Government
appointed the Napier Commission whose report, issued in 1884,

[20] Mackenzie, *Hundred Years*, p. 191.

led to legislation designed to mitigate the prevailing discontent.[21]
But despite alleviating measures crofting continued to decline.
The tillage acreage of sixty-two predominantly crofting parishes in
the Highlands and Islands fell from 70,000 in 1886 to 66,000 in
1910 and to 38,000 in 1952. Cattle numbers went down from 95,000
in 1886 to 84,000 in 1910 and to 58,000 in 1952. Sheep, however,
showed a slight but very far from proportionate increase.[22]  It must
not be assumed that all landlords regarded their Highland estates
as purely money-making or sporting subjects. Many indeed were
most kindly disposed toward their tenants and spent money freely
for the good of the district. They constructed roads, planted trees,
reclaimed land from the moor to form farms and promoted local
industries such as weaving and knitting. In years of scarcity such
as those associated with the failure of the potato crops of 1845 and
1846 some landlords, in addition to other relief measures, gifted
large amounts of food to their people.

Osgood Mackenzie's *Hundred Years in the Highlands* shows
how assiduously his family tried to maintain the old friendly relations
between chief and people and to develop the agriculture of the
district on approved lines. His mother, on behalf of the trustees,
strove to abolish the run-rig system in Gairloch and to provide a
four-acre croft for each of the five hundred small tenants on the
estate. At the time of the potato famine able-bodied men were
given work in the construction of the Gairloch to Loch Maree
road, a sum of £10,000 being borrowed by the estate for the purpose.
At that time, too, Mrs Mackenzie acted as doctor to the whole
parish of Gairloch with its population of 5,400.[23]

The story of developments in Glenurquhart at the close of the
eighteenth and the beginning of the nineteenth centuries is typical
of those Highland estates where landlords strove to make changes
that would benefit their tenantry. Sir James Grant, who owned
Glenurquhart from his succession in 1773 until his death in 1811,
abolished kind and service rents, instituted the crofting system,
founded two villages, encouraged the erection of stone-built houses,
promoted flax, potato, turnip and rye-grass culture and insisted on
a regular rotation of crops being practised. He discouraged emigration and found work for the people in the construction of roads,

[21] *Report of the Commission of Enquiry into Crofting Conditions*, Cmd. 9091,
1954, p. 10.
[22] *op. cit.*, pp. 13-15.
[23] Mackenzie, *Hundred Years*, pp. 30, 36, 37.

bridges and river embankments, in spinning and weaving, in planting trees and in land reclamation.[24]

Developments of sporting estates, however harmful to some agricultural interests, brought much wealth to the Highlands. The Glengarry portion of the Macdonnell estates is said to have been purchased by Lord Dudley in 1840 for £9000 and to have been sold to the Right Hon. Edward Ellice in 1860 for £120,000. In thirty years the Ellice family spent £274,749 on the property, the greater part being paid in wages.[25] But despite the money spent by wealthy proprietors, and despite the legislation of 1886 and later years, the stock improvement schemes of the Department of Agriculture for Scotland, the great amount of State aid provided, the reports of various committees, the increasing attention given to the Highlands and tourism, the Highland problem has not yet been solved. Against the background of a poor soil and inclement climate, poor natural resources, the division of the land into holdings too small to provide occupiers with either full-time employment or an adequate living, poor communications and high freightage rates, the problem seems almost to defy solution. The development of forestry may help, as it has already done in limited areas; so too may the extension of hydro-electric schemes.

Orkney, which today is held to be one of our most progressive counties, was not always so. As has been noted, so badly did it suffer from misrule after being ceded to Scotland that its people were in despair. Writing of its agriculture in 1795 Sir John Sinclair pointed out that, unlike the other northern counties of Scotland, it had shown no increase in population during the preceding forty years. The one-stilted plough was then in use and continued to be used until about 1810. Sinclair erroneously concluded that Orkney was unsuitable for grain-growing because its climate was apparently too cold to mature the crops properly. Proprietors attempting to consolidate the run-rig lands into farms met with great opposition and some had to desist. Others, determined to continue, were stigmatised as oppressors and " mesterfu " men.[26] Long after improvements had been well advanced in the mainland counties Orkney remained backward. Contributors to the second *Statistical Account*, writing in the late thirties and early forties of the nineteenth

[24] Mackay, *Urquhart and Glenmoriston*, pp. 442 ff.
[25] Lees, *County of Inverness*, pp. 339-40.
[26] *Crofters Commission Report*, App., p. 272.

century, commented on the extent of land still occupied in run-rig.
Even then tenants were still thirled to certain mills.

Harvesting was sometimes done by pulling up the grain by the
roots. The pulled grain, instead of being bound into a sheaf, was
bundled by being tied round near the heads and dumped on its
bottom so as to form a kind of cone.[27] This system of " gaiting ",
as it was called, was well suited to get the crop into sufficiently good
condition for stacking and, until recently, was practised in some
Scottish counties with rye-grass grown for seed. In North Ronaldsay
the division of the land into squared farms and the confining of the
native sheep to the shore lands took place in 1832,[28] but it was not
until much later that the run-rig lands on the mainland of Orkney
were consolidated into separate farms. Incidentally the North
Ronaldsay and the Shetland breed of sheep remain as survivals
of the old Norwegian breed, the former living largely on seaweed.
Curiously enough, both turnip and rye-grass seed were harvested
in Orkney and exported to the mainland in the 1830's, even before
turnips were extensively grown as a root crop for feeding to
cattle. Thus at the time of the writing of the second *Statistical
Account of Scotland*, 2-3 tons of turnip seed grown in the parish of
Holme and Paplay were being exported annually to Edinburgh and
other places.[29] The long-continued preference of the Orcadian
farmer for the " grey " oat is explained by the fact that the liberal
use of shell sand, which was largely employed as a manure, caused
" sagging " or " segging " in the white oats. In time widespread
improvements in the cultivation of land were everywhere evident
and the status of the cottars was raised to that of crofters holding
land direct from the landlord.

The first attempts to improve cattle were made early in the
nineteenth century by introducing animals of the Highland breed,
the Dunrobin strain being favoured. By about the forties of the
century bulls of what was then known as the Teeswater breed were
being imported and Orkney cattle soon began to be esteemed as
" good doers " by the mainland farmers who fattened them. But
the most important factor in Orkney's development was the establishment in 1833 of regular steamboat communication between
Kirkwall and Leith.[30] This enabled farmers to have their store
cattle sent to the southern markets. In markets like Aberdeen

[27] *N.S.A.*, VOL. XV, Orkney, p. 21.
[28] *op. cit.*, p. 109.                          [29] *op. cit.*, p. 222.
[30] R. Watson, " Agriculture in Orkney ", in *S. J. Agric.*, III (1920), pp. 307 ff.

cattle from Orkney came to enjoy a high reputation. In course of time Aberdeen-Angus bulls came into favour and the greatest attention was given to stock improvement, so much so that today it is generally agreed that Orkney leads most, if not all, other Scottish counties in the average quality of its beef cattle. Another feature in the development of Orkney farming was the influx of farmers from Aberdeenshire in the nineteenth century. Just as Aberdeen-shire had benefited earlier from the coming of farmers and farm managers from the Lothians, so Orkney benefited from these new arrivals who helped to set the pace of its farming. In 1830 the cultivated acreage in Orkney was 25,000; by 1870 it had risen to 70,000 and by 1923 to 93,000.[31]

Today Orkney occupies an honourable place in Scottish agriculture. It carries a heavier poultry population per acre of arable land than any other Scottish county; the average quality of its commercial beef cattle is notably high while nowhere is land reclamation being pursued with greater zeal than in this northern group of islands. In the depression between the two World Wars Orcadian farmers were adding to their arable acreage by carving out fresh fields from unreclaimed moorland, while in the years following the Second World War about 1 per cent. annually was being added. Elsewhere comment is made on the overhead increase in the number of stock kept in Orkney. As cattle must be kept indoors in Orkney during the winter the problem of accommodating increasing numbers became acute, but the ingenious Orcadian farmer has solved it by building lean-to byres to existing walls. The general standards of housing, both for human beings and for stock, though lower than those of the mainland, have been much improved. In 1847 a Mr Denison, overtaken by a storm, sought shelter in the dwelling-house of a cottar. The home measured some 14 × 12 ft. and contained one box bed, 5 ft. 8 in. long, 3 ft. 10 in. broad, in which a man, his wife and six of a family slept; a shelf above the foot of the bed provided a sleeping place for two out of the six. The cottar was highly intelligent and chatted for three hours on questions of Church and State.[32]

Shetland, a crofting rather than a farming county, has a very much poorer soil than Orkney. So long as its crofts could provide occupiers with the essentials of living (housing, food and firing),

---

[31] Alex. Calder, " Orkney's changing conditions ", in *Scot. Agric.*, XXXII (1952-53), pp. 37 ff.

[32] *Crofters Commission Report*, App., pp. 274-5.

PLATE IV

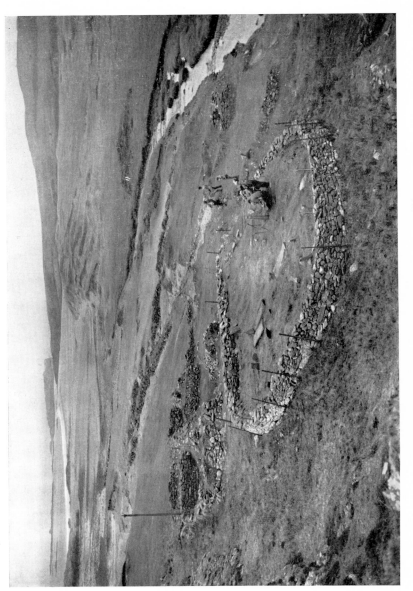

The desolation of former generations—Rhum

and allow cottage industries such as spinning, weaving and knitting, or fishing to be practised, there was not the same incentive to improve agriculture as in Orkney. Macgillivray, writing in 1920,[33] gives rather a doleful picture of the backward state of Shetland's agriculture at that time. Except in the more fertile parts such as Dunrossness parish and the Tingwall valley, agriculture was still very backward. Much of the cultivation was done by hand labour, mixed gangs of ten or twelve persons digging the land. A certain amount of ploughing was done by Shetland ponies, teams of four being employed, but the soil was merely scratched. Even harrowing was still done by hand labour and run-rig was still common. In the more fertile parts, however, the methods adopted were similar to those employed on the mainland. But in certain respects Shetland has attained fame. It was the first county in Great Britain officially declared to be free from bovine tuberculosis; it also possesses its own distinctive breeds of horses, cattle, sheep and farm dogs.

[33] James Macgillivray, " Agriculture in Shetland ", in *S. J. Agric.*, III (1920), pp. 414-28.

# CHAPTER XVIII

# LAND SETTLEMENT

Soil and climatic influences...Emergence of croft and small-holdings...Land settlement...Late eighteenth and early nineteenth centuries...Good and poor planning...Effects of industrial development and cheap food policy...Results of introduction of sheep-farming in Highlands...Congested areas...Fair rents...Security of tenure...New holdings and enlargements...Land Settlement Acts and the Highlands... Rural depopulation...Board of Agriculture for Scotland... Plots for unemployed...Fifty years of Land Settlement... Post-war policy.

FROM THE AGRICULTURAL STANDPOINT Scotland is not one but several countries, each with varying conditions of soil and climate determining its system of farming. The deep, level and fertile soils of the eastern arable districts, favoured by adequate sunshine and none too heavy a rainfall, are well adapted for the growth, maturing and ingathering of wheat, barley, oats, sugar beet and potatoes and, generally speaking, for large-scale arable farming. The more humid conditions of the south-west are well suited for dairying on moderately-sized farms and the cooler and drier climate of the north-east for arable farming coupled with stock-raising and fattening again on moderately-sized farms; but in the Highlands and Islands, where both soil and climate are unsuited for arable farming, only pastoral systems can be pursued with reasonable hope of success. There the extent of land capable of being ploughed is limited; the soils, even where ploughable, are thin and infertile, while the dull and humid climate militates against the ripening and harvesting of cereal crops. Arable must therefore be subordinated to pastoral farming, the purpose being to provide food for the cultivator and winter feed for the stock. Cropping as opposed to grazing is confined to narrow fringes of land lining the sea coast or bordering the sides of rivers and lochs. To support any considerable population holdings must of necessity be small and cultivation of the available good soil intensive; in short, this is the reason the crofting system of land settlement prevails in the Highlands.

The term " croft " in Scotland is generally applied to any self-contained and separately-occupied small unit of from one to ten or more acres, exclusive of outrun—a fair average being from four to five acres arable. Outside the Highlands and Islands the croft is run largely as a miniature self-contained arable farm, its individual small fields being fenced for grazing; where the land adjoins the hills, a limited amount of rough enclosed grazing may go with the croft, but as a rule the stock is grazed largely on the rotation pastures. In most parts of the Highlands and Islands a different system is followed, whether the arable land is in scattered unfenced patches or is in a single compact block. The holdings are usually grouped into townships, the stock being pastured on common grazings associated with these townships, while the rotation pastures are used as hay meadows. After the harvest of the grain and potato crops the whole croft in most Highland townships becomes common pasture, a practice which militates against the growing of turnips.

It would be interesting to know when the term " croft " first emerged. Before the eighteenth century it is seldom met with in documents, probably because it was applied only to the few small units of land rented direct from the proprietor. Before that time most occupiers of the smaller areas of land were subtenants of the tenant-in-chief and were referred to as cottars or pendiclers. Beneath them in status were the grassmen or herdsmen and the " dry house " cottars, who had only a kailyard attached to their houses. Nevertheless, the term " croft " does occur in early documents as, for instance, in the deed wherby two " croftis " were gifted in 1280 to the Abbey of Kelso,[1] while in 1542 the holding of Newcassey on the Coupar Abbey estate was let in six " croftis " to three tenants.[2] Why three tenants one may ask ? About this time there was a move on the Coupar Abbey estate to consolidate holdings and possibly this applied to the smaller pieces of land. Even in the northern Highlands, where one might least expect it, the term is mentioned in Lovat's feu charter of 1584, which refers to M'Hucheon's, M'Alesteris' and other crofts.[3] But in the Highlands the move to consolidate the small scattered patches of arable land appears to have made little headway until the agricultural revolution of the eighteenth century was well begun. Gradually,

---

[1] *Liber de Calchou*, Latin text, p. 95.
[2] *Coupar Abbey Rental Book*, VOL. II, p. 184.
[3] Grant, *Social Development*, pp. 258-9.

however, the advantage of consolidation came to be realised. The self-contained arable unit was not affected by the constant disputes about the measurements and allocation of the former run-rig lands; it enabled the tenant to reap the reward of his labour and it eliminated waste of time in walking from one to another of the scattered patches. Enlightened proprietors like those of the Gairloch and the Glenurquhart estates encouraged the movement, got rid of the tacksmen, reallocated their lands and let the new holdings direct to the tenants. In 1803 the Duke of Argyll cut up several of the larger farms in Tiree into self-contained holdings calculated to be large enough to sustain a family with ease. Individual occupancy was insisted upon and run-rig was abolished.[4] Crofting had now come to stay in the Highlands. The parts played in this process by the clearances and the adoption of the potato as a food crop were doubtless considerable. Crofting, however, so far from solving the problem of land settlement in the Highlands, seemed merely to aggravate it.

In various ways all the available fertile land was used up with the result that as population increased and standards of living rose the crofts were too small. The average Highland crofter could neither grow all the crops he needed nor keep all the stock he wanted, and these disabilities, along with insecurity of tenure and a high rent, were his main grievances. There were others—poor houses, a wet and boisterous climate with poor land on which to grow his crops. If there were an access road to his holding—possibly there was none—the chances were that it was a poor one. Everything he had to buy was highly priced and anything he had to sell had to be sold cheaply. Freight rates for the Hebridean islands were high and it was the crofter who had to foot most of the bill. The customary large families of the nineteenth century and the lower incidence of epidemic diseases intensified the twin problems of feeding the people and of finding employment for the rising generation. During the early years of the agricultural depression of the last quarter of that century the Highland crofter had indeed many disabilities and grievances. A new approach to problems of land tenure and settlement was overdue and, as mentioned, the Government appointed the Napier Commission.

On the mainland, apart from the Highland counties, the re-division of land at the time of the agricultural revolution, coupled with the rise in population and the development of rural industries,

[4] Argyll, *Scotland*, pp. 430-1.

was reflected in the establishment of self-contained farms, crofts and lotted lands as distinct from run-rig under joint occupancy. In poorer areas, particularly those in the north-east, quite a number of smallholdings and crofts were at this time set up in addition to such farms as were large enough to justify the keeping of at least a pair of horses.

Sometimes these smallholdings were established by tenants and cottars displaced by the consolidation of run-rig land into farms. Rather than leave their native district they carved crofts for themselves out of the unreclaimed moorland. Long leases and possibly some assistance in building houses were inducements to this end. In other instances, the establishment of crofts owed its origin to well-planned estate development schemes designed to provide a number of holdings each large enough to keep a cow. The tenants were to be employed in various ways—as estate workmen, country tradesmen, merchants, roadmen, etc. Nor were the needs of the aged overlooked: retired couples, no longer able to look after a farm, found in the croft an easy, economical and attractive way in which to spend their latter days.

As an instance of a well-planned and co-ordinated system of land settlement the estate of Durris in Kincardineshire may be cited. The plan adopted was to make, in the light of the circumstances prevailing in the mid-nineteenth century, the fullest use of the whole estate, to provide sufficient holdings of all sizes up to the 200-300 acres mark, and to ensure that not only would there be an ample supply of married workers other than those permanently employed on farms, but also that the circumstances of these workers would be eased by the occupancy of a croft as subsidiary to their main employment. The crofts kept no horses, but in the layout of the estate provision had been made for setting up certain small-sized holdings, the occupiers of which welcomed extra work for their horses either in cultivating the land of the crofts or in carting for the estate owner, the wood merchant, the building contractors or the road authority. In such circumstances the crofter had no need for more land unless perchance he wished to change his occupation and devote himself entirely to agriculture. In that event the holdings were so graded as to enable him to lease in succession holdings commensurate with his financial resources. In this way the enterprising man could climb the farming ladder. It may be observed that land additional to what was required to keep a cow and her calf, would have been nothing but an embarrassment to a crofter

T

in full employment. Throughout the nineteenth century this system operated well.

But not all estates were laid out on this principle. On the poorer portions of the adjoining parish of Fetteresso there was, as a result of haphazard settlement, a preponderance of poor small-sized holdings, so that as time went on, tenants could not find outside employment, while the holding itself could not provide full and profitable employment for an able-bodied man. Expedients such as taking in boarded-out orphans from the cities were resorted to, but by the twentieth century the fate of these holdings was sealed. The difficulty about land settlement schemes is that they usually cater only for current needs and are too inflexible to be readily adapted to altered circumstances.

Yet another type of planned land settlement scheme was evolved in the latter part of the eighteenth and the first part of the nineteenth century. Its aim was praiseworthy if its fate was unfortunate. The plan was to link up rural industries with agriculture. Small towns and villages were established, particularly in north-east Scotland, where householders could pursue such crafts as weaving and spinning or could establish themselves as country tradesmen —blacksmiths, carpenters, masons, tailors, etc.—and at the same time derive part of their living from the land.

In the planning of many of these villages and towns the land earmarked for houses and gardens within the village or town was rented on long lease or perpetual feu, but each occupier was entitled to rent elsewhere on the outskirts a portion of land large enough to support a cow. This movement began in north-east Scotland in or about 1750, when the Banffshire village of Tomintoul was founded [5] and about that time Lord Findlater, the noted improver, completed his planning of the town of New Keith.[6] There, out of a barren muir, plots 30 ft. by 70 ft. were marked out and were taken up by feuars who, in addition to the rent of their lotted land, paid 10s. a year for them. A few years later, and on the same principle, Lord Fife founded the villages of Fife-Keith and Newmill of Keith. The abundance of peat as well as of reclaimable land in the locality was a deciding factor in the selection of sites for these villages. The feuar was thus enabled to provide himself with food and firing. Grantown was founded in much the same manner in 1776,[7] while Dufftown, Aberchirder, and New Pitsligo are other

[5] N.S.A., vol. xiii, Banffshire p. 305.    [6] F.S.A., vol. v, p. 420.
[7] N.S.A., vol. xiv, Inverness-shire p. 440.

examples of this movement. Many of the New Pitsligo men became masons and found useful employment, up till the time of the First World War, in building and repairing farm-houses and steadings in Aberdeenshire and Banffshire. So long as the country industries flourished these settlements prospered. Unfortunately, however, hand-loom weaving, spinning, knitting, tailoring, dressmaking, the making of boots and shoes, etc. could not withstand factory competition, and so, deprived of their main means of livelihood, many tenants had to give up their lotted lands. Some of these were used as grass fields and others were taken over by small farmers in need of additional land.

The agricultural depression which began in the late 1870's weighed heavily on crofters and on tenants of holdings of an uneconomic size. Fewer people were employed on the land; drainage and reclamation schemes were slowed down and labourers with crofts or lotted lands had more difficulty in finding work. Unless full-time employment could be found locally the croft was no asset for it tied the holder to the district. Moreover, the lure of higher wages, shorter hours, holidays, and better housing and social amenities in the towns, told heavily against life on the croft, associated as it was with small returns and hard work. The larger type of smallholding, those of less than 30 acres arable, also suffered. They were too small to justify keeping two horses but without two horses ploughing was impossible. Co-operation with another holder, each providing a horse for the plough team, was in theory the solution; in practice it usually failed to work, and outside employment for a pair of horses became increasingly difficult to find. Holdings in the poorer parts of the east suffered most. By the 1880's most landlords, except only those in the Highlands, had assumed the burden of providing adequate farm buildings on their estates. The high outlays involved in so doing, in relation to the low rents, obliged proprietors to refuse to repair or renew the houses on many of the crofts and smaller-sized holdings. Death duties, increased local taxation and rising income tax were beginning to take effect. The first Marquis of Aberdeen and Temair, a most generous landlord, was sometimes obliged for economic reasons to refuse to renew tumble-down dwelling-houses and buildings on the smaller holdings. Such holdings were then attached to larger neighbouring farms. In consequence of this policy the opinion gained ground that, if landed proprietors would not, or could not, replan their estates to meet the needs of prospective smallholders, the State should assume the responsibility.

Although public opinion was moving in that direction it could hardly be said that, in the Lowlands, much serious discontent about land settlement was expressed until the twentieth century. In the Highlands and Islands it was otherwise. There the people had built their own houses, but their crofts were too small to support families without the help of some subsidiary employment, and the only remedy seemed to be to enlarge the holding. The clearances, apart from the hardships involved, had fostered a profound sense of grievance; the people thought that the land had been stolen from them. They had other complaints. They and their forefathers had reclaimed their crofts from the heather and had erected their houses, but the fact that someone else owned the land deprived them of any real security of tenure or compensation for improvements. Their rents were based, not on the original value of the land, but on higher competitive figures. Their grazing rights, quite apart from their crofts, had either been curtailed or lost when sheep farms were created. At a time when facilities for keeping a few extra sheep and cattle might have tipped the balance by converting an uneconomic holding into a low-level economic subject, it seemed to them unreasonable to be restricted to under-sized crofts and to limited areas of common grazings. Many crofts, too, had been subdivided and many families had no land at all. In the nineteenth century good stone and lime houses were being built in the Lowlands but in the Highlands and Islands, where the proprietors had not assumed responsibility for providing houses, no crofter was foolish enough to build a good house for himself when possibly, at the whim of his landlord, he might be turned out without compensation. Security of tenure, fair rents, more land and better communications were demanded, and there was much agitation which defects in education and in the machinery of justice did nothing to lessen. An immediate solution to the problem was required. Highlanders as a race had played a notable part in the development of the Empire. They were famed for their bravery as soldiers. As pioneers they had succeeded where others, reared under less rigorous conditions, had failed; and at home, men born and reared on Highland crofts had risen to positions of eminence, *e.g.* clergymen, doctors, schoolmasters, etc. Though uneconomic the Highland croft was a good training ground. All this prompted the question whether, in the national interest, something ought to be done to improve the lot of the Highland crofter and, after investigation, the Government took an affirmative view. Practical measures to this end meant the enlargement of many holdings, the reduction of rents and provision for security of tenure. The Crofters' Holdings (Scotland) Act was accordingly passed in 1886 and, although applicable only to the Highlands, it was to be the precursor of several Acts dealing with land settlement. Some of the more important were the Congested Districts (Scotland) Act 1897, applicable only to the Highlands; the Small Landholders(Scotland)Act 1911, and the Land Settlement Acts 1919 and 1931, the three latter applicable to Scotland as a whole.

The 1886 Act gave the right of security of tenure and fair rent. A Crofters' Commission was appointed to relieve land congestion in the crofting areas. At first this body directed its efforts mainly to enlarging holdings but later it was given powers to create new ones. The purpose of the Congested Districts (Scotland) Act 1897 was to enable the Congested Districts Board to provide, equip and adapt land for occupation by crofters and fishermen and to develop industries associated with, or supplementary to, crofting, *e.g.* weaving and fishing. These measures soon led to considerable improvement in conditions throughout the Highlands and helped to stay rural depopulation. Crofters, now that heritable security of tenure was assured, began to replace their black houses by substantial stone-built and slate-roofed structures. The Congested Districts Board provided the crofters with good male animals to encourage the breeding of better stock and instituted other remedial measures.

Meantime, however, the rural population of Scotland was steadily falling. As noted, the great agricultural depression which had begun in the late seventies, meant that less land was cultivated and fewer workers employed. In 1881 the number of persons engaged in agriculture was 240,000; thirty years later it had fallen to 198,000. The fall had been most pronounced among shepherds and farm workers, over a fifth of whom had left the industry. Many had gone to the towns where steady employment at higher wages, and better houses equipped with more modern facilities, could be had; others had emigrated. Many crofts and small-sized holdings in the poorer areas were no longer occupied as individual units. The decline in rural population was everywhere manifest, being most pronounced in areas remote from markets and in those where environmental conditions were least attractive. In 1921 in the upland Aberdeenshire parish of Glenbuchat there was less than 50 per cent. of the population recorded in 1871.[8] Outmoded houses,

---

[8] *The Scottish Countryside*, being the Report of the Scottish Liberal Land Inquiry Committee 1927-28, Scottish Liberal Association, 1928, p. 5.

low wages, poor travelling facilities, low prices for all agricultural produce, coupled with lack of opportunities, changes in the dietary habits of the people and the lure of the towns, were reasons assigned for this great drain on the population of the countryside. The Board of Trade returns showed that male agriculturists constituted the largest class of emigrants.[9] Clearly there was something far wrong with the industry. The nation, however, failed to identify the policy of cheap food and Free Trade as one of the main causes of rural depopulation. In the search for a remedy the effects of the Crofters' Holdings Act were examined and the land policies of other European states were studied. In Germany, France and Holland the acreages under cultivation had risen steadily in the years of depression while ours had fallen. In Denmark land reclamation had been continuous and output per acre had increased. Yet in all these countries the most important groups of holdings were those under fifty acres in extent. Denmark, which in area is only about one-half the size of Scotland, had three times the number of holdings.[10] The solution to the land problem thus seemed to many to lie in the creation of more smallholdings. It was thought that these would provide opportunities for young men to become independent. They would also attach people to the soil and ensure the better use of land. Accordingly in 1911 the Small Landholders' (Scotland) Act was passed. A Land Court was set up to revise rents and settle legal disputes. The Board of Agriculture for Scotland was brought into being in 1912 and in 1929 it became the Department of Agriculture for Scotland. The Board's remit was wide, for its function was to develop agriculture generally, land settlement being merely one of its responsibilities. For this latter purpose it had powers to create new holdings and to enlarge existing ones.[11] The task which the newly created Board had to tackle was formidable. Thousands of people applied for new holdings or enlargements of existing ones,[12] but the funds allocated for settlement were quite inadequate to meet the demand so that progress at first was very slow and in the crofting counties impatience became evident. Then followed the 1914-18 war and for the time being land settlement was almost suspended.[13]

[9] *The Scottish Countryside*, being the Report of the Scottish Liberal Land Inquiry Committee, 1927-28, Scottish Liberal Association, 1928, p. 10.

[10] *op. cit.*, p. 29.

[11] B.O.A.S., 1st report, 1913, pp. iv-vii.

[12] *op. cit.*, p. xi.

[13] B.O.A.S., 4th report, 1916, p. x.

The end of the war saw measures designed to speed land settlement and in 1919 the Land Settlement (Scotland) Act [14] was passed to give the Board additional powers to acquire land, to equip new holdings, and to make advances to holders to purchase livestock, seeds, implements, etc. At that time agriculture was most prosperous. Many ex-soldiers, whose wartime experiences had given them a fondness for outdoor life, applied for holdings and the official policy was to give ex-service men priority. Lloyd George had promised ex-soldiers that theirs would be " a land fit for heroes to live in ". But in spite of a greatly augmented land settlement staff and additional funds, applications came in so fast that they could not be disposed of in reasonable time. By the end of December 1921 [15] 18,162 applications for new holdings and enlargements had been received. The apparent slowness in the rate of settling people on the land exasperated many applicants, and in some parts of the Highlands land was forcibly seized.

The situation was to some extent relieved by emigration from the Highland counties. The depression in farming, which set in by 1921, further reduced the list. Many applicants, too, were found to be unsuitable either because of lack of experience or shortage of capital. By 1923, however, the number of new holdings and enlargements was 1236 [16] and the task of settling suitable applicants had become less formidable.

Lord Pentland, Secretary of State for Scotland, when piloting the Small Landholders' (Scotland) Act through Parliament, had defined the type of holding visualised as one that would employ a man and his wife economically. The definition was, however, somewhat elastic. A smallholding five to ten acres in extent might satisfy a holder specialising in pigs or poultry, or able to devote his skill and energies to market gardening. But the drawback of creating a holding of this type was that the holder and his family might occupy the house and use the holding merely to supplement earnings from some form of whole-time employment. This was not, and never had been, the objective of the legislators. Applicants accustomed to traditional methods were apt to think that the best policy for smallholdings was to run them as miniature farms relying mainly on family labour. Many of the holdings formed in arable areas extended to about fifty acres. Where, however, the land

[14] B.O.A.S., 8th report, 1920, pp. vi-vii.
[15] B.O.A.S., 10th report, 1922, p. 118.
[16] B.O.A.S., 12th report, 1924, p. 87.

settlement scheme was near a good retail market several holdings
of the small specialised type were established.[17] In the Highlands,
because of the limited extent of arable land and other circumstances,
neither type was suitable.   There either existing holdings were
enlarged or large sheep farms were acquired and the sheep stock
handed over to sheep stock clubs, loans being provided at low rates
of interest.   To ensure uniformity it was eventually decided to
bring all newly formed holdings under landholders' tenure.[18] This
meant the fixing of a fair rent by the Land Court, the benefit of
security of tenure and the assurance of compensation for all
improvements.

The continuous and ever-deepening depression in agriculture—
and in industry in general—in the early thirties decided the Government to alter its previous policy of establishing small-sized farms
to one of setting up small 5-10 acre units specialising in pigs, poultry
and horticultural products.   This policy found expression in the
Act of 1934. It was intended to establish 1000 holdings of this type,[19]
to be set up in industrial areas where markets for produce were
close at hand.

To ease the circumstances of the unemployed during the great
trade depression of the thirties, plots varying in size from a quarter
to one acre were provided in many areas adjacent to towns.
By May 1938, 1883 plot holders had been settled.[20]   These
operated under the guidance of officers of the Department and of
advisers in poultry-keeping and horticulture from the agricultural
colleges.

A review of the land settlement policy made in 1938 showed
that from 1886 to 1938 11,577 applications for new holdings or
enlargements [21] had been granted.   By this time the Department
had become a very large landowner, possessing nearly half a million
acres.[22]   It would be unwise to judge the results of land settlement
from any single angle.   Land settlement schemes were costly but
smallholders established by the Department weathered the agricultural depression as well as, if not better than, larger farmers.
A considerable number of people were now making a living under
greatly improved conditions.   The smallholding provided a ladder
of opportunity for agricultural workers and the sons of farmers or
smallholders.   Most failures had occurred in the period 1919-24,

[17] D.O.A.S., 27th report, 1938, p. 40.      [18] op. cit., p. 36.
[19] ibid.                                    [20] op. cit., p. 37.
[21] op. cit., p. 38.                         [22] op. cit., p. 39.

when the selection of applicants, because of the preference extended to ex-service men, was not so meticulous as it later became. These, too, were the years when the effects of the post-war depression were most acutely felt. In many cases the agricultural output of land under smallholdings was increased, and in nearly all cases many more people were able to obtain a living from the land than had hitherto been possible.[23] Housing conditions in the Highlands and Islands had been vastly improved and by the beginning of the 1939-45 war the old black house had all but disappeared in many districts of the Hebrides.

Land settlement had not, however, solved a problem peculiar to the Highlands, viz. the provision of part-time employment sufficiently remunerative to enable holders to attain a decent standard of living. The development of forestry and its integration with sheep-farming and crofting had often been advocated as a practical solution. Certainly tree-growing, where it can be successfully practised, works in well with crofting, and the passing of the 1945 Forestry Act will doubtless make for the closer integration of the two industries. Another factor which will affect future land settlement in the Highlands is the development of hydro-electric schemes.

On the outbreak of the Second World War land settlement schemes had to be suspended, but a fair number of applicants were settled as holdings became vacant, while plans were drawn up for the disposal of some of the land taken over by Agricultural Executive Committees or by the Department of Agriculture. Small-sized, intensively-run holdings specialising in pig and poultry husbandry were hard hit by the severe restrictions on supplies of feeding-stuffs for the smaller farm animals. In not a few cases the holder returned to his former employment or sought a new one, using his house merely as a residence, and leaving the land to be worked either by a neighbour or by the labour and machinery services administered by the Agricultural Executive Committees.[24]

In the Agriculture (Scotland) Act 1948 provision was made for the creation of holdings up to seventy-five acres in extent or £150 in rental.[25] This change accorded with the general trend towards increased mechanisation in agriculture after the 1939-45 war. This trend may affect the economic stability of smallholdings and regrouping may have to be resorted to. The Act also empowered

---

[23] D.O.A.S., 27th report, 1938, p. 40.
[24] D.O.A.S., *Agriculture in Scotland 1939-48*, p. 73.
[25] *op. cit.*, p. 75.

the State to provide loans not exceeding three-quarters of the working capital required for the holding.   The high cost of land and buildings at this time, however, retarded new settlement.   In 1952 no new schemes were instituted although constructional works on fifteen previously formed holdings had been completed.[26]

[26] D.O.A.S., *Agriculture in Scotland*, report for 1952, p. 25.

CHAPTER XIX

# DIFFUSION OF KNOWLEDGE[1]

The first agricultural writers...The Society of Improvers, The Edinburgh Society, the Select Society, the Highland Society...Buchan Society...Gordon's Mill Club...Eighteenth-century writers...Statistical Account...County reports... Transactions of Highland Society...Beginnings of agricultural journalism...Instruction in veterinary science, forestry and agricultural science...Edinburgh Chair of Agriculture... Liebig...Agricultural Chemistry Association...Experimental stations...Cheese-making...Developments in agricultural education...Colleges of agriculture...Research stations.

FAMED AS SCOTTISH FARMING was to become in the nineteenth century, at the beginning of the eighteenth it was vastly inferior to English agriculture or indeed to that of most Western European countries. It could scarcely have been otherwise. For the three centuries after Bannockburn the country had been so distracted by wars, political strife, and misrule that the arts of peace were perforce neglected. Even after the Union of the Crowns in 1603 Scotland was jealous of and mistrusted her southern neighbour, while poor communications between the two countries inhibited intercourse. The two nations differed, indeed, in religion, law, education and agricultural methods, and desire for a closer under-standing was non-existent. This explains why Scotland, at the beginning of the eighteenth century, lacked knowledge of the advantages of enclosures, fallowing, sound rotational methods, and growing turnips and clover for feeding to cattle in winter—practices already established in parts of the southern kingdom. Nor, it appears, did returned soldiers of fortune, such as Scott's Dugald Dalgetty, seek to introduce the improved practices which they had seen during their continental campaigns. Indeed, at the end of the seventeenth century, the dominant characteristics of Scottish agri-culture were apathy to or ignorance of improved methods of farming. By that time many English writers had produced books on

[1] This chapter is reprinted (with some minor alterations), by permission, from *T.H.A.S.*, 6th ser. 1 (1956), pp. 1-19.

agriculture.[2]   There had been Walter of Henley, who has left us his manuscript on Husbandry, written in the thirteenth century.  Three centuries or so later we find the names of John Fitzherbert, Thomas Tusser, Barnaby Googe, and Gervase Markham.  The seventeenth century produced many well-known English farming writers.  Then it was that, through the writings of Sir Richard Weston, Samuel Hartlib, Andrew Yarranton, and Walter Blith, new rotations came to be adopted, turnips and red clover grown, and the advantages of drainage and enclosures began to be realised.  But right up to nearly the end of that century Scotland produced no agricultural writers.

In the Spalding Club Collections for the shires of Aberdeen and Banff there is a letter written in the year 1683 giving precise details of the mode of agriculture then followed in the North of Scotland. The writer, Alexander Garden, the laird of Troup in Banffshire,[3] describes the common system of husbandry—infield and outfield; the kinds of soil—black (loam) peat, clay, and " haslie "; the weeds —principally charlock, spurrey, and thistles; the measures taken to fertilise the soil—dunging, composting, folding, and burning dried peat-soil furrows; the yields of grain—three and four fold; the method of restoring exhausted outfield land to fertility—allowing the plants indigenous to the soil to grow until a cover of vegetation was established, then ploughing twice.  The prominence given to this letter in agricultural literature reflects how very little was known about Scottish farming up to that time.  What is known has been pieced together from passing references by travellers and historians, from the records of old rent rolls or of the Barons' or Abbots' Courts, from laws on the subject and from descriptions by various writers of the eighteenth century.  It was in 1683, however, that the first known treatise on gardening was published by John Reid, named *The Scots Gard'ner*, which recommends the potato for garden cultivation.[4]  The potato was also mentioned in Sutherland's *Hortus Medicus Edinburgensis* (1683), the name given to the catalogue of plants grown in the garden attached to Edinburgh's School of Medicine.

But for a treatise on farming we have to turn to *Husbandry Anatomized*, to give it a shortened title, published by James Donaldson,

---

    [2] Ernle, *English Farming*, pp. 473 ff.
    [3] *Collections for a History of the Shires of Aberdeen and Banff*, ed. J. Robertson, Spalding Club, Aberdeen 1843, pp. 103-06.
    [4] Reid, *The Scots Gard'ner*, 1683 edn., VOL. II, p. 107.

an Edinburgh printer who claimed to have been brought up to farming. The book appeared in 1697 and was apparently the first known Scottish book on agriculture.[5] Although Donaldson was prone to theorise and to over-estimate yields and incomes, many of his views were sound and pointed to several weaknesses in the Scottish farming of his time. He advocated fallowing, extolled the virtues of dung, lime, sea ware, and " vigitables of all kinds providing they be first putrefied or rotten," deplored the prevalent habit of over-stocking, and recommended potatoes as a profitable crop for men with large families. But he was much too optimistic in thinking, as he did, that heather-clad land could be made to yield 32-40 bushels of wheat per English acre merely by paring off the heather, burning it, cultivating the land and sowing the wheat. He expressed his opinion about tenant right and considered that more use might be made—evidently in farmers' gardens and not for stock—of parsnips, turnips, onions, and potatoes. His book was dedicated to Patrick, Earl of Marchmont and the Lords of the Privy Council. Donaldson clearly felt that he had a message for the people of Scotland, by whom, however, it was apparently not too well received. Some of his ideas came from the English writer Markham, a " hack " writer whose views were none too reliable. In 1699 an anonymous author, thought to be Lord Belhaven, published a pamphlet, *The Countrey-man's Rudiments*, advising East Lothian farmers on how to labour and improve their land.[6] In it he drew attention to the difference between Scottish and English farming and commended some of the best practices then existing—fallowing and liming, etc. Whether these publications had much, if any, influence in promoting agricultural improvements in Scotland is not known, but probably they helped to spread knowledge. But knowledge, to become effective, must be followed by action and to stimulate action there must be enthusiasm. No better media of arousing enthusiasm have so far been devised than lectures, meetings and discussions, and for these Scottish agriculture is much indebted to her agricultural societies.

---

[5] James Donaldson, *Husbandry Anatomized, or an Enquiry into the present Manner of Teiling and Manuring the Ground in Scotland for the most Part; and several Rules and Measures laid down for the better Improvement thereof, in so much that one third part more Increase may be had and yet more than a third part the Expence of the present way of Labouring thereof saved*, p. 20.

[6] J. A. S. Watson and G. D. Amery, " Early Scottish agricultural writers, 1697-1790 ", henceforth cited as Watson and Amery, " Early writers ", in *T.H.A.S.*, 5th ser. XLIII (1931), p. 62.

The first of these was "The Honourable the Society of Improvers". Founded in July 1723,[7] it came to an untimely end in the fateful year 1745. But in its short life it exercised a remarkable influence. It roused Scottish agriculture from its centuries-long apathy and set in motion the movement which was later to make our agriculture world famous. Its membership of 300 was most distinguished and included dukes, peers and knights, lords of the Court of Session and professors of the University, lawyers, judges, and landlords—all dedicated to the cause of furthering agriculture and other Scottish interests. Thomas Hope of Rankeillor, who drained Straiton's Loch, now part of the spacious Edinburgh "Meadows", was its inspired President, but the Secretary, Robert Maxwell of Arkland, a Galloway laird, seems to have been its moving spirit. An indefatigable experimenter and pioneer, to benefit his fellows he was prepared to risk and lose all, as indeed he did, for his wife, the Lady Arkland as she was called, was at one time reduced to keeping a shop in High Street, Edinburgh. The Society did notable work. It discussed all innovations pertaining to agriculture—new crops, new implements, new ways of management of stock and land—and generally made agriculture a fashionable theme. In *The Heart of Midlothian* Scott is true to the spirit, if not to the details, of history when he credits the Duke of Argyll with the possession of Devonshire cattle, with establishing an experimental farm in Dunbartonshire and with being a distinguished agriculturist,[8] but makes the mistake of alluding to the Board of Agriculture about the year 1740, or more than half a century before it was established. In 1724 the Society prepared an interesting booklet on fallowing, the growing of turnips, flax and hemp, the processing of flax into linen, and the sowing and harvesting of grass and clover seeds[9] (evidently the authors, presumably Hope, the President and Maxwell the Secretary, thought that clover seeds could be harvested in Scotland). For us this production is of interest, since it provides among other things information on cereal yields of that time. These were much as Garden of Troup had stated earlier, three to four times the seed sown, whereas in England they probably averaged five. The booklet recommended the sowing of turnips and stipulated that each plant should be one foot away in all directions from the next. The wide influence of

[7] Alexander, *Notes and Sketches*, p. 25.
[8] Sir Walter Scott, *The Heart of Midlothian*, Chapter xxxvii.
[9] Society of Improvers in the Knowledge of Agriculture in Scotland, *A Treatise concerning the manner of Fallowing of Ground, Raising of Grass-seeds, and Training of Lint and Hemp*, Edinburgh 1724.

this Society led to the formation of constituent societies elsewhere and of course helped to disseminate knowledge.

Meantime, imprisoned in Edinburgh Castle for his part in the Risings of 1715 and 1719, was a staunch Jacobite, Brigadier William Mackintosh of Borlum, Inverness-shire. After his college days at Aberdeen, and possibly at Oxford, he had returned to his Inverness-shire estate to initiate improvements in farming and tree-planting. Now in captivity he felt he had a message for his fellow-countrymen, and so he devoted his time to writing essays on agriculture. He protested vigorously against short leases, rack rents, the lack of fallowing, and the reprehensible and by then out-moded custom of unrestricted and onerous servitudes. He recommended enclosing land, growing turnips, sowing grass seeds, and making hay; he advocated the planting of trees, suggested the establishment of an agricultural college, and discussed the relative merits of hedges and stone fences, etc. This forthright writer was far in advance of his times. Characteristically his book was addressed to the most noble Lords & Honourable Gentlemen of the Scots nation in the British Parliament by a Lover of His Country.[10] It was published in 1729 and his essay on the husbandry of Scotland [11] appeared in 1732.

From 1733 onwards various books on Scottish agriculture appeared. One of the most interesting of these was a treatise [12] produced in 1735 by a constituent society of the Society of Improvers and styled " A small Society of Farmers in Buchan ". It conveys a graphic picture of the situation confronting farmers of that period. So wedded were they to age-old practices and customs that bare fallowing as a means of cleaning land would have been condemned as wasting land for a season. No better advice was offered by this Society regarding weed control than the practice of young stock grazing the leaves of the grassy weeds amongst corn brairds and harrowing the brairds to destroy the seedlings of annual weeds.

Although there was then a pathetic lack of knowledge it is refreshing to find the treatise condemning over-cropping, stigmatising it as the inhuman practice of wounding so unmercifully the sides of our common mother earth. The treatise was a criticism of exacting landlords and of land-scourging tenants, and portrayed the dire straits of the people in regard to food. Later publications were

[10] W. Mackintosh, *An Essay on Ways and Means of Inclosing, Fallowing, Planting, &c. Scotland, and that in Sixteen Years at farthest*, Edinburgh 1729.

[11] W. Mackintosh, *An Essay on the Husbandry of Scotland, with a proposal for the further Improvement thereof*, Edinburgh 1732.

[12] The treatise is reprinted in Souter, *Agric. Banff.*, pp. 33-85.

more critical of the practice of Scottish agriculture and more adventurous in their suggestions. An essay by Francis Home (1719-1813), published in 1757, indicated a desire for further knowledge on the nutrition of plants. Home insisted on the dependence of agriculture on " Chymistry ".[13] The Minute Book of " The Farming Club " at Gordon's Mill, 1758-1765—a club numbering amongst its members no fewer than six professors of Aberdeen University— criticised such features as over-cropping with grain crops, overstocking, neglect to enclose land, change seed corn, and the failure to grant long leases, to forgo servitudes, to adopt the system of stallfeeding animals with turnips and potatoes, and to pursue a constructive improvement programme in animal breeding and management.[14]

It was to this club that the Aberdeenshire improver, Sir Archibald Grant, is supposed to have dedicated a pamphlet of ninety-two pages entitled *Dissertation on the Chief Obstacles to the Improvement of Land and introducing better Methods of Agriculture throughout Scotland* (1760). The author's name is not given, but the arguments and criticisms suggest that the production was Grant's. At club meetings many topical subjects were discussed—oxen versus horses as draught animals, Jethro Tull's theory of horse-hoeing, the enclosing of land, etc. By correspondence and personal visits members would ascertain what improvements were in progress in the Lothians or in Norfolk. Barclay of Ury took part in the discussions, and at their fortnightly meetings the members rationed themselves to a plain dinner costing not more than eighteenpence per person, drinks included. After about six years' existence the club seems to have expired.

From Sir Archibald's pen came other dissertations and pamphlets which condemn wholeheartedly the common errors of the Scottish agriculture of his time, and suggest such improvements as enclosing land, adopting suitable crop rotations, summer fallowing, change of seed, sowing land down to pasture for a period of years, liming, proper cultivations, and growing new crops such as turnips and the different clovers. In his " Memorandum to the Tenants of Monymusk ", issued in January 1756, he berates them soundly for their laziness and failure to adopt new methods.[15] Amongst other innovations which he commended was the Yorkshire plough.

[13] Ernle, *English Farming*, p. 216.
[14] J. Wilson, " Farming in Aberdeenshire ", pp. 76-102.
[15] *Monymusk Papers*, ed. H. Hamilton, p. lxx.

The sixties of this century saw the publication of several books and treatises on farming. Sir Archibald Grant's dissertation has already been mentioned; in 1762 the Rev. Adam Dickson of Duns published the first of two volumes of *A Treatise of Agriculture*. The second volume dealing with crops and rotations was issued in 1769 and the complete work ran to two more editions.[16] Many parish ministers of the time were often pioneers in agriculture, for education and travel had widened their outlook, while their glebes provided opportunity for experiments. Another clerical writer, the Rev. William Thom, gave advice to landholders and farmers. Still other writers in the sixties and early seventies of the century were Lord Kames and a Mr George Fordyce. Sometimes the name of the author was not disclosed. Agriculture was now enjoying a larger reading public. The contemporary *Scots Magazine* encouraged contributions on farming and quoted passages from books on the subject.

One of the most observant and far-seeing agricultural writers of that time was James Anderson, the very remarkable tenant-farmer of Monkshill, Udny, Aberdeenshire. From his pen in 1775 came his two-volume *Essays relating to Agriculture and Rural Affairs* which in four years reached a third edition. His observations on pastures and rotational grazing are refreshingly modern, although at times he was too much of a theorist. He was made a Fellow of the Royal Society and an LL.D of Aberdeen University. Anderson wrote a number of books and also edited a magazine, *The Bee*. Incidentally, he corresponded with George Washington, President of the United States.

In 1776 *The Gentleman Farmer*, a notable book, appeared from the pen of Lord Kames. At least six editions were published. Like Anderson, Kames was critical of some of the prevailing methods and implements. Anderson had described the old Scots plough as " beyond description bad "; of the wooden pegged harrow Kames wrote that it was " more fitted to raise laughter than the soil ". The systems of outfield and infield, of high ridges and of sowing turnips broadcast came under his lash. Jethro Tull's theory about plant roots ingesting particles of soil was exploded. By weighing soil in pots before and after the plant was grown Kames found that there was no apparent difference in weight.[17]

[16] Watson and Amery, " Early writers ", pp. 71-3.

[17] A. McCallum, " A great agricultural improver, Lord Kames ", in *Scot. Agric.*, XVIII (1935), p. 340.

U

East Lothian at this time was in the van of agricultural progress, and the Wight family of Ormiston, East Lothian, were noted pioneers. Robert, the tenant of Muirhouse, the first we read of, was closely associated with the original improvements instigated by Mr Cockburn.[18] It was, however, to his son Alexander that Cockburn was largely indebted for carrying out the improvements in agriculture which were to make Cockburn famous. In time Alexander's son Andrew was to make a notable contribution to farming literature. On Lord Kames's suggestion Andrew Wight was chosen to report on methods of husbandry pursued, and on all circumstances pertinent to agricultural practice, on the annexed estates. His excellent reports led to his being asked to extend his survey to the whole of Scotland. In his travels he visited many improving landlords and farmers, discussed and suggested improvements, praised efforts, and was always a most careful recorder. So precise were his descriptions that from the six books which contain his reports we get a vivid impression of the extraordinary progress that Scotland's agriculture was then making. Wight was the noted rider of Scotland's shires, for in the period 1778-84 he visited every mainland county except Argyll.[19]

The last quarter of the century was famous for its agricultural writers. In England Arthur Young, the most gifted of all, had by the early nineties produced his graphic and accurate descriptions of the agriculture of many parts of England, France, and Ireland. In 1784 he began his *Annals of Agriculture*, a monthly magazine to which George III occasionally contributed under the pseudonym of " Ralph Robinson ", his shepherd at Windsor.[20] The study of agricultural books, treatises, and articles was now the vogue, while the translation into practice of ideas gleaned from the agricultural literature of the period was proving to be profitable both individually and nationally. Output in farming was on the increase; prices were rising and Britain's population was growing.

Then in the nineties appeared a notable work relating to Scotland and its agriculture, the first *Statistical Account of Scotland*. In twenty-one volumes it described the social, industrial, and agricultural conditions of every Scottish parish, giving details of the numbers of people, stock, crops, modes of cultivation, improvements in farming, etc. The work was initiated in 1790, the first volume

---

[18] A. McCallum, " Cockburn of Ormiston ", in *Scot. Agric.*, XXI (1938), p. 39.
[19] Watson and Amery, " Early writers ", pp. 76-8.
[20] Ernle, *English Farming*, pp. 195-6.

was published in 1791 and the last in 1799. Most men would have been appalled at the task, but Sir John Sinclair, who conceived the idea and saw the work completed, was of different mould. This work will be a monument for all time to the zeal and tenacity of purpose of this remarkable man.[21] Not content with this achievement Sinclair, who in 1793 had become President of the newly appointed Board of Agriculture, decided on agricultural surveys for every county in Great Britain. The first complete county survey, made mainly between 1793 and 1795, was followed by a second some years later. Information from these county and parish surveys enabled him to produce his *General Report* on Scottish Agriculture as well as his Code of Agriculture. Sinclair also wrote voluminously on naval, military, financial, legal, and sociological subjects. To him Scottish agriculture is largely indebted for important developments in the formative years at the turn of the eighteenth century.

At this time there were developments in agricultural journalism. Imbued with the desire to spread knowledge of new methods, the Highland Society began in 1799 to publish its prize essays. Reaching a wide-spread reading public they did much to enlighten landlords and farmers about the current improvements in farming, forestry, etc. So valuable did they prove that they have been continued ever since. The ground covered was wide and varied, as a glance at the Index to the first, second and third series of the *Transactions*, covering the years 1799-1865, shows.[22] They ranged from roofing slates to rollers, rails on roadways, ragweed, ryegrass, rakes, reaping machines, and reclamations. Noted seedsmen and pasture experts like Charles Lawson of Edinburgh and Scottish-born George Sinclair of Woburn enlightened landlords and farmers about pastures; noblemen like the Earls of Airlie, Cawdor, and Seafield told how they formed their extensive plantations; distinguished clergymen with a love of farming, like the Rev. Dr Singer of Dumfriesshire and the Rev. Dr Farquharson of Alford, Aberdeenshire, the latter an F.R.S., aired their views on many subjects—sheep diseases, grasses, cereal varieties, irrigation, " distempers " of corn, pulse and root crops. Amos Cruickshank, the famous Shorthorn breeder, described his reclamation of fifty acres of moorland on his farm of Sittyton. James Hogg, " the Ettrick Shepherd ", was a contributor. Professors Anderson and Johnston wrote on many subjects ranging from pigeons' dung— then a much esteemed fertiliser—coal ashes, sewage, spurious guano,

---

[21] Anderson, *The Scottish Nation*, VOL. III, pp. 463-71.
[22] *Index to the Transactions of the Highland and Agricultural Society*, 1866.

to oilcakes and the valuation of artificial fertilisers. The wealth of material in the earlier *Transactions* was enormous, and although circulation was limited to proprietors and the larger farmers their educational value was great, for members of the Society were leaders everywhere in thought and action. Nor was the Highland Society alone in encouraging pioneers in agricultural development to describe their experiences or give expression to their thoughts, for, as has been pointed out, the *Scots Magazine* had opened its pages to agricultural writers. In 1800 the first issue appeared of the *Farmers' Magazine*, a quarterly devoted to farming and rural affairs. It was jointly edited by Robert Brown, farmer of Markle, and by Dr Somerville of Haddington until the latter's death when Brown edited it alone. So popular did it become that five editions had to be printed.[23] Loudon, in his *Encyclopaedia of Agriculture*, 1835 edition, stated that this magazine did more to enlighten Scottish farmers than any other work.[24] It was carried on until November 1825, James Cleghorn succeeding Brown as editor.

As the nineteenth century wore on, specialist agricultural journalists appeared, some of whom were attached to the daily newspapers and others to weeklies devoted entirely to agricultural news. Amongst these journalists some well-known Scottish names appear. Five Macdonalds, four of them brothers, reared on an upland Banffshire farm, and one a nephew,[25] attained important positions in agricultural journalism. One of them founded *The Farmer and Stock-breeder*, the first agricultural journal to have a circulation of 100,000. All five had an eye for farms, stock and implements, a flair for acquiring information, a zest for matters agricultural and a gift for writing. There were others, eminent in a bygone generation—Young, McNeilage, Cameron, Mackay, and McCulloch. Thus agricultural literature did not die with Arthur Young and Sir John Sinclair, Lord Kames, Wight and Anderson, but was maintained by writers who, as Lord Ernle said, " wrote with the knowledge of specialists and with the simple ease of practical men of the world."[26] Today the tradition is being well maintained, and Scotland is proud of her agricultural writers and journalists. The tempo in the diffusion of agricultural knowledge has been much quickened of late years and this can be largely attributed to an excellent agricultural press.

[23] Ernle, *English Farming*, p. 209.
[24] Loudon, *An Encyclopaedia of Agriculture*, henceforth cited as Loudon, *Encyclopaedia*, 3rd edn. 1835, p. 131.
[25] Watson and Hobbs, *Great Farmers*, p. 283.
[26] *op. cit.*, p. 286.

Right up to the time of the First World War the State assumed no direct control over agriculture and farmers were at liberty to grow what crops they pleased and keep what stock suited them best. But the proprietors, proud of their estates and conscious that good farming enhanced their value, strove by precept and example to encourage good and to prevent bad farming. Their home farms became the experimental and demonstration stations of the times, their leases the instruments for preventing bad farming, and the agricultural literature of the period the means of keeping themselves abreast of advances in all farming matters.

Another feature of the last quarter of the eighteenth century was the setting up in 1790 of a Chair of Agriculture in Edinburgh University. This was the first of its kind in Britain, if not in the world. The teaching of agriculture had been advocated by Mackintosh of Borlum, and his arguments had been supported in 1743 by the Society of Improvers. Indeed, Maxwell, the Secretary of the Society, gave lectures on agriculture in 1756, his example being followed by two Edinburgh professors, Cullen and Wallace, but it was not until 1790 that these efforts and those of Lord Kames and some of his friends found practical expression in the establishment of a Chair of Agriculture.

The first three occupants of the Chair (Coventry, Low, and Wilson), to eke out their small emoluments, did valuable work in collating existing knowledge and giving it orderly arrangement.[27] Incidentally between 1868 and 1893 the Highland Society contributed to the Professors' salary.[28] Aberdeen was quick to follow Edinburgh in making provision for the teaching of agriculture. In 1790 £1000 was left by Dr Fordyce, a noted Aberdeen graduate, to establish a Lectureship, but this money was so tied up with liferents that it was only in 1840 that a lecturer could be appointed.[29] John Shier, the first lecturer, took his duties seriously; he revised Davy's *Agricultural Chemistry*, founded an agricultural museum, and doubtless paved the way for one of his successors, Thomas Jamieson, to set up an Agricultural Research Association.

The attempt to induce Edinburgh University to undertake the teaching of veterinary science was less fortunate. In 1816 efforts were made to establish a Chair of Comparative Anatomy embracing

[27] Watson and Hobbs, *Great Farmers*, p. 83.
[28] *op. cit.*, p. 269.
[29] James Hendrick, " In the beginning : the University of Aberdeen and North of Scotland College of Agriculture ", in *Agricultural Progress*, xv (1938), p. 71.

veterinary physic and surgery.    The project was dismissed as implying adjuncts scarcely compatible with University life.[30] · Undismayed by this refusal, and conscious of the profound ignorance of the horse doctors of the time, the Directors of the Highland Society, who had backed the project, extended their patronage to a course of lectures to be given by William Dick, a Scottish graduate of the Veterinary College of London, and also to the award of certificates for veterinary proficiency.    Dick's skill, zeal and determination were soon to play a most important part in the development of veterinary education in Scotland.    The " old white lion ", as Dick has been aptly termed, turned out men who later acquired world reputations.[31]    He rescued his subject from obscurity, gave it the dignity it merited, and established the Royal (Dick) Veterinary College, now part of the University of Edinburgh.

The Highland and Agricultural Society's activities in spreading knowledge were by no means limited to the publication of informative essays and the material assistance given to the promotion of veterinary education.    In 1858 it instituted examinations for diplomas in agriculture and dairying, provided grants-in-aid to agriculture and allied sciences, and in 1876 it persuaded the Science and Art Department at South Kensington to add the " Principles of Agriculture " to its syllabus.[32]    It also took steps to ensure that theories in agriculture were verified by field tests.    Failure to observe this rule had sadly misled Sir Humphry Davy, the foremost chemist of his time, who had been employed by the first Board of Agriculture at a salary of £100 a year.[33]    Knowing that plants were composed mainly of carbon, hydrogen, and oxygen he concluded that they derived much of their carbon and oxygen from the soil.    Humus, he thought, was merely a stage in the life-cycle of the dead to the living plant.    Basing his ideas on the belief that carbon and hydrogen were supplied in part at least by the soil through decaying vegetation, he thought that oils would be good manures.[34]    He was also wrong in supposing that the carbon in soot could readily be made soluble by the action of oxygen and water.    It was left to Liebig, a young German chemist, to explode Davy's theory.[35]    He pointed out that the carbon,

[30] " Historical account of the veterinary development of the Highland and Agricultural Society ", in *T.H.A.S.*, 4th ser. XI (1879), pp. 121-9.

[31] Watson and Hobbs, *Great Farmers*, p. 268.

[32] *op. cit.*, p. 269.          [33] *op. cit.*, p. 72.

[34] James Hendrick, " The Society and agricultural science ", in *T.H.A.S.*, 5th ser. XLIII (1931), p. 28.

[35] *op. cit.*, pp. 29-30.

hydrogen, and oxygen in plants were got from the " carbonic acid " of air and the " water " in the soil. He qualified the prevalent idea of " corruption being the mother of vegetation ". The needs of the plant in respect of carbon, hydrogen, and oxygen could be met from the air and from water, but it was otherwise with " the ammonia compounds " and " the alkaline phosphates " as he termed them. The principles of manuring, he considered, were related to supplying mineral substances to the soil in sufficient amount as largely determined by the ash content of the crop. Liebig's theories marked a great advance in knowledge of plant nutrition, but he allowed them too free play. Had he checked them by weighing the crop responses he would have found, for instance, that the ash content of turnips gave no clue to the manurial requirements of that crop. Instances like these emphasised the need for carefully conducted field trials. The volume of contradictory statements contained in the essays published by the Highland Society further proved the need for such trials being carried out, if necessary over a series of years.

Realisation of this induced Sir John Sinclair in 1821 to press for the establishment of an experimental farm. Other requests followed, but the Highland and Agricultural Society, to whom the requests were addressed, did not feel justified in embarking upon such a costly project. Nevertheless in 1848 they appointed a chemist, Dr Thomas Anderson, but this was after a number of farmers in Midlothian had formed in 1842, at the instigation of Mr Finnie, Swanston, the Agricultural Chemistry Association of Scotland. Its objects were twofold—analyses for members and the extension of knowledge. To aid this Association the Society gave substantial grants, allowed it the use of their rooms and published the results of its work in their *Transactions*.[36]

Experimental stations were eventually set up by the Society at Harelaw in East Lothian and Pumpherston in West Lothian, while the chemists appointed to the Society did much useful service through local farming associations in following up the work of the Rothamsted Experimental Station in England and checking it under local conditions of soil and climate. Although the main efforts of the local associations were related to livestock and root and grain shows, or to the hiring of stallions to travel their districts, many of them carried out useful local manurial trials. Long before the

---

[36] E. M. Crowther, " Experimental agriculture ", in *Advancement of Science* (British Association), new series, 1951, p. 236 ; Hendrick in *T.H.A.S.*, 5th ser. XLIII (1931), pp. 36-7.

agricultural colleges had come into being, Scottish farmers were well aware of the importance of applying phosphates to turnips and nitrogenous manures to hay and grain crops, and it was to the credit of Thomas Jamieson, the chemist of the Agricultural Research Association at Aberdeen, that in 1880 the value of finely ground mineral phosphates for acid soils was realised.[37]  At Rothamsted, on a different soil, insoluble phosphates had failed to yield good results.

Another step taken by the Highland Society to spread new knowledge was to send a promising young Scotsman, James Johnston, to England to learn from Elkington, the famous English drainer of that time, the secrets of his success.[38]  On his return to Scotland, Johnston's advice was much in request but it was left to James Smith of Deanston to make Scottish agriculturists fully aware of the benefits of drainage.  In 1831 he published his *Remarks on Thorough Drainage and Deep Ploughing*, a book which did much to promote the great drainage schemes of the thirties, forties, and fifties of the last century.

Ayrshire had long been famed for its Dunlop cheese, for which the great industrial area of the west provided a ready market, but not content with local successes Ayrshire cheese-makers wanted a wider market.  So when the Highland Society provided classes at their annual show for English varieties of cheese they strove to produce such English cheeses as the Gloucesters, but their efforts did not gain the success desired.  In 1850 after the Glasgow Highland Show it was reported that English-made cheese still brought 15s. per cwt. more in the market than the Scottish make.  Accepting this as a challenge, the Ayrshire Association sent two commissioners to the cheese-making districts of England to report on the kind of cheese most suitable for Scottish conditions.  The Cheddar was recommended, and Mr and Mrs Joseph Harding from Marksbury, Somerset, were induced to come north and teach Scottish cheese-makers how to make it.[39]  This venture was markedly successful and ere long Scottish-made Cheddar was reported to be almost up to the standard of the best Somerset.[40]  In 1889 a permanent school in dairying was set up on a farm near Kilmarnock and was assisted by grants from the Highland and Agricultural Society.  Later this school was to become the Dairy School for Scotland.

[37] Crowther in *Advancement of Science*, 1951, p. 241.
[38] Watson and Hobbs, *Great Farmers*, p. 262.
[39] *op. cit.*, p. 166.          [40] Ramsay, *History H.A.S.*, p. 310 *n*.

Although Edinburgh University had set up a Chair of Agriculture no provision had been made for the teaching of such cognate subjects as agricultural chemistry and botany until Professor Robert Wallace, the fourth occupant of the Chair, persuaded the University to provide instruction in these subjects and to establish a degree in agricultural science.[41] This step was of major importance in enabling teachers of agricultural science to be properly trained. Some of Edinburgh's first graduates became noted pioneers of agricultural education and research throughout Great Britain and the Empire. Sir William Somerville (1887), Sir Thomas Middleton (1888), Gilchrist (1889), and Seton (1894) were amongst the University's earlier graduates. Glasgow was less fortunate than Edinburgh at this time, for it did not have a Chair of Agriculture and therefore depended on private enterprise for instruction in the subject. Primrose McConnell (of Note-Book fame) gave a course of lectures for one session in 1883. Three years later Mr (later Sir Patrick) Wright began a course, and the following year he was attached to the staff of the Technical College. By 1891 a small but enthusiastic staff of teachers had been gathered together.[42]

Up to 1890 little or no material help, however, had been given by public bodies towards agricultural education, and only the well-to-do could afford this type of instruction. The Paget Committee (1886) recommended a grant-in-aid for the purpose, and local authorities were later empowered to provide technical instruction, including agriculture. Little, however, could be done to promote either centralised instruction or instruction throughout the counties until what was known as " whisky money ", about £750,000 a year for Great Britain and Ireland, became available.[43] This was money originally collected by Government for the purpose of compensating dispossessed publicans, and subsequently largely applied by local authorities for promotion of technical education. Lecturers from the Glasgow Technical College now began to give talks in the neighbouring counties. Funds were made available towards the support of the dairy school at Kilmarnock, and two counties, Lanark and Kirkcudbright, appointed whole-time instructors. At Aberdeen

[41] Watson and Hobbs, *Great Farmers*, pp. 82-3.
[42] John Kirkwood, " In the beginning : the West of Scotland College of Agriculture ", in *Agricultural Progress*, xxv (1950), pp. 69-70.
[43] J. A. Hanley, " Agricultural education ", in *Agriculture in the Twentieth Century, Essays in research, practice and organisation to be presented to Sir Daniel Hall*, henceforth cited as *Agriculture in the Twentieth Century*, Oxford 1939, pp. 91-4.

the Fordyce Lectureship was expanded into a School of Agriculture conferring degrees and diplomas in the subject, the first session being held in 1895-96.[44] In the Glasgow area the progress made in the nineties induced some zealous Directors of the Highland and Agricultural Society associated with the area to seek further developments. An agricultural college for the south-west was suggested, and there was also a demand for an experimental farm. It was decided in 1899 to establish a college and to acquire twenty acres of land for experimental purposes. In 1900 the newly founded college moved into premises in Blythswood Square, Glasgow, while dairy teaching and experimental work was located at Kilmarnock, where the old dairy school had functioned.[45] Later, in 1902, it was considered desirable to build a new dairy school there. The Highland and Agricultural Society contributed generously towards this project and they also increased their annual grant.[46] The munificent gift of the Auchincruive Estate, Ayr, by John Hannah, a Girvan farmer, has since enabled the West of Scotland College to develop much of its research, teaching, experimental and demonstration work at that centre.

The east of Scotland in 1901 and the north in 1904 followed the example of Glasgow in founding Colleges of Agriculture in Edinburgh and Aberdeen respectively for instruction in agriculture, dairying, poultry-keeping, horticulture, and bee-keeping in their particular areas, the counties of which were by now in close liaison with the colleges. Arrangements were made with the universities for the awarding of degrees; the colleges awarded diplomas and in the west of Scotland, in particular, students were prepared for the national diplomas in agriculture and dairying. In 1900 the examination for the National Diploma in Agriculture replaced the old examination in agriculture conducted by the Highland and Agricultural Society, that body having come to an arrangement with the Royal Agricultural Society of England to hold a joint examination. A similar arrangement had been reached in 1897 for holding joint examinations leading to the National Diploma in Dairying.[47]

The three newly-established agricultural colleges entered with zest upon the task of providing instruction to students attending

---

[44] Hendrick in *Agricultural Progress*, xv (1938), p. 71.

[45] Kirkwood in *Agricultural Progress*, xxv (1950), p. 70.

[46] Proceedings at Board Meetings, in *T.H.A.S.*, 5th ser. xv (1903), pp. 443-4.

[47] Proceedings at Board Meetings, in *T.H.A.S.*, 5th ser. x (1898), p. 506; XII (1900), pp. 463-4.

their central classes, and to farmers and their wives and daughters in the counties. The number of students rapidly increased, and evening lectures in agriculture, veterinary hygiene, dairying, and poultry-keeping were well patronised throughout the counties. Despite obvious disadvantages in the carrying out of trials on private farms, much useful experimental work was done. Farmers learned the advantages of using more prolific strains of cereals, of employing better grass seed mixtures, and of supplying adequate amounts of fertilisers to the various crops.

In 1910 the Development Commission was set up and Sir Daniel Hall, first as Commissioner and later as full-time Adviser, did invaluable work in planning the development of agricultural education and research. At the same time additional funds became available.[48] The West and North of Scotland Colleges put in strong demands for farms for investigational work of a long-term nature. Such work required a degree of control and expenditure which private farms could be expected neither to give nor to bear. Farms were accordingly acquired by the West and the North of Scotland Colleges of Agriculture and, some years later, by the Edinburgh and East of Scotland College.

Until the Scottish Board of Agriculture was established in 1912 Scottish agricultural interests had generally been looked after by the second Board of Agriculture in London, established in 1889,[49] but the administration of educational grants in agriculture had been entrusted to the Scottish Education Department. On the formation of the Board of Agriculture for Scotland, however, control of these grants was vested in their hands.[50]

The outbreak of the 1914-18 war restricted scientific developments in agriculture, but during the war it became clear that such developments could no longer be neglected. The production of food at home had assumed a new significance; the toll exacted by diseases and pests was enormous; soil science was in its infancy; much had to be learned about the need for, and the function of, lime and manures on the soil, the breeding and nutrition of plants and animals, and the nature, treatment, and prevention of diseases and pests. By 1919 money seemed to be plentiful, and the successful termination of the war had fostered a feeling of optimism not warranted by circumstances. A large programme of research work was

[48] Hanley in *Agriculture in the Twentieth Century*, p. 99.
[49] H. E. Dale, " Agriculture and the Civil Service ", *op. cit.*, pp. 3-4.
[50] B.O.A.S., 1st report, 1912, p. xix.

visualised, and to ensure that the results would be passed on to farmers it was planned that adequate experimental, advisory and educational facilities would be provided.

Some work in connexion with plant breeding had been done during the nineteenth century by Scottish breeders of oats, potatoes, and turnips. The first Scottish cereal breeder of note was an East Lothian farmer, Patrick Shireff,[51] who had a flair for detecting good single plants amongst cereal crops. As a rule natural cross-pollination in cereals is rare, so the chances of a superior variety being produced are small, while the possibility of its recognition is still more remote. Nevertheless, cross-pollination does occur occasionally and if the product happens to be recognised as superior, and its seed is multiplied in isolation to preclude danger from admixture with other seeds, the industry may be benefited. Pursuing this policy Shireff managed to select some superior varieties of wheat and oats. In his later days he turned to hybridisation as a speedier means of producing superior strains but died before attaining any marked success. Nevertheless, John Garton, the founder of the great seed firm of Garton's, Warrington, by this means succeeded in breeding his famed Abundance oat,[52] which was largely used by Scottish farmers.

New varieties of potatoes are derived from seeds contained in the potato " plum ". These " plums " may grow naturally as a result of self-fertilisation, or they may be the product of cross-fertilisation. In crossing, potato breeders of the nineteenth century were largely guided by the principle that like produces like, and doubtless used selected parent plants with certain desirable characteristics such as cropping power and resistance to blight. But until the Mendelian principles were generally made known in 1901, breeders, so far as the transmission of heritable qualities was concerned, were working largely in the dark. Moreover, in the assessment of the varieties they produced they were greatly hampered by lack of scientific training and proper testing facilities.

Scottish oat growers, before the outbreak of war in 1914, had benefited greatly from the use of varieties produced in England, Sweden, and Canada. But such varieties were not suited to all the soil and climatic variations of Scotland. This fact undoubtedly spurred oat growers to demand their own breeding station. There

[51] H. Hunter, "Developments in Plant Breeding", in *Agriculture in the Twentieth Century*, p. 225.
[52] Watson and Hobbs, *Great Farmers*, p. 81.

was another weighty argument for such a station in Scotland. Wart disease in potatoes had become serious during the 1914-18 war. Fortunately certain varieties had been found to be immune and English growers came increasingly to depend on getting seed of these varieties from Scotland. As the range of good immune varieties was limited there was a strong case for increasing their numbers, and it was felt that this could best be attained by the establishment of a plant-breeding station in Scotland.

True to its traditions the Highland and Agricultural Society gave valuable aid in furthering this and other projects. In July 1918, while the war was still at a critical stage, a proposal that a grant of £2000 should be made by the Society for the institution of a station for research in plant breeding in Scotland was confirmed.[53] Early in 1919 the Society decided to convene a meeting to discuss possible steps to investigate animal diseases, and in the following year awarded a grant of £1000 to the Animal Diseases Research Association.[54] In 1922 a grant of £500 was given to a committee on research on animal nutrition formed by the University of Aberdeen and the North of Scotland College of Agriculture.[55] This committee had, two years before, been promised a sum of £10,000 by a Mr John Rowett of London, a benefaction which resulted in the establishment of the world-famous Rowett Research Institute. In 1927 the Society donated £1000 for the endowment of a Department of Research in Animal Breeding in the University of Edinburgh.[56] Two grants aggregating £1500 were voted by the Society in 1929 to the Hannah Dairy Institute at Ayr.[57] By the generosity of a Mr Macaulay, a Canadian, the establishment of a Soil Research Institute at Craigiebuckler, Aberdeen, became possible in 1930, and to this Institute the Highland and Agricultural Society gave a grant of £500.[58] Grants on a pound-per-pound basis were made in all these cases by the Government. Thus by the early 1930's Scotland had six Agricultural Research Institutes, while each of its three Agricultural

[53] Proceedings at Board Meetings, in *T.H.A.S.*, 5th ser. XXXI (1919), p. 383.
[54] Proceedings at Board Meetings, in *T.H.A.S.*, 5th ser. XXXI (1919), p. 371 ; XXXIII (1921), p. 420.
[55] Proceedings at Board Meetings, in *T.H.A.S.*, 5th ser. XXXV (1923), pp. 406-07.
[56] Proceedings at Board Meetings, in *T.H.A.S.*, 5th ser. XXXIX (1927), p. 420 ; XLI (1929), p. 407.
[57] Proceedings at Board Meetings, in *T.H.A.S.*, 5th ser. XLII (1930), pp. 417, 420, 433.
[58] Proceedings at Board Meetings, in *T.H.A.S.*, 5th ser. XLVIII (1936), pp. 431, 453.

Colleges was equipped with an experimental farm, a staff of agricultural economists and of specialists and, in addition, the county extension advisory officers.

The impact of scientific knowledge on agriculture was of material help in enabling farmers to weather the storms of the inter-war depression. Farmers were taught how to use the foods given to animals to better advantage, and how to combat many stock and plant diseases, particularly those connected with sheep and pigs, turnips and potatoes. Critical examination of some commonly accepted practices revealed the great importance of the early sowing and planting of crops. Thus it was shown that delays in sowing oat crops after certain optimum dates might result in a daily decline in the oat yield of a quarter of a cwt., or in the case of turnips of half a ton per acre. The greatest material help given by the Colleges during this period, however, was in the use of better grass seed mixtures, particularly those containing wild white clover seed. Not only did the second and third year pastures become much more productive, but grassy weeds like onion couch (*Avena elatior bulbosus*) and twitch (*Triticum repens*) were suppressed, while the arable crops following the temporary pastures became much more luxuriant. The stepping-up of crop and pasture production was accompanied by an immediate increase in stock numbers. In Orkney, for instance, the cattle and sheep population both rose by 70 per cent. in the first half of the twentieth century. Had the times been more prosperous even better results would have been got in the inter-war period. As it was, the foundations were being laid for the great advance in technical efficiency that was to serve both nation and farmer so well in the 1939-45 war.

Striking developments in agricultural education and research took place after the end of the Second World War. The struggle had revealed the great potentialities, as well as the shortcomings, of home agriculture. To ensure a sound basis for British economy, very high output of home-produced food was a prerequisite. This envisaged the full utilisation of agricultural research and the stepping-up of the technical efficiency of the farmer by providing facilities for obtaining and assimilating expert advice. Practical recognition of these ideas has been afforded by the establishment of new research institutes, centres, and organisations for dealing with problems related to horticulture, hill farming, agricultural engineering, poultry and animal breeding, and genetics. The setting up by the Agricultural colleges of a Veterinary Investigation Officer Service has done much to shed light upon certain animal diseases. Another development of the post-war period was the acquisition of the Bush and Dryden Estate by Edinburgh University, a move which not only established closer liaison between the research stations and the teaching and advisory departments of the University and the East of Scotland College, but also ensured the fuller integration of science with practice. Fifteen years after the outbreak of war the value of Scotland's agricultural output had been increased by 50 per cent.— a result largely attributable to the impact of science on agriculture.

# CHAPTER XX

# LIVESTOCK

Cattle in prehistoric times...Introductions from the Continent...Shorthorned and polled types...Sixteenth and seventeenth century importations...Early efforts at improvement in Scotland...Falkland cattle...Enclosures...Baldoon cattle... Irish imports...The food question...Bakewell and his disciples ...Shorthorns, Aberdeen Angus, Galloways, Highlanders and Ayrshires...Milk recording...William Harley, John Speir ...Clydesdale breeders...Robson of Belfort and Cheviots... Blackfaces ... Border Leicesters ... Pig breeding ... Overseas breeds...Diseases and pests.

THE MATERIAL FROM WHICH SCOTTISH as well as English breeders were to evolve the many breeds of livestock which were later to attain world fame was unpromising. It was of mixed origin; most of the animals were small and by present-day standards badly shaped. This is not surprising, for up to the time of the agricultural revolution of the eighteenth century the breeding of farm animals was indiscriminate and haphazard. The promising heifer on the unenclosed common grazings was far more likely to mate with an athletic and leggy bull than with one possessing the qualities that are now prized in a beef animal. Ability to roam, and to live on poor pasture in summer and on poor winter provender was of more importance than size, shape or milking qualities. To give the stock a fair chance to survive the winter, a number of the younger animals were slaughtered in autumn; and since those with the most flesh were selected, they were not available for breeding. Natural selection, too, tended to promote hardiness and liveability without reference to size or shape. While there was some incentive to breed strong animals for draught purposes, large animals did not find favour in Aberdeenshire. They ate too much.

In prehistoric times two distinct types of wild cattle were to be found roaming the forests in north-western Europe—cattle being forest animals. One of them, *Bos primigenius*, was a very large animal with a span of horns even wider than the West Highlanders. A skull a yard in length in the British Museum indicates the animal's great size. The other breed, *Bos longifrons*, was smaller and had a short, thick-set head, a short body with fine bones, and small horns. Skulls containing flints suggest that this type of cattle was hunted in Britain during the Stone Age.[1] It is from these breeds mated with domesticated cattle imported from Europe that our native cattle are believed to have been descended. Their colours are not known for certain, but the fact that black or dun is characteristic of British breeds now native to the most mountainous and remote parts of these islands, has suggested that black was the common colour. But reddish hairs found in bog butter and on the remains of hide-covered weapons confutes this idea. All theories about the early development of our cattle are largely guesses. The dominant yellowish-brown colour of present-day West Highland cattle or the prevailing black colour of the Shetland ponies have been largely induced by adherence to fashion: the original colour of the Highland cattle was largely black.[2] Light-coloured animals were supposed to be soft.

In the first millennium B.C. continental invasions are supposed to have introduced other cattle to Great Britain—the Celtic short-horned type—and these animals were probably crossed with *Bos longifrons*. There was possibly another importation in the days of the Romans. Their cattle were white in colour and the fact that the present-day wild park cattle are white and have somewhat similarly shaped horns suggests some affinity to Italian cattle. With the Anglo-Saxon invasion probably came still another type—the red-coloured animals, the origin doubtless of the Shorthorn, Lincoln, Red Sussex and Devon breeds common in areas where the Saxons settled. The Norsemen came mostly to Britain to harry and to rob, but they settled in north and west Scotland and it has been thought that they introduced polled cattle. This may or may not have been the case; the finding of the skull of a polled animal in the midden of the Roman camp at Newstead casts great doubt on this theory. Yet the Angus Doodies, the Buchan Hummlies, the Galloways and former polled breeds in Sutherland and Skye, had characteristics common to some Scandinavian breeds[3] while their distinctive colour seems to have been brindled or dun. From this admixture our present-day breeds have been largely evolved. The

---

[1] F. H. Garner, *The Cattle of Britain*, London 1944, pp. 9-10.

[2] Mackenzie, *Hundred Years*, p. 15.

[3] Garner, *Cattle in Britain*, p. 10 ; James Wilson, *The Evolution of British Cattle and the Fashioning of Breeds*, London 1909, pp. 45-69.

X

Norman-French invasion did not include cattle. Importations of Dutch cattle to England in the sixteenth and seventeenth centuries could at that time have had little effect in Scotland. Only one breed, the Falkland or Fife, said to have been introduced from England in the time of James IV, seems to have gained a foothold.

Throughout the Middle Ages, and indeed right till near the end of the eighteenth century, Scottish cattle were small with disproportionately large heads and gaunt frames. In winter they were more or less starved; in summer they were stinted of grass, overstocking being prevalent. From birth onwards the calf was poorly nourished with the result that the plough ox was weak and undersized. In England eight animals sufficed to pull the heavy wooden ploughs but in Scotland people spoke of the " twal owsen " plough. They even had names designating the pairs, first the " wyners ", next the " steer draughts ", then in succession the " fore-throcks ", the " mid-throcks ", the " hind-throcks " and lastly the pair designated " fit on land " and " fit in fur ".[4]

It is generally supposed that on the occasion of the marriage of Margaret Tudor to James IV, her father Henry VII of England presented his son-in-law with some English-bred cattle. Whether the intention was to improve the Scottish breeds for working purposes is not known, but their name of Falkland or Fife cattle was derived from their original location—the royal palace of Falkland.[5] They were reputed to be good work oxen but in the less fertile lowland parts such as Aberdeenshire it was difficult to provide these relatively large animals with sufficient food. Nevertheless, young work oxen from Fife were finding their way to the north-east in the latter half of the eighteenth century. For the next eight or nine years they were worked, and aged animals were sold, often to the dealers who had brought them north, but they were usually past their best as work oxen long before that time. In 1766 Aberdeenshire farmers were criticised by a committee of the Farming Club at Gordon's Mill for " the infrugal way they take to replace the cattle that are past their labour ".[6]

Before systematic breeding began to be practised in the eighteenth century " survival of the fittest " seems to have effectively determined the different breeds found in Scotland. In the relatively mild climate of the south-west the hardy, thick-coated, out-of-doors

[4] J. B. Pratt, *Buchan*, Aberdeen 1858, p. 480.
[5] Alexander, *Notes and Sketches*, pp. 69-70.
[6] Wilson, " Farming in Aberdeenshire ", p. 87.

Galloways were evolved. In the western and northern Highlands and Islands the no less hardy or even hardier Highlanders, mostly black or dun in colour, were predominant, the Skye and Sutherland stocks being superior. In arable areas, where cattle were housed, less hardy types were developed—the Buchan Hummlies, the Aberdeenshire Horned, the Angus Polled, the Kyle, the Fife, etc.

But apart possibly from such minor efforts as the introduction of the Fife or Falkland breed to improve the size of cattle in Scotland, no systematic attempt to breed superior animals from native stocks appears to have been made until the seventeenth century, when Sir David Dunbar of Baldoon, Galloway, formed his famous park. In this enclosure, two and a half miles long and a mile and a half broad, he could " keep in summer and winter a thousand bestial " and could mate " his two hundred milch cows " with superior bulls. His pastures must have been good, for most of the cows calved annually.[7] At four years of age his cattle, usually sold for fattening on the rich pastures of Norfolk, were much larger than the normal Scottish cattle of the period. They were so large that a drove of 340 of them, being driven through England in 1682, were mistaken for Irish cattle and were seized. Before the mistake could be rectified 60 were knocked on the head. (At that time England's fiscal policy forbade imports of Irish cattle.)[8] The incident, however, reflects the prevailing small size of Scottish cattle. The same year, 1682, was also the year of Sir David Dunbar's tragic death, the main incidents concerning which were used by Scott in *The Bride of Lammermoor*. Dunbar's successor at Baldoon continued his improvement policy and petitioned the Scottish Privy Council for permission to import from Ireland " six score young cows of the largest breed ". They were to be used only for breeding and he undertook to import no more. At this time the trade in Scottish stores with England was increasing and soon afterwards other breeders in the south-west were following Sir David's example by forming parks and pursuing a constructive breeding policy. Sir George Campbell of Cessnock, for instance, formed a park where he kept " superior horses and cattle ".[9] He, too, asked permission to import animals from Ireland. These attempts at improvement were isolated and did little to influence the size and character of the general run of our cattle. Little or no progress could be recorded until there were enclosures

[7] Chambers, *Domestic Annals*, VOL. III, p. 152.
[8] *R.P.C.S.*, 3rd ser. VOL. VIII, pp. 156-7.
[9] Chambers, *Domestic Annals*, VOL. III, p. 153.

on individual holdings, for only then could an owner ensure the mating of his females with superior bulls. Animals also had to have sufficient food at all times of the year if they were to live and thrive. The indiscriminately-bred animal—the product of natural selection —was often better fitted to endure hard conditions than one which, however well bred, was unlikely to survive in winter on a starvation diet.

English farmers were the pioneers of livestock improvement and the first to demonstrate its possibilities was Robert Bakewell of Dishley Grange, Leicestershire (1725-95). Employing his individual methods he was highly successful in improving the Longhorn breed of cattle, and even more so in the case of the Leicester breed of sheep. Before his time cattle had not been bred for beef. Indeed, the calf that showed signs of putting on flesh rapidly was generally slaughtered for veal. This meant the retention for breeding of the more scraggy animals. Bakewell decided to retain for breeding the best animals as judged from the butcher's point of view. To achieve this he was at pains to examine and record the good and the bad points of every carcass. Beef and mutton were his sole objectives; milk and draught qualities he ignored.[10] We now know that it was by close inbreeding, careful observation and the use of proven sires, that he obtained his remarkable results in so short a time. His bull Twopenny was not only mated with his own mother but was also bred to their daughter, while the product of that mating was bred to his half-sister—again by Twopenny.[11] Through inbreeding Bakewell was able to perpetuate and to intensify the most desirable qualities in his animals. Refusing to sell his best males, he hired them out and carefully observed their progeny. If the hired bull or ram did well he was taken back and retained for home use. The fame of Bakewell's Leicester sheep spread afar, and Scottish breeders took them north to lay the foundations of the Border Leicester breed. Some Scottish hill sheep farmers even tried to introduce Leicester blood into their flocks; but what the animals may have gained in size was lost in hardiness;[12] animals so bred were unable to convert the rough hill herbage into mutton and wool and at the same time retain vitality. Bakewell's Longhorn cattle failed to hold their own with the Teeswater breed which was later to develop into the Shorthorn. His contribution to breeding

[10] Ernle, *English Farming*, p. 185.
[11] Wilson, *Evolution of British Cattle*, p. 119.
[12] Watson and Hobbs, *Great Farmers*, p. 176.

PLATE  V

Lambing time on Inverness-shire hills (Blackface breed)

knowledge lay not so much in the breeds he originated as in demonstrating the possibilities of systematised breeding; to that extent the world of livestock is indebted to him.

Two of his admirers, the brothers Collings from near Darlington, determined to do for their local breed, the Teeswater, what Bakewell had done for the Longhorn.[13] They acquired the famous bull Hubback and by inbreeding, produced the renowned bull Comet. The fame of the Teeswater, or Shorthorn as it was beginning to be called, was by now spreading, and other breeders were soon making their names and adding renown to their breed. Amongst these were some Scottish farmers who, having learned the secret of turnip growing and rotational farming, were anxious to match crop with livestock improvements. By 1789, Robertson of Ladykirk, Berwickshire, and General Simson of Pitcorthie, Fife, had brought some of the animals north to Scotland. These were believed to have been the first Teeswater cattle to be brought so far north, but this is doubtful, since Wight reported that in 1779 Mr Udny of Udny had an English " shorthorned " bull at his Aberdeenshire farm.[14] Whatever the truth, the Teeswater breed, because of its ability to put on flesh rapidly, to mature early and to impress these qualities on its offspring when crossed with native cows, grew in fame. Rennie, the noted farmer of Phantassie, East Lothian, acquired some of the Ladykirk breed, bred them pure and by exhibiting them spread abroad their fame.

Largely owing to the efforts of Rennie and Sir John Sinclair, the Highland Society staged their first livestock show on Boxing Day 1822. Although Rennie won only three first prizes he exhibited twenty-three bullocks of the Teeswater breed. Their outstanding merits impressed visitors and the fame of this breed spread afar.[15] There were no prizes for sheep at this show but eight New Leicester two-year-old wethers were exhibited as well as " two beautiful pigs ". A sale held by Rennie at Phantassie in 1827 was an important event in the subsequent development of the Shorthorn in Scotland. Two men from the north-east—Captain Barclay of Ury, the son of the famous improver, and Hay, of Shethin, Tarves, Aberdeenshire—were buyers. Barclay's purchase of females enabled him to breed his animals pure. Up till this time bulls of the breed had been mainly

---

[13] J. Sinclair, *History of Shorthorn Cattle*, London 1907, p. 25 ; Robert Wallace, *Farm Livestock of Great Britain*, Edinburgh 1885, p. 62.

[14] Wight, *State of Husbandry*, VOL. III, p. 605.

[15] Ramsay, *History H.A.S.*, pp. 162-3.

used, north of the Tay, to mate with native cows. Hay bought
Jerry, a famous bull and, in the parishes around Tarves, the
Aberdeenshire Shorthorn was later to attain high perfection.

Barclay, despite his Quaker ancestry, was a noted sportsman.
He had remarkable physical strength and endurance, but like many
men of his class and all who boxed, hunted, attended cock-fights,
etc., he was given to betting and in consequence sometimes found
himself in financial straits.[16]  Apparently this failing obliged him
in 1838 to dispose of his famed Shorthorn herd. Fortunately, however, he did not cease to breed Shorthorns; only seventeen days
after disposing of his herd he started another. English-bred females
of the bluest blood were bought for him by Wetherell, the auctioneer
who had sold his first herd.[17]  Though lacking the weight of flesh
of his first females the cows mated well with two bulls which had
been kept back from the sale, both sons of a bull named Monarch.
Their progeny and the progeny of another of Monarch's sons which
was later brought back to Ury, constituted a second famous herd.
When it was dispersed in 1847 most of the animals were retained
in the north-east, where Aberdeenshire Shorthorns, under the
master hand of Amos Cruickshank, of Sittyton (variously known
as the " Sage of Sittyton " and the " Herdsman of Aberdeenshire "),
and other notable breeders, were later to attain world-wide
fame.

Now that bone meal was in regular use turnips were being grown
extensively in Aberdeenshire.    Because of the abundance of
succulent winter feed which turnips provided and the high quality
of the oat straw produced, winter fattening of cattle became the
major farming enterprise of the county.    Great attention was
therefore given to breeding animals with a wealth of flesh—animals
that would mature early and fatten on turnips, straw and some oats
or a little oilcake.    Hence the Cruickshank brothers, Amos and
Anthony, strove to provide a type of bull that would cross well
with the native cows to produce the kind of animal most suitable
for fattening for the London market.[18]  Unless an animal was
inherently good it was not selected for purchase or retained for
breeding whatever the length of its pedigree or its showyard honours.[19]
On 29th November 1859, after twenty years of unremitting effort, an

    16 Watson and Hobbs, Great Farmers, p. 144.
    17 Isabella Bruce, The History of the Aberdeenshire Shorthorn, Aberdeen 1923,
p. 22.
    18 Watson and Hobbs, Great Farmers, p. 145.
    19 Bruce, Aberdeenshire Shorthorn, pp. 130 ff.

outstanding animal, Champion of England, was calved at Sittyton. Although by no means perfect, he had the qualities—wealth of flesh, constitution and early maturity—which his breeders were seeking and he proved remarkably prepotent in transmitting them. The blood of this bull became concentrated in the Sittyton herd. His best sons and grandsons were used as stock bulls, but it was only when American buyers discovered the merits of Sittyton-bred Shorthorns that the herd became famous; on the vast prairies of America the descendants of Sittyton bulls throve amazingly well. By his skill and single-mindedness Amos Cruickshank had brought great fame to Scotland. William Duthie, his pupil, and many other Aberdeenshire families—Marrs, Campbells, Durnos, Gordons —and later the Macgillivrays in Ross-shire and others elsewhere, were to prove worthy successors to the Quaker farmer.

Coincident with the creation of beef Shorthorns was another great development in cattle breeding. From 1810 to the end of the century the Aberdeen-Angus was in process of being established, improved and even more widely recognised as a breed of outstanding merit. The breed owed nothing to England in respect of blood; it was created entirely from native material in the counties of Angus and Aberdeen. The story has often been told of how young Hugh Watson, who had just been set up by his father in the farm of Keillor, near Coupar Angus, set out one summer day in 1810 for Trinity Market, Brechin, to purchase animals to augment the numbers, and perhaps improve the quality of the herd (given to him by his father) of half-a-dozen of the " best and blackest cows ". He bought " ten best heifers and one bull ".[20] Using the methods of his many friends in the Shorthorn world, but ever mindful of the type he wished to produce, he soon won success. Two fat animals which he sent to Smithfield Show in 1829 created a minor sensation. One of them, a heifer, possessed both remarkable wealth of flesh and fineness of bone. Earl Spenser, later to become the first President of the Royal Agricultural Society of England, was so impressed by her perfection that he had a medal struck bearing her image.

But had it not been for William McCombie of Tillyfour (1805-80) the Aberdeen-Angus might, because of the growing popularity of the Shorthorn, have been only one of many local breeds. McCombie had been born to the cattle trade, his father having been one of the greatest cattle dealers of the time. At a Falkirk tryst he might

[20] Watson and Hobbs, *Great Farmers*, p. 156.

stance as many as 1500 cattle. Wishing his son to follow a less precarious occupation he sent him to college, but there young William would not settle. He was allowed to come back to the farm, the drove road with its perils and excitement and the staging of cattle at the great trysts and fairs, where his " eye for a beast ", trained by an expert and exacting parent, was the most important asset. And so he became one of the great Scottish cattle dealers of his time.[21] Young McCombie was quick to realise the great potentialities of the Angus cattle of Hugh Watson, Keillor, and his contemporaries. Against powerful Shorthorn competition the breed, in its early stages and despite the classes in which it could compete at the various shows, seemed hardly likely to increase or to spread. But McCombie had faith in the " blacks ", and in this he had the support of Torr, an open-minded, unbiased English Shorthorn breeder. Undaunted he carried on Watson's work on his Aberdeenshire farm of Tillyfour which was high-lying and cold (the name means " cold house ") but eminently suitable to bring to perfection a breed whose carcass qualities have been developed to the highest degree. Under McCombie's master hand the breed achieved high distinction and earned a world reputation. At Smithfield in 1867 his steer Black Prince created such a sensation that Queen Victoria had it taken to Windsor. In 1878 the Tillyfour group of polled cattle won first place at the International Show at Paris in competition with fifty-nine other British and Continental exhibits.[22] It was a magnificent triumph for McCombie and for the breed which he had done so much to advertise and to perfect. The second prize also went to the breed, this time to the Ballindalloch herd. From McCombie's time onward the Aberdeen-Angus breed ranked with the Scottish Shorthorn and the Hereford as one of the world's three best beef breeds. The success of the Aberdeen-Angus and its crosses, at Smithfield and at Chicago, have since been outstanding. It has been customary to refer to Hugh Watson as the founder of the breed, to McCombie as its builder and deliverer, and to Sir George Macpherson Grant (1839-1907) of Ballindalloch as its refiner. For many years after McCombie's time the Ballindalloch herd did much to show the world that, in proportion of fat to lean and of meat to bone, the breed and its crosses could excel.[23]

[21] McCombie, *Cattle and Cattle-Breeders*, pp. xii, xiii.
[22] *op. cit.*, p. xv.
[23] J. Macdonald and J. Sinclair, *History of Polled Aberdeen or Angus Cattle*, Edinburgh 1882, pp. 79-85.

Its ability to transmit these qualities to its offspring is indeed remarkable.

At the early Highland Shows and indeed until about 1860, there were no separate classes for Galloways as distinct from Aberdeen-Angus. Although labelled " polled " animals the two types were otherwise rather widely different. The Galloway was bred, reared and kept out of doors on rough moorland grazing and in consequence was hardy though slow to mature. Early in the nineteenth century its type was well established, but no single outstanding breeder came forward to proclaim its fame. It was rather a case of many improvers, such as Lords Selkirk, Daer and Galloway, and the Murrays, Herons, Maxwells, Gordons, Maitlands, McDowalls and Cathcarts, whose combined efforts created a breed that fulfils a particular function and which, as instanced by recent numerous successes at Smithfield, occupies a high place amongst beef breeds.[24]

Like the Galloway, the West Highlander had been largely evolved, through natural selection, to thrive out of doors on poor food in a rainy, cold climate. In the eighteenth and early nineteenth centuries Skye-bred and Sutherland-bred animals were eagerly sought by breeders in other parts of the Highlands. Improvers were not wanting for this picturesque breed and many folds on the mainland and in the Hebrides, particularly that of Balranald in North Uist, rose into prominence. The breed was developed for beef and has often, at Smithfield and elsewhere, shown that for this purpose its performance is most creditable.

Apart from the Shetland there is only one dairy breed native to Scotland, the Ayrshire; this appears to have been evolved in the latter part of the eighteenth century. Often called the poor man's cow, its function at first was to produce milk from none too nourishing feed. The milk was either sold as such or was made into butter or cheese. About 1808, long before the Highland Society had thought of a show for stock, farmers in the Kilmarnock district instituted one, and this helped to stimulate improvement. But shows for dairy cattle are of only limited value if milk production in the animal is ignored. William Harley, a dairyman on the outskirts of Glasgow, had recognised this principle early in the nineteenth century. Morning and evening, he weighed the milk given by his cows, tested the proportion of cream in the milk and, in 1829, published a book on the " Harleian Dairy System ".[25] He was far in advance of the times, and as has happened to many another

---

[24] Watson and Hobbs, *Great Farmers*, p. 161.  [25] *op. cit.*, pp. 165-68.

pioneer, his system eventually took root only much later—about seventy years in fact—when the Fenwick Farmers' Society began milk recording. But it was largely left to a farmer on the outskirts of Glasgow to persuade farmers generally that, in the absence of recorded milk yields, efforts to improve performance would achieve little.

John Speir of Newton, Cambuslang, the man in question, was one of the first to recognise the inadequacy of a breeding policy for dairy cattle that was based purely on showyard points. In 1903 as a director of the Highland and Agricultural Society he induced his fellow-directors to set aside £200 for a limited scheme of milk-recording and butter-fat testing, to be inaugurated that year.[26] Speir wisely insisted that butter-fat testing should be included. On many of the south-western farms, where Ayrshires predominated, cheese was made. The greater the yield of milk and the higher its butter fat percentage, the greater was the amount of cheese obtained from the cow's seasonal milk yield. In herds devoted to producing milk for cheese-making telling comparisons could be got by recording the milk yields from cows of the same breed, calving at much the same time, grazing the same pasture and subjected to the same climatic conditions. The first tests were made on farms in the counties of Ayr, Dumfries and Wigtown. Since that time the story of the Ayrshire breed has been one of steady and indeed striking progress. Fashionable showyard points, like small-sized teats which bear no relation to production, were given progressively less emphasis. The growing practice of milk recording had in many ways a pronounced educational value.

Long before milk producers elsewhere in Britain had realised the importance of eliminating bovine tuberculosis from their herds and of keeping them free from infection, Ayrshire breeders in the south-west were doing their utmost to clean up their herds. One farmer would decide to get rid of his reactors and his neighbour would often follow suit: in due time large islands free from the disease would be progressively formed and later expanded. Surplus breeding animals from the areas concerned were in great demand all over the kingdom for the establishment of attested herds. For many years in the forties and early fifties of the twentieth century, Ayrshire breeders reaped rich harvests from their skill, fore-sight and determination. In part at least this was an outcome of the work of pioneers in milk testing. With that of John Speir, the

---

[26] John Speir, " Milk records ", in *T.H.A.S.*, 5th ser. XVI (1904), pp. 170 ff.

names of James Dunlop, John Dunlop and Adam Montgomery should be linked as Scotland's pioneers in milk recording.

If we except the breeds of the Shetland and Highland ponies Scotland has produced only one outstanding breed of horses, the Clydesdale. The old native horses were probably not unlike the Highland garron. It is not known for certain whether it was by crossing such native mares with the six black stallions brought over from Flanders by a Duke of Hamilton that the Clydesdale breed was evolved; what is known is that a superior breed of horses, which existed in Upper Clydesdale in the eighteenth century, was characterised by weight, activity, docility and hardiness. As soon as the " twal owsen " wooden plough was abandoned in favour of Small's iron swing plough Clydesdale stallions were hired by agricultural societies everywhere. In the early days stallion shows and ploughing matches played a great part in furthering the interests of the breed, which in its early days produced two outstanding sires in Prince of Wales, owned successively by Lawrence Drew of Merryton and Riddell of Blackhall, and Darnley, also owned by Riddell.[27] These two breeders did notable work in the seventies and eighties of the last century. Through the former stallion some Shire blood is supposed to have been infused into the Clydesdale. At a later date the Montgomery brothers did much to fix the modern type. They owned the famous stallion Baron's Pride and shipped large numbers of Clydesdales overseas. Since their day many outstanding horses have been bred by notable breeders who, despite the competition of the tractor and the gradual disappearance of horses from the farm, still carry on with zest and enthusiasm. The noted veteran breeder, James Kilpatrick, alive at the time of writing, bred and owned many famous animals.

When Wight of Ormiston made his tour of the Border country in 1778 he was greatly impressed by the work done in improving the Cheviot breed of sheep by a young Northumbrian, Robson by name, who had crossed the Border to take the Roxburghshire sheep farm of Belford on Bowmont Water.[28] By the skilful use of rams he succeeded in improving the conformation of his flock and in increasing its clip without impairing the ability of the animals to graze and live on high land with a stormy climate. Two types of Cheviots —the North-country and the South-country—were developed later.

[27] Archibald Macneilage, " Famous Clydesdale sires ", in *T.H.A.S.*, 5th ser. IX (1897), pp. 143 ff.
[28] Wight, *State of Husbandry*, VOL. II, p. 364.

The former was evolved from Cheviots brought north by Sir John Sinclair in 1792 [29] and by other pioneer Cheviot flock-masters who migrated from the Borders and Northumberland in the early years of the nineteenth century. Their object was to produce finer wool than that produced by the Blackface breed. In the north of Scotland, where much of the moorland is relatively flat and has a much lower stock-carrying capacity than the typical moorland of the Borders, there was particular need for a type of sheep that would be an agile walker, able to negotiate freely the soft parts of the hill—the " flow ground " as it is called. This circumstance obliged northern sheep farmers to develop a longer-legged animal with longer and deeper sides than the more blocky type of the Borders. To enable these sheep to attain sufficient size on the relatively poor northern grazings the ewe hoggs, instead of being wintered on the hills, were wintered on low ground and only the strongest of the gimmers (yearlings) were mated. In course of time, a larger type of Cheviot— the North-country type—was developed. Its neck is longer than that of the South-country type, and its ears, instead of being carried erect, are more inclined to the horizontal.

Showyard standards are not always safe guides. In the dairy cow they give no real indication of milking capacity; in the pig they do not show whether the sow is likely to be a prolific breeder or a good mother, so that at weaning time she will have a large litter of young that will later achieve a high live weight gain in relation to the food consumed and will yield carcasses which will satisfy the bacon curer and his customers. In the hill and mountain breeds of sheep the essential feature is hardiness and ability to live and thrive on a diet of very coarse herbage. The type favoured in the showyard may or may not have the ability to withstand the storms and privations of a winter on the hill, to produce a strong lamb and to provide it with an adequate supply of milk. In the middle 1850's false values were assigned in the showyard to certain types of blocky Cheviots,[30] but the severe winter of 1859-60 brought many owners of such sheep to their senses. In fact until British breeders realise that performance is the final test, there will be a continuing risk that they will be misled into selection by showyard standards. The famous breeders Bakewell, Amos Cruickshank and Robson always made utility and performance their prime objectives and Robson linked these qualities to environment.

[29] William Barber, " Breeds of Scottish sheep: Cheviots ", in *T.H.A.S.*, 5th ser. XXVI (1914), p. 125.                    [30] *op. cit.*, p. 127.

PLATE VI

Lambing time near the Pentlands (Cheviot breed)

The hardy Scottish Blackface—descended, it is supposed, from sheep brought from England—has had no lack of improvers but none did so much for this breed in the early days as Robson of Belford did for the Cheviot breed. The Blackface is the breed of the heather moors rather than of the grassy hills and its hardiness enables it to exist on some of the poorest and highest hills of Scotland. Although a mountain breed, the Blackface provides lambs that can be killed at a reasonable size when only five months old, a quality which may probably have been incorporated, about the middle of the nineteenth century, by Howatson of Glenbuck, Lanarkshire. Incidentally, there was already a famous ewe stock on this farm in the eighteenth century. Howatson produced a blocky sheep which was easily fattened, but whose open wool trailed on the ground—an objectionable feature in time of snow. Another type was produced by the Archibalds of Overshiels,[31] whose aim was hardiness combined with a close coat of wool. The battle between the prevailing show-yard standards and those demanded by utility has continued through the years but the mutton qualities of the breed have been progressively developed. The sheep championship at Smithfield was once won by Blackfaces. But one wonders whether mutton qualities have been over-emphasised to the detriment of other essential features in a mountain breed.

The third of Scotland's breeds of sheep is one which, though small in numbers, is of great importance. The Border Leicester is kept, not for mutton production, but for the valuable crosses which it produces with both the Cheviot and the Blackface. It is a branch of the Leicester breed that Bakewell improved; when Andrew Wight of Ormiston toured the Border district in 1779 he found excellent Leicester sheep at Mertoun,[32] where the Border Leicester was afterwards largely developed. For half a century the Mertoun flock was self-contained, no animals being brought in. Close inbreeding must have been pursued,[33] but the value of the breed for crossing with the Blackfaces and Cheviots was improved. The crosses inherit in remarkable degree the style, character and prolificacy of the male parent; the female crosses make excellent mothers, and when mated in turn to Oxford or Suffolk rams give progeny which exhibit the advantages of three-breed crossing and provide the near-ideal mutton carcass.

[31] Watson and Hobbs, *Great Farmers*, p. 181.
[32] Wight, *State of Husbandry*, VOL. II, p. 376.
[33] Watson and Hobbs, *Great Farmers*, p. 178.

At no time has there been any distinct Scottish breed of pigs. Scottish pig-owners were content to follow their English fellows. Sporadic attempts to introduce certain English breeds have been made but until lately only one, the Large White, became firmly established. The formation in 1933 of the Pig and Bacon Marketing Boards drew the attention of breeders to the shortcomings of commercial stock from the point of view of the bacon curer. Steps towards improvement were taken, but the scarcity of pig feed following the outbreak of the 1939-45 war, and the failure by the Ministry of Food to offer sufficient inducements for the production of quality carcasses, restricted further advance in this direction. Soon after the end of the war it seemed to some breeders that a short cut towards improvement could be achieved by importing Landrace pigs, a breed evolved to meet the British demand for uniformly high quality bacon. The Government acceded to a request to allow the introduction of this breed, and as the Danish Government had prohibited the export of their native Landraces the animals were bought in Sweden in 1949. A second consignment of 103 Swedish-bred Landraces imported in 1953 realised at auction an average of £913 per head.[34] Thereafter enthusiasm for Landraces ran riot; selection was disregarded and inferior animals were retained for breeding. Moreover it was shown that the best animals of the Large White breed could achieve quite as good a performance as the Landrace. Slowly the lesson was learned that what matters is not so much the breed, but rather more the methods employed to select for breeding individuals within the breed. Consequently, litter recording, progeny testing and accredited breeding stations as a means of improvement are now in use.

One other breed of livestock for which credit largely belongs to overseas breeders is the British Friesian. Before the prohibition of imports of cattle from abroad, which was imposed to reduce the risk of introducing diseases, large numbers of black and white Dutch cows from Holland[35] were landed at Leith and Aberdeen as well as at the eastern ports of England.[36] They were famed as milk

[34] *The Scottish Farmer Album*, 1954, p. 165.
[35] G. Hobson, " British Friesian cattle ", in *T.H.A.S.*, 5th ser. xxx (1918), p. 40.
[36] Before February 1877 imported Dutch cattle did not have to be slaughtered. Between 1877 and 1889 such cattle had to be slaughtered but from 1889 to 1892 they were allowed to enter free subject to inspection. In 1894 further restrictions were imposed and in 1896 imports of live cattle were prohibited altogether by an amendment to the Contagious Diseases of Animals Act.

producers, though at that time the quality of their milk was not high. But so valuable were they as converters of food into milk that, when imports were prohibited, a number of farmers in the Inverness district and elsewhere tried to establish herds from the available material. Their difficulty, however, was to obtain suitable bulls of the same breed. At last, in 1909, a British Friesian Society was formed and a herd book was instituted, animals being at first admitted on inspection. In 1914 the importation of sixty animals from Holland was allowed [37] and this was followed by other importations at later dates from South Africa, Canada and Holland. An animal of considerably larger frame and requiring more food than the Ayrshire, the British Friesian is unexcelled as a milk producer and the circumstance that, generally speaking, the dairy farmer gets no premium for milk of high butter-fat percentage has tended to make the breed popular, particularly in England. The Ayrshire, its great rival at the London Dairy Show, is by far the more popular in Scotland. It should be added that since the institution of the British Friesian Herd Book there has been a distinct up-grading with respect to the butter-fat content of Friesian milk.

No record of the improvement in stock breeding would be complete without mention of the great progress made in the elimination and control of stock diseases. Cattle were particular sufferers from infectious diseases. Since 1839 there have been repeated outbreaks of foot-and-mouth, and pleuro-pneumonia first appeared in 1840.[38] Hugh Watson's herd was stricken by it. In 1865-66 rinderpest wrought great havoc in Scottish herds, many being wiped out. Energetic action was demanded, and the Cattle Diseases Prevention Act passed on 20th February 1866, made compulsory the slaughter of affected animals. In a single week in March of that year over 10,000 animals were slaughtered in Britain; but by the last week of June the number slaughtered weekly had fallen to 338, and by the end of the year the week's toll had dwindled to 8.[39] Rinderpest, pleuro-pneumonia in cattle and glanders in horses were finally eliminated and a great measure of control established over foot-and-mouth disease, but recurrent outbreaks of this and also of swine fever continue, infection being introduced either by migrating birds, or by food imports from countries affected by these

[37] Hobson in *T.H.A.S.*, 5th ser. xxx (1918), p. 55.
[38] Ernle, *English Farming*, p. 375.
[39] *Report on Cattle Plague during the years 1865, 1866 and 1867.* Cmd. paper 4060, 1868, App. I, p. 4.

troubles. Of late years remarkable progress has been made towards the eradication of bovine tuberculosis and in the control of contagious abortion, mastitis, and two bovine venereal diseases. The veterinary research worker continues to study the nature of the diseases in order to discover methods of control. With the chemist, he provides protective vaccines and sera, the Government administers regulations; the veterinary practitioner carries out the field work, while the farmer plays the part of willing co-operator.

In respect to sheep progress has been no less remarkable. Sheep scab disappeared from Scotland in 1941. Means have been found to deal with liver fluke and other internal parasites, while the recently introduced D.D.T. dips have been most successful in combating external parasites. Inoculation can prevent such diseases as braxy, louping-ill and lamb dysentery. Light has been shed on the cause and treatment of the " pine " diseases. Major losses in sheep can now largely be attributed either to undernutrition or to mal-nutrition, and until practical measures are devised to resolve these problems, particularly in the case of mountain sheep, a fairly high casualty rate seems likely to continue. We can gauge the degree of success achieved in the control of some of the diseases mentioned, not by the number of sporadic outbreaks which continue to occur but by considering, in the light of experience, what would have happened in the absence of prompt measures wisely administered.

CHAPTER XXI

# POULTRY AND BEES

Neglect of poultry...Origin of hens...Arrival in Britain...
Hens as rent...Capons...Medieval egg production...Intro-
duction of light and American breeds...Incubators...Poultry
school for Scotland...Influence of the agricultural colleges...
Egg-distributing stations...Post 1914-18 war developments...
Trap-nesting...Egg-laying competitions...Disease problems...
Accredited stations...Hatcheries...Economies in labour...Fold
units...Battery method...Electricity...Built-up litter...Sex-
linkage...Sexing...Egg grading...Tenth World's Poultry
Congress...Wild and domesticated bees...Bees in medieval
times...First Scottish writers on bees...Bar-frames...Bee
diseases.

THROUGHOUT THE NINETEENTH CENTURY, and indeed up to the
year 1920—a period when attention was being lavished on the
breeding, care and management of the larger livestock—little
heed was given to poultry. Specialist breeders there may have been,
but few were farmers, and in any case they were more concerned
with show points or breeding birds for the table than with egg
production. The subject received little notice in the farming press
for the nineteenth-century Scottish farmer was no lover of hens,
which he was wont to say always died in debt. He resented their
habits of roosting in his cart and implement sheds, of nesting in
his stacks and of trampling down grain just before harvest. He may
even have grudged the modicum of oats which his wife took daily
from the corn bing in the barn. No one, indeed, could say with
certainty whether or not hens died in debt for no poultry accounts
were kept. Yet on many Scottish farms the farmer's wife was
expected to keep the house, *i.e.* to buy groceries for the household,
including those for boarded single servants of both sexes, and even
to clothe her children, on the proceeds of sales of butter, eggs and
poultry. Scavengers the poultry certainly were, for much of their
food was literally picked up. For these reasons farmers tolerated
them but by and large were indifferent to their welfare.

A native of the Middle East, the domestic hen arrived in Britain
much later than most other farm animals. It is supposed that

Y                                          337

trading Phoenicians or the Belgae may have brought her here. Little mention of poultry occurs in ancient farming manuscripts, treatises or books—probably their presence was taken for granted; but the anonymous author of *Hosebonderie* describes how they were managed on English manor farms in the thirteenth century, where under the care of the dairywoman each hen was expected to provide annually 115 eggs and seven chickens, " three of which ought to be caponised ".[1] If hens realised such expectations in those days, no progress in egg performances can have been made until the outbreak of the 1914-18 war, for it is doubtful if the farmyard hens of 1914 averaged 115 eggs a year. Examination of the results of egg-laying competitions instituted in England in 1920 made possible a sifting out of the more efficient breeds and strains for egg production, and the estimated average annual production per bird rose from 120 in the earlier to 175 in the later trials.[2] Since the birds in these trials represented the best stock it may reasonably be presumed that average production on farms in 1920 was no more than 100 eggs a year. There is also the interesting fact that, in the Middle Ages, only two eggs per hen were demanded as teinds. Since these were presumed to be a tenth part of a hen's produce, exclusive of hatching requirements, it seems possible but scarcely credible that a hen's average annual output was then only thirty to forty eggs.

Frequent reference is made to poultry in later medieval times. When rents were paid in kind poultry were usually mentioned as one item. Sometimes a stated number of capons had to be handed over; at other times the term used was " pultre " and sometimes " cocks and hens ". Thus in the Coupar Abbey rent roll the farm of Mill of Keithock had to supply five dozen capons and four dozen fed geese[3]—no small order then. In Glenisla most of the tenants had to supply geese as well as poultry. " Ane " or " twa " geese or " geis " and " ane " or " twa pultre " was a common item in the rent roll of small tenants.[4] In other rent rolls the capon, because of its size and tenderness of flesh, was reckoned to be the equivalent of two " pultre ". Incidentally by the end of the eighteenth century the caponising of male birds appears to have been discontinued. It was reckoned that although a capon was worth so much more than

[1] Ernle, *English Farming*, p. 17.
[2] *op. cit.*, p. 470.
[3] *Coupar Abbey Rental Book*, VOL. I, p. 178.
[4] *op. cit.*, VOL. II, pp. 144-5.

a mature cock he had to be kept until he was three or four years old and in the meantime he had cost much more.[5] Hens that roosted in the cupples of the dwelling houses were termed " reek hens " and down the ages until the middle of the nineteenth century were esteemed as the largest and the best of their kind.[6] The hen-wife of the eighteenth century and later was employed by some landlords to collect the " reek hens "—described as " properly fed fowls "—which the laird was to receive in part payment of rent, as witness Alexander who makes Meg Raffin, the hen-wife, one of the characters in his nineteenth-century Aberdeenshire classic.[7] Ducks are not mentioned in early documents and turkeys were unknown until their introduction from America.

In the urge to erect orderly, substantial stone and lime farm buildings, so prominent a feature of nineteenth-century farm architecture, the hen was not forgotten, for substantial hen-houses were erected to house the mongrel flocks which roamed the farm-yard. But these hen-houses harboured diseases and parasites and hens were wont to roost in trees or on the frames of coup-carts in the cart shed. As for nesting, stable mangers, straw and grain stacks and secluded spots in thickets of tall weeds were often pre-ferred to the orthodox nesting boxes. Bulky and ill-balanced foods were largely provided. Into a big pot of boiled turnips and potatoes —boiling was supposed to increase the value of the food—oat and other milling offals would be dumped and the whole mixed. This, with some scattered oats, was the normal feed which the farmer's wife gave her hens, but for chickens she would spare some oatmeal. This kind of food for hens was ill-suited for the production of the protein-rich egg, but the protein deficiency of the food was to some extent made good by the hen herself; she would pick up seeds, insects, worms and the short protein-rich leaves of grass and clover. She began to lay in spring and continued laying until she became broody. She may or may not have been allowed to hatch a setting. Throughout the summer and possibly part of the autumn she would lay intermittently but she produced few eggs in winter. There were no rings on the legs of the hens to tell the farmer's wife the ages of her individual birds; these she guessed by the abundance or scarcity of leg scales. Birds which survived the common farmyard

[5] Souter, *Agric. Banff*, p. 265.

[6] T. MacLelland, " General view of the agriculture of the Stewartry and of the county of Wigtown ", in *T.H.A.S.*, 4th ser. VII (1875), p. 13.

[7] Alexander, *Johnny Gibb o' Gushetneuk*, Chapter XIX.

poultry diseases might exist for a few years as pensioners, producing some eggs each spring and possibly rearing a few chicks. The late date of natural hatching prevented most pullets from maturing sufficiently to begin laying before the onset of winter; it was probably nearly Easter before they produced eggs. On Easter Sunday on many farms the farmer's children would be given a treat—their first egg of the season, possibly one of the few they would be privileged to get. Eggs, though cheap by modern standards, were then too expensive for use in many farming households.

There were specialist breeders of some of the new breeds that had come in from Asia in the nineteenth century—the Bramah, the Cochin and the Langshan; but most breeders were more concerned with show points or with the production of a large table bird than with specialising in egg-producing strains. The Leghorns, Anconas and Minorcas—all light breeds from the Mediterranean—partially supplied this need, but they were, under the conditions of the times, poor winter layers. It was not until better methods of poultry-keeping were introduced that the value of these light breeds came to be appreciated. Other breeds were introduced from America, e.g. the Rhode Island Red; they were more heavily feathered than the lighter breeds and, under good management, they and their crosses laid well in our comparatively cold winter climate.

Two thousand years ago the Egyptians knew the art of incubating eggs without the assistance of the hen, but not until 1883, when the Hearson incubator was introduced, did artificial hatching become possible in Britain.[8] This valuable invention enabled pullets to be hatched sufficiently early in spring to come into lay in autumn, and to continue to lay all winter. The incubator was, in fact, the foundation of all later developments such as the production for sale of day-olds and broilers and also of the battery and the built-up litter systems.

Soon after the beginning of the twentieth century poultry-keeping began to attract attention. The newly-established Scottish colleges of agriculture, realising the backward condition of the poultry industry, made it their business to see that farmers and their wives should get the best advice possible. But they were severely handicapped by lack of fully qualified teachers. To meet this difficulty the West of Scotland Agricultural College in 1906

[8] Edward Brown, *Poultry Breeding and Production*, London 1929, VOL. II, p. 597.

set up a poultry school alongside the Dairy School of Scotland,[9] and a few years later it became possible to appoint instructresses in both these subjects for most Scottish counties.  In exceptional cases the larger counties were provided with two instructresses, while the smaller or less important often shared the services of a single instructress.  Systematic instruction in poultry-keeping was commonly given in the winter months, the summer being devoted to demonstrating up-to-date methods of cheese- and butter-making; but this instruction, with advisory visits to farms throughout the year, soon convinced farmers and their wives of the value of adopting more up-to-date methods.

When the Board of Agriculture for Scotland was set up in 1912 it took over from the Congested Districts Board a poultry improvement scheme, whereby crofters in the Congested Districts areas could get settings of eggs from flocks of pure-bred poultry kept at approved stations for 1s. a dozen, the Board paying to station holders 1s. 6d. bonus for each dozen sold.[10]  This scheme was extended to the whole of Scotland in 1913, when 149 approved stations for the distribution of eggs were set up.  Before approving these stations the Board arranged that the college instructresses should visit all prospective station holders and satisfy themselves that the quality of the birds, and also the housing, feeding and management of the flock conformed to certain standards.  Visits of this nature led to the weeding out of poorly qualified applicants and to the general grading-up of the quality of the birds and methods of management.  So satisfactory was the scheme that, in its third year of operation, the number of approved stations had increased from 149 to 261, Aberdeenshire and Orkney leading the field.  About this time, for reasons already outlined, incubators were becoming more popular on general farms.  To encourage their use among those less able to purchase them a scheme was introduced in 1915 offering assistance for purchase to small farmers, cottars and farm servants.[11]  In the following year the Board staged at Corstorphine a demonstration showing how poultry should be housed, fed and managed.[12]

The collapse of grain prices in 1921 led farmers to become more "poultry-minded".  Gradually they realised that grain could be more profitably disposed of through the medium of a well-managed

[9] Kirkwood in *Agricultural Progress*, xxv (1950), p. 71.
[10] B.O.A.S., 1st report, 1913, pp. xxx, xxxi.
[11] B.O.A.S., 5th report, 1917, p. xxvi.
[12] B.O.A.S., 6th report, 1918, p. xxvii.

poultry flock than by sale to a grain merchant.    Greater egg production in poultry flocks was called for, and with this end in view the
Board sought advice from the colleges and leading producers.
Visual inspection of birds kept by station holders did not, it was
thought, go far enough since it did not reveal heritable laying
capacity.    To make good the lack a trap-nesting scheme, introduced
in 1921, encouraged approved station holders to record the egg
production of their birds for a specified period during their first
year.    Eventually trap-nesting became compulsory for all approved
station holders.    Meantime in 1923 the Board had set up at Seafield,
near Edinburgh, a laying-test station for a hundred pens of hens and
eighteen pens of ducks, each pen accommodating six birds.    The
testing period ran for eleven months from the middle of October
and the results were published.[13]    This venture was well supported by
breeders, and much interest was shown in the trials by the now
rapidly expanding industry;  the numbers rising from about four
million in 1913 to five million in 1926.    By 1932 they had gone up
to seven and a half millions.    But despite this gratifying expansion
all was not well.    The egg-laying trials did not yield the expected
results, and bacilliary white diarrhoea, a disease transmissible to
chickens by reacting hens, was exacting a heavy toll.    Fortunately
it was found that reactors could be detected by a blood test and in
1929 only hens passing this and the trap-nesting test were accepted
for the Category A station list; [14] by 1933 all stations were required
to keep blood-tested stock.[15]

Poultry keepers were by this time confronted by another new
and puzzling disease termed fowl paralysis, while mortality rates
in general remained at too high levels.    In their eagerness to obtain
high egg production per bird owners had overlooked such important
factors as liveability and longevity.    Moreover, the growing trade
in day-old chicks provided all-too-easy opportunities for the
spread of diseases.    Following the findings of a Poultry Technical
Committee set up in September 1935 to enquire into poultry
diseases, a Poultry Commission was established to regulate the
distribution of breeding stock, while additional powers were taken
to control the spread of poultry diseases.    To provide prospective
buyers with information about sources of eggs and chicks most
likely to be free from diseases the Board, now the Department

[13] B.O.A.S., 13th report, 1925, pp. 52-3.
[14] D.O.A.S., 18th report, 1930, p. 53.
[15] D.O.A.S., 22nd report, 1934, p. 38.

of Agriculture, instituted their scheme of registration of accredited poultry stations. This scheme was a great success and the number of stations rose from 99 in 1939 to 894 in 1948.[16] The corollary to this scheme, now that greater numbers of chickens were being obtained from hatcheries, was the institution in 1943 of the Accredited Poultry Hatcheries Scheme.

The inter-war period saw many important developments. The colony system, which had been introduced before 1914, was widely adopted with advantage to the health of the birds and economy in food. It was, however, wasteful in labour, and the need to economise in this respect led to the invention of many labour-saving devices. Brooder houses, equipped with automatic fountains and feeders, enabled chickens to be reared much more cheaply than under the former foster-mother system; larger incubators were built while the fold unit, which in part replaced the colony house system, economised in labour and helped to fertilise poor land. About the beginning of the thirties, the cage or battery method of poultry-keeping was devised. Birds were confined in individual cages which could be placed one above the other in three or four tiers. The system was advantageous in using a minimum of floor space per bird, in detecting unprofitable birds and, where good arrangements for feeding and watering the birds and removing the droppings were provided, in the saving of labour. Where properly balanced rations were given the system gave good results and it was particularly suitable for winter egg production. Electric light could be automatically switched on at a very early hour so that a " working " winter day of fourteen hours could be arranged at little extra cost, and with great advantage to winter egg yields. Recent developments in this system have been in the direction of economising on labour, food and water being conveyed to the birds at intervals on a power-operated belt system.

The built-up litter system, developed in America as a result of labour shortage,[17] has recently made great progress in Scotland. The method employed is to add fresh litter to the soiled litter in the houses. At first this method aroused misgivings as it was thought outbreaks of disease would follow. In practice, however, it was found to work well under certain conditions. Investigations showed that where success was achieved the droppings were broken

---

[16] D.O.A.S., *Agriculture in Scotland 1939-48*, p. 109.
[17] *Intensive Methods of Poultry Management*, Ministry of Agriculture and Fisheries Bulletin, 1953, p. 2.

down by bacteria and other micro-organisms, and a dry litter with some nutritional value was produced. To enable this litter break-down system to operate properly in Scotland the birds had to be installed in properly insulated and ventilated houses in early autumn while the weather was still warm. Once started, the fermentation process in the litter will, under suitable conditions of management, continue all winter. No other system of poultry management, however, demands so high a level of day-to-day skill. Like the battery system, it provides opportunity for the use of electric light to increase winter egg production. The poultry-yard system is a compromise between this system and the older semi-intensive system.

The years between 1920 and 1953 saw other developments. Farmers at first largely abandoned natural methods of hatching and rearing chicks and adopted the incubator and foster-mother systems. Later, hatching began to be carried out increasingly in special hatcheries and day-old chicks were brought long distances to be auctioned. Since egg production alone was the aim of many farmers the practice of supplying only female chicks became popular and this was done by either of two methods. By cross-mating birds of certain pure breeds sex-linked chickens were produced, the cockerel in such instances being readily distinguishable by its colour from the hen chick. The second was by visual examination of the out-ward sexual parts of day-old chicks. Operators, however, had to be specially trained for this work.

In no other branch of farming have production methods changed so drastically as in poultry-farming. Even at the time of writing new developments were being introduced, like the production of broilers[18] and the use of antibiotics in chicken food. In methods of marketing sweeping changes have taken place. Eggs are now mainly graded for freshness and weight, but comparatively little has been done in practice to grade poultry for table use and great developments along this line are foreshadowed.

In 1954 the tenth World's Poultry Congress was held in Edin-burgh.[19] Some 2000 members and associate members from many parts of the world attended. An admirable exhibition was staged, illustrating the various breeds of poultry, the different systems of

[18] Thomas Whittle, " Chicken for the table ", in *Scot. Agric.*, XXXIV (1955-56) pp. 126-31.

[19] T. Milne, " Impressions of the Tenth World's Poultry Congress ", in *Scot. Agric.*, XXXIV (1955-56), pp. 104-07.

hatching, rearing and management, the production of eggs and birds, and the methods employed in marketing poultry products. This was supplemented by another illustrating recent advances in education and research. The plenary and sectional meetings were well attended and much light was shed on many genetical and disease problems peculiar to this industry.

The story of Scotland's poultry industry in recent years is one of remarkable advance. Her hen population rose two and a half times in the forty years between 1913 and 1953,[20] and this despite the severe handicap imposed by the 1939-45 World War when available poultry feed was drastically reduced. The value of the output from the industry in 1954 was exceeded only by two other products, milk and fat and store cattle. Since one-ninth of the total output of Scotland's farms, on a sale basis, is contributed by poultry,[21] this branch can no longer be dubbed " the Cinderella of farming "; indeed no other branch except pig husbandry has advanced so rapidly of late years.

Bee-keeping has its enthusiasts but at no time has it been one of the general enterprises peculiar to Scottish farming. From early times the bee has been mentioned in writings: Virgil described its habits; it was probably the Romans who brought the domesticated bee to Britain, but verification of this is lacking. Mead, a liquor derived from honey—probably from wild bees—was used by the ancient Britons and one of the early Scottish laws decreed that anyone following and locating a swarm of bees was entitled to possess them. We know, too, that churchmen in medieval times paid much attention to bees, which provided them with honey and wax. Honey, being the only form of sugar then known, was invaluable, and was used in liquids, foods and medicines, while wax was in demand for candles, for salves and other medicinal purposes.[22] To those interested, bees were a source of pleasure and profit. It would seem that after the Reformation, bee-keeping declined in Scotland, but after the end of the sixteenth century treatises such as Charles Butler's *Feminine Monarchie* (1609), John Levett's *Orderinge*

[20] *Agricultural Statistics, Scotland*, (1922) PART I, p. 14, and 1950, PART I, p. 23.

[21] D.O.A.S., *Scottish Agricultural Economics*, VOL. V, 1955, p. 6.

[22] Ernle, *English Farming*, p. 18.

*of Bees* (1634) and Richard Remnant's *Discourse or Historie of Bees* (1637) were produced in England.[23]   More appeared in the seventeenth century, but none originated from Scotland although Scotsmen are known to have kept bees in straw " scapes ".   In the *Monymusk Papers*, John Middleton, the gardener at Pitfeichie, relates how he proposes to kill one of the " scapes " and keep another, and how he sowed mustard near the beehives.[24]

James Bonner, a Scottish bee enthusiast, commented in 1795 on the small number of hives in Scotland and suggested that the stocks might readily be increased twenty-fold.[25]   At that time honey was imported on a large scale from eastern Europe, Danzig being apparently one of the principal ports.   Bonner suggested that if more interest were shown in bee-keeping Scotland could produce all its home requirements.   The prevalent method of smoking the hive and killing all the bees in order to get at the honey and wax he regarded as " barbarous ", and he went on to describe his own system of preserving the life of the bees and securing the honey.[26] This advice was not, however, followed in Scotland generally until the next century.   Thomson in *The Seasons* aptly describes the procedure adopted to get at the honey.

> And fix'd o'er sulphur, while not dreaming ill,
> The happy people in their waxen cells.
> Sudden the dark oppressive steam ascends ;
> And, used to milder scents the tender race,
> By thousands tumble from their honeyed dome,
> Convulsed and agonizing in the dust.

That bee-keeping was not extensively practised in Scotland in Bonner's time is borne out by the paucity of reference to it by parish ministers in the first *Statistical Account* and by the County Reporters.   Three parishes, all in Aberdeenshire, were mentioned as keeping bees.   Birse, where heather and clover adjoin, was credited with 300 stocks.[27]   Kinellar had 39 hives[28] and several tenants kept bees in Lumphanan.[29]   In the summer of 1791 two men in the parish of Birse are said to have each " exported " 500 lb. of honey, the price ranging from 6*d*. to 10*d*. a pound.[30]

[23] Ernle, *English Farming*, p. 106.
[24] *Monymusk Papers*, ed. H. Hamilton, pp. 92, 98-9.
[25] James Bonner, *A new Plan for specially increasing the number of beehives in Scotland*, London 1795, p. viii.
[26] *op. cit.*, p. 24.
[27] *F.S.A.*, VOL. IX, p. 118.
[28] *op. cit.*, VOL. III, p. 497.
[29] *op. cit.*, VOL. VI, p. 384.
[30] *op. cit.*, VOL. IX, p. 113.

The invention abroad of the bar-frame in 1851 did much to stimulate bee-keeping. A hive known as the Stewarton Hive was widely adopted in Scotland, but in the main and until almost the end of the century, most of the colonies were housed in straw skeps.

The establishment of the agricultural colleges and the appointment of itinerant lecturers and advisory officers in bee-keeping did much to stimulate the industry during the current century. Incidentally, more than a century ago, Bonner had advocated the employment by bee societies of skilled bee keepers for advisory work.[31] Nowadays the straw skep is a rarity. Modern hygienic methods of obtaining the honey have been introduced and practised; much honey is now sold in the comb and, in favourable seasons, averages of more than a hundredweight per hive have been obtained. From time to time bee keepers have had to contend with diseases such as fowl brood and acarine disease. For long the origin of the latter remained unknown until Dr Rennie, an Aberdeen research worker, discovered that it was caused by a parasitical mite invading the tracheal system of the insect. Scotland is fairly well favoured for apiculture because of the abundance of white clover in the temporary pastures of her cultivated lands and her natural resources of heather, but these advantages are offset by relatively sunless summers. While considerable developments seem possible in bee-keeping it is unlikely to become more than a spare-time occupation.

[31] Bonner, *New Plan for . . . beehives in Scotland*, p. 228.

# CHAPTER XXII

# GRASSLANDS

Grass parks on monastic estates...Introduction of red clover...
Pioneers of sowing grasses and clovers...Work of Grant,
Cockburn and the Earl of Haddington...Dr Anderson on
grasses...Reseeding...Virtues and failings of rye-grass...
Yorkshire fog on peaty soils...Cocksfoot and timothy...
Rotational grazing...George Sinclair and Charles Lawson...
Introduction of Italian rye-grass and alsyke clover...Robert
Elliot, Somerville, Middleton, Gilchrist and Findlay...Im-
provements effected by slag and wild white clover...Cruick-
shank's work on clay farm in Aberdeenshire...Influence of
agricultural colleges...Assessment of improvement...Feeding
values of grasses...Grass conservation...Grass drying and
ensilage...Grassland management...High manuring and strip
grazing...Moorland pasture problems.

INCORPORATED IN CERTAIN SIXTEENTH-CENTURY LEASES between the
tenants of Galloraw and of Balbrogie and the Coupar Abbey
estate were conditions which have given rise to some speculation on
the question whether the custom of sowing grass seeds in the laying
down of cropped land to rotation pastures was practised then, as it
is today. The tenants in question were bound to prepare certain
parks, after they had been cropped for two years, some for broom
and others for pasture.[1] Thereafter these parks, now enclosed, had
to remain down for seven years before being cropped again while
the grass ones had to be hained for the use of the Abbey. This has
been taken to mean that grass seeds were sown, but it would be
unwise to assume this in the absence of corroborative evidence.
Scottish soils were so full of the seeds of acid-loving grass weeds
like bent and Yorkshire fog that there was probably little difficulty
in getting a " take " of these grasses without artificial aid. In all
probability the word " prepare " in the lease meant fencing the
fields, for it was distinctly stated that cattle had to be excluded from
the broom field. Garden, writing in 1683 about the need for outfield land to " lye in grass " for a period of years, implies that this
was done by allowing indigenous plants to establish themselves.[2]

[1] *Coupar Abbey Rental Book*, VOL. I, p. 180; VOL. II, p. 169.
[2] *Collections for a History of the Shires of Aberdeen and Banff*, Spalding Club,
Aberdeen 1843, pp. 103-06.

Even in the twentieth century one Kincardineshire farmer excused his failure to sow grass and clover seeds in a certain field by saying that the grass grew naturally, and, as for clover, it was a waste of money to sow it because it never grew.

Whatever the facts of the matter the general belief is that it was not until the new system of rotational cropping, founded on the field cultivation of turnips and clover, was introduced into Great Britain that the sowing of grass and clover seeds came to be practised. The man responsible for this was a royalist squire, Sir Richard Weston from Surrey who, because he was a Catholic as well as a King's man, had to flee the country at the time of the Civil Wars.[3] Evidently in 1644 he had visited the Low Countries where, near Antwerp, he saw a field of clover whose wealth of vegetation attracted his eye. It had been cut three times in the season, and so greatly was he impressed with the crops grown and the rotations practised in Flanders, that, in the following year, he wrote his book *A Discours of the Husbandry used in Brabant and Flanders* and dedicated it as a " legacie " to his sons.

It is now known that while the book was still in manuscript, a copy fell into the hands of a writer named Hartlib who pirated it. Hartlib's book was published in 1651 under the title *Legacie*. At a later date another writer made use of Weston's material. The effect of the publicity on the subject of new crops and rotational farming, coupled doubtless with the practical work of Weston after his return to England, was to familiarise readers with these new rotational systems and with the sowing of clover seeds. Weston, a shrewd observer, recommended that the seeds should be sown in late March and throughout April, and that the land should first be well cultivated and limed. The quantity of clover seed recommended was ten pounds to the acre. Once the plants were well established the land could, he advised, be left down for five years. Progress in Britain was doubtless slow for nobody was likely to sow grass and clover seeds in open fields which after harvest became common grazing. Land had first to be enclosed to protect the plants from stock. In 1775 Dr Anderson, an Aberdeenshire farming writer, gave the date when the sowing of such seeds came into common practice in Britain as about a century earlier,[4] and his statement agrees with much other evidence. We know that rye-grass seed was being sown

---

[3] Ernle, *English Farming*, p. 107 ; Peter and Charles Lawson, *Agrostographia*, 5th edn. Edinburgh 1860, p. 11.

[4] Anderson, *Essays*, VOL. II, p. 135.

on the Chilterns towards the end of the seventeenth century. But
it was not until about 1708 that a start was made in Scotland. The
credit for introducing the practice is generally ascribed to the
English-born wife of Lord Huntly, afterwards second Duke of
Gordon. To her northern home she introduced fallowing, hay-
making and the sowing of the seeds of at least tall oat grass. The
Earl of Haddington is said to have been sowing grass and clover
seed as early as 1708 but this seems somewhat doubtful. What is
certain is that Grant of Monymusk, one of Scotland's first improvers,
shows an item in his accounts for March 1719 relating to the
purchase of nine firlots of grass seed for his Aberdeenshire lands;[5]
the particular kinds are not detailed. Both the Earl of Haddington
and Wight, a tenant on the Ormiston estate, are definitely known to
have been sowing grass and clover seeds between 1720 and 1730. The
practice was, however, criticised severely by East Lothian farmers,
their view being that land designed by God for the nourishment
of man, was being misused to produce food for stock. But enlightened Scottish agriculturists were by that time beginning to recognise
the value of these improvements. Maxwell, Secretary of the Society
of Improvers, extolled clover, pointing out that the plant received
much of its nourishment from the air. He also explained how rye-
grass seed should be harvested. Another development of the practice
of sowing these seeds was to lay down land to pasture by sowing it
with seeds gathered from good old pastures : in 1730, we find Sir
William Nicolson of Glenbervie, Kincardineshire, sowing grass
seeds derived from the natural pastures of the district.[6] The view
was evidently widely held, in the second half of the eighteenth
century, that good pastures could be produced by sowing seeds
obtained from the best natural pastures. We find, for instance, that
the policy parks at Glamis Castle were sown down about 1773 with
seed from some of the best natural pastures in Yorkshire,[7] while
the distinction seems to have been drawn even then between seed
obtained from cultivated " white clover " and what we now know
as the " wild white clover ". One writer mentioned that a Hamp-
shire neighbour " sowed the wild white clover which holds the
ground and decays not ".[8]

Another idea, rather widely prevalent at the end of the eighteenth

---

[5] *Monymusk Papers*, ed. Hamilton, p. 72.
[6] Robertson, *Agric. Kincardineshire*, p. 293.
[7] Lawson, *Agrostographia*, p. 17.
[8] Watson and Hobbs, *Great Farmers*, p. 119.

century, was that old pastures were better than new, an assumption which Dr Anderson denied in his *Essays relating to Agriculture*. Not every old pasture was, in his opinion, so good that it could not be improved by being ploughed and resown with the seeds of superior pasture plants, thus ensuring that the land would be colonised only by such plants.[9] Old pastures, he pointed out, contained considerable proportions of inferior plants. Anderson was far ahead of his time. He stressed the importance of leafiness and winter greenness in grasses,[10] advocated what we now know as rotational grazing[11] and pointed out that rye-grass tended to produce flower stalks and seed, had a shallow root system, did not resist drought well and hence was not nearly so valuable a grass as was commonly supposed.[12] His association with Linnaeus, the celebrated Swedish botanist, who along with colleagues and correspondents had studied the palatableness of some six hundred plants for stock, interested Anderson in assessing their grazing value.[13] A report on the subject by Linnaeus had been translated into English by Stillingfleet,[14] but he, unfortunately, used only the Latin names of the various plants, so Anderson published the names in English.[15] His enthusiasm for some of the natural grasses—the poas, the smaller-leaved fescues and Yorkshire fog—and his dislike of rye-grass made him over-estimate the value of these grasses. He erred in thinking that, by cultivation alone, better strains of these plants could be evolved. At the time he wrote his essays, timothy, so called after Timothy Hanson, an American, had only recently been introduced from North Carolina, so that Anderson had little opportunity to assess its merits. Cocksfoot, like timothy a native of Europe but also introduced from North America, had, he thought, certain possibilities but he deemed it too aggressive and tufty for use in a seeds mixture and observed that stock were not really fond of it. His comments on both these grasses were qualified, however, by his observation that he had had too little opportunity to assess their value.[16]

Dr Singer, the Dumfriesshire reporter, observed in 1812 that when a crop of rye-grass hay was allowed to become over-ripe the land was scourged[17]—a view previously put forward by Anderson. Singer also reported on the use made of Yorkshire fog in establishing

[9] Anderson, *Essays*, VOL. II, pp. 135-8.
[10] *op. cit.*, pp. 160-72.
[11] *op. cit.*, pp. 196-201.
[12] *op. cit.*, pp. 155-72.
[13] *op. cit.*, pp. 242 ff.
[14] *op. cit.*, Appendix, p. 237.
[15] *op. cit.*, Appendix, p. 238.
[16] *op. cit.*, pp. 171-5.
[17] Singer, *Agric. Dumfries*, p. 238.

swards upon newly reclaimed mossy lands. Large amounts of the various clover seeds, red, white and yellow, used to be sown; some proprietors like Lord Cathcart in fact stipulated the amounts to be sown, in leases granted for thirty-one years.[18] Doubtless the heavy seedings of clover then customary reflected the general difficulty in establishing satisfactory clover " takes " on land that was either too acid or was too deficient in plant nutrients. Even that shrewd observer Lord Kames recommended over-heavy seedings of the clovers—24 lb. to the acre.[19] He did not, however, underestimate the virtues of white clover; indeed he described it as the best pasture plant. One very useful purpose for rye-grass was in laying down meadows fertilised by town sewage. Thus the meadows at Craigentinny, fertilised by the sewage from Edinburgh, formerly yielded successive cuttings of rye-grass throughout the growing season.[20]

Faulty as the grass seed mixtures of the time may have been, they helped to put the Scottish rotational system, in which temporary grasses were included, on a sound footing. By balancing summer with winter keep, by restoring fertility to the over-cropped soil, by spreading out the work of the farm throughout the year, and by helping to rid the arable land of such a troublesome weed as couch, temporary pastures were made complementary to arable crops. On poorer land, too, these pastures, though less close in the " pile " or " sole " than good natural grasslands, were generally much more productive.

Anderson's dislike of rye-grass was not altogether unjustified. Repeated saving of seed from crops sown in the previous year had led, even then, to the predominance in commerce of short-lived, seedy types; hence the search for leafier, more persistent and more productive strains, some of which were produced and their seeds marketed. The most noted was Pacey's or Peacy's, which appeared in commerce about the beginning of the nineteenth century. Singer, reporting on the agriculture of Dumfriesshire, described Pacey's rye-grass as a strict perennial which came early, produced more leaves and had better spikes and more seed than the ordinary sorts.[21] A superior strain appears also to have been selected by the farmer of Lampits near Carluke in Lanarkshire.

[18] Lawson, *Agrostographia*, p. 16.

[19] Henry Home, Lord Kames, *The Gentleman Farmer ; being an attempt to improve Agriculture, by subjecting it to the test of Rational Principles*, henceforth cited as Kames, *Gentleman Farmer*, Edinburgh 1766, p. 126.

[20] T. B. Franklin, *British Grasslands*, London 1953, p. 93.

[21] Singer, *Agric. Dumfries*, p. 239.

Indefatigable in its efforts to encourage agricultural experiments the Highland Society devoted much attention to grass problems. In 1828 it offered a handsome premium to competitors who would determine the comparative advantages of laying down land to pasture with and without a nurse crop. The Society was also concerned about the best means of stocking pastures. About this time two Scotsmen were to add much to the store of knowledge on pasture formation. George Sinclair, a Berwickshire man who had entered the service of the Duke of Bedford, made an intensive study of pastures and of their composition. In his *Hortus Gramineus Woburnensis*[22] he prescribed seed mixtures for temporary and permanent pastures. The other Scot was Charles Lawson of the seed firm of Peter Lawson and Son of Edinburgh which, from about the year 1810, had been experimenting with different grasses and clovers. In 1833 the results of Lawson's studies were given to the public—first in the *Quarterly Journal of Agriculture* and latterly in the booklet *Agrostographia or Treatise on the Cultivated Grasses* of which six editions were printed. The extravagant use of seed, so characteristic of the practice half a century earlier, was still common. The firm felt that they had a mission, and the seeds mixtures which they advocated for one year's hay and two years' pasture aggregated little more than 50 lb. of seed per acre. Recommendations were made for different kinds of soil and for short- and long-duration leys.

To Peter Lawson and Son we owe the introduction of Italian rye-grass. It was apparently first obtained from Hamburg in 1831: Thomson of Banchory also appears to have brought home some seeds that year. In less than twenty years, by which time seed was being procured from home sources, 25,000 bushels were being sold annually. Other plants were experimented with; one of them, the tussock grass, *Poa flabellata* from the Falkland Islands, was thought to be suitable for the peaty maritime soils of Orkney and the Hebrides. In 1834, Stephens, a drainer, introduced alsyke or "hybrid" clover from Sweden. Lawsons at once realised its value and recommended its use in mixtures.[23] By their careful assessment of the value of the more important pasture plants combined with business integrity, Lawsons were able to extend their connexions to many parts of the world, and at the same time to raise the standard of the British seed trade. Although in the light of modern knowledge

[22] G. Sinclair, *Hortus Gramineus Woburnensis*, London 1816.
[23] Lawson, *Agrostographia*, p. 20.

Z

their seed mixtures were not ideal, they served to bring about considerable improvements. The Lawsons realised, though perhaps not fully, the value of cocksfoot and timothy and they were of great service to farmers in recommending much smaller amounts per acre of rye-grass and clover seed than those which had been customary. Sad to record Charles Lawson, who instigated the great work of this firm, died in poverty.[24]

Despite the precept and example of Lawson and others, progress in the knowledge of different pasture plants and seed mixtures was disappointingly slow. For temporary pastures two bushels of home-seeded and home-dressed perennial rye-grass per acre, along with a pound or two of cocksfoot, four pounds of red clover (purchased under such various names as broadleaved red, cow grass, and perennial red), one pound of alsyke and a pound of ordinary short-lived white clover, composed up to the twentieth century the standard mixture for one year's hay and two years' grazing. Ayrshire farmers specialised in the growing of rye-grass seed for sale but shortages of rye-grass seed on Aberdeenshire farms were often made up by dressed seed from the hay loft. Fortunately, since the seed of perennial rye-grass usually germinates well and since much of the hay crop was fairly mature before being cut, good takes were generally obtained though by the third year the rye-grass plants had largely disappeared except on the best soils. In dry summers, too, rye-grass pastures on light land " burned " badly and in any season cattle intended for immediate fattening had to be taken indoors by about the end of August and fed mashlum and early turnips.

The great and prolonged agricultural depression which started in the 1870's caused much of the poorer land to be laid down to permanent grass. The Scottish farmer, in his ignorance, used his ordinary seeds mixture with the result that after two or three years few plants were left of the sown grasses and clovers; their places were taken by bent, Yorkshire fog, mat grass, rushes and many other weeds. The plight of the English farmer was often worse, for he had been accustomed to use the seed of short-lived plants for a one year's hay crop. Much of his land, now abandoned for cropping, was in fact not seeded, being simply allowed to tumble down to grass and in due time being colonised by plants natural to the area. The quality of the resultant swards was determined by the particular species that became established and by the management of the self-sown pastures. Some of the famed cattle-fattening

[24] Watson and Hobbs, *Great Farmers*, p. 129.

pastures of Leicestershire and Rutland were self-seeded, but most self-seeded pastures were inferior in quality and productivity.

To focus attention on these defects Faunce de Laune of Sitting-bourne, Kent, contributed an article on the laying down of permanent pastures to the 1882 *Journal of the Royal Agricultural Society*.[25] Rye-grass, in his opinion, was no better than a weed and should not be used in pasture mixtures. He maintained that it was so aggressive in its early stages that it crowded out other desirable long-lived plants, yet it was itself so short-lived that it quickly left room for weeds. De Laune's provocative paper excited much speculation. Amongst those interested was Robert H. Elliot, a Scot who had acquired a fortune in India. Returning home he bought the Roxburghshire estate of Clifton near the English border and in 1887 took over the farm of Clifton-on-Bowmont, extending to 1,250 acres of which 450 were arable. There he experimented with various kinds of pasture plants. Much of his soil was of the poor, thin type often associated with arable land skirting the hill-sides, and his work led him to believe that it could best be brought into fertility by forming a good pasture, composed of deep-rooting plants, and ploughing down the resultant turf. He regarded grass not merely as a feed for stock but also as a fertiliser and soil builder, transferring plant nutrients from the subsoil to topsoil. A century earlier Dawson of Frogden had realised the value of grass as a restorer of fertility; his view was that the fertility of all but the best land in Scotland could be restored after a course of cropping only by sowing it down and allowing it to remain in grass for a period of two to four years.[26] " Farming in a circle, unlike arguing ", wrote Lord Ernle more than a century later, " proved a productive process ".[27] The adoption of the ley rotation to complete the circle had long before put Scottish agriculture on the map. But mere restoration of fertility was not Elliot's final objective; it was rather the pro-motion of fertility. This, he thought, could best be done by sowing the seed of the longer-lived and deeper-rooted grasses and other pasture plants, and by leaving the land down to grass for at least four years. The plants selected had thus to be persistent, deep-rooted, palatable to stock, and able to resist both drought and the

[25] Faunce de Laune, " On laying down land to grass ", in *Journal of the Royal Agricultural Society of England*, henceforth cited as *J.R.A.S.E.*, 2nd ser. XVIII (1882), pp. 229-64.

[26] J. S. L. Waldie, " William Dawson 1734-1815 ", in *Agricultural Progress*, XXVI (1951), PT. II, p. 96.

[27] Ernle, *English Farming*, p. 174.

invasion of inferior species. With the help of Hunter, a Chester seeds merchant, he set out to discover such plants. Rye-grass was discarded as unsuitable, but use was made of cocksfoot, the taller fescues and tall oat grass, of late-flowering red clover and kidney vetch with the herbs burnet, yarrow and chicory—drought-resistant plants, some of which had been advocated a century earlier by Singer of Dumfries.[28] Elliot thought that these herbs contained nutrients which were lacking in the grasses and clovers.

Accordingly he set out to show that pastures could be made to build up the fertility of soils through deepening them, extracting plant nutrients from the subsoil and storing them in the turf while also promoting better physical conditions. A firm believer in the fertilising properties of good pastures, Elliot in his enthusiasm over-stressed their manurial effects. Self-confident in his views and pronounced in his prejudices he derided any farmer who questioned his ability to grow a full crop of turnips without either dung or artificial fertilisers. Yet we find elsewhere in his book that he himself used artificial fertilisers, though probably at a later stage, for his turnips; he erred in thinking that his deep-rooted plants would transfer sufficient fertility from the subsoil to the topsoil to permit the production of a succession of first-class crops : he also overdid the number of species in his mixtures and he under-estimated the value of rye-grass. Nevertheless, he drew attention to the value of cocksfoot, to the need for drought resistance and persistence in pasture plants, to the importance of a leguminous base and to the soil-building properties of pastures. Had the merits of wild white clover been known in his time, and had he used sufficient lime and phosphates to ensure its luxuriant growth, he might have achieved revolutionary results. Firm in his beliefs the " daft Laird ", as he was dubbed locally, wrote, lectured and showed visitors round his fields so willingly that his work became widely known. A born experimenter, he criticised the Government of the day for doing so little to encourage experimental and educational work in agriculture. Though a pathfinder he was preacher rather than scientist; his Clifton Park system did not achieve all that he claimed; but the value of his work in disclosing some of the latent possibilities of pastures in relation to soil improvement was indisputable.

Across the Border in Northumberland, three other pathfinders,

[28] R. H. Elliot, *The Clifton Park System of Farming*, London 1943, pp. 41 ff. ; Singer, *Agric. Dumfries*, p. 243.

all progressive Scots, were at work on pasture problems about Elliot's time. Somerville, the first of these, approached the problem of improving poor pastures from a different angle. By manuring the poor, bent-ridden pastures of Cockle Park (the Northumberland County Council farm) with finely ground basic slag, a source of phosphate previously deemed useless as a fertiliser, he obtained astonishing results. The slag-top-dressed Tree Field pastures became a carpet of thriving white clover, and the sheep grazing them put on three times as much weight per acre as those on the control plot. They even put on a half more liveweight, on the 10-cwt. per acre slag plot without other food, than those on the " cake but no manure " plot; moreover they left almost three times as much profit as the latter.[29] Middleton, who succeeded Somerville, developed his work, but when he in turn left Cockle Park to be succeeded by Gilchrist, there was another development in pasture improvement. While continuing to demonstrate the effects of basic slag, Gilchrist applied his mind to seed mixtures, his object being to determine the most valuable plants from the standpoint of production, tolerance one to another in the mixtures, drought-resistance, endurance and cheapness. By trial and error he evolved the famous Cockle Park mixture [30]—simple, cheap, effective and admirably adapted for temporary pastures. When the merits of wild white clover were discovered shortly before the beginning of the First World War, Gilchrist was one of the first to recommend its use.

While Gilchrist was experimenting with his seeds mixtures another worker, William Findlay of Aberdeen, was engaged in similar investigations. A keen investigator, but extremely cautious, Findlay on his small plots at Craibstone determined the influence of one plant, or one crop, on another and why red clover grew in one place and failed elsewhere: he observed the influence of different manures, seeds and preceding crops on the yields of rotation hay and succeeding pastures, and worked on many other baffling problems. Like Gilchrist, he evolved simple, cheap and effective grass and clover seed mixtures. Long before the Seeds Act was passed Findlay had advised farmers to buy only seeds with a guarantee of purity and germination, and he was adamant on the question of the strain of red clover. So decided were his views, so respected were his opinions, and so effectively did he argue with farmers and

[29] Watson and Hobbs, *Great Farmers*, p. 137.
[30] *op. cit.*, p. 138.

seed merchants about the importance of this matter, that in the north-east farmers refused to sow and seedsmen refused to stock red clover seed from France, Chile, or any country where there was doubt about the hardiness of the strain. Like Gilchrist, Findlay was one of the first to draw attention to the wonderful grazing and fertilising properties of wild white clover. The numerous scattered small plots, sown with seed of wild white clover which he supplied to former students of the North of Scotland College of Agriculture, retained their greenness throughout the winter, were constantly grazed by stock in summer, and, when ploughed, yielded heavy cereal crops.

The notable work of Somerville, Middleton and Gilchrist at Cockle Park was in one respect matched in Scotland by that of an Aberdeenshire farmer, James Cruickshank. The farming of the cold clays of Buchan which had bankrupted many a hard-working tenant, acted as a challenge to him.[31] Abandoning the growing of turnips—always a precarious crop on these clays—he grew mashlum—mainly beans and oats—instead, and ensiled the crop in a tower silo, the first of its kind in Scotland. When his land came to be laid down to pasture he was at pains to sow a good mixture containing the seed of wild white clover, and to apply heavy dressings of slag. As early as 1910 [32] he was buying wild white clover seed, being probably the first Scottish farmer to do so on any scale. The result was a marvellous transformation. Former almost derelict land produced the finest of pastures and, when ploughed, yielded between four and five times as much grain per acre as it had done previously.[33]

The discovery of the merits of wild white clover was perhaps the greatest in British agriculture since the worth of artificial fertilisers had come to be recognised nearly a century earlier. Rotation pastures, instead of deteriorating in the second, third and sometimes later years, became even more luxuriant with age; animals grazing them could often be fattened without oilcake or other supplements and, instead of fading away after June or July, as they had formerly done, the pastures continued to grow on steadily until October. The wild white clover banked fertility in the land for the use of succeeding crops; the nitrogen gathered by its roots nourished the sown grass plants and so repelled invasion by weeds

[31] James Cruickshank, "Clay farming and ensilage", in *T.H.A.S.*, 5th ser. XXXVII (1923), pp. 23, 33.
[32] *op. cit.*, p. 29.      [33] *op. cit.*, p. 31.

while the more luxuriant follow-on grain crop had a pronounced smothering effect on such weeds as might have survived. Cleaning the land for the fallow crop, previously an arduous task, now became easy; the former middens of weeds disappeared, for few perennial weeds were left to gather.

The agricultural colleges quickly spread the good news of the wonderful effects of wild white clover; its introduction was an important factor in mitigating the effects of the 1921-39 depression. If grain and potato prices fell much below the cost of production, more stock could be kept because of the improvement not only of the pastures but of all crops, and output in terms of total produce was significantly increased.

One difficulty associated with grassland improvement had been the determination of the relative nutritive values of the different species of pasture plants and their strains. Their bulk, earliness and palatability could be observed visually and their respective results on the stock grazing them could be noted. Thus bent and Yorkshire fog pastures, though productive enough in quantity, were deemed inferior because stock did not thrive so well on them as, say, on rye-grass—white clover pastures. Obviously, then, the bulk and weight of the produce of the different pasture plants might be misleading, and some better method of assessment than by the eye was necessary. Somerville had indicated one method by recording actual liveweight increases on experimental plots. Another worker, Dr David Wilson (afterwards Sir David Wilson of Carbeth), attempted a solution by a chemical analysis of plants. The results of his researches were published in the 1886 and 1889 *Transactions* of the Highland and Agricultural Society. He showed that the younger the growth of the grass, the greater was its feeding value, and that as grass approached maturity it gradually became more fibrous and less digestible. He found that the young leaves of grasses might be more than twice as nourishing, on a dry-matter basis, as those cut at an older stage, and showed that at a given early stage of growth there was but little difference in chemical composition between one species and another.[34] His researches convinced him that the partiality of animals for different grass species at various stages of maturity was closely associated with their chemical analysis and nutritional value. The value of his work was not fully appreciated until thirty or forty years later when, in the making of dried grass

[34] David Wilson, " The nutritive value and produce of grass and clovers ", in *T.H.A.S.*, 5th ser. I (1889), pp. 1-45.

and grass silage, wide differences became apparent in the chemical analysis and feeding values between the processed feed made from grasses which had been cut at different stages of growth.

Despite the depression in farming the inter-war years saw far-reaching and striking developments in grassland husbandry. The breeding of more prolific, more persistent and leafier strains of pasture plants became the objective of scientific workers both in State-aided and privately owned plant-breeding establishments. It was no easy task, since straightforward assessments based on the weight of produce were far from reliable guides in selection. The strains produced had to be assessed for palatability, earliness or lateness of growth, leafiness, persistence in face of competition from other species in the mixture, and reaction to varying soil and climatic conditions and to different systems of management. Even when superior strains of grasses were evolved the maintenance of their purity was no easy matter because of the danger of wind-pollination by neighbouring less desirable strains. Many other problems were tackled with vigour and zest. Following up the work initiated by Dr Wilson, workers at Cambridge drew attention to the high nutritive qualities of young leafy grass. This paved the way for progress in grass drying and ensilage. Engineers, working in collaboration with chemists and other scientists, devoted much attention to designing efficient grass-driers. Other machines were developed to ease the problems of collecting and loading grass cut in the short leafy stage and intended for silage or for drying.

During the First World War German workers had evolved a system whereby the productivity of grasslands could be greatly increased by the application of heavy dressings of fertilisers, particularly those rich in nitrogen. To make the fullest use of pastures so treated a system of rotational grazing was evolved. By concentrating stock on relatively small areas, without restricting their grazing needs, pastures could be grazed down to a low level within a day or two. These portions were then rested on the principle that leaf makes root and root leaf, the stock meantime being similarly grazed in rotation on other areas. By the time all these areas had been grazed and sufficient time allowed for recovery the first-grazed area was bearing a thick but relatively short sward of leafy herbage. The advantage of the system was that there was little waste from the tramping, dunging and urinating of the animals, while the whole energy of the grass plants, instead of being dissipated in flower and seed-production, was devoted to producing highly nutritious leaves. Developments in the use of electrical fences made this system of rotational grazing a practical proposition. But owing to grass having different growth rates throughout the season it was not an easy system for beginners; it called for the exercise of sound judgment on the part of those in charge.

At Aberystwyth work of far-reaching importance was done by Professor Stapledon in training the students to become " grass-minded ". There every aspect of grassland husbandry was investigated. One of his pupils, Martin Jones, who had come to Scotland, did notable work in drawing attention to the very important part that correct management could play in determining the output and the period of useful life of a sward. He also showed how the problem of wintering ewe lambs inexpensively off the hill could be eased by reseeding in-bye land and conserving the grass so produced for use *in situ* by the animals during the early winter months.[35] Other notable work has been done by Dr Gregor of the Scottish Society Plant Breeding Station in providing superior strains of pasture plants and in demonstrating the value of the complementary aspect of improvement in pastures.

Unfortunately the inter-war agricultural depression discouraged farmers from attempting changes involving considerable expenditure. The use of wild white clover in grass seed mixtures had enabled production from rotational grass to be greatly stepped up, and most farmers were therefore content with that form of improvement; other improvements were made only after the ploughing-up campaign was launched in 1939, and the necessity for making fuller use of our grasslands, so as to release land for cropping, came to be realised.

Grassland improvements initiated on farms during the war were projected right into the post-war period when the great increase in supplies of lime and fertilisers, combined with the introduction of subsidies and the prevailing attractive prices for produce, induced farmers to grow more grass on fewer acres. The results obtained were most gratifying. Using stock-equivalent figures, to make allowance for the reductions in horses and sheep between the years 1938 and 1954, it would seem that by the latter year the equivalent of more than 200,000 extra cattle were being grazed on 200,000 fewer acres of grass.

Important as this aspect of grassland improvement is in raising

[35] D.O.A.S., *Hill Farm Research, Report of the Scottish Hill Farm Research Committee*, 1951, pp. 39 ff.

output, it does not exhaust its possibilities. More than a century ago John Boswell referred to the correlation between grass and cropping by pointing out that, without grass, severely cropped land cannot be restored to full fertility and that, without cropping, grass cannot be made to continue at the maximum level of production.[36] The possibilities of exploiting grassland as an aid to cropping are great; equally great are the possibilities of raising grassland output through the plough and cropping.

Scotland is a hilly country, and rather less than a quarter of its land surface is under crops and grass; of its total surface area of 19 million acres no fewer than 11 million are classified as rough grazings. These, with their associated in-bye lands, support a population of two and a quarter million ewes besides followers, and partly feed a cattle population of about a tenth of a million. The character of these grazings varies greatly, some being predominantly heathery and others just as predominantly grassy. Where the rainfall is heavy or the land is wet *molinia* (white bent) may dominate the pasture. Some plants, notably the so-called cotton grass, which is confined to the boggy land and is untouched by stock in summer, are valuable in providing animals with a palatable and highly nutritious food in early spring—a time of year when other nutritious feed is extremely scarce. In a snowstorm, when pastures cannot easily be grazed, the green shoots of the heather plant are of particular value to stock.

The commonly accepted and widely practised methods of improving these rough grazings have been systematic burning of the old heather plants to induce the growth of more nourishing leaves of young plants, open drainage to trap surface water, opening up the bogs to encourage the growth of sweeter and more palatable herbage, flushing slopes with spring water charged with lime, and the control of bracken. When these age-old methods were introduced is not known, but it seems unlikely that much by way of improvement was done on hill lands until the first half of the nineteenth century. Prosperous times, from then until 1879, encouraged farmers to practise these means of improving hill grazings. Furthermore the reclamation at this period of considerable areas of in-bye land, which enabled more winter keep to be grown, enhanced the stock-carrying capacity of hill farms. But despite these improvements the stock-carrying capacity of many hill grazings declined. This was

[36] Sir R. George Stapledon, " Grassland ", in *Agriculture in the Twentieth Century*, p. 218.

particularly true from 1879 and onwards for the next sixty years and was attributed to such factors as the reversion of the former green crofting areas to their original herbage.[37] and to the spread of bracken and aggressive grasses like *molinia* and *nardus*. This deterioration has stimulated the ecological study of plant communities, a subject which had been neglected up to the time in question. Noted pioneers in this aspect of grassland were the late Dr W. G. Smith of Edinburgh and his brother.

Soon after the outbreak of the Second World War it became apparent that, if the hill grazings of Scotland were to produce more food and wool for the nation, special measures would have to be taken. A committee—the Hill Sheep Farming Committee— appointed to deal with the matter recommended among other things that State assistance should be provided to rehabilitate hill farms and restore the land to fertility, that more research should be undertaken on problems connected with hill sheep farming, that the minimum of restriction should be applied in regard to heather burning, and that the breeding of hardy stocks of cattle on the hills should be encouraged, so as to prevent further deterioration of the pastures and wherever possible to promote improvements.[38] Many of these recommendations have been adopted, generous assistance being provided by the State.

Since the publication of the Committee's report much publicity has been given to the value of cattle on the hills as a means of increasing overall productivity. In individual instances, such as Glenlochay in Perthshire, very considerable increases in output in sheep and wool have followed from the cumulative effects of adding limited numbers of cattle to the sheep stock and of applying other known means of improvement. In Lochaber, on moorland at a low elevation, cattle kept on the ranch system have replaced sheep, winter keep being provided by cropping both old arable and newly reclaimed land. On the Aberdeenshire-Banffshire border, a windswept dry heather moor, with associated old arable land, has been converted from a low-grade sheep farm carrying a hill ewe with its lamb for every ten acres into a flourishing cattle ranch carrying a superior cow and calf for every eight acres.

A complete answer to the problem of fully utilising our hill grazings has, however, yet to be found. The abundance of summer is

---

[37] J. Macdonald, " Agriculture of Sutherland ", pp. 83-4.
[38] *Report of the Committee on Hill Sheep Farming in Scotland*, Cmd. 6494, 1944, pp. 86-7.

largely wasted. The seasonal increase in the regular breeding flocks or herds kept on the hills goes but a small way to provide enough stock to convert the summer vegetation into useful animal products. Of necessity, the numbers of these breeding animals must be restricted to what the grazings can support during the winter season with the help of some low or in-bye land or of purchased hay. Much prominence has been given to the problem, and many extravagant suggestions for more cattle on the hills have been put forward, but the experience gained by a few pioneers does suggest that by keeping an appropriate ratio—usually a low one—of hardy cattle to sheep, and by the adoption of other known means of improvement, the output from our hills could be considerably increased. The problem is, however, largely economic, and the absence of reliable information on the economic aspects of the different systems of improvement practised is undoubtedly a deterrent to progress.

The importance of all aspects of hill farming has, however, been considered so great that a Hill Farming Research Organisation has been established and three hill farms, representative of the main areas associated with hill sheep farming, have been acquired for research and experimental purposes. The problems studied will be many. Some will be connected with the breeding of hill sheep, others with their nutrition, while one of the most important will be to determine the optimum level of nutrition for a hill ewe at various stages of its life and to discover how that level can best be achieved.[39]

[39] A. R. Wannop, " The hill farming research organisation ", in *Scot. Agric.* XXXIV (1955-56), pp. 178-80.

PLATE VII

Cattle on the hills, Ross-shire

## CHAPTER XXIII

# THE POTATO

Arrival in British Isles...Value as food and crop...First mention in Scottish literature...Garden and table curiosity... Introduction to Scotland...Opposition...Value recognised... Use confined to autumn and winter months...Early kinds recommended...Lazy-bed cultivation in Highlands...Dominant role as crop, north and west...Effects on population... Partial crop failures...The rival turnip...Disastrous seasons... Blight...Relief measures...Check in rise of Highland population...Depopulation...Effects elsewhere in Scotland...Breeding new varieties...Paterson's Victoria, Nicoll's Champion, Findlay's Up-to-Date...Scottish seed-potato trade...Wart disease... Scottish-grown wart-immune seed...Inspection of growing crops...Synonyms...Registration of new varieties...Research into diseases...Rise in yield...Export trade...Early potato industry...Virus-tested stock...McIntosh...Scientific breeding...Economic value.

T HE FACT THAT AFTER ITS INTRODUCTION to the British Isles, Scotland took so long to adopt the potato as a crop and as an article of food, is a reflection on her insularity and conservatism. Almost a hundred years elapsed after the plant had been brought to England and the south of Ireland, supposedly about 1586-88,[1] before there is any known mention of its having been grown in Scotland. The need for it was certainly great. The people of Scotland were often short of food, particularly in the seventeenth century, and in the closing years of that century famine conditions were specially severe; yet the potato could provide a valuable article of human food and the plant was well suited to Scottish conditions. No other food crop could be grown in satisfying amount on so little land or for so small an expenditure of labour; it was appetising and nourishing and contained the valuable Vitamin C, the deficiency of which in Scottish diets up till 1750 accounted for the general prevalence of scurvy. Kail, a specific against that trouble, was formerly unknown

---

[1] R. Salaman, *The History and Social Influence of the Potato*, henceforth cited as Salaman, *History of the Potato*, Cambridge 1949, pp. 148-57; Whitehead, *Potato*, p. 16.

in many part of the Highlands, and as late as 1794 scurvy was noted, not only in the growing industrial towns where gardens were few, but also in some lowland country parishes.[2]  One reporter in the first *Statistical Account* noted in 1795 that scurvy had become much less common because of the more liberal use of vegetables.  Doubtless the improvement was due, in large measure, to the growing use of potatoes as a food.[3]

In Ireland the potato had quickly become popular.  It could be successfully grown on most soils; it suited the " lazy-bed " system of cultivation, and possibly under Ireland's somewhat humid conditions, may not have suffered greatly from the " degenerative " virus diseases spread by green-fly.  Incidentally it is doubtful if insect-borne virus diseases were present in Britain before 1750. The fact that in Ireland the tillage land was only allowed to be grazed by stock after the end of October (by which time the potato could be lifted) obviated one of the difficulties that militated against its cultivation in England.  There the potato made far less headway than in Ireland, presumably for such reasons as the opening up of the unfenced fields for grazing immediately after the grain harvest, the hidebound regulations of the Open Field system which admitted of no variation in cropping,[4] and the relative suitability of the land in England for cereals, particularly wheat.

Despite frequent contacts in the seventeenth century between Scotland and Ireland and between Scotland and the Low Countries, where the potato was also extensively grown, no mention of this valuable plant is made in Scottish literature until 1683.  In that year John Reid in *The Scots Gard'ner* recommended its use as a garden vegetable and gave directions for its cultivation.[5]  At that time the only gardens, apart from the kail yards, were those owned by the nobility.  Again in 1683 we find the potato included in the list of plants in the physic garden attached to Edinburgh's School of Medicine.[6]  Evidently it was then a curiosity, its appearance on the table being limited to some special occasions in one of the wealthier households.  In 1701 it figured in the Duchess of Buccleuch's household-books as a purchase, a peck costing 2s. 6d.

Nobody conceived the use of the potato as a staple food for ordinary people or as a valuable food-producing plant that could be

---

[2] *F.S.A.*, VOL. XI, p. 193.          [3] *op. cit.*, VOL. XV, p. 143.
[4] Salaman, *History of the Potato*, pp. 202-03.
[5] Reid, *The Scots Gard'ner*, 1683 edn., pp. 107, 116, 120 ; *The Gard'ners Kalendar*, Edinburgh 1683, pp. 4-7.
[6] James Sutherland, *Hortus medicus Edinburgensis*, Edinburgh 1683.

grown in the field until Donaldson, the first Scottish writer on farming, recommended it, in his *Husbandry Anatomized* [7] to " husbandmen " or others who had large families. Donaldson was presumably well aware that in Ireland the potato was an important food crop that could be successfully grown on the lazy-bed system; he was in many respects a theorist and his recommendation was not adopted by Scottish farmers of the period. Another writer, presumed to have been Lord Belhaven, [8] had been impressed by the use of the potato in Flanders and recommended his countrymen to grow it; but once again the results were disappointing. Gradually, however, the plant came to various parts of Scotland, and passing as it were from the dining halls of the mansions by way of their kitchens to the poorer dwellings, was adopted as a staple food crop. A cadger brought it in 1717 to Strathaven in Lanarkshire [9] and from England it was taken by pack horses to Edinburgh about the year 1720. We know that John Cockburn was growing potatoes in his garden at Ormiston in 1724 and from his correspondence with Wight, his tenant, we gather that in 1726, if not earlier, he was growing them in a field at Ormiston; he wrote of the profit realised on a quarter of an acre and assured Wight that he would have a good crop of barley on the land where he had grown potatoes. [10] Robertson, the Kincardineshire reporter, stated that an old soldier had brought the potato from Ireland to Marykirk about 1727, but that he stayed only one year and nobody followed his example. [11] The potato came to the county of Kirkcudbright from Ireland in 1725. [12] For other lowland Scottish counties the dates of its introduction are given as between 1729 and 1739. A Kilsyth man, Thomas Prentice, is said to have been the first to grow potatoes in the open field, the date being 1728, [13] but Cockburn's correspondence with Wight lays the claim open to doubt. In any case field culture seems to have been thought impracticable—on account of the supposed

---

[7] Donaldson, *Husbandry Anatomized*, p. 117.

[8] John Hamilton, 2nd Baron Belhaven, *The Countrey-man's Rudiments ; or, an Advice to the farmers in East-Lothian how to labour and improve their Ground*, Edinburgh 1699, p. 32.

[9] Salaman, *History of the Potato*, p. 389.

[10] Anon. in *Farmer's Magazine*, 1804, pp. 135, 440 ; Cockburn, *Letters*, pp. xxv, 21 *n.*, 98 *n.*

[11] Robertson, *Agric. Kincardineshire*, p. 277.

[12] J. E. Handley, *Scottish Farming in the Eighteenth Century*, London 1953, p. 180.

[13] Patrick Graham, *View of the Agriculture of Stirlingshire, with observations on the means of its improvement*, Edinburgh 1812, p. 172.

delicacy of the plant—until Robert Graham, another Kilsyth man, showed how it could be done successfully in 1739.[14] His subsequent renting of land for its cultivation, in the neighbourhood of six of the principal towns in Scotland's lowland belt, helped to popularise it.

In the Highlands and Islands the potato was apparently introduced only in 1743 when, as has been stated, Clanranald brought some tubers from Ireland and forced his clansmen in south Uist to grow them.[15] Martin Martin, in his book on the Western Islands of Scotland, published in 1703, mentions that the potato was used as a food in Skye[16] at that time. This however, seems unlikely, in view of the reluctance of Clanranald's people (who had many comings and goings with Skye) to accept it. Salaman in his book *The History of the Potato* evidently misinterpreted Pennant by suggesting that that author stated that the potato was introduced to Tulloch in Perthshire about 1722. What Pennant stated was that Alexander Christie set up the first bleaching ground at Tulloch about fifty years ago, *i.e.* about 1722, and was the first person to introduce the right culture of potatoes into this country.[17] Although no mention is made in the first *Statistical Account* of the date of its introduction to Skye, Nicolson states in his *History of Skye* that it was introduced soon after 1750.[18] By 1756 it had arrived in Lewis, and possibly in some of the parishes in Orkney and Shetland; the *Statistical Account* reporters for these latter areas give only approximate dates for its introduction.[19] From the Islands it probably spread to the western mainland areas of the Highlands. It seems that the minister was often the first in the parish to adopt the crop. In Assynt, Sutherland, the parish minister successfully experimented with potatoes in 1765, and in the following year persuaded his parishioners to grow them.[20] In some inland parishes of the Highland counties they appear to have been grown as early as 1754, which was the date of their introduction to Fortingal.[21] In Boleskine and Abertarff in the centre of mainland Inverness-shire the potato was introduced about 1764.[22] Curiously enough, so great was the

[14] *F.S.A.*, VOL. XVIII, pp. 282-6.
[15] Walker, *History Hebrides*, VOL. I, p. 251.
[16] Martin, *Western Islands*, p. 201.
[17] Salaman, *History of the Potato*, pp. 363-4 ; Pennant, *Tour*, VOL. II, p. 112 *n.*
[18] Nicolson, *History of Skye*, p. 305.
[19] Salaman, *History of the Potato*, pp. 364, 382.
[20] *F.S.A.*, VOL. XVI, p. 187 *n.*
[21] *op. cit.*, VOL. II, p. 459.                    [22] *op. cit.*, VOL. XX, p. 30.

prejudice against the plant that people of the lowland Moray Firth parish of Ardersier, in which Fort George is situated, refused to grow it, and largely in consequence suffered great privations after the disastrous harvest of 1782.[23] Even in 1790 they were still refusing to grow potatoes. The probable reason was that Ardersier, like other lowland parishes bordering the Moray Firth, had a soil and climate well adapted to growing grain crops, so that the people saw no particular need to resort to any new crop to augment the supply of food. At this time this parish in most years exported a considerable amount of grain.

The situation was different in the Highlands and Islands where poor, thin, stony and peaty soils were ill adapted for the growth of cereals and the rainy climate militated against successful ripening and the securing of the grain crop. While in ordinary years the returns from grain crops were small, in poor harvests it was not uncommon to reap little more than the seed sown. To people who were constantly facing food shortages and who, at least in the islands, had often to resort to shell-fish for nourishment,[24] the potato was a welcome addition to the food supply. It was most adaptable to their soils and to their lazy-bed system of cultivation and until 1845 was not affected by " blight ". At a time when settled rule and rising standards of health were reflected in an increasing population, the potato provided a sure means of augmenting the food supply both of the people and of their stock. Walker, in his *Economical History of the Hebrides*, wrote that eleven years after its introduction to Lewis the potato replaced bread for half of the year.[25] Later he noted that the haulms were being cut as food for animals while still green, a practice which he deprecated.

Why, we may well ask, only half the year? The probable explanation is that, when the crop was first introduced, the people grew only late varieties and were still unfamiliar with methods of storage. Consumption began only in August or September, and ceased soon after December.[26] After it had become an established practice to store potatoes in earth-covered pits on the ground—or in frost-proof houses [27]—they continued to be used until sprouting started in April, after which no more were eaten until the new crop was

[23] *F.S.A.*, VOL. IV, p. 90.
[24] Nicolson, *History of Skye*, p. 306.
[25] Walker, *History Hebrides*, VOL. I, p. 187.
[26] Kames, *Gentleman Farmer*, p. 117.
[27] Thomson, *Agric. Fife*, p. 188 ; S. Smith, *View of the Agriculture of Galloway*, henceforth cited as Smith, *Agric. Galloway*, London 1810, p. 144.

ready. Even after the beginning of the nineteenth century when it was customary to use them up till June, Neill, a prominent horti-culturist, drew attention to the fact that, since people did not grow early and second early varieties, they were deprived of potatoes from June until September. Neill recommended the following varieties as earlies: Ashleafed, London Early, Superfine and differ-ent sorts of Early Dwarfs. For second earlies he advocated Cumber-land Royal, Early White Kidney, Early Manly, Early Red and Early Flat, the last being much the best.[28] Incidentally he advised sprouting the seed tubers in the case of earlies. Of the late varieties grown at this time we know little. They were largely classified by their shape and colour, and are referred to as the Long White, the Red, the Purple, the Dun, the Pink Eye and the Long Kidney.[29]

At first the cultivation of the crop was carried out entirely by the spade or, in the Highlands, by the *càschrom*. Large-sized tubers were selected for seed, probably because people thought that they would produce large-sized tubers. The seed tubers were cut, care being taken to ensure that each piece had an eye. The setts were either covered with earth or were dibbled in. Lord Kames seems to have been one of the first to advocate the use of the plough in growing the crop in the field.[30] Dawson of Frogden, the father of Berwickshire agriculture, by developing turnip-growing in drills also showed how eminently suitable potatoes were for drill culti-vation. In the Hebrides, however, lazy-bed cultivation continued to be common.

With ever-widening knowledge of how best to cultivate, to manure and to store the potato and also of its value as a food, it became increasingly popular. This was particularly true of the Highlands, which had been rudely shaken by the Forty-Five rebellion. There it grew well on newly-broken virgin land; it responded to dresssings of dung, seaweed, peat ashes and, in inland areas, to bracken cut in the green state. Moreover, its cultivation fitted in well with the lazy-bed system and with the seasonal requirements of the kelp industry which, towards the end of the eighteenth century, had become highly profitable. Thus its introduction slowed down the rate of emigration and, in part, enabled crofters who had been displaced by the clearances, to eke out a living on new holdings in their native areas. Finally the potato was a valuable food for stock

[28] D. Duncan and P. Neill in Sinclair, *General Report*, VOL. IV, pp. 419-21.
[29] *F.S.A.*, VOL. VIII, p. 338.
[30] Kames, *Gentleman Farmer*, p. 116.

in winter. For feeding to animals two large-growing coarse varieties
—the Yam, probably the same variety still known under that name
as a "rogue", and the Tartar, were grown.[31] In the Lowlands,
horses, cattle, sheep, pigs and poultry were fed on potatoes as were
also cattle and sheep in the Highlands. The potato was indeed the
root of scarcity. According to Chalmers the population of the five
counties of Argyll, Inverness, Ross and Cromarty, Sutherland, and
Caithness rose from 211,381 in 1755 to 309,228 in 1821.[32] But in
spite of this increase food was more plentiful than it had been before
the Forty-Five. Macdonald, writing in 1811 about the Hebrides,
estimated that potatoes constituted four-fifths of the food of the
people and that one-fourth of the total quantity grown was fed to
animals.[33]

From Islay and Kintyre large quantities were shipped to the
Clyde ports. Even townsfolk would sweep the streets to get horse
droppings as manure for their few drills leased from a neighbouring
farmer. In such cases the farmer supplied the horse and his subtenant the hand labour; but farmers were so willing to sublet their
land for potatoes, to get it thoroughly cleaned and manured, that
they sometimes gave it rent free. Married farm workers engaging
themselves for the year, would stipulate for the produce or use of
so many yards of drills—often 1000-1600 yards. Cottagers grew
the crop freely. Lord Kames' dictum that the potato was a comfortable food for "low people" was indeed true.[34] At the beginning of
the eighteenth century the potato had graced only the tables of the
rich; in the end it became the mainstay of the poor. So popular
did it become that the minister of Banff reported that landlords were
at first apprehensive lest the increasing production should lower
the price of grain.[35]

Reporters in the first *Statistical Account* and many travellers
hailed the potato as the "saviour" and "mainstay" of the people,[36]
"the richest present the New World ever made to Europe".[37] At
the time in question it seemed to be an unmixed blessing, although
Walker maintained that the ease with which it could be grown
encouraged laziness. Salaman has said that in some parts men were

[31] Somerville, *Agric. E. Lothian*, p. 139 ; F.S.A., VOL. XVII, p. 167.
[32] G. Chalmers, *Caledonia*, VOL. V, Paisley 1890, p. 5.
[33] Macdonald, *Agric. Hebrides*, p. 232.
[34] Kames, *Gentleman Farmer*, p. 117.
[35] F.S.A., VOL. XX, pp. 326-7.
[36] *op. cit.*, VOL. XIX, p. 249 ; VOL. XVIII, pp. 200, 283.
[37] *op. cit.*, VOL. XVII, p. 166.

eating as much as 8 lb. per head per day. Previous figures in connexion with the Islands [38] show that the crofters of Skye were apt to neglect their cereal crops and concentrate on the potato. It had assumed a dominating role in the food habits of the Highland people—so much so as to invite disaster in the event of a crop failure. Fathers subdivided their holdings so as to allow their sons to marry, the potato, for the time being, having solved the food problem of the croft.

Partial failures occurred in the early years of the nineteenth century but the causes of these failures are obscure. Prominence was given in the *Transactions* of the Highland and Agricultural Society to reports describing a partial failure in the year 1833,[39] when the seed tubers seem to have failed to sprout. The prevailing custom of cutting seed and of leaving the cut setts in a heap before planting, coupled with the circumstance that the spring of that year was exceptionally warm and sunny and the ground was dry, may have been the chief cause. In other cases partial failure of the crop seems to have been due to skin diseases attacking the sprouts. The year 1835 brought a serious failure of the crop in the Highlands, but this seems to have been the result of an exceptionally cold and wet season.[40] Cases were also reported of potatoes rotting in the pits, and of their being frosted. One of the volumes of the *Transactions* of the Highland and Agricultural Society gives an interesting account of how Sir George Mackenzie raised new varieties from the true seed. The production of new varieties seems, however, to have been rare at that time.

In the closing years of the eighteenth and the opening years of the nineteenth century the great field rival to the potato was the turnip. The two had many points in common; they had been introduced about the same time; both were cleaning crops, and both yielded large amounts of food per acre. The potato was, however, more suited for human consumption than the turnip which was better suited to animals. In the Highlands the turnip never made much headway, mainly because of lack of fencing and the fact that the arable ground became common pasture after harvest; but it was otherwise in the arable districts of eastern Scotland, particularly after supplies of phosphatic manures (bone meal and superphosphate) became available. But despite the relatively important

[38] See p. 278.
[39] Articles on the failure of potato crops, in *T.H.A.S.*, 2nd ser. v (1834), pp. 27-44.                          [40] Salaman, *History of the Potato*, pp. 374-5.

PLATE VIII

Healthy                    Unhealthy (Leaf curl)

Healthy                    Unhealthy (Mosaic)

POTATOES: EFFECTS OF VIRUS DISEASES

place of turnips in east Scotland, the potato was up till 1845 the more important crop in parts of Perthshire. This was explained by its being grown largely for shipment to London.[41]   Indeed, during the first part of the nineteenth century so much land was devoted to this crop in the Perth area that many farmers in that neighbourhood reduced the fertility of their farms.

Such lowland farmers as grew too many potatoes for sale, in common with the Highlanders who had become too dependent on the crop, received a severe shock in 1845 when a serious attack of " blight " led to a crop failure. This was a new disease which had evidently reached Europe from America, where it had been recognised in 1843.[42]   It would seem from certain accounts that it affected some Scottish potato crops in 1844, but its grave nature was not realised until 1845 when, in a few midsummer days, it blackened and killed the haulms in many areas. Up till July the weather had been good but thereafter it was cloudy, foggy and rainy. Fortunately, the crops in the northern Highlands and Islands were less seriously affected than in many parts of Scotland; in Argyll and Islay a third of the crop was lost. Such a loss, in an area where the potato was the people's staple food, was serious enough, but worse was to follow. In 1846 "blight" reappeared and this time did much more damage. It swept the land, leaving in its trail only putrefying vegetation. Such tubers as had been formed mostly rotted in the ground. The loss for the Highlanders was calamitous. In Ireland, which had a similar visitation, the situation was too grave to be dealt with by relief measures. Thousands of people died from starvation, while dysentery and other diseases associated with famine carried off many thousands more. Between the censuses of 1841 and 1851 the population of Ireland fell by more than 1,600,000. Fortunately the problem in the Highlands and Islands was of much smaller dimensions. Relief committees, instituted in Edinburgh and Glasgow, collected £100,000 which was largely spent on oat-meal;[43] many Highland proprietors provided their tenants with large amounts of meal. In those years Norman, the twenty-second chief of the MacLeods, spent so much of the family inheritance in supplying the wants of his tenants that in order to recoup his fortunes he turned wage-earner, accepting a post as a clerk in the Home Office,[44] while Osgood Mackenzie's mother never at that time left

[41] N.S.A., VOL. X, Perthshire, p. 185.
[42] Salaman, *History of the Potato*, p. 291.     [43] *op. cit.*, p. 376.
[44] Nicolson, *History of Skye*, p. 354.

the family estate of Gairloch.　So short were supplies of potatoes
that even the better-off families in the Highlands could not purchase
them, and Osgood, as a boy, had instead to eat rice, which he disliked.[45]
In Glenurquhart, Gairloch, Lewis and elsewhere much money was
spent by generous proprietors on relief works.

The potato famine of 1845-47 brought to a close this hundred-
year period of rather unhealthy Highland development.　During
that time the potato had become the mainstay of the common people
of the Highlands and Islands; despite emigration and constant drift
to the towns its introduction had enabled the population, and the
area of arable land, to be greatly increased and had, generally
speaking, mitigated hardships; it had fostered the subdivision of
holdings and also the creation of independent crofts as distinct from
land held in run-rig.　No plant in the history of the Highlands had
exerted so profound an influence on the lives of the people.　Moreover, it had come to the Highlands when the old way of life under
the clan system had been rudely disrupted.　But now that the potato
was known to be vulnerable to "blight", a new era of progressive
decline was ushered in.　The census year 1841 saw the Highland
population at its peak and each successive census thereafter marked a
decline.　In Skye, for instance, the first census taken in 1801 indicated a population of about 16,000; by 1841 a peak figure of 23,000
had been reached; by 1901 the population stood at only 13,800 [46]
and by 1951 it was down to 8,265.

Elsewhere in Scotland, since there was much less dependence on
potatoes, the disasters of 1845 and '46 were less severely felt.　In
certain respects these disasters benefited agriculture.　Perthshire
farmers, by paying more attention to the growing of turnips and
the fattening of cattle, raised the general standard of their farming.
Moreover, by 1860 a fresh development in potato variety production
had started.　The " Lumper ", one of the most popular varieties
grown before 1845, had been found to be extremely susceptible to
" blight ", and the general failure of all varieties at that time to resist
the disease was considered to be due to the worn-out and enfeebled
condition of the plant.[47]　Revitalisation was thought to be the
remedy, and since most of the varieties then in existence in Britain
did not readily set " plums " owing to the anthers not being fully

[45] Mackenzie, *Hundred Years*, p. 29.

[46] Nicolson, *History of Skye*, pp. 401-2.

[47] Mrs Paterson, " On the cultivation of the potato ", in *T.H.A.S.*, 4th ser.
VIII (1876), pp. 122-6.

developed, new varieties were accordingly introduced from various countries and from these introductions " selfed " seedlings were obtained. One of the most notable potato raisers of the period was William Paterson (1810-70) of Dundee. He procured potatoes from several countries and, depending mostly on the selection of " selfed " seedlings rather than on deliberate hybridisation, he produced a large number of distinct varieties. One of these, the well-known Victoria, was raised in 1856 and marketed in 1863. The production of this variety raised the standard of potato growing in Britain. Some half-a-dozen other raisers adopted Paterson's methods, one of the most notable being another Forfarshire man, John Nicoll (1830-90), who won fame as the breeder of Champion, raised in 1863 and marketed in 1876. This variety had considerable powers of resistance to "blight" and in the disastrous season of 1879 it with-stood the attacks of this disease better than other varieties.[48] Because of its "blight" resistance and its excellent cooking qualities it became popular for home consumption. In Ireland Champion was to become a favourite potato, and it continued to be widely grown as late as the period between the two World Wars.

The next notable Scottish breeder was Archibald Findlay, a potato merchant and farmer of Markinch in Fife. His Up-to-Date (1891) was an outstanding main crop variety,[49] yielding large crops of well-shaped, smooth-skinned tubers. It was also suited to warmer countries and became a favourite variety in South Africa. With the introduction of this superior cropping variety Scotland's seed potato trade, hitherto of modest dimensions, began to expand. Findlay was the raiser of several other varieties, among the best known being British Queen and Majestic. His Eldorado is said to have fetched £150 for a single pound during a period of boom.

In one respect Scotland's much reviled climate has been a great asset to her agriculture. Aphids (greenfly) the transmitting agents of some of the worst of the degenerative virus diseases, do not infest potato crops in Scotland to nearly the same degree that obtains under the warmer and less windy conditions of England's summer. In consequence, Scottish-grown potato seed is far less likely to be affected with certain insect-borne virus diseases than seed grown in England. Although the reason why Scottish seed should have been relatively free from leaf curl was unknown at the beginning of the

[48] Salaman, *History of the Potato*, pp. 166-7.
[49] *op. cit.*, p. 168.

nineteenth century, Yorkshire farmers were already getting their seed either from a moorland district or from Scotland. Tuke, who wrote one of the reports on Yorkshire, mentions this practice and Brown, who reported on the agriculture of the West Riding, observed that the farmers avoided curl by getting seed from Berwick.[50] According to Walker leaf curl is supposed to have come from Lancashire by imported seed. It was first observed in the Lothians about 1773.[51]

It must not be supposed that all Scottish-grown seed is free from insect-borne virus diseases. There is evidence that potatoes were suffering from curl at the beginning of the last century; this is to be found in the general reports on the agriculture of Midlothian,[52] Fife [53] and Perth.[54] In Midlothian about 1810 it was noted that the disease rarely occurred on farms over 400 ft. above sea level. The control practised was to get seed from a higher and later district. Thomson, the Fife reporter, also alluded to this practice while Robertson, the Perth reporter, stated that seed obtained from Dunira near Comrie was free from the trouble. Another Robertson, the reporter for Kincardineshire, found that the curl did not occur in that county.[55] So high was the reputation of Scottish-grown seed that many years ago English farmers began to procure their seed from Scotland, largely on a farm-to-farm basis. Scottish farmers who had migrated to south-eastern England in the 1880's and 1890's and who found that the seed brought with them from the north gave much larger crops than that grown locally, did much to extend the practice. But long before 1914 the trade in Scottish-grown seed potatoes had been greatly expanded and had largely been placed in the hands of merchants.

About the time of the outbreak of the 1914-18 war wart disease threatened the potato-growing industry with disaster. No remedy for infected land was known and, at a time when food imports were imperilled by enemy submarines, there was deep concern about the future of potato growing. But the timely discovery that certain varieties were immune to the disease saved the situation. The

[50] Robert Brown, *General View of the Agriculture of the West Riding of Yorkshire*, Edinburgh 1799, p. 101 ; J. Tuke, *General View of the Agriculture of the North Riding of Yorkshire*, London 1794, p. 150.

[51] Walker, *History Hebrides*, VOL. I, p. 257.

[52] Robertson, *Agric. Midlothian*, p. 108.

[53] Thomson, *Agric. Fife*, p. 186.

[54] James Robertson, *General View of the Agriculture of the County of Perth*, henceforth cited as Robertson, *Agric. Perth*, Perth 1799, p. 173.

[55] Robertson, *Agric. Kincardineshire*, p. 278.

remedy was to allow only immune varieties to be planted on infected land. English growers, aware of the benefits of planting Scottish seed, naturally looked to Scotland to supply the required immune seed. Scotland's seed potato growers and merchants and her Board of Agriculture responded to England's appeal. Immune varieties were planted to produce seed which had to be true to type and free from impurities according to a prescribed standard. To facilitate control a voluntary scheme for the field inspection of growing crops was instituted in 1918 by the Scottish Board of Agriculture.[56] So successful was this that, at the request of the seed potato trade, it was later extended to embrace non-immunes. Another development resulting from the wart disease outbreaks was the realisation that potatoes were affected with many diseases that had previously been ignored or had passed unnoticed. Steps were accordingly taken towards investigating the cause and determining measures for control. Much confusion was also caused by the multiplicity of names given to individual varieties. Thus the popular variety Up-to-Date had nearly two hundred synonyms, some of which were also applied to other varieties.

Since the number of wart disease-immune varieties possessing such other desirable qualities as cropping power, cooking quality, shape and resistance to certain diseases was relatively few, a great impetus was given to breeders to produce new immune varieties. Steps were also taken to clear up the confusion in nomenclature, to record the distinctive features of each variety and to classify all varieties as immune or non-immune. A Potato Synonym Committee was appointed to do this and it was later entrusted with the work of registering new immune varieties of superior merit. Up till and including 1951 only twenty varieties had been deemed worthy of registration, so exacting were the tests applied.[57]

Meantime much good work had been done under the Scottish potato inspection scheme in purifying and in building up healthier commercial stocks. In 1922 stocks true to variety and substantially free from degenerative and other diseases were designated " stock seed " and from time to time standards for stock seed have been raised. In 1932 a health-grading inspection scheme for all crops was introduced. Further steps were taken later to build up virus-tested stocks from single plants. In the development of this work Dr McIntosh of the Department of Agriculture for Scotland took

---

[56] D.O.A.S., *Agriculture in Scotland*, 1951, p. 10.
[57] *op. cit.*, pp. 14-15.

a leading part. Largely as a result of these measures the yield of potatoes gradually rose. Thus the average Scottish yield had risen from 5.6 tons per acre in 1891-1900 to 7.2 tons in 1941-50.[58] For Great Britain as a whole a slightly smaller rise was recorded. The provision of sufficient high-grade potato seed from Scotland and Northern Ireland was of immense benefit to the nation during the 1939-45 war and the immediate post-war years, when food was still scarce. Before 1939 some 100,000 tons of seed potatoes were despatched annually from Scotland but in 1943-44 (a peak year) the amount had risen to 473,000 tons. While most Scottish-grown seed goes to England a growing trade has been established with a number of the Mediterranean countries and with South Africa.

For more than a century and a half Scotland has exported potatoes. In the first *Statistical Account* reporters tell of potatoes being sent in the closing years of the eighteenth century to English ports from places as far apart as Kirkinner (Wigtown), Crail (Fife) and Elgin, while Peterhead once exported potatoes to Norway.[59] Mention has already been made of Perthshire farmers sending their potatoes to London. Blight in 1845 and 1846 caused a temporary setback but the trade later revived, " red soil " potatoes from the Dunbar area being highly esteemed in London. As far up the east coast as Ross-shire potatoes were grown for English tables. With the recent development of the Scottish seed potato trade less ware is now available for export, most being required for home consumption. But ware potatoes are still sent in considerable amounts to the north of England, particularly in summer. The warm Ayrshire coastlands between Ballantrae and Largs are eminently suited for growing early potatoes and quantities in excess of Scottish requirements in summer are marketed in the north of England. Since Ayrshire farmers began to grow early potatoes for sale a highly developed and specialised industry has been established. Epicure, bred by Clark and placed on the market by Sutton of Reading in 1897, has been found to be the most suitable variety. On many holdings early potatoes are grown year after year on the same fields, a practice which has unfortunately led to soil infestation by potato eel-worm. Notwithstanding this good crops have continued to be grown and the industry is highly remunerative.

With so large a stake in the seed potato trade, much attention has naturally been focused in Scotland on the breeding of new varieties. Up till the time of the 1914-18 war and for some years thereafter, the principles of Mendelian genetics had not been used by potato breeders. Most popular varieties had indeed been produced by selection of seedlings either produced from "self" seeded berries, or by deliberate hybridisation. In the late twenties, however, a new generation of potato-breeders sprang up; the genetical factors associated with the inheritance of resistance to various diseases were studied at the Scottish plant-breeding research station and the knowledge applied, the names of Black and Cockeram being particularly associated with this work. Progress in the breeding of varieties immune from wart disease encouraged scientific breeders to produce varieties immune from or highly resistant to blight and various kinds of virus diseases.[60] By securing parents resistant to those diseases, and by pursuing a policy of repeated back-crossing— so as to incorporate desirable and eliminate undesirable features —excellent progress has been made. Unfortunately, the potato industry as a whole seems rather unwilling as yet to adopt these newer varieties, the reason being that consumers and hence customers for seed potatoes, dictate the kind of potato which the Scottish farmer shall plant; and there is always a reluctance on their part to accept a new variety in place of an old and trusted variety. An outstanding private breeder of the inter-war period was Donald Mackelvie of Arran.

Two hundred years have elapsed since the potato began to be generally adopted as a crop and as a food in Scotland. In these two centuries the crop has had a profound effect on the social and economic development of the country. In the Highlands it was the means, during the first of these centuries, of greatly augmenting the food resources of the area. Because of its adoption the population of the Highlands was greatly increased on a self-supporting basis, but too great dependence upon a single crop brought disaster when the crop failed. The policy of expediency brought retribution. But overall the potato has undoubtedly been a great asset to Scotland. It has provided a cheap, nourishing, appetising and health-giving food. In times of emergency, when imports of food have been restricted, it has been the means of ensuring that the nation would not starve.

Psychologically the potato has had a most stimulating effect on both scientific workers and practical farmers. No crop has presented so many problems, but none has responded so well to

[60] Salaman, *History of the Potato*, p. 174.

remedial measures. The very success which has attended investigation and the application of scientific knowledge has encouraged investigations with other crops. Economically, the potato is the mainstay of many farmers. From the point of view of agricultural output the general value of the potatoes sold is higher than that of any other crop. The adoption and exploitation of the crop in Scotland has indeed been of great benefit both to farmers and to the nation.

PLATE IX

Planting potatoes by hand

# CHAPTER XXIV

# FARM IMPLEMENTS

Mid-eighteenth century Scottish implements...Winnowing
machines and barley mills...Inherent prejudices...Evolution
of two-horse ploughs...Small's contribution to implement
design ... Development of ploughs ... Steam cultivation ...
Threshing machines...Meikle's invention, 1786...Need for
reaping machinery...Bell's reaper, 1828, and recognition of
his work...Scots develop drilling practices...Whin mills...
Potato-lifters and planters...Turnip-lifters...Milking machines
...Modern developments.

THE CENTURY 1750-1849 WAS one of striking progress in the
invention and use of improved farm implements, and much
of the credit belongs to Scotland. For hundreds of years
only the simplest, crudest and clumsiest of farm tools had been in
use. Except in the Highlands ploughing was done by the cumbrous
wooden plough, and harrowing largely by the wooden-toothed
harrow, an implement ridiculed by Lord Kames. The teeth of such
harrows, made from roots of whin or thorn, were taken home at
night to be sharpened in the fire; mallets were employed to break
down stubborn clods. In the Highlands the inefficient ristle plough
was used to cut the land in front of a light plough in places where
ploughing by animals was possible, while in whole parishes at the
end of the eighteenth century the turning over of the land was done
solely by the *càschrom*. Twelve men equipped with *càschroms*
could turn over one Scots acre in a day[1] and the work could be
speeded by means of the sickle plough. These, along with the
spade, graip, shovel and the mattock (a kind of shoulder pick)
provided the tillage equipment. Horse collars were made of straw,
ropes and halters from hair or hemp or even twisted fir roots.

These implements and appliances were matched in their crude-
ness by the equipment for the harvest field, the barn and the road.
Sickles and scythes were used to cut the grain crops and flails to
thresh the corn, while the winds of heaven, harnessed to create a
draught between the two opposite doors of the barn, separated the

---

[1] Macdonald, *Agric. Hebrides*, p. 152.

chaff from the grain.  Creels on the backs of human beings or of
horses, sledges (some of them shafted and called " slides "), and
a very primitive form of low cart, the tumbler or tumbril (a rough
wooden platform mounted either on solid wooden wheels or on
three pieces of wood pinned together like a butter firkin and revolving
with the axle trees), conveyed sheaves from field to stackyard and
dung from fold to field.  These tumblers cost only half-a-crown to
make.  In 1723 " crowds of people " were astonished to see a
" strange sight "—a cart carrying a small load of coals from East
Kilbride to Cambuslang.[2]  English travellers like Edward Burt
viewed with disgust the spectacle of women in the Highlands
carrying dung in creels to the lazy beds.[3]  Even today the practice
is not unknown.[4]  Content to struggle on with rude and ineffective
tools—they knew of none better, even after better had been invented
—the people were slow to adopt anything new.  " Why change ? "
they would ask.  " What was good enough for our forebears is
good enough for us ! "  " Why have a cart when there are no roads
or only such so-called roads as are unfit to carry a cart ? "  Ignorance
was matched by conservatism and general apathy towards improvement.

The year 1710, however, was eventful.  Andrew Fletcher of
Saltoun, a fiery republican but an ardent lover of Scotland, had
previously visited Holland and had been impressed by the method
of making pot or pearl barley.  On his return to Scotland he sent
his clever wheelwright, James Meikle, to Holland to discover how
Dutch barley mills were made and how the barley was processed.
Meikle agreed to go after ensuring that his wages and expenses
would be met and that his widow would receive a lump sum of
five pounds in the event of his death.[5]  His mission succeeded and
on his return he built a barley mill at Saltoun which he worked with
Fletcher's brother, Henry.  The latter's wife was determined, however, that no one else should discover their method of pot barley
making.  Accordingly she sat in the mill office all day taking orders
for the famous Saltoun pot barley and prevented unauthorised
persons from entering the mill.  But the most interesting part of
the story, from the farming angle, is that from the machines he had
seen in Holland Meikle was able to construct Scotland's first

---

[2] Graham, *Social Life*, p. 167.

[3] R. H. Coats, *Travellers' Tales of Scotland*, Paisley 1913, p. 107 ;  Burt,
*Letter*, xx, VOL. II, p. 152.

[4] Wendy Wood, *Mac's Croft*, London 1946, Chapter II.

[5] Somerville, *Agric. E. Lothian*, pp. 294 ff.

winnowing machine. While the Fletcher family enjoyed a monopoly of pot barley manufacture as a result of Meikle's ingenuity, his fanner was unfavourably received; it was regarded as " an infernal machine "; it attempted to "interfere with the laws of God "; it produced " the Devil's wind ". In *Old Mortality* Scott portrayed the hostility to the fanner in Mause Headrigg's words: this " new fangled machine for dightin' the corn from the chaff " was " impiously thwarting the will o' Divine providence ".[6] If Scott was wrong in antedating the invention of the fanner by half a century, he at least epitomised the prejudice against its use. Not until 1737, according to Graham,[7] was another fanner produced, although it is recorded that a man called Rogers chanced upon a disused fanner in a Leith granary in 1733.[8]

What of the plough ? For centuries the rude old Scots wooden plough had held pride of place in the eastern arable districts, as did the still ruder types in the western areas. In England attempts had been made, as early as the sixteenth century (see for instance Barnaby Googe's *Foure Bookes of Husbandrie*) either to devise or to introduce better ploughs.[9] But in Scotland no new or improved models were heard of until the Earl of Stair, about the year 1730,[10] introduced a Dutch plough for which a patent was secured, while a somewhat similar plough, the Rotherham, patented in 1730, was made on factory lines at the Yorkshire town from which it took its name. These ploughs were evidently a great improvement on the old Scots plough, but it seems that in Scotland neither the Dutch nor the Rotherham plough came to be widely used, and it was not until 1763, when James Small started to make his famous swing plough at Blackadder Mount, Berwickshire, that real progress began. Small, having served his apprenticeship as a wright and blacksmith at Hutton in Berwickshire, went to England, where he doubtless became familiar with ploughs of the Rotherham type. On his return to Scotland he settled at Blackadder Mount where he began to make his famous two-horse swing plough, known as " Small's Chain or Swing Plough ". Some important new features were incorporated in this plough. It had a feathered share and a curved instead of a

---

[6] Sir Walter Scott, *Old Mortality*, Chapter vi.

[7] Graham, *Social Life*, p. 202.

[8] G. E. Fussell, *The Farmer's Tools 1500-1900*, henceforth cited as Fussell, *Farmer's Tools*, London 1952, p. 159.

[9] Barnaby Googe, *Foure Bookes of Husbandrie, by M. Conradus, Herebachius, newly Englished and Increased*, 1577 ; Fussell, *Farmer's Tools*, p. 37.

[10] Fussell, *Farmer's Tools*, p. 46.

straight mouldboard. Iron displaced wood in the vital parts—the
mouldboard, the sheath and the head, sufficient strength being thus
obtained with less bulk and weight. By repeated trials Small determined the shape of share and mouldboard best suited to cut the
furrow and turn it with the minimum resistance. Spring balances
were used to measure the draught, and soft wooden mouldboards
to show how friction could be evened out and reduced. Having
arrived at the desired shape of mouldboard he took his wooden
patterns to the Carron Iron works where the wearing parts were
cast in iron.[11] Small claimed that the plough was made according
to basic mechanical principles which he analysed in the book which
he wrote on the subject.[12]

Unlike Meikle's winnowing machine, Small's plough was an
immediate success; in this instance there was no question of the
laws of God being outraged. Wight reports that all that could be
urged by Paton of Grandholm near Aberdeen in defence of the
cumbrous old Scottish plough, powered as it was by eight, ten or
twelve oxen or their equivalent, was that there was some virtue in
that the animals did not all pull together; some at any given time
were sure to be in need of rest.[13] The advantages of Small's plough
were obvious. At a competition at Dalkeith spectators were amazed
to see one man with two horses and one of Small's ploughs doing
much better work than was possible with the old Scots plough and
its team of four men and from eight to twelve oxen.[14] But Small's
triumph was evidently not complete, for some progressive proprietors like Lumsdaine of Blanerne,[15] who had ordered a Small
plough, complained that their men could not work it. On investigation Small would usually find that the horses were not adequately
trained and indeed he had often to train both horses and men. The
news of this wonderful plough, and of the new method of ploughing,
spread quickly. Of the forty ploughs coming forward at an Alloa
ploughing match in 1791, all were of Small's design, and all were
pulled by two horses driven by the ploughman himself.[16] In
Longforgan parish in the 1790's there were well over a hundred
ploughs, all of Small's design. The news of Small's plough reached
"Farmer George" at Windsor, and an Alloa ploughman was

---

[11] Sinclair, *General Report*, VOL. IV, pp. 352 ff.
[12] J. Small, Introduction to *Treatise on Ploughs and Wheel Carriages*, henceforth cited as Small, *Treatise on Ploughs*, Edinburgh 1784.
[13] Wight, *State of Husbandry*, VOL. III, p. 594.
[14] Sinclair, *General Report*, VOL. IV, p. 356.
[15] *ibid.*                                    [16] *F.S.A.*, VOL. VIII, p. 604 *n.*

asked to demonstrate before His Majesty how Scottish farmers ploughed their land.[17] In more remote districts, however, such as the high parts of Aberdeenshire, the "twal owsen" plough remained in fairly common use as late as 1792.[18] The sight of one in Culsalmond parish, in the early years of the nineteenth century, was unusual enough to cause comment.

In Lanarkshire, whether from prejudice in favour of a local make of plough—the Rutherglen—or because Small's mouldboard was too concave to press aside the many stones in parts of that county, Small's plough was not received with enthusiasm.[19] In Kincardineshire this latter difficulty was overcome by making the tail end of the board convex.[20] Although some English writers of the time gave it high praise Small's plough was used only in the northern counties of England. Loudon in his *Encyclopaedia* (1828) commended its use,[21] while a writer in the *Quarterly Journal* of 1828 took English farmers to task for failing to adopt either Small's plough or some other akin to the Rotherham. The ploughs in common use, he pointed out, were in the matter of construction at variance with the plainest mechanical rules. Four horses and two men were often doing work which could be done by half that number.[22]

Being an altruist, Small determined that his inventions should be used to benefit farmers generally. He took out no patents and allowed blacksmiths everywhere to copy his design. In his workshops, latterly set up in Leith Walk, Edinburgh,[23] he made all kinds of farm implements, rollers, harrows, winnowing machines, ploughs and carts. Every farm tool manufactured by Small was based on known mechanical principles and advantages, and in his treatise on *Ploughs and Wheel Carriages* (1784)[24] he explained why, by "dishing" the wheels of vehicles, the mud gathered by them in soft ground or on bad roads was thrown clear of the wheel and not into the naves and axles. By tapering the axles and slanting them downwards, the spokes of these dished wheels, as they turned round underneath the cart, became upright in relation to the road, while the wheel

---

[17] *N.S.A.*, VOL. VIII, Clackmannanshire, p. 47.
[18] Alexander, *Notes and Sketches*, pp. 34-5.
[19] Fussell, *Farmer's Tools*, p. 50.
[20] Robertson, *Agric. Kincardineshire*, p. 235.
[21] Loudon, *Encyclopaedia*, pp. 390-1.
[22] " On the plough ", in *Quarterly Journal of Agriculture*, I (1828-9), p. 429.
[23] Sinclair, *General Report*, VOL. IV, p. 359.
[24] Small, *Treatise on Ploughs*, pp. 202 ff.

itself bore less heavily on the inner end of the axle. The dishing of the wheels allowed the sides of the cart to be sloped outwards and thus enabled a given load to be carried in a shorter cart. This made it easier for the horse to be turned. The Scottish one-horse " coup " cart became so popular that the English waggon, introduced by Barclay of Ury and drawn by four, six, or even eight horses, never gained a real foothold in Scotland. It was quite unsuited for hilly roads.[25] Famous cart makers, like Simpson of Peterhead, could boast that their carts would last a century, so sound was the design, so careful the selection of wood and so skilful the workmanship. Simpson on being twitted that he had not made much money replied, " No, but I have made good carts ".

Despite his inventions Small died a poor man in 1793, at the early age of fifty-two. He had over-exerted himself and had lost money on his book *Ploughs and Wheel Carriages* which, incidentally, had provided his rivals with valuable information. " Small," wrote Sir John Sinclair, " had such a propensity to be useful that he laid personal interest too much aside—a man possessed of more public zeal and of a greater turn for mechanical invention has rarely appeared in any age or country." [26]

Improvements to and adaptations of Small's plough were made in due time. Veitch of Jedburgh made one, and Finlayson of Muirkirk designed another specially for use on mossy land.[27] By adding a furrow wheel Wilkie provided a means of steadying the plough. Double mouldboard ploughs were invented for setting up and splitting ridges. For ploughing steep lands across the slope, " one-way " or " turnwrest " ploughs were invented by Finlayson and by Smith of Deanston.[28] A drainage plough was designed by McEwan of Stirling; with its two coulters and shovel-shaped share it cut a furrow slice 18 in. wide and 14 in. deep.[29] Twelve horses were required to draw it and by repeated excavations the earth was brought to the surface from a considerable depth. Many of these ploughs are illustrated or described in Loudon's *Encyclopaedia of Agriculture*, and in Pidgeon's article in the 1892 *Journal of the Royal Agricultural Society of England*. It remains to be mentioned

[25] Robertson, *Agric. Kincardineshire*, p. 237.
[26] Sinclair, *General Report*, VOL. IV, p. 358.
[27] Loudon, *Encyclopaedia*, p. 392.
[28] Fussell, *Farmer's Tools*, p. 68.
[29] D. Pidgeon, " The evolution of agricultural implements ", henceforth cited as Pidgeon, " Evolution of implements ", in *J.R.A.S.E.*, 3rd ser. III (1892), p. 255.

that Smith of Deanston invented a subsoil plough which, as described in Chapter XXV, was valuable for drainage.[30] Incidentally, Small's claim to have designed a plough on mechanical principles aroused some academic criticism in the early years of the nineteenth century: none of which, however, was very effective.[31]

While Scottish makers in the early part of the nineteenth century were adapting ploughs of various kinds for Scottish conditions, some English makers, who had set up factories, were catering for an overseas trade. Howard of Bedford was sending ploughs all over the world, while Ransome of Ipswich, who had discovered the secret of case hardening, was developing the idea of building a plough whose working parts could be removed and replaced by new ones in the field.[32] The wrought iron share of the Scottish swing plough required constant sharpening, an operation which cost money and entailed much loss of time in journeys to and from the smithy. Scottish farmers were not easily persuaded to part with their well-tried, strongly-built, swing ploughs, but towards the end of the century " Yankee " ploughs were introduced. Built largely of wood they were light, had replaceable parts with short concave boards, broad feathers, skim coulters and short handles. In draught the " Yankee " was lighter than the swing plough, it took a wider furrow, and it ploughed the land at a more uniform depth. On light deep land it did good work, and it was much used to turn over stubble and "red" land. On thin and stony land, however, its lightness and lack of stability and the fact that the ploughman had less control over it than he had over the swing plough, prevented it from becoming popular. Moreover, it required to be carefully set to ensure good work. Cropping results reflected no appreciable difference in favour of one kind or the other, but the fact that the wearing parts of the " Yankee " were replaceable saved much time in travelling to and from smithies and was a distinct mark in its favour.[33] The introduction of American ploughs had a salutary effect on plough-making in Scotland. Factories specialising in the making of ploughs and other farm implements began to realise that short mouldboards, the use of chilled steel and of replaceable parts had their merits which, however, had to be embodied with the best features of the Scottish swing plough. Movable-point shares and

[30] Watson and Hobbs, *Great Farmers*, p. 16.
[31] Fussell, *Farmer's Tools*, p. 50.
[32] Watson and Hobbs, *Great Farmers*, pp. 54-6.
[33] John Barclay, " The American chilled plough in comparison with the Scottish swing plough ", in *T.H.A.S.*, 5th ser. IV (1892), pp. 33-6.

detachable feathers and tail pieces were made and the boards tended
to become shorter. The skim was substituted for the knife coulter,
thus allowing dung spread on dunged stubbles, or the foggage of
leys, to be effectively turned in. By about the turn of the century
the manufacture of these short-boarded ploughs was proceeding
apace.

Coincident with the improvement in ploughs at the end of the
eighteenth century came improvements in other tillage tools. Iron
teeth replaced the ineffective wooden teeth of the harrow. At first
the frames to hold the teeth were made of wood in various shapes—
square, triangular and rhomboidal.[34] Some were dragged squarely
behind the horses; others were attached by a corner so that no
tine would follow in the same path as another. Finlayson of Muirkirk invented a drag harrow, mounted on wheels, to tear up the
furrows and loosen the roots of perennial weeds in preparation for
the turnip crop. By means of a lever and by the forward pointing
shape of the teeth, the depths could be regulated.[35] The chain
harrow for rolling together the roots of weeds exposed on the surface
was one of Smith of Deanston's inventions.[36] Rollers made of stone,
wood and latterly of cast iron were used, instead of mallets, to
crush clods and smooth the ground for the scythe.

Towards the end of the eighteenth century great improvements
were made in cart and plough harness; leather straps and iron
chains replaced twisted hair, heather or fir roots, and the barbarous
custom of harnessing implements to horses' tails, which had
persisted in some parts, was finally abandoned.

As early as 1834 the Marquis of Tweeddale, who had developed
a great interest in land cultivation and improvement, drew the
attention of the Highland and Agricultural Society to the possibilities of using steam engines for drawing ploughs. In 1837 the
Society offered a premium of £500 to the maker of an effective
steam plough, but although the offer was renewed annually until
1843 no award was made. In that year, however, Heathcoat (also
spelt Heathcot and Heathcote), an English maker, was induced
to take his large steam-operated plough, at considerable expense,
to Lochar Moss near Dumfries. This plough had done good work
on mossland in Lancashire and a large number of people attended

---

[34] Fussell, *Farmer's Tools*, p. 68.
[35] Loudon, *Encyclopaedia*, p. 403.
[36] James Slight and R. Scott Burn, *The Book of Farm Implements and Machines*,
ed. Henry Stephens, Edinburgh 1858, p. 254.

PLATE X

Robot potato planter

Robot transplanter

MODERN MACHINERY

a demonstration staged at Lochar. The engine remained stationary and the plough was drawn by means of a long rope wound on to a drum and passing round a large pulley anchored at the other end of the moss. The story had a dismal ending. After working for three days this heavy plough was left overnight on the moss, and by next morning it had disappeared.[37] The moss was unconquered and was seemingly unconquerable. It remained for Fowler of Leeds to solve the difficulties of harnessing steam power effectively to the plough, but steam ploughs could be economically worked only by contractors or large farmers, and in Scotland, where the general system of farming was organised to employ horses to advantage from the end of the grain harvest to the middle of the following June, they did not become popular. Nevertheless Bradley, a farm pupil at Fenton Barns, East Lothian, in the early 1870's reported having seen from that farm the smoke of six " steamers " ploughing at one time.[38] These were owned by individual farmers.

The most spectacular efforts in steam cultivation of land in Scotland were those associated with the great Sutherland reclamations. These were begun in 1872 in the Lairg area. Work was done at first with an old set of Howard's steam ploughing tackle which had been employed in reclaiming the farm of Upper Brora; but this proved too weak for the task. In the summer of 1873 a huge plough specially built by Fowler and Co. of Leeds was used. In four successive seasons it turned over 1829 acres. At the beginning of this reclamation scheme hidden boulders and tree stumps caused many stoppages and breakdowns. The Duke of Sutherland, assisted by his farm manager, largely mastered this difficulty by employing a disc coulter to cut the ground to a depth greater than that at which the share was set. On striking any major obstacle the plough rode over it.[39] Another development in large ploughs for reclamation work came in the Inverness area from Hugh Paris, who made a great plough to be drawn by oxen. Many acres of moorland, including part of the historic battlefield of Culloden, were transformed by this plough from waste into arable ground.[40] At the time of writing this plough could still be seen at Cradlehall Farm, Inverness. In the twentieth century there were great developments in adapting ploughs to tractors. Multiple furrow ploughs,

[37] Ramsay, *History H.A.S.*, p. 434.
[38] Bradley, *Squires and Farmers*, p. 78.
[39] J. Macdonald, " Agriculture of Sutherland ", pp. 32 ff.
[40] W. Macdonald, " Agriculture of Inverness ", p. 23.

operated from the driver's seat on the tractor, became common. For reclamation work many powerfully-built single ploughs were designed, in all of which were embodied the principles laid down so long before by Small.

Threshing by flail was a hard, back-breaking and costly operation and was never very effective since some of the grain was always retained in the straw. It thus seemed natural to visualise some kind of mechanical contrivance that would do better and quicker work with less physical exertion. With this end in view Menzies, a Scot, invented a threshing machine as early as 1732.[41] It embodied the principle of the flail and was driven by water. Straw threshed by hand flails in the ordinary way yielded more grain when passed through this machine. The difficulty with this, as with all machines designed on the principle of the mechanised flail, was that it quickly broke in pieces. In 1758 Stirling, a Dunblane farmer, invented a thresher designed on another principle. Sheaves of grain were fed into the top of an enclosed cylinder, $3\frac{1}{2}$ ft. high and 8 ft. in diameter, inside which was a perpendicular shaft fitted with four arms. These arms beat out the grain, which was separated from the straw and chaff by riddles and fanners. The machine worked fairly well with oats, but with wheat and barley it was apt merely to break off the heads.[42]

It was left to Andrew Meikle, the son of James who built the first Scottish barley mill and winnowing machine, to produce the first reliable thresher. He heard of a machine, built on an entirely new principle by Ilderton, a Northumbrian. The unthreshed grain was forced between a drum and a set of revolving rollers which were ranged round the drum and pressed against it by springs. It rubbed rather than beat out the grain, but the rubbing process was apt to cause damage. Meikle had earlier been working on threshers based on the flail principle, but on seeing a model of Ilderton's machine, he abandoned this idea and designed a new thresher on Ilderton's principle.

His first machine fell to pieces, but undeterred he built another. It was produced in 1786 and was a success. The sheaf was fed through fluted rollers to a revolving drum equipped with beaters to knock out the grain. At first there seems to have been no arrangement to separate the straw from the chaff and the grain.[43] Probably Meikle designed some kind of revolving rake to draw away the

---

[41] Somerville, *Agric. E. Lothian*, p. 75.
[42] *op. cit.*, p. 76.     [43] *op. cit.*, pp. 76-7.

straw, but nothing definite is known about this. At all events three people, Gladstone of Castle Douglas (1794), Bailey in Northumberland (1798) and Palmer (1799) claimed to have invented these revolving rakes.[44] In Smith's *General View of the Agriculture of Galloway* there appears a drawing of such a mill—one of Gladstone's makes, operated by a water wheel on the chain bucket system. By 1810 Gladstone had erected 200 mills on farms. Modern shakers came into use later: Docker of Findon [45] claimed to be using them in 1829 and Ritchie of Melrose in 1837.[46] The fanner was incorporated into the threshing machine soon after it was invented, and sieves were used to separate weed seeds from the grain. Meikle, like Small, did not patent his machine, so far as Scotland was concerned. Accordingly he profited little by his invention, and it is recorded that a public subscription was raised to provide for his old age. In England, developments in threshing machines were restricted almost entirely to portable machines, owned by contractors and operated by steam power. By 1810 great progress had been made in perfecting these machines, and in 1883 Howards of Bedford succeeded in incorporating a straw-binding apparatus with their threshers.[47]

By the end of the eighteenth century the modern patterns of many of the horse-drawn implements of the farm had been evolved but the greatest need of all—a machine to reap the crops—had still to be met. Hand labour was exclusively employed, except for carting the grain to the stackyards. The hours of work in harvest were long and arduous and, as the crop ripened, the anxiety of the farmers grew lest winds should shake the ripened but uncut oats or break off the matured heads of the standing barley. Speed in cutting was desirable, otherwise serious losses by shaking were always possible; but the scythe or sickle set the pace of cutting and considerable loss was often incurred.

The idea of mechanising the principle of the scythe had long been the dream of English inventors, but no machine designed on this principle had been successful. An inventor named Plucknett, however, abandoned that idea and introduced a circular steel plate sharpened at the edges, notched at the upper side, and revolving parallel to the ground. Gladstone of Castle Douglas improved upon

[44] Pidgeon, " Evolution of implements ", p. 239.
[45] Smith, *Agric. Galloway*, pp. 370-5.
[46] Pidgeon, " Evolution of implements ", p. 239.
[47] Fussell, *Farmer's Tools*, p. 176.

the idea. The Highland Society was at first interested in Gladstone's machine but later withdrew its support. A machine made on Gladstone's principle, however, won the premium offered by the Dalkeith Farming Society, then a very prominent, progressive and wealthy body.[48]  Meantime, James Smith of Deanston, of drainage fame, was experimenting with another type of rotary cutting machine but this unfortunately broke down in the trials. Undeterred, Smith entered for the competition in 1813 and was awarded a consolation prize. In 1815 his machine received favourable comment from the Highland Society but it did not become popular, and Smith was too busy at the time to perfect it.

It was left to Patrick Bell, a divinity student, to devise a reaper on the principles that are now largely adopted for reaping machines. On seeing a pair of hedge shears sticking in a hedge on his father's farm in the Carse of Gowrie the idea of mechanising them flashed into his mind. This was in 1826; he built his machine; then in 1828 came the day for testing it in a barn where there was a standing crop of oats, artificially planted in soil brought in from the field. The barn trial was successful, but would the machine work in the harvest field ? Fearing derision if it should prove a failure and possibly some opposition if it were a success (since labour-saving devices were then unpopular), the test was carried out during the hours of semi-darkness. In the excitement of the test an essential feature was forgotten and the machine failed to work. Bell and his brother were in despair until they discovered their mistake, after which they got the machine to work.[49]  Public trials were held at Powrie Farm on 10th September 1828 and the machine received a favourable report in the *Quarterly Journal of Agriculture*.[50]  The Highland Society awarded Bell a premium of £50 which only partly covered his expenses. Like Small and Meikle before him, Bell did not take out a patent. It was left to country blacksmiths to make other machines and they did not make them well. By 1832 only ten were working,[51] but meantime some had been sent abroad, and detailed descriptions of them were published in various journals.

What part, if any, Bell's reaper played in the success of the Cyrus McCormick American machine will never be known. All that

[48] Fussell, *Farmer's Tools*, p. 117.

[49] J. Hendrick, " Patrick Bell and the centenary of the reaping machine ", in *T.H.A.S.*, 5th ser. XL (1928), p. 68.

[50] " Description of new reaping machine and implements ", in *Quarterly Journal of Agriculture*, I (1828-29), pp. 217-19, 331-2.

[51] Watson and Hobbs, *Great Farmers*, p. 51.

we know is that three years later McCormick produced a reaper embodying some of Bell's principles. McCormick's machine, instead of using the principle of the scissors, cut the grain by means of a saw-toothed straight blade, supported by fingers and working backwards and forwards.[52] He and his father had indeed been at work on reaping machines for some years, but they may well have got ideas from descriptions of Bell's machine. The McCormick machine was soon developed and produced in American factories, whereas in Scotland Bell's machine was neglected. Only in 1851, when the McCormick and another American machine, the Hussey, were shown at the Crystal Palace Exhibition did someone recall Bell's machine, a specimen of which had been in use for years on his brother's farm. The American machines were challenged, and contests took place, the first in 1852 at Perth where the Bell defeated a Hussey-Crosskill machine, and another in 1853, when a Bell improved by Crosskill won against a McCormick.[53] By 1860, however, the Hussey was preferred in East Lothian to the more cumbrous Bell.[54] As for Bell he completed his divinity studies and became parish minister of Carmyllie, Angus. Indifferent to worldly fame or fortune he was content with his past achievement and with his pastoral duties. Public recognition came late, only in 1868 when the Highland and Agricultural Society, forty years after the event, presented him with a piece of plate and the sum of £1000, in recognition of his invention of "the first efficient reaping machine".[55] In the meantime extensive developments followed the 1853 reaper contest. The best features of the two rival types were combined. Bell's clippers were replaced by McCormick's serrated saw-tooth blade. Instead of the grain being delivered in a swathe, devices were adopted whereby two men on the machine could lay it out in a form convenient for hand binding. The manual-delivery machine was in turn superseded by the self-delivery type and enterprising Scottish manufacturers began to make them at Stirling, Maybole and Ayr.[56]

Early in the century hay collectors had been introduced from America. Morton's *Cyclopaedia of Agriculture* of 1856 contains an illustration of a Scottish horse rake, but no progress was made in

[52] Fussell, *Farmer's Tools*, p. 127.
[53] Watson and Hobbs, *Great Farmers*, pp. 52-3.
[54] Scot Skirving, "Ten years of East Lothian farming", in *J.R.A.S.E.*, 2nd ser. 1 (1865), p. 109.
[55] Ramsay, *History H.A.S.*, p. 431.
[56] Fussell, *Farmer's Tools*, pp. 134-5.

devising satisfactory machines for cutting hay. The ordinary reaping machine was apt to choke when cutting grass and did not cut close enough to the ground to satisfy farmers. Not until the production of strong and durable mowers mounted on two driving wheels and having a relatively short cutting bar, with freedom of movement on the ground and a high-speed blade, was the mower a complete success. Progress in hay-making machines between 1850 and 1875 was stimulated by the Royal Agricultural and other English agricultural societies. By the latter year mowers had assumed their present form and subsequent improvements have been more in matters of detail rather than in applying new principles.[57]

The invention of the mower was followed in the early seventies by that of the binder, a machine which at first tied the sheaves with wire. Other developments followed quickly. In 1879, a year fateful for British farming, a string-tying binder was exhibited with some unlooked-for consequences.[58] The binder enabled vast overseas areas of rich wheat-growing lands to be brought into cultivation and the exploitation of these areas was the immediate cause, not only of the agricultural depression in Britain, but also of some of the disastrous soil erosion which occurred in the American West. At home the binder eased the labour problem of the harvest and lowered grain harvest costs; but many farmers trying to dispose of grain at less than its cost must have reflected ruefully on what the invention had meant.

About 1701 a noted Englishman, Jethro Tull (1674-1741), invented the drill sowing machine. Drill sowing had many advantages over broadcasting. It economised seed by depositing it at a uniform depth, and allowed horse and hoes to pass up and down between the rows, so that weeds could be effectively controlled. Fallowing and crop-growing could thus proceed together. But Tull, like many another with advanced ideas, was a step ahead of his times. His methods and machines remained largely uncopied. Indeed Arthur Young, writing of him in 1770, stated that the spirit of drill husbandry had died with him;[59] he was discredited by his own countrymen, but the fault was not entirely theirs, for Tull was given to too much theorising and to overstating his claims.

Fortunately Scotsmen took up his system and, having adapted it for a particular purpose—the growing of roots in drills—perfected it. Craik, a noted Galloway improver, designed drills to sow grain,

---

[57] Fussell, *Farmer's Tools*, pp. 144-8.
[58] *op. cit.*, p. 137.          [59] *op. cit.*, pp. 101-02.

as well as turnip seed, in rows.[60] This meant widely spaced rows with room for horse hoe cultivation during the summer. In the Border country Dawson of Frogden, following the example of Dr John Rutherford of Melrose in growing turnips in drills, developed a better system, and taught his ploughman in 1762 the art of setting up ridges on the top of which the seed could be sown.[61] An Aberdeenshire laird, Udny of Udny, is credited with the discovery of the "bobbin john" for sowing small seeds in drills. It was merely a tin can with a nail hole punched in the bottom. When the can was filled with seed and let down by an attached stick the seed could be made to trickle out as the tin was shaken. Drill-sowing barrows were made at a later date and in course of time were adapted for sowing two rows at a time. One of these is described in the first *Statistical Account* for Longforgan parish.[62] Progress in mechanisation was slow. Although this particular machine is known to have worked in 1791, we find the Highland Society in 1827 giving a prize to a man named Wightman for a like machine.[63] Early in the nineteenth century bone meal began to be used to fertilise turnip land and in the 1831 volume of the Highland Society's *Transactions* a combined two-drill turnip seed and bone meal sower is described. It was designed by Nicol of Guildy.[64] In Loudon's *Encyclopaedia of Agriculture*, 3rd edition, a better machine, the front wheels of which were bevelled, is mentioned; it was made by French, a Northumbrian.[65] In East Lothian grain drills were made which allowed seed to be sown in rows nine inches apart; this enabled hand hoeing to be done.

Scoular and Sons of Haddington devised an ingenious broadcast sowing machine, 18 ft. long, by making the seed box in three sections.[66] The centre section was 9 ft. long and the others each 4½ ft. long. When the end sections were folded round, the machine could pass along roads or go through gateways. Horse hoes were evidently in use on Scottish farms in 1814 since, in the appendix to his *General Report*, Sinclair included the expense of horse-hoeing in his estimated cost of raising a turnip crop.[67]

[60] Smith, *Agric. Galloway*, pp. 370-5.

[61] Waldie, "William Dawson 1734-1815", in *Agricultural Progress*, XXVI (1951), PT. II, p. 97 ; Sinclair, *General Report*, VOL. I, p. 554.

[62] *F.S.A.*, VOL. XIX, p. 511.

[63] Fussell, *Farmer's Tools*, p. 113.

[64] *T.H.A.S.*, 2nd ser. II (1831), p. 205 ; Fussell, *Farmer's Tools*, p. 112.

[65] Loudon, *Encyclopaedia*, p. 411.

[66] Fussell, *Farmer's Tools*, p. 112.

[67] Sinclair, *General Report*, VOL. IV, p. 340.

By the middle of the nineteenth century Scottish farms were well equipped with horse-drawn cultivation and sowing implements. Stationary threshing machines were mainly used on the larger farms in the main arable areas. In the invention and development of these machines Scotsmen had taken no small part, as witness their invention of the reaping and threshing machines and their work on the different kinds of ploughs, harrows, cultivators, and carts. But from the middle of the century onwards the lead in development of agricultural machinery passed to America, though many English farm machinery manufacturers became world famous for their reliable ploughs, harrows, cultivators, threshing mills and reapers.

The whin mill, a food-processing implement which hitherto has received little notice in agricultural books, may deserve mention. The date when gorse was first used as forage in Scotland is uncertain. We know that broom had been used for this purpose from the fifteenth until the eighteenth centuries but, although many may have noticed that the tender shoots of whin were occasionally grazed by sheep and goats, no one in Scotland seems to have thought that practical use could be made of this plant until, probably, the eighteenth century. At any rate, in 1725, someone did point out that the sowing and use of whins for stock food—a practice prevalent for the previous hundred years in Wales—was making headway near London and that whins were used for cattle feeding.[68] Mention is also made about this time of whins being propagated, for cattle, by Grant of Monymusk.

Before gorse could be made fit for stock it had to be bruised to make the spines harmless and such instruments as flails and wooden mallets were used for the purpose. Then someone developed the process of crushing the branches with a heavy stone roller which was passed over them repeatedly. The roller, so tapered that it could be drawn in a small circle by a horse attached to the outer end (the inner end being pivoted) was dragged round in a circular stone-paved path on the surface of which the whins were strewn. The remains of these stone rollers for crushing whins are still to be found in Aberdeenshire; the best known and most effective way of crushing the whins was, however, by the grindstone-shaped type of whin crusher, some specimens of which are still to be found in the north and north-east of Scotland. One is to be seen at the farm of Beechwood at Inverness and another at the Rowett Research

[68] James Ritchie, " Whin mills in Aberdeenshire ", in *P.S.A.S.*, LIX (1924-25), pp. 128 ff.

PLATE XI

Potato harvester (Elevator type)

Potato harvester (revolving end type)

MODERN MACHINERY

Institute near Aberdeen. These crushers measured about four feet in diameter and were twelve or more inches broad. Like the stone rollers they were trundled along in a circular stone-paved path, being maintained upright by a pivoted shaft to the outer end of which a horse was attached. The whins, strewn in the pathway, were watered to facilitate crushing.

While, according to Ritchie,[69] whin branches in Scotland were taken from naturally grown bushes—there is little evidence of their having been specially grown—it is interesting to note that in the 1870's a Ross-shire farmer, Gordon at Udale [70] in the Black Isle, had sown whin seed on some of his poorest land. The plants were cut annually by a mower and afterwards crushed by an iron and steel machine, Mackenzie's " Gorse Masticator", made by a Cork firm. Annual yields of ten to twelve tons per acre were obtained over a series of years. The roots of the whin appear to have fertilised the soil, for although the land was naturally very poor and everything that grew was carried off during the period the land was under whin, the following crop of oats yielded four quarters per acre, or about four bushels short of the country average at the time.

Mention is made in the first *Statistical Account* of whins being used for stock feed during the hard winter of 1782-83 in the Nairnshire parish of Cawdor ;[71] but failure by other reporters to comment on their use suggests that they came into use in Scotland between the end of the eighteenth century and about 1840 by which latter date turnips began to be extensively grown. Doubtless they continued to be used long after this time as was the case at Udale. One whin mill was still in use in Aberdeenshire in 1890.[72]

So long as potato-growing on farms was confined to home consumption farmers were content to lift tubers by the graip, perhaps occasionally putting a single or double plough into the drills and ploughing them up. After the plough they might be scattered by graips to facilitate picking; but, in view of the small quantities grown on individual holdings, there was no particular urge to use speedier means to lift and gather them. With the development of the growing of ware potatoes for sale to the large towns and cities

[69] James Ritchie, Jnr., " Whin bruisers and whin mills ", in *S.J. Agric.*, XIII (1930), pp. 390 ff.

[70] James Macdonald, " Agriculture of Ross-shire ", in *T.H.A.S.*, 4th ser. IX (1877), pp. 110-17.

[71] *F.S.A.*, VOL. IV, p. 352.

[72] James Ritchie, Jnr., " Whin bruisers and whin mills ", in *S.J. Agric.*, XIII (1930), p. 398.

the problem of harvesting main crop varieties of potatoes became urgent. On farms particularly suitable for potatoes large acreages were grown and the tubers had to be gathered in the all too short period of good weather between the ingathering of the cereal crop and the approach of winter. A night's frost might do untold damage while wet weather might put a stop to the lifting. Hence the need for a potato-lifting machine. The answer to the problem was the rotary spinner lifter, invented by Hanson and patented in 1855.[73] Other patents were taken out but it is strange, in view of the traditions of the Highland and Agricultural Society's interest in developing farm machinery, that no trials with lifters were apparently organised by that body earlier than the 1870's. In 1871 mention is made of six machines tested on a farm near Perth. All the makers were Scottish, mostly from the Coupar Angus and Dundee areas. Although these machines did good work, and each was awarded a silver medal, none was outstanding in performance.[74] Further trials were carried out and on 10th October 1876 the two best machines, the Bisset and the Aspinall, were tested one against the other at Liberton Mains, Edinburgh. The comment of the judges was none too favourable. The potatoes were expelled from the soil far too rapidly and many of the tubers were split or had badly broken skins.[75] No award was made. Further development on diggers of the spinner type aimed at correcting this fault.

Notwithstanding its drawbacks the spinner type of digger continued to be used on most potato farms for the next half century or more. It had the merit of lifting crops quickly and so long as pickers could be got in sufficient numbers there was no particular need to develop better machines. By the late 1920's, however, elevator diggers were beginning to become popular. They lifted the potatoes more cleanly and laid the tubers close together in a row, so that they could be picked more quickly. But on wet soil or where the land was covered with weed growth, they did not work well. With the ever-growing difficulty of getting sufficient pickers, the demand at the time of writing was for a machine which would not only lift potatoes cleanly and without undue bruising but would also obviate the need for gatherers. A completely satisfactory machine has not been evolved.

Although the need for a labour-saving machine for potato

---

[73] Fussell, *Farmer's Tools*, p. 187.

[74] Proceedings at Board Meetings, in *T.H.A.S.*, 4th ser. VOL. IV (1872), App. A, p. 14.

[75] Proceedings at Board Meetings, in *T.H.A.S.*, 4th ser. IX (1877), pp. 339-40.

planting was less urgent, the Highland and Agricultural Society did their utmost in the seventies of last century to encourage the production of such a machine. In the 1877 volume of their *Transactions* mention is made of a trial of planters at Liberton in 1876.[76] In the same issue is an account of turnip-lifters.

Despite the long depression dating from the late 1870's which hindered progress in agricultural machinery, many developments took place apart from reapers and binders. New hay-making machinery, potato dressers, turnip-lifters and cutters, sprayers, manure-distributors and cultivation implements were produced. The arrival of the tractor, about the time of the First World War, induced agricultural engineers to design farm implements for tractor power and in this field there have been remarkable developments, the combine-harvester being a striking example.

Until 1889 various attempts, but all unavailing, had been made to develop an efficient milking machine. In that year Murchland of Kilmarnock patented his machine. John Speir of Newton, Cambuslang, reported not unfavourably upon it, but it was not until the principle of intermittent pulsation was introduced that real progress was made. At last the Lawrence-Kennedy machine was evolved and, according to Stevenson, secured for Scotland the credit of producing a really satisfactory mechanical milker.[77] It was by no means perfect but it paved the way for future developments.

It is not part of the purpose of this book to discuss the most recent developments in agricultural machinery. The use of the tractor for power and haulage and the problem of reducing labour, for instance, have called for the redesigning of many agricultural implements. Rapid progress has been made and the need for adequate tests and disinterested advice has been recognised by the establishment of a sub-station of the National Institute of Agricultural Machinery at Howden, Mid Calder, and by the provision of teaching and advisory services by the agricultural colleges. Important as these are, we must not forget that the principles employed in the modern machines which till the land, sow the seed, harvest and thresh the crop have been largely evolved by Scots during the past two centuries. Farmers today owe much to such inventors and designers as the two Meikles, Small, Bell and Murchland.

[76] Proceedings at Board Meetings, in *T.H.A.S.*, 4th ser. (1877), pp. 337-8.
[77] W. Stevenson, " Milking Machines ", in *Standard Cyclopaedia of Modern Agriculture*, ed. Sir R. P. Wright, VOL. IX, pp. 25-9.

# CHAPTER XXV

# DRAINAGE AND BRACKEN

Early underground drainage, stone, broom, brushwood and
turf drains...Springs...Elkington's methods...Retentive sub-
soils...Horse-shoe tiles...Smith of Deanston...Systematic
underground drainage...Subsoil ploughs...Cylindrical pipes
...Government loans...Hill drainage...Arterial drainage on
monastic estates...Eighteenth and nineteenth century schemes
...Need for legislation...State-aided arterial drainage schemes
...The bracken menace...Grants for bracken destruction.

IT CAN READILY BE IMAGINED that at the time of the agricultural
revolution the traditional system of draining, by high " rig " and
low furrow, was much criticised.    Dr Anderson, for instance,
describes it as marring operations to a high degree.[1]  But the system
had some good features, it did help to rid the land of much surplus
water while it also served to divide one man's rig from another's.
Following the consolidation of scattered rigs into enclosed fields
and self-contained farms, the need for small divisions no longer
existed.    Moreover, the baulks between the rigs were so much
wasted land, and were often overgrown with objectionable weeds;
they obstructed and even prevented cross cultivation, and generally
hindered good farming.    Some other system had to be devised.
What happened was that on sloping land, where the subsoil was
reasonably porous, the ridges were simply levelled.    In such cases,
except where there were springs, drainage was no problem; but with
a retentive subsoil and where there was not much slope, levelling
alone deprived the land of the means of drainage.    Resort was
therefore had to the Roman system of underground drainage as
mentioned by Palladius.[2]  Where a spring was encountered a
trench leading away from the spring was dug to a depth of $2\frac{1}{2}$ or
3 ft., and was filled with stones to within a foot of the surface.
Underground drains of this type were made by Barclay of Ury.[3]
At Jordanston and Balharry, near Alyth in Perthshire, a more
elaborate drain was made, with stones laid in the bottom of the

---

[1] Anderson, *Essays*, VOL. I, p. 136.
[2] Palladius, *De re rustica*, BK. VI.
[3] Robertson, *Agric. Kincardineshire*, p. 326.

drain.[4] Side walls of stone, four, five and six inches high and spaced three to six inches apart were built and were bridged with flat stones. Sinclair mentions this type [5] in his *General View of the Agriculture of the Northern Counties*, and Dr I. F. Grant tells of her pleasure in discovering the so-called dutch [6] which her ancestor made in 1775. Such stone-built drains were appropriately named " box " drains in Forfarshire; those filled with small stones tumbled in were named " syvers ". In other cases the cavity was made by two flat stones placed together so as to form an inverted V.[7]

Anderson, in his *Essays on Agriculture*, gave the world a learned dissertation on springs and underground—as opposed to surface—water and expressed the opinion that the best way to deal with a spring was by means of open ditches dug just above it or above any line of springs. The water could thus be intercepted and led away.[8] The disposal of such surface water as refused to sink through a non-porous subsoil posed another problem. Anderson, who disliked the old high-backed ridges, was opposed to their retention merely to provide drainage. Where drainage was required he plausibly, but rather unconvincingly, recommended a moderately high-backed narrow ridge with a shallow furrow separating each ridge. Some people, he observed, had gone so far as to copy the methods of Essex farmers by having an underground drain at each ridge-dividing furrow, but this he considered unnecessary and unduly expensive.[9] He was careful to point out, however, that he lacked experience in the drainage of deep strong clays. In Essex and Suffolk it had long been customary for farmers to underdrain land, spacing the drains regularly and closely. With the aid of special drainage tools these drains were made very narrow towards the bottom. In depth they varied from two to two and a half feet. The cavity at the bottom was then, for lack of other suitable material, filled with boughs of thorn, heath or alder. Sometimes the filling was intended only to support the soil until a natural arch could be formed, and not infrequently temporary expedients such as twisted ropes of straw or hopvine were employed for the purpose; sometimes

[4] Robertson, *Agric. Perth*, p. 270.

[5] Sinclair, *Agric. Northern Counties*, p. 39.

[6] Grant, *Highland Farm*, pp. 44, 215.

[7] J. Headrick, *View of the Agriculture of the County of Angus or Forfarshire*, Edinburgh 1813, p. 392.

[8] Anderson, *Essays*, VOL. I, p. 116.

[9] *op. cit.*, p. 119.

2 C

again a wooden plug would be drawn along.[10]    The noted Berwick-shire improver Dawson of Frogden, who had lived for several years in England, practised these methods on his return to Scotland. He used broom, with the bare stalks undermost so as to leave a passage for the water. Drains of this type are said to have lasted for thirty years.[11]    Kerr, a Berwickshire farmer, drained a field at Ayton in this way, the drains being at intervals of five yards.[12]    At Haining in Peeblesshire heath formed into small but long-shaped bundles was laid in the bottom of the drain; [13]    for this purpose the tough stalks of heather that had survived burning were in particular demand.    Elsewhere broom and brushwood were used to fill the cavity at the bottom of the drain.    On peaty land, turf drains were made by casting a wide trench to a certain depth; at this depth the trench was narrowed, forming shoulders on which broad turves, with the vegetation side downwards, could be laid to form a bridge.[14] In stiff soils the bottom of the drain was narrowed to a V-shape and a turf, shaped to fit the drain but with the bottom sliced off, was inserted to form a cavity.[15]    These were appropriately designated wedge drains.

A rather ingenious suggestion, made by Anderson, was to pierce the non-porous stratum by a pit sunk down until the underlying stratum was reached.    He had evidently met with success by doing this in places where marshy pieces of land were being reclaimed.[16] Such pits were filled with stones and the water, which had been pre-vented from escaping by the non-porous stratum, disappeared.    They could be sited at some distance from the wet spot so long as there was a connecting drain.    In Roxburghshire this system was employed to some extent,[17] while English drainers had hit upon the device about the same time.[18]    Elkington, an English drainage expert and an adept at finding where water would rise to the surface, became famous for his system of drainage.    It was most effective in dealing with underground as opposed to surface water.    His crowbar was compared to the rod of Moses.

[10] Ernle, *English Farming*, p. 366.
[11] R. Douglas, *General View of the Agriculture in the Counties of Roxburgh and Selkirk*, henceforth cited as Douglas, *Agric. Roxburgh*, Edinburgh 1798, p. 131.
[12] R. Kerr, *View of the Agriculture of the County of Berwick*, London 1809, p. 361.
[13] Wight, *State of Husbandry*, VOL. III, p. 24.
[14] Robertson, *Agric. Perth*, p. 272.
[15] Ernle, *English Farming*, p. 366.
[16] Anderson, *Essays*, VOL. I, pp. 127-8.
[17] Douglas, *Agric. Roxburgh*, p. 129.
[18] Ernle, *English Farming*, p. 366.

Getting rid of surface water (as opposed to spring water) in cases where the subsoil was uniformly retentive was difficult. Deep drainage at wide intervals was useless since much of the water never reached the deep drains; stone drainage at frequent intervals was expensive, particularly in places where stones were scarce. Thus for long land of this type remained undrained. The East Lothian farm of Fenton Barns, later to attain something near world fame for its excellent crops and management, nearly ruined the Hopes who tenanted it; until it had been drained it failed to yield good crops.[19] A solution was reached by stages, a notable one being the invention of the horseshoe tile or "mug". Sir James Graham of Netherby, a landowner on the Cumberland side of the Border, had much flat, wet and unproductive land. On hearing good accounts of tile drainage in Staffordshire he sent a man to enquire and to learn how the tiles were made. On his return, Sir James began to manufacture horseshoe tiles of various diameters—3, 4, 6 and 8 in.—according to the size of the drain. So satisfactorily did these tiles act on his home farm that, on the renewal of leases, he bound his tenants to drain their land to his satisfaction, his own contribution being to supply the tiles.[20] In the *Transactions* of the Highland Society, Yule described this work, which began some time after 1819. Another account of the improvements at Netherby is given as an appendix to *Reports of Select Farms*.[21] His example was followed by one of the Dukes of Portland who set up a tile works and commenced extensive drainage on his Cessnock estate in 1826.[22]

Tile drainage having come to Scotland in this way, it was left to James Smith of Deanston to perfect the system. Smith, a cotton manufacturer with an ingenious turn of mind, took over his uncle's Perthshire farm at Deanston in the year 1823. It was a poor, unproductive subject, the low parts waterlogged and overgrown with rushes, the higher parts infested with bracken, broom and heather. Smith's uncle had tried to drain the land, but the non-porous subsoil prevented the surface water from reaching the deep drains he had laid. Shallower drains, 18 in. deep, at more frequent intervals, were tried. The improvement was still inadequate, and at this stage Smith took charge. Using the earlier methods of Essex

[19] Watson and Hobbs, *Great Farmers*, pp. 98-100.
[20] J. T. Yule, " On the mode of drainage by means of tiles as practised on the estate of Netherby ", in *T.H.A.S.*, 2nd ser. II (1831), pp. 388 ff.
[21] *Farm Reports ; Netherby, Cumberland*, pp. 62-8.
[22] A. Sturrock, " Report on the Agriculture of Ayrshire ", in *T.H.A.S.*, 4th ser. I (1869), pp. 29-30.

farmers, he drained the land systematically, putting in "leaders" 4 ft. deep in the hollows with receiving drains 3 ft. deep to convey the water from parallel collecting drains, laid 2½ ft. deep and from 16 ft. to 21 ft. apart.[23] Still the results did not satisfy Smith and he concluded that the subsoil was not sufficiently porous to allow the water to percolate freely downwards and sideways to the drains. Obviously something was needed to break up the subsoil. Hand trenching was too expensive and in any case, as ordinarily carried out, it meant bringing to the surface some cold and inert material; the trench plough was also open to this latter objection. Smith, therefore, adopting the principle of the common plough, but leaving off the wide share and the mouldboard invented his subsoil plough, which was designed to follow in the furrow made by the ordinary plough.[24] Success was at once achieved; the whole of the farm was subsoiled, and in due time it was converted from a barren, unfruitful subject into a veritable garden.[25] Landlords and farmers came from afar to see it, and Smith, a true benefactor, gave them hospitality and expert advice.

Smith and his drainage system became famous and in 1831 he published a pamphlet called *Remarks on Thorough Draining and Deep Ploughing*. Giving evidence in 1836 before the Committee on Agricultural Distress, he asserted that "frequent" drainage, followed by subsoil ploughing, was a most desirable method of bringing wet soils into full production. Crops on wet land could be grown successfully when otherwise they would fail.[26] Throughout Scotland he travelled, advising proprietors and others who sought to drain land. His advice usually led to excellent results but, as often happens with new methods, enthusiasm was carried to extremes; subsoiling was overdone and unnecessarily expensive drainage was carried out. Nevertheless, Smith's system gave a great impetus to land drainage. The accounts of different parishes in Stirlingshire in the second *Statistical Account of Scotland* impress the reader by the prominence given to this subject. In this county there were at least seven tile works and there may have been several more.[27] The invention of the cylindrical tile about this time by

---

[23] "The late James Smith of Deanston", in *Journal of Agriculture*, new ser. IV (1851), pp. 457-74.

[24] Watson and Hobbs, *Great Farmers*, pp. 16-17.

[25] Ernle, *English Farming*, pp. 366-7.

[26] Watson and Hobbs, *Great Farmers*, p. 18.

[27] *N.S.A.*, VOL. VIII, Stirlingshire, pp. 14, 55, 68, 84, 109, 125, 158, 173, 202, 269, 277, 285, 327, 372, 384, 429.

PLATE XII

Hill drainage: making surface drains

Reade, a Kentish farm worker, did much to stimulate land drainage and from 1843 several works were making round tiles.

Underground drainage with drains narrowly spaced is expensive and is worthwhile only as a long-term improvement. Much capital expenditure is required to bring wet land into full production and although agriculture, by the late thirties, was becoming more prosperous, neither landlord nor tenant could afford to spend lavishly. In order to lessen costs efforts had been made to substitute machine for hand labour. For instance, McEwan, a Stirlingshire man, invented a drainage plough: but hand drainage, despite the expense, continued to be the vogue.[28]

In 1840 an Act was passed enabling landowners, subject to the approval of the Court of Chancery, to raise loans for drainage and in 1846 £2 million of public money was set aside under statute to provide loans for this form of improvement, repayment being spread over twenty-two years. Scottish landlords responded quickly to this offer; a further £2 million were offered, and the Private Money Drainage Act of 1849 enabled private companies to be formed to lend money for land improvement. Thanks to these loans a very large acreage of Scotland's arable land was underdrained at this time but, unfortunately, much of the drainage was carried out at too great a depth and with pipes that were too small. Joseph Parkes, who had done excellent work in Lancashire in draining a moss, had found that under such conditions deep drains answered best and had mistakenly concluded that deep drains should be chosen for all classes of land. Unfortunately his advice was preferred to Smith's who was of opinion that for most land, and particularly for clays, collecting drains should be about 2 ft. 6 in. deep. On much heavy land the clay above the pipes prevented the water from getting down to the pipe so that the drains either did not function at all or did so imperfectly.

Just when the surface drainage of moorland grazings was first practised is unknown but before the end of the eighteenth century it was being carried out on the Border hills. Effective in improving the pasture and in lessening the losses of sheep from liver fluke, this form of drainage continued to be practised from that time and throughout the whole of the nineteenth century. Unfortunately some of the systems were badly laid out. Instead of traversing the slopes of the hills at a gentle angle, and thus receiving the surface water that was apt to collect in the hollows, they frequently ran up

[28] D. Pidgeon, " Evolution of implements ", p. 255.

and down the slope, thus failing to intercept surface water and
sometimes causing erosion. Another form of hill land improvement
during the earlier part of the nineteenth century was irrigation by
waters from alkaline springs. By the careful siting of open drains
along the slopes of the hills, lime-charged waters issuing from
springs were made to spill over the downward slopes, so promoting
the growth of valuable herbage plants. Akin to this form of improvement was the old practice of flooding land to form water-meadows.
Under the direction of a Gloucestershire flooder six water-meadows
were laid out on the Pitfour estates in Aberdeenshire between 1801
and 1806 and at first they appear to have answered well.[29] The
Craigentinny sewage meadows, previously mentioned, were first
established about the middle of the eighteenth century. At one time
the practice was fairly widespread in Scotland but it seems quickly
to have fallen into disuse.

The great spurt in land drainage, which began shortly before
Queen Victoria ascended the throne, came opportunely. Agriculture
was then regaining prosperity, and both landlords and tenants
were disposed to spend money on land improvements. Without
such improvements as drainage the great potential benefits of
artificial fertilisers could not have been fully realised. Properly
drained land could be worked early in the spring and crops could be
timeously sown; certain plant diseases were avoided and weeds
were more easily controlled; stock became healthier and much
better crops were harvested. Before the depression of the seventies
most of Scotland's arable land, where drainage had been required, had
been underdrained.

Drainage and hard times, however, go ill together and after the
depression of the eighties had set in drainage work on farms notice-
ably declined. Farmers and landowners were content to do only
the most urgent maintenance works. The 1914-18 war revealed
that considerable areas of arable land were suffering from excessive
wetness. To carry out the work at economic cost as well as to
economise on labour an American drainage machine, the Buckeye,
was brought over and did good work on suitable soils. But the great
fall in prices of farm produce after 1920 militated against its use,
while the cost was almost as high as that of hand drainage. To
encourage drainage and to provide employment for workers during
the trade depression that followed the post-1914-18 war boom, the
then Board of Agriculture for Scotland offered drainage grants for

[29] Keith, *Agric. Aberdeenshire*, pp. 445-52.

approved work on a percentage of cost basis. Most of the work done was related primarily to existing drainage systems which were patched up, renewed or supplemented. Considerable advantage was taken of this scheme.

Such mechanised drainers as were employed in the inter-war period showed no pronounced advantage over hand labour. Rising costs and growing labour shortages during the 1939-45 war led, however, to the invention of more suitable machines. One notable hill drainage machine, the Cuthbertson, has been widely employed in this and other countries, while others have come into use for underground drainage. Excavators of various types have also been extensively used for arterial drainage. In 1950, when State grants of one-half of the approved expenditure were being given to farmers and landowners to assist the drainage of agricultural land, the amount paid out in Scotland for 5162 schemes was £339,498.[30] This expenditure was exclusive of the cost of arterial drainage schemes carried out by the Department of Agriculture's own engineers.

Although the hilly and undulating nature of much of Scotland's surface provides good natural drainage, there are areas of flat but potentially fertile land which could only be brought into full production by the removal of surplus water and the lowering of the water table. As has already been related the monks of Inchaffray and of Melrose and Coupar Abbeys did notable work in carrying out large drainage schemes and in ensuring that drainage works were properly maintained. The neglect of the Inchaffray scheme after the Reformation led to the passing in 1696 by the Scots Parliament of a special Act anent the making of the Inchaffray Pow.[31]

The passing of former Church lands into the possession of private owners seems, however, to have been detrimental to the process of drainage, and the cutting of a new channel through rocks for the stream at Loth in Sutherland in the early part of the seventeenth century was evidently exceptional for the period.[32] During the agricultural revolution of the eighteenth century many proprietors were induced to undertake arterial drainage. Mention has already been made of the drainage of Straiton's Loch in Edinburgh and of the release of a great extent of fertile land for cropping at Ardincaple on the Clyde. Forfar Loch was lowered considerably, partly to reclaim the wet lands on the margin and in part to get access to its

[30] D.O.A.S., *Agriculture in Scotland*, report for 1950, p. 37.
[31] *A.P.S.*, VOL. X, p. 67.  [32] *F.S.A.*, VOL. VI, p. 313.

deposits of marl.[33]   The Carse of Gowrie was transformed from areas of bogs with isolated islands (inches) of dry land into its present-day flourishing condition.   The drainage of this fertile tract presented special problems;   the weirs of the then existing mills was one,[34] and another was to secure sufficient way-go for the surplus water of the flat land next to the hills.   The remedy devised by one landlord at a later date was to provide a new drainage outlet for the far-away lands by placing the outflow pipes a few feet below the level of the then existing pows (the local name for large ditches) which still continued to operate.

The prosperous condition of agriculture just before and at the time of the Napoleonic Wars partly accounted for much of the large-scale drainage work carried out at this period.   Thus to prevent flooding on the farm of Hallyards, Meigle, an embankment half a mile long was built at the joint expense of two neighbouring proprietors, while the north bank of the Tay from Errol to Invergowrie Bay was protected by an embankment several miles long.   Between Kirkcudbright and Tongland an embankment over a mile long was erected.[35]   The fact that most of Scotland was portioned out in large estates, and that few arterial schemes were the concern of more than two or three proprietors, enabled such schemes to be planned and carried through on a co-operative basis. Many a proprietor, too, was able to make a large main ditch within his own estate, and in consequence many small arterial schemes were readily promoted and completed in the early part of the nineteenth century.

Towards the middle of that century, however, difficulties arose in arranging for joint schemes and in ensuring their proper maintenance.   A vast amount of underground drainage was being carried out about this time and proprietors of upper lands sometimes experienced trouble in getting an adequate outlet for their drainage water.   Legislation was accordingly promoted, taking the form of the cumbersome Drainage Act of 1847.

Neglect to maintain arterial drainage works, particularly during and after the 1914-18 war, combined with the breaking-up of large estates and the creation of many occupier-owned farms, led to much dissatisfaction about procedure in cases of dispute.   The Land Drainage (Scotland) Act of 1930 provided machinery to regulate

[33] Wight, *State of Husbandry*, VOL. I, p. 275.
[34] Robertson, *Agric. Perth*, pp. 367, 369.
[35] Smith, *Agric. Galloway*, p. 229.

arterial schemes which affected two or more properties. It also enabled the Department of Agriculture for Scotland to enter upon land to execute large arterial drainage schemes and to recover the estimated betterment value of the land, the difference between that value and the cost being met by a State grant. This Act set in motion schemes on the Kelvin, the Clyde and the Annan.

The outbreak of the 1939-45 World War revealed the fact that, in numbers of places, increased production was being seriously hampered through lack of proper arterial drainage in the catchment areas of many of the small rivers and streams. During the long period of the agricultural depression little or nothing had been done to maintain them in proper condition. Accordingly legislation in the shape of the Agriculture (Miscellaneous War Provisions) Act 1940 was passed empowering the Department to require landlords to carry out drainage schemes, the cost of which would be unlikely to exceed £5 per acre for the extent of agricultural land estimated to be benefited.[36] Under this Act the State provided grants of 50 per cent. of the cost. A considerable number of schemes were completed, the work usually being done by the Department's excavating machines. In 1941 the Land Drainage (Scotland) Act was passed and by the end of 1948 the aggregate expenditure incurred on the ten arterial schemes then completed under this Act was £143,471.[37] Much good work was done but failure of landowners to execute the follow-on works in the areas affected prevented the full benefits of these schemes being realised.

It also became evident at this time that existing legislation did not provide the answer to the larger problems of arterial drainage. In the upper valley of the Spey, for instance, much of the land had been rendered practically useless by periodic flooding and a high water table. Lochar Moss, Dumfriesshire, provided another perplexing problem, as did Barr Loch, Renfrewshire. Considerable areas of fertile land in Strathmore were subjected to periodic flooding. This position led to the appointment in 1947 of a committee (the Duncan Committee) to consider the necessity of further large-scale drainage and to make recommendations. The Committee's report was published in June 1950,[38] but its recommendations did not lead to the passing of new legislation. Lochar Moss, for which a scheme was propounded more than 200 years ago, remains to be tackled, as

[36] D.O.A.S., *Agriculture in Scotland 1939-48*, p. 39.
[37] *op. cit.*, p. 81.
[38] *op. cit.*, p. 37.

do many other areas which could be made fertile only at considerable cost.

Another major problem, which in the mid-years of the twentieth century warranted State aid, was bracken eradication. Bracken is a plant almost always regarded as harmful to farming interests. It is a weed peculiar to uncultivated grazing areas, on the best parts of which it may become dominant, even to the complete suppression of useful edible plants. Maggot-struck sheep are apt to seek its shade and if overlooked by the shepherd may perish. Thus before D.D.T. dips were introduced heavy losses were sometimes incurred especially in warm summers such as that of 1933. Before sheep were introduced to the Highlands bracken was better controlled; it was often cut green for manure or used for litter in its more mature state. Again, cattle help to restrict its growth by treading, but when land is grazed by sheep alone the plant becomes more luxuriant and spreads rapidly. No practicable method of keeping it in check, other than hand-cutting, was known and with rising costs after the 1914-18 war hand-cutting tended to fall into disuse. The result was that many of the best portions of our hills deteriorated seriously. Following representations by farmers a Government grant-aided bracken eradication scheme was introduced in 1936 [39] and was continued during the war years; a committee was also appointed to investigate possible means of controlling the menace. The life history of the plant was studied, the efficacy of various mechanical and spraying devices tested, the costs of the various control systems were ascertained and the possibilities of introducing diseases or predatory insects were explored. So far, a satisfactory solution to the problem has still to be found. The number of bracken-infested acres in Scotland is estimated to exceed half a million.

Drainage and bracken are thus two of Scotland's major agricultural problems. Inadequate drainage prevents some of our most fertile arable lands from becoming fully productive, while much of our best hill grazing lands are unable to produce plants of high nutritive value owing to bracken encroachment.

[39] *Report of the Committee on Hill Sheep Farming in Scotland*, Cmd. 6494, 1944, p. 29.

## CHAPTER XXVI

# HORTICULTURE

Early horticulture promoted by Church and Crown...Gardening after the Reformation...Edinburgh's seed and nursery trade...First Scottish book on gardening...Eighteenth-century market gardening...Clydeside orchards...Paisley and its flowers...Effect of road and rail transport...The tomato industry...Strawberries and raspberries...Research...Fruit preservation...French gardening...Allotments...Statistics.

FOR THE EARLY DEVELOPMENT of her horticulture Scotland is indebted to the Church of medieval times. Hailing as many of them did from countries where apples, pears, cherries, and plums were common, and where vegetables of many kinds were served with meals, the monks and lay brethren of the abbeys determined to find out whether these fruits and vegetables could be grown in Scotland. History and tradition alike testify to the large measure of success that was achieved. Fruit trees planted in the gardens of abbeys and priories continued to flourish long after the Reformation, and in the vicinity of many the tradition of good gardening was carried on in private gardens. The apple Arbroath Oslin, said to have been introduced by an Arbroath abbot from the Continent, is still grown, and thus perpetuates the name of the ancient Arbroath Abbey garden.[1]

Robertson, writing in the early years of the nineteenth century, related how the remains of the Priory orchard at Beauly were still visible.[2] One pear tree in a normal season would yield 64 bushels of fruit, while at nearby Easter Lovat an apple tree covered a space of ground 47 ft. in diameter.[3] At the old Abbey of Deer in Aberdeenshire Ferguson, the owner at the beginning of the nineteenth century, marvelled at the pains taken by the monks hundreds of years earlier

---

[1] George Hay, *History of Arbroath*, Arbroath 1876, p. 56. In Sinclair, *General Report*, VOL. IV, p. 435, this apple is described as an excellent early table apple which grows freely from cuttings.

[2] J. Robertson, *General View of the Agriculture in the County of Inverness*, London 1808, p. 203.

[3] P. Neill, " On the gardens and orchards of Scotland ", in Sinclair, *General Report*, VOL. II, p. 177.

to ensure that their fruit trees should yield their utmost.  Three feet down, under a layer of rich soil, was a paved causeway of granite, underneath which was a bed of sand one foot thick, underlaid in turn by another causeway which overtopped a layer of soil.[4]

From Dunbar's *Social Life in Former Days* we read how, in 1566, the Dean of Moray made a contract with his gardeners that they would "labor the gryt orcheart and gardings of the said Dene's manss within the Channorie of Elgin indewring the space of thrie yeirs and sall dycht and sned [prune] all the tries and sall gude [manure] theme with sufficient muk [dung]".[5]  Over a century later, in 1684, many grafts of several named varieties of apples and pears, including "the Great-Summer-Bon-Chrestein Peare" and "the Great-French-Bergamot-Peare" were sent by a man named Hunter to the laird of Gordonston in Moray.  The letter announcing their dispatch is headed Murehouse, probably a place in the vicinity of Edinburgh.[6]  Edinburgh about this time enjoyed considerable repute in horticulture.  This is borne out by the following account from a nurseryman and seedsman of the name of Miller, sent to Sir Robert Gordon in the year 1718.

> Account of Garden Seeds, Garden Toolls, etc. furnished to Sir Robert Gordon by William Miller *—18th December 1718.
>
> 2 ounces Silver-Firr seed
> 4 ounces Great-Pine
> 4 ounces Cypruss
> 4 ounces Pynaster
> 2 ounces Pitch-Firr
> 8 pound Lym-Tree seed whereof 4 pound and 10 ounces but yet furnished
> 8 pound Yew-Tree seed
> 6 pound Scots-Firr
> 14 pound French Furzz
> 1000 Hors-Chestnutts
> 1 bushell of Walnutts
> 1 bushell of Chestnutts
> 8 pecks Holley Berries
> 1 peck Filberd-Nutts
> 2½ pound Hornbeam seed
> ½ pound Apple seed, not yet sent
> ½ pound Pear seed, not yet furnished
> 4 bushels Ackorns
>
> * Miller rented the gardens at Holyrood Abbey.

---

[4] Keith, *Agric. Aberdeenshire*, p. 365.
[5] Dunbar, *Social Life in Moray*, p. 147.
[6] *op. cit.*, p. 148.

1 parcel of Ellem seed cost me
Three dozen of largest Garden-Spades
Three Syths
One longest Garden-Line

The account also included :—Peas (8 varieties), Beans (3 do.), Radish (2 do.), Onion (2 do.), Turnip (2 do.), Cabage (4 do.), Letuce (3 do.), Leek, Parsneep, Carrot, Colliflower, Sweet-Majorum, Beet-rave, Sellery, Pompion and Gourd, Cress Coucumer of severall sorts, Melon, Purpie, Charvill, Smooth Spinage, Shellot, Persly, Clairie, Sumner and Winter Savory, Thym, and Beet Chord. The total account was £30. 9s. 0d.

In 1729 Dunbar of Thunderton, Moray, was supplied by Miller with two hundred and forty " fruit trees of the finest kinds ",[7] while a still existing firm of Edinburgh nurserymen, Dickson's, was established some time about 1700.[8]

The principles of horticulture, however elementary they may have been as judged by modern standards, were well understood in medieval times by certain Scottish kings. David I, for instance, had a garden at the base of Edinburgh Castle Rock which he personally superintended, and in which he practised the grafting of trees,[9] and Alexander III employed a gardener at Forfar. But these instances were doubtless exceptional. For centuries very few of the nobility or of the common people were interested in horticulture.

In 1683 John Reid, a Scot, published an informative book on gardening. The first part describes the layout of the garden, formality being then the fashion. The second, which concerns the propagation and improvement of fruit trees, bushes and kitchen " hearbes ", describes among other things how potatoes, then almost unknown, should be planted, stored and prepared for the table. The reader is advised when planting to cut the tubers into many pieces making sure that each piece has an eye.[10] The institution of the now famous Royal Botanic Garden, Edinburgh, dates back to this time. Designed as a garden for medicinal plants, it was founded by Sibbald, who later became Edinburgh's first Professor of Medicine.[11] In 1670 he acquired a plot of land for the garden and in 1675 the project received the support of Edinburgh Burgh Council.

[7] Dunbar, *Social Life in Moray*, pp. 148-9.
[8] R. L. Scarlett, " Market gardening in the Lothians ", henceforth cited as Scarlett, " Market gardening ", in *Scientific Horticulture*, x (1951), p. 201.
[9] Neill, in Sinclair, *General Report*, VOL. II, p. 46.
[10] Reid, *The Scots Gard'ner*, 1683 edn. VOL. II, p. 107.
[11] The Royal Botanic Garden, Edinburgh, *Brief Descriptive and Illustrated Account*, 1934, p. 5.

While horticulture in those days may have been more or less beyond the comprehension of the common people, professional gardeners were well versed in the subject and Scots gardeners were already in high repute outside their native land—as witness the employment of Scott's Andrew Fairservice in a Northumberland garden.[12] In the Western Highlands, however, there were no gardens—not even at the houses of the chiefs. Lochiel is said to have been the pioneer in gardening for by 1734 he had established a garden at Auchnacarry, and entertained his guests, in August of that year, with a hotch-potch of peas, carrots and turnips.[13] Cockburn's letters (1727-43) to his gardener Charles Bell at Ormiston, written about the same time and already referred to, are most revealing; they provide evidence of wide knowledge of horticulture, agriculture and forestry and of his zeal in promoting improvements.

About 1746 Henry Prentice began to cultivate white peas, potatoes, turnips and other culinary plants for the Edinburgh market, and used a horse and cart to convey them.[14] Up till that time Edinburgh's supply had been limited to the amount that could be carried in baskets. Evidently Musselburgh was a favourite area for vegetable growing; in 1763 Edinburgh's supply came mainly from that district, women with creels on their heads " crying " the produce in the streets. By 1771 there were 32 market gardeners in the Edinburgh district, and they owned 29 carts; 126 acres were devoted to the industry. By 1812 there were 76 market gardeners owning 55 carts and at this time some 400 acres were under fruit and vegetables; rents up to £10 and even £15 per acre were being paid.[15]

The valley of the Clyde below Lanark had long been a favoured area for tree fruits—apples, pears and plums. About the beginning of the nineteenth century it was estimated that about 340 acres were devoted to horticulture in Lanarkshire and that 250 of these were on the steep banks of the Clyde.[16]

The similarity in the exposure, configuration and character of the soil in the Clyde valley to that of the Midlothian North Esk doubtless explains the development of plum orchards near Lasswade. There too, and also at Roslin, strawberry-growing was important

---

[12] Sir Walter Scott, *Rob Roy*, Chapter xiv.
[13] Neill, in Sinclair, *General Report*, VOL. II, p. 105.
[14] Robertson, *Agric. Midlothian*, p. 133.
[15] Neill, in Sinclair, *General Report*, VOL. II, pp. 80-1.
[16] J. Nasmith, *General View of the Agriculture of the County of Clydesdale*, Brentford 1794, p. 132.

in the early years of the nineteenth century and parties from Edinburgh used to visit Roslin in strawberry time in order to enjoy this delicious fruit. Robertson, the writer of the *General View of the Agriculture of Midlothian* gives the acreage of strawberries as 200, but Neill, probably with more accuracy, estimated it at half that figure.[17] In 1799 there were nearly a score of tree fruit orchards in the Carse of Gowrie,[18] and Leslie, writing about that time, stated that Moray pears were the best in Scotland.[19] The Rev. Joseph Smith, who contributed to the first *Statistical Account* for the semi-Highland parish of Birse in Aberdeenshire, states that in one particular year the apples from one tree grown at Mid Strath realised a guinea.[20]

Not until about the end of the eighteenth century did cottage gardening, with its combined vegetable and flower culture, make headway in Scotland. Kail had long been grown as a specific against scurvy and cabbages are said to have been introduced by Cromwell's soldiers,[21] but except in gentlemen's gardens no other vegetables had been regularly grown. Doubtless the adoption of the potato encouraged people to lay out and fence their gardens, and to cultivate flowers and other vegetables. At the beginning of the nineteenth century Paisley artisans were noted for their interest in flowers. A clergyman of the time attributed this to the fact that many were devising the most exquisite designs of patterns for textiles, such as the noted Paisley shawl. Be that as it may, in their spare time they devoted much attention to the cultivation of different kinds of flowers—tulips, hyacinths, anemones, polyanthus, auriculas, pinks and carnations. They excelled particularly in pinks, individual growers having as many as eighty choice varieties. Some growers specialised in breeding new varieties and some actually sent them to London.[22]

Provincial vegetable and flower shows did much to promote cottage gardens, while the Highland Society also encouraged the movement by their prize competitions. Unfortunately, the practice of building houses close to the streets of Scottish towns and villages

[17] Neill, in Sinclair, *General Report*, VOL. II, p. 91.

[18] Robertson, *Perth Agriculture*, p. 228.

[19] W. Leslie, *General View of the Agriculture of the Counties of Nairn and Moray*, London 1813, p. 236.

[20] *F.S.A.*, VOL. IX, p. 113.

[21] C. Rogers, *Scotland, Social and Domestic*, Grampian Club, London 1869, p. 108.

[22] Sinclair, *General Report*, VOL. IV, pp. 422-6.

hindered development; but in most country towns and suburban districts great care and attention were devoted to the growing of flowering trees, shrubs and flowers. Favourite flowers in old-time cottage gardens were white narcissi, marigolds, wallflower, London pride, violets and polyanthus. For perfume, almost indispensable for church attendance, so insanitary and musty was the state of many of the old churches, thyme, southernwood, spearmint, and the red cabbage rose were planted, while for medicinal purposes there were such plants as the tansy, horehound, wormwood and rue.[23]

Since the end of the First World War the large Scottish estate gardens, formerly run on munificent lines, have declined because of reduced incomes, high taxation and higher costs, particularly in wages. Some have been turned into commercial concerns but others continue bravely to exist, usually on a much reduced scale. Such gardens are frequently open to the public, the fees for admission going largely to some charitable purpose. While the decline in estate gardening is to be regretted there has been a marked advance in late years of the standard of ornamental displays in municipal gardens.

In the main, apart from the Lothians, Clydeside and the Carse of Gowrie, Scotland's horticulture was developed to meet only local needs. Gradually, with the development of railway and more particularly road transport, Lothian growers sought markets further afield in Glasgow and other industrial towns of the west of Scotland and occasionally as far south as London. It is reckoned that almost two-thirds of the volume of vegetables now grown in Scotland are produced in the Lothians.[24]

The earlier part of the nineteenth century saw considerable developments in fruit growing in the Clyde valley, to meet the growing needs of the rising population of Glasgow and district. According to a contributor to the second *Statistical Account*, over sixty varieties of apples and twenty-four of pears were grown there.[25] There had been very few varieties of plums which, to begin with, were grown on their own root stocks, but with the introduction of grafted trees the number of varieties increased. Gooseberries were extensively grown and orchard fruit was marketed by dealers who purchased the season's crop and undertook the picking and marketing. Until

[23] Neill, in Sinclair, *General Report*, VOL. II, p. 68.
[24] Scarlett, " Market gardening ", p. 197.
[25] *N.S.A.*, VOL. VI, Lanarkshire, p. 744.

the advent of steamboats the fruit of the area found a profitable local market, but with the introduction of regular steamer services between Glasgow and English and Irish ports, competition with fruit grown elsewhere had to be faced, and lower prices ruled. Crops in these days, we are also informed, often failed because of " blights " or caterpillar damage.

From 1870 onwards there were new developments: strawberries and raspberries especially began to be more extensively grown. Indeed from 1880 until 1910 the basic horticultural crop of Clydeside was strawberries, which were either disposed of as fresh fruit or consigned in barrels to jam manufacturers throughout the country. The importance of the strawberry industry to Lanarkshire may be gauged from the fact that in one year something between 1200 and 1400 tons were despatched by rail from the county.[26] In the nineties very low prices ruled for strawberries and in one year the price fell to £8 per ton, i.e. less than a penny per pound. Fortunately, after the turn of the century, a new marketing procedure was developed. Soft fruits were consigned in non-returnable baskets and cases, and large quantities were sold in the towns in the north of England and in Scotland. Some time between 1908 and 1913 strawberry and apple growing in Clydesdale reached its peak. Thereafter there was a decline, but gooseberries and plums held their own. Apples became more difficult to sell in competition with the more attractively coloured and packed imported varieties, and both the strawberry and raspberry acreages fell. Further reductions took place during the 1914-18 war but this trend was reversed after hostilities ceased. Unfortunately in 1920 a new strawberry disease, red core root rot, appeared in plantations. This disease, already widely prevalent throughout the world but at that time unidentified, came to be known as the Lanarkshire disease. For a long time no practical remedy was known and many Clydeside growers had to give up strawberry production.

Fortunately, with the decline in strawberry and tree fruit growing, Clydeside growers found in glasshouse production a profitable alternative enterprise. Glasshouses for tomato production, on which this industry is mainly based, were first built about 1895. At first no particular design of house was followed but before the outbreak of the First World War the type now in common use was evolved and standardised, heating being usually done on the low

[26] R. D. Reid and B. A. Lovatt, " Horticulture in Lanarkshire ", in Scot. Agric., XXXIII (1953-54), p. 36.

2 D

pressure hot water system. To control diseases and pests most growers have adopted the practice of sterilising their soil annually by steam. Recently the crops grown have given yields varying from 28 to 60 tons per acre with an average of about 35 tons. Half the glasshouse area in Lanarkshire is believed to be devoted exclusively to tomato culture. Many tomato growers use their glasshouses in the off-season to produce late-flowering chrysanthemums, early daffodils and tulips, pot plants, lettuce, etc.; the amount spent annually by Lanarkshire men on Dutch bulbs has been estimated at £10,000. Where glasshouses are used during part of the year to produce out-of-season flowers, growers are often at a disadvantage in regard to the early and late stages of the tomato crop. This is, however, offset by returns from the other products, and such growers find it possible to retain the services of their more skilled workers throughout the year.[27]

In one respect the Lanarkshire tomato industry is under a handicap. The area is colder than most other tomato-growing areas so that fuel costs are relatively high. Nevertheless, the skill of the average Lanarkshire tomato grower in the production and marketing of this crop has, so far, enabled him to withstand the competition of his fellows in England, the Channel Isles and Holland.

The establishment of the agricultural colleges at the beginning of the century was of great significance to horticulturists. The intensive cultivation practised in commercial gardens and glass-houses provides ideal conditions for the multiplication and spread of diseases and pests, a circumstance which calls for skilled advice on their recognition and on preventive and remedial measures. Horticulturists, too, as a class cultivate a wide variety of crops. Some may be interested only in vegetable culture, others may specialise in glasshouse production, others again are fruit growers and a fourth class—nurserymen—may devote their energies entirely to the propagation of flowers, shrubs and trees. Successful growers have thus to acquire a wealth of technical knowledge on the nutrition and management of their crops, and it was to meet these needs that the horticultural departments of the agricultural colleges were established. Besides serving commercial growers the colleges were called upon to advise cottage gardeners and allotment holders on their many problems. Day and evening classes were held

[27] R. D. Reid and B. A. Lovatt, "Horticulture in Lanarkshire", in *Scot. Agric.*, XXXIII (1953-54), p. 96.

at the central colleges, extension lectures given and advisory visits made. During the great trade depression of the 1930's, when there was large scale unemployment, special officers were appointed to give instruction and advice to unemployed workers who had been supplied with plots.[28]

It was early realised that, however well trained and knowledgeable advisory officers in horticulture might be, they would be certain to encounter many problems quite outside their competence. Thus in the case of a hitherto unrecognised disease such as strawberry red core root rot, the disease's cause, its recognition, its mode of spread, and its control, were matters appropriate to research workers. In time much was learnt about the disease, but the question of how to grow a healthy crop on infected land remained unanswered until certain American varieties were discovered to be highly resistant to the disease. A highly resistant variety might, however, be useless commercially: it must combine superior cropping powers with other desirable qualities. Here again science came to the rescue. The Department of Agriculture set up a strawberry breeding unit. Through a process of crossing, back crossing and most rigorous selection, Robert Reid, a Lanarkshire man with a flair for plant breeding, managed, with the aid of other workers and after many years of toil, to produce varieties which combined many desirable qualities. The result was a revival in strawberry growing and of confidence within the industry.[29]

The raspberry industry, which had flourished in the Blairgowrie district at the beginning of the century, also had an unhappy experience. It was crippled by diseases, in its case largely virus infections. In the 1920's a new variety, Lloyd George, with superior cropping powers was introduced and proved so satisfactory that it very largely displaced other varieties. Unfortunately, its susceptibility to certain virus diseases led to a progressive loss in cropping power. Remedial measures of a two-fold pattern were taken. A New Zealand stock of Lloyd George, which had remained healthy, was imported, while new varieties of raspberries, bred at the horticultural research station at East Malling in Kent, were introduced. So satisfactory did these varieties prove that the raspberry industry in Perthshire and Angus quickly revived.[30] To combat the spread of disease and to ensure that, when buying plants, growers would get

[28] D.O.A.S., 22nd report, 1934, pp. 15, 21.
[29] D.O.A.S., *Agriculture in Scotland*, report for 1953, p. 13.
[30] *ibid.*

stocks free from visible disease and true to kind, the Department of Agriculture for Scotland in 1929 initiated schemes for the inspection and certification of small-fruit stocks. Except for a break during the 1939-45 war these valuable schemes continued in operation. At the time of writing the average yield of raspberries, which had slumped to under a ton per acre, is nearly three tons. Strawberries were giving somewhat similar yields,[31] although previously the average had been of the order of only a ton per acre. The story of the revival, in these latter years, of raspberry and strawberry growing in Scotland provides an excellent example of improved production through the successful co-operation of growers, advisory officers, research workers and the administrative services of a Government department. The gratifying progress in dealing with diseases has stimulated other developments, better care and management of plantations, improved methods of fruit marketing and the winning of new markets.

An important development in Scottish horticulture was the acquisition in 1950 of the 170-acre farm of Mylnefield, near Dundee, for a Scottish Horticultural Research Institute.[32] The new organisation incorporates the Scottish raspberry unit previously controlled by the East Malling station and the strawberry unit set up earlier by the Department of Agriculture for Scotland. At this Station tests will be made of the local application of knowledge gained at East Malling, Long Ashton, the John Innes Institution and other centres in England where much useful investigation has been carried out.

No account of horticultural development in Scotland would be complete without reference to allotments. These attained prominence during the First World War, the number provided by burgh councils and other public bodies rising from 1685 in 1914 to 42,277 in 1918.[33] Thereafter the movement declined but a revival occurred during the great depression of the thirties when there was widespread unemployment. The unemployed were encouraged by the Scottish National Union of Allotment Holders and the Society of Friends to take up allotments, a joint committee being formed to assist unemployed miners and others to obtain and cultivate these small units. Assistance was given for the purchase of seeds, seed potatoes, fertilisers and gardening tools[34] while, as has been said, instructors were

[31] D.O.A.S., *Agriculture in Scotland*, report for 1953, p. 13.
[32] id., report for 1950, p. 55.
[33] B.O.A.S., 7th report, 1919, p. lix.
[34] D.O.A.S., 24th report, for 1936, p. 59.

appointed by the agricultural colleges to advise plot holders. During the Second World War allotments again attained prominence and a peak number of 83,746 was reached in 1943. It was reckoned that during the six years of the war, some 141,000 tons of horticultural produce were grown on allotments in Scotland.[35]

The quick-freeze method of preserving fruit began to be applied in Scotland in 1946 and by 1953 four factories were operating. In the latter year 600 tons of quick-frozen Scottish raspberries were exported to America,[36] and considerable amounts of frozen strawberries and raspberries were marketed at home. Large amounts of these fruits are also canned. In Angus and Perthshire considerable acreages of peas are grown on farms for canning.

Another interesting feature of Scotland's horticulture is the development of French gardening in the Lothians where it is believed the largest French gardens in Great Britain are located.[37] Another development, overhead irrigation for vegetable crops grown in the open, suggests that Scottish growers have kept abreast of modern developments.

In the year 1957 10,661 acres in Scotland were under vegetables, 997 acres under tree fruits, some with small fruit below and 9532 acres under small fruits not under orchard trees. These figures showed a decline, so far as tree fruits are concerned, on previous years. The Department of Agriculture for Scotland estimated the value of the horticultural output for Scotland for 1956-57 at just over £3½ million.[38]

[35] Sir R. B. Greig, " The dig for victory campaign 1940-45 ", in *Scot. Agric.*, xxv (1944-46), p. 229.

[36] *Scot. Agric.*, xxxiv, (1954-55), p. 113.

[37] Scarlett, " Market gardening ", p. 198.

[38] *Scottish Agricultural Economics*, vol. viii, p. 8.

## CHAPTER XXVII

# THE CO-OPERATIVE MOVEMENT

Birth of co-operation in Britain...The Rochdale Society...
Agricultural co-operation in Denmark...The Farmers' Supply
Association...Agricultural Organisation Societies in England
and Scotland...Government grants...Initial and war-time
difficulties...Post-1914-18 war developments...Purchasing and
selling societies...Egg-grading...Wool marketing...Develop-
ment in co-operative selling by dairy farmers...Effect of
Marketing Acts...Marketing Boards...Milk...Potatoes...Pigs
and Bacon...Wool...Difficulties and criticisms of boards
...Benefits to farmers...Co-operative societies in general.

THE CO-OPERATIVE MOVEMENT IN THIS COUNTRY was the child of
Britain's industrial development age, an age that brought
great but unevenly distributed wealth.  Factory and mine-
owners, shipping and railroad capitalists and others became rich
whereas the generality of workers, who toiled long hours for small
pay, remained poor and even downtrodden.  They usually had
large families, for children of tender years were wage-earning assets.
A report published in 1842 on the employment of children makes
unhappy reading; from it we learn that to augment the incomes
of the poor and to swell the profits of the well-off, children of seven
and eight years were in some collieries harnessed like dogs to draw
trucks.[1]

When the whole family was in employment a bare living could
be eked out but little or nothing could be set aside for a rainy day
and, as periods of unemployment were frequent, families were apt
to get into debt with local shopkeepers.  Debts mounted and often
enough it was not in the shopkeeper's interest that they should be
repaid for, while he wished to retain his customer, he also wished to
exact a high price.  Even factory-owners were apt to exploit poorly
paid employees by stipulating that part of their wages should be
spent in shops belonging to the owners or in those in which they had
an interest.  Discontent was rife and far-seeing workers realised that
unless they themselves could exercise control of the buying markets

---

[1] Arthur Bryant, *English Saga*, p. 51.

they would be powerless to remedy matters. By combining to form a society they might go right beyond the wholesaler and perhaps own factories. But over and above the purely business side of the issue other arguments in favour of co-operation were apparent. It promoted the spirit of brotherhood and gave the lower classes an opportunity to manage their own affairs; unlike joint-stock companies co-operative societies were not out for high profits for shareholders; their object was but to pass on benefits to their members in proportion to the value of goods purchased.

The first co-operative society was formed at Rochdale in 1844,[2] and survived the perils of infancy. It was quickly followed by others established mainly in industrial towns. Attempts at boycott by shopkeepers merely strengthened them. The movement was extended and was copied in Europe and in the United States. Curiously enough, while co-operation at this time did not appeal to British farmers, the reverse happened in Denmark, where the first co-operative society established to purchase goods for members was formed exclusively of farmers. In time the Danish societies became co-operative selling societies aiming largely at supplying British shopkeepers with standardised breakfast-table produce. The movement in Denmark was run purely on business lines, and was not governed by social or moral aspirations.[3] In course of time the agricultural co-operative movement spread to other European countries.

Not until 1884, when the Farmers' Supply Association was established in Leith, did co-operation find favour with Scottish farmers.[4] Its primary object was not to supply its members with goods on favourable terms but rather to ensure that the seeds and artificial manures purchased were of guaranteed purity and quality. But almost without exception Scottish farmers remained individualistic in the matter of buying their requirements or selling their products. Yet farming conditions during the great agricultural depression were not dissimilar to those experienced by workers in Rochdale and elsewhere in the early phases of the Industrial Age. Many farmers were deeply in debt to merchants for their seeds, manures and feeding-stuffs, for few had the wherewithal to pay cash down or settle accounts for goods within a month. The

[2] Trevelyan, *Social History*, pp. 546-7.

[3] Lionel Smith Gordon, *Co-operation for Farmers*, London 1918, pp. 122-3.

[4] T. G. Henderson, " Agricultural Co-operation in Scotland ", henceforth cited as Henderson, " Co-operation in Scotland ", in *T.H.A.S.*, 5th ser. XLI (1929), p. 71.

merchants for their part were accommodating since it suited their convenience and trade. For seeds and manures they did not press for payment until next year's order was due. High prices were charged but, when payment was made, a seemingly generous discount was given and farmers, thinking that they were not being too harshly dealt with, gave next year's order to the old firm. A remedy for this state of affairs was sought by some of the more enlightened farmers and landlords.

To understand the background of the development of agricultural co-operation in Scotland it may be pointed out that of the country's 75,000 agricultural holdings some 50,000 or so are small holdings of under 50 acres arable. Of these over 16,000 are under 5 acres in extent and are mainly located in remote areas in the Highlands and Islands. Their distance from markets, with consequent high freight charges, their small agricultural requirements, and the limited amount of saleable produce severely handicapped these very small-scale farmers. Had they been able to buy or sell in bulk, they could have saved greatly on transport, handling and the prices of their requirements. It was reasonable to assume, therefore, that the advantages of co-operation would be greatly appreciated by all classes of smallholders, particularly in remote areas.

In 1905 the Scottish Agricultural Organisation Society was brought into being, with aims similar to those of its English equivalent, established in 1901. These societies had a two-fold object, (a) to spread the co-operative movement amongst farmers, and (b) to organise trading societies and provide advice to enable them to run their businesses on sound lines. Buying societies, for instance, would be told where best to buy goods and selling societies informed of the best markets for produce. The Scottish and the English Organisation Societies were non-trading concerns: the former was entirely self-supporting and continued so for some years and many proprietors contributed liberally to its upkeep in its initial stages.[5]

About twenty years elapsed after the establishment of the Farmers' Supply Association before the next society, the Tarff Valley Agricultural Co-operative Society, Ltd., came into being;[6] while in 1905 another was formed by crofters in the far-away small

[5] Horace Plunkett Foundation, *Agricultural Co-operation in Scotland and Wales*, henceforth cited as *Agric. Co-op.*, London 1932, p. 3.

[6] C. J. M. Cadzow, " Fifty years of co-operative service in Scotland ", in *Scottish Agriculture*, xxxv (1955), p. 43.

island of Eday in Orkney. Its chief aim was to promote the interests of their poultry enterprises.[7] This latter society applied for aid to the Highland and Agricultural Society and the directors made a grant of £12. About the same time the tenant farmers of the Durris estate, Kincardineshire, combined to form a purchasing society and in 1906 the North Eastern Agricultural Society was formed with headquarters at Aberdeen.

By 1909, the first year for which figures are obtainable, forty-eight societies were in being, most of which were small purchasing concerns in the Highlands and Islands, but through lack of purchasing power and for other reasons they made little headway. In 1912 the Scottish Agricultural Organisation Society received its first grant from the Development Commission. This enabled it to make greater efforts to strengthen the movement, efforts which, however, were to some extent hampered by the existence of a rival organisation—the Scottish Smallholders' Organisation Society.[8] Nevertheless, the former society soon doubled its constituent societies and took steps to co-ordinate and systematise their activities. All popular movements, however, in the early stages when enthusiasm runs high, are apt to develop too quickly to be healthy, and in the formation of the first Scottish agricultural organisation societies enthusiasm often outran discretion, with unhappy results. But in Scotland casualties were less frequent than in England and Ireland and only four societies had to be wound up.[9]

The outbreak of war in August 1914 checked progress. People had more serious matters to think about and staffs were depleted. Societies in remote districts suffered from shortage of supplies and transport difficulties and some had to close down when their key men joined the Forces. Immediately after the war the Organisation Society set out to develop the co-operative movement among farmers and smallholders as quickly as possible. Victory had engendered a feeling of optimism and the Government were now offering greatly increased grants on a pound per pound basis. A special grant facilitated the appointment of a Gaelic-speaking organiser.[10] Despite overlapping by the rival organisation which was also Government-aided,[11] great progress was made, no fewer

[7] Proceedings at Board Meetings, in *T.H.A.S.*, 5th ser. XVIII (1906), pp. 425-8.

[8] Henderson, " Co-operation in Scotland ", p. 72.

[9] *Agric. Co-op.*, p. 7.

[10] B.O.A.S., 8th report, for 1920, p. lxi.

[11] *Agric. Co-op.*, pp. 7, 10.

than 176 societies being registered by 1920. But many of these societies were insubstantial, existing only in name. The slump of 1921 caused another setback but fortunately the Scottish agricultural co-operative societies were not carrying heavy stocks of goods, and did not suffer badly. Nevertheless, the parent society found itself in financial difficulties because Treasury grants were reduced. This slump, however, had one salutary effect. No good purpose was being served by the existence of two rival organisations doing the same work, covering much the same ground, and both in receipt of Government aid. Following an enquiry the Scottish Smallholders' Organisation was closed down.

Soon after 1925 prospects brightened. An annual grant of £100 was made by the Highland and Agricultural Society of Scotland,[12] while other grants came from the National Farmers' Union, the Scottish Chamber of Agriculture and at a later stage the Scottish Farm Servants' Union. Co-operation was on lines in accord with the principles of these latter bodies and the influential backing thus given was of the greatest value to the Society's development. The Treasury, too, loosened its purse strings and enabled grants up to £4500 a year to be earned,[13] benefactions which allowed the Society to enlarge its staff and expand its activities. But its story can perhaps be best illustrated if we consider briefly the principal lines along which the subsidiary societies were developed.

The S.A.O.S., as the Scottish Agricultural Organising Society was known, found great scope in its early years for the formation of supply societies in remote areas of the Highlands and Islands, for there the greatest economies in the bulk purchase and transport of materials could be made. Unfortunately, many of these societies were weak and insubstantial and later the policy followed was to reduce the number of the smaller and strengthen the larger and more mature concerns. This could be done either by allowing the weak society to dissolve and persuading its members to join a larger one, or by one of the larger societies absorbing the smaller. The most notable of these large-scale supply societies is the North-Eastern Agricultural Co-operative Society at Aberdeen. It is equipped with oil-crushing and artificial manure processing plant, and fills admirably the role of supplier to the highly developed agricultural area stretching from East Angus in the south to Moray

---

[12] Proceedings at Board Meetings, in *T.H.A.S.*, 5th ser. xxxix (1927), p. 414.

[13] B.O.A.S. 16th report, for 1928, p. 67.

in the north; its turnover in 1954 was about £1¾ million.[14] In that year 28 supply societies were in operation, with an aggregate membership of over 14,000 and a turnover of over £3 million. These 28 societies do not include such selling societies as provide agricultural requirements subsidiary to their main function of selling farm produce, usually eggs.

In Orkney hen population per acre of arable land was, and is, the highest in Scotland and markets for eggs had to be found outside the county. It was in Orkney that the S.A.O.S. found the greatest scope for the establishment of egg-collecting and marketing societies. Opportunity was taken in 1912 to establish an egg-selling agency at Leith,[15] where most of the Orcadian eggs were sent by boat. By 1929 over one-fifth of all Orcadian eggs were handled by local co-operative societies in the county, but not all of these eggs were sold through the Leith agency. Some egg-grading appears to have been done by these collecting societies, many of which supplied their members with groceries and occasionally with feeding-stuffs, artificial manures and seed oats.

A marked advance in egg-marketing was recorded in 1927 when the Aberdeen Egg Producers, Ltd. established a society at Turriff.[16] Eggs were collected by vans within a radius of up to twenty miles and were tested and graded on up-to-date lines. At glut times the eggs were cold-stored. From the outset this society met severe opposition from private traders, and to counter this it adopted the plan of selling groceries. Thanks to the determination of its promoters and the loyalty of its four to five hundred members the society survived. Its enlightened methods of handling eggs enhanced the reputation of Aberdeenshire eggs and helped producers to obtain much better prices. During the 1939-45 war and the immediate post-war years these egg-collecting societies acted as agents of the Ministry of Food. The value of the eggs and poultry which they handled in 1952 was over £3 million and 47 per cent. of the eggs passing through Ministry of Food Egg Packing Stations were handled co-operatively.[17]

In 1924 after an internal reorganisation and a change in policy by the S.A.O.S. a committee was appointed to consider the important question of wool marketing, and as a result Scottish Wool

[14] Scottish Agricultural Organisation Society, henceforth cited as S.A.O.S., *Report* for 1954, p. 14.
[15] Henderson, " Co-operation in Scotland ", p. 75.
[16] *ibid.*
[17] S.A.O.S., *Report*, 1950-52, p. 15.

Growers Ltd. was registered in 1926.  Amongst its 458 members at this time were some of the largest sheep farmers in the country.  All classes of wool were dealt with; the business was run on commission lines, each member receiving the price realised for his wool, less expenses.  By 1931 the membership had increased to 690 and the society was handling nearly a fifth of the Scottish clip.[18]  At the beginning of the 1939-45 war the Government assumed control of wool sales and prices and appointed the Society an authorised merchant to act on its behalf.  In anticipation of the decontrol of wool steps were taken after the war to promote a Wool Marketing Board and one was formed in October 1950.  Producers in the Islands, where local wool was manufactured, were given the option of selling their wool either privately or to the Board.

In the marketing of livestock auction marts have for long played an important part in Scottish farming.  Many were founded by individuals who converted their businesses into joint-stock companies; others were formed by farmers, who subscribed the capital, employed auctioneers and distributed profits as dividends according to the number of shares held.  One Kincardineshire joint-stock company, largely farmer-owned, paid a bonus on sales transacted for its members and in 1909 this company changed its status to that of a co-operative society.[19]  By 1932 three co-operative marts were functioning.  This system of selling fat stock as live fat animals in auction marts has, however, often been criticised as wasteful in practice, the contention being that the marts had to have their commission, the dealers and wholesale butchers, who purchased the animals, their profit, and that unnecessary expense, waste of time and needless loss of weight were involved in animal transport, first to the marts then possibly to other marts and finally to the slaughterhouse.  Another criticism was that at some of the smaller marts there were buyers' rings.  The S.A.O.S. contended that the supply of fat stock could not be properly regulated unless sales by auction were replaced by sales through slaughterhouses controlled by the producers and possessing facilities for grading and cold storage.  In 1928 the first co-operative slaughterhouse operating more or less on these lines was opened at St Boswells.[20]  Largely through miscalculations its initial story was not one of unbroken success, but it survived and on the outbreak of the Second World War was taken over by the Ministry of Food who became the purchasers of all fat stock.  This

[18] *Agric. Co-op.*, pp. 142-3.
[19] *op. cit.*, p. 146.          [20] *op. cit.*, p. 147.

experiment in handling meat, coupled with the experience gained during the period of control, had been carefully noted by the Scottish National Farmers' Union and in anticipation of the de-control of meat a Fat Stock Marketing Scheme was put forward in 1952 by the three Farmers' Unions of the United Kingdom.[21] The scheme was not accepted by the Government when it announced the forthcoming decontrol of meat in November 1953. Instead a Fatstock Marketing Corporation was brought into being in 1954 by the Farmers' Unions. Formed under the Companies Act and financed by the banks, this voluntary marketing agency was em-powered by the Government to administer price guarantees under the Agriculture Act 1947 for the livestock it handled. The animals consigned by producers to the Corporation were paid for on a dead meat and grade basis very much on the lines suggested in the proposed Fat Stock Marketing Scheme—a scheme which many farmers hoped would in time find acceptance.

The story of the milk-selling societies illustrates the strength and the weakness of co-operative selling societies and of the effect of their experiences in inducing dairy farmers to sell their milk through a marketing board. Before 1914 a number of milk-selling co-operative societies had been formed, principally in the west of Scotland; for the most part they sold as much liquid milk as they could to milk-retailing firms. One, which was established at Inver-ness about 1912, was associated with a milk-retail business, and its members were induced by price incentives and quotas to maintain regular supplies throughout the year. Milk surplus to members' quotas was paid for at lower prices. In the operations of some of these societies the principle of a pool price monthly payment was adopted. On the decontrol of milk after the 1914-18 war the Scottish National Farmers' Union, representing the liquid milk producers of the south-west, collaborated with the co-operative dairy associations in arranging prices with the milk-retailing com-panies. For some years this arrangement worked well. Owing, however, to increasing quantities of milk being offered for sale—partly because some cattle-rearing and fattening farmers were switching over to milk production, and in part because of the widening of the gap between the prices of milk for consumption as liquid and milk for manufacture into butter and cheese, two com-modities which had fallen in price, difficulties arose over the question

[21] *Marketing of Fat Stock*, report of National Farmers' Union of England, Scotland and Ulster, 1952.

of surplus milk.  So acute did the situation become that the system of collective bargaining broke down.

In an attempt to avoid a return to individual marketing the Scottish National Farmers' Union, in collaboration with the Scottish Agricultural Organisation Society, drafted a scheme for setting up a central agency which would secure a market for all milk produced by its members.  The bulk of the milk would be sold to the retailers as liquid milk on the basis of contract quantities, the residue being sold for manufacture.  The scheme was approved and the Scottish Milk Agency came into being in 1927, a branch being set up in Aberdeen.  For a time all went well, but once again difficulties arose over the disposal of surplus milk.  Moreover, certain former members who had become disloyal to the agency, along with outsiders, competed with the agency for the disposal of their milk.  In some instances milk was offered for sale at $3\frac{3}{4}d$. per gallon.  By 1931 the main society had become moribund and only the Aberdeen branch survived.[22]  The experience gained from this setback, however, was invaluable.  It was realised that so long as a competitive minority of producers of a perishable product such as milk remained outside the organisation, and so long as control of production throughout the year was inadequate, co-operative milk-marketing would be unlikely to succeed.  Success postulated that all producers should be brought in.[23]

A partial solution to the problem was found in the Agricultural Marketing Act 1931, whereby a majority of producers could, with the consent of the Government, compel a minority to observe regulations governing the sale of a particular product.  To determine this matter, producers had to be registered and a poll taken.  If two-thirds of the producers voted in favour of a marketing board then such a board could be set up.  But before a board could operate properly powers were necessary to control home-grown and imported supplies.  This was effected by the Agricultural Marketing Act 1933,[24] in anticipation of which the S.A.O.S., in conjunction with the National Farmers' Union for Scotland, drew up a scheme for the establishment of a Scottish Milk Marketing Board.  The Aberdeen and the northern milk producers, believing that their interests would be best served under local control, set up their own boards in 1934.  These were known as the Aberdeen and District

[22] *Agric. Co-op.*, p. 135.          [23] *op. cit.*, p. 136.
[24] A. W. Ashby, " Agricultural conditions and policies 1910-13 ", in *Agriculture in the Twentieth Century*, p. 70.

Milk Marketing Board and the North of Scotland Milk Marketing Board respectively. The three Scottish Boards purchased all milk produced for sale in their areas except milk sold by producer-retailers for whom special arrangements were made. The maximum amount was sold as liquid milk to the retailers; the remainder (except a certain amount sold to England) being disposed of either to manufacturing companies or processed by the Boards into cheese, butter, cream, milk powder, etc. The proceeds of milk sold were pooled and producers received the pool price less expenses.

Although the necessary two-thirds majority of producers had been obtained in setting up the Scottish Milk Marketing Board there was bitter opposition from some producer-retailers. To enjoy the advantages of the scheme these producers were subjected to a levy of so much per gallon. One critic characterised this as " pure unadulterated organised daylight robbery " and after the establishment of the Board some objectors refused to pay the stipulated levy. There were legal proceedings and eventually the case went to the House of Lords who decided against the Board and the rate of levy was reduced. The Scottish Milk Marketing Board, however, continued to function.

The system of price pooling obviously favoured producers who had formerly produced milk for manufacture. Owing to the low world price of cheese and butter they benefited by sharing in the higher price received for liquid milk. Equally, of course, producer-retailers, who formerly sold most part of their milk as liquid milk, now had to bear through the levy part of the loss incurred in the disposal of surplus milk for manufacture. They seemingly ignored the protection afforded them against competition, and the possibility of such competition becoming very acute, since with the aid of modern appliances clean milk can be transported long distances and remain fresh for three or four days.

A criticism often levelled against the Boards was that they created a monopoly with power to exact an unduly high price from consumers. At the time of their establishment there was little evidence to support this, but in view of such a possibility measures were taken later to protect consumers' interests.[25] The Agricultural Marketing Act passed in 1949 gave Ministers wider powers to protect the national and consumer interest under marketing schemes and at the same time, by permitting direct representation of Ministers on Marketing Boards, gave the Government greater authority in

[25] Astor and Rowntree, *British Agriculture*, pp. 429-30.

regard to their operations.   The formation of the Milk Marketing Boards put the whole milk-producing industry on a sound basis. Without them conditions would have been chaotic and in that event many producers might have switched to some other farming enter-prise and thereby endangered supplies of milk.   Nor should it be overlooked that through the Boards' activities the Government were enabled to institute an enlightened policy that was to have far-reaching effects on human and animal health.   The school milk scheme, financed in part by the Exchequer, encouraged milk-drinking by children with advantage to their health.   Milk-drinking by adults was stimulated by the creation of milk bars and by propaganda, again in part financed by the Government.   By the payment through the Boards of 2d. per gallon for tuberculin-tested milk, dairy farmers were encouraged to establish tuberculin-tested herds and to produce cleaner milk.[26]   Government assistance was given to the Boards to facilitate the sale of surplus milk.   The Boards tackled their work with energy and effected considerable economies in the handling and processing of milk;  they spared no effort to improve the quality of the milk, and when control ceased and the Ministry of Food no longer bought milk the Boards became the agencies through which the guaranteed prices for milk were paid. The establishment of artificial insemination stations with substations some years after the close of the 1939-45 war was evidence of their desire to promote efficiency in production.   Incidentally the first artificial insemination centre in Scotland was set up at Hoddam by a co-operative society, the Dumfriesshire Cattle Breeders Ltd. Societies with somewhat similar objectives were set up in connexion with grass-drying and chick-hatching.

Chaotic conditions in years of abundant potato crops obliged producers to look for means of regulating supplies and to some extent controlling prices.   Producers therefore welcomed the Marketing Acts which enabled them to set up a Potato Marketing Board for Great Britain.   This board, unlike the Milk Marketing Boards, was not a purchasing body but it exercised a two-way control over supplies.   Each producer was given a basic acreage, only to be exceeded on payment of an acreage penalty, while, by determining the size of the ware riddle according to the abundance or scarcity of the crop, supplies coming on to the market were largely regulated.   If despite these safeguards prices slumped in

[26] James MacIntosh, " The evolution of milk production ", in *Agriculture in the Twentieth Century*, pp. 419-20.

early winter, as they were apt to do in years of plenty, the Board could peg them by buying largely for forward delivery. In years when the crop was very short, imports above those customary for early potatoes were allowed. With commendable zeal the Potato Marketing Board set out to solve the problem of disposing of the surplus in years of plenty. In continental Europe potatoes were used to make starch and industrial alcohol, but before much progress in this direction could be made in Great Britain the Second World War had broken out. Nevertheless, a factory for drying potatoes for stock feed had been set up at Wisbech.[27]

Pigs were also badly affected by price slumps and for years had been subject to recurring cycles of good times and bad. In good times more pigs were produced and the sellers' market soon became a buyers'. One such crisis, which faced producers at the beginning of 1932, led to the appointment of a Government commission to draw up a reorganisation scheme. It recommended that a quota should be applied to supplies from abroad and that a contract system for home-produced pigs should be established. A Pig as well as a Bacon Marketing Board was subsequently brought into being, the objective being to secure a guaranteed minimum price for bacon pig producers. This was to be effected by contract between producers and curers, the price of pigs to vary with the market price of feeding stuffs, but unfortunately the scheme was beset with difficulties. Curers often ran short of supplies and other arrangements had to be made. Moreover, a pig can be killed either for pork or for bacon and the Board had no control over the supply or sale of pork pigs. If farmers thought that they would make more for their pigs by selling them at the age of five months for pork than by keeping them on for bacon they chose the first alternative.[28] The scheme for the marketing of bacon pigs could only be worked satisfactorily if regular supplies reached the curers, and as this did not happen some means remained to be found to control steady supplies of bacon pigs throughout the year and to ensure sufficient—but only sufficient—supplies of pork pigs to meet the seasonal demands.

A special feature of the agricultural co-operative movement in Scotland is the assistance given to the development of markets for items of produce which, strictly speaking, are not agricultural but which in crofting areas are linked with agriculture, e.g. handicrafts

[27] Astor and Rowntree, *British Agriculture*, pp. 124-9.
[28] *op. cit.*, pp. 218-24.

2 E

such as tweeds and knitted goods, seaweed and fishing products. Lobsters, too, are a considerable source of revenue to some fishermen-crofters, but summer-caught lobsters have to be sold more cheaply than those caught in winter, and in summer casualties in transport are considerable. Trials to solve this problem were instigated. Through the Crofters' Supply Agency, two storage ponds were hired in which to keep summer-caught lobsters until winter when prices are higher and casualties in transport are fewer. Transport by air was also experimented with.[29]

The net cast by the Organising Society has been wide, for it embraces activities ranging from livestock improvement schemes and insurance societies to different kinds of supply and marketing organisations. The policy now followed is to concentrate not so much on the formation of new societies but rather on strengthening existing societies by amalgamation or otherwise. Educationally, too, the Organising Society has done good work. Although many members of the agricultural co-operative societies may obtain part of their requirements or sell part of their produce privately, and are therefore not 100 per cent. wedded to co-operation, it is estimated that two-fifths of the occupiers of farms and crofts in Scotland are members of such societies and therefore converts to the principle of co-operation. Furthermore the adoption of its principles, even by those outside the co-operative societies, has led farmers to accept marketing boards for milk, potatoes and wool as most desirable institutions.

In a broader sense, too, the acceptance by farmers of the principles of co-operation has effected a change in their day-to-day relationships. They have become much more public-spirited, more ready to share their experiences or give their private time and, in general, to subordinate personal interests to the higher cause of serving the industry to which they belong. While self-help has been the basis of community enterprise, co-operation has proved itself to be the basis of community welfare.

[29] S.A.O.S., *Report* 1950-52, p. 20.

# LIST OF ABBREVIATIONS AND OF
# WORKS COMMONLY CITED

*Agric. Co-op.* = *Agricultural Co-operation in Scotland and Wales*, Horace Plunkett Foundation, London 1932.

*Agriculture in the Twentieth Century* = *Agriculture in the Twentieth Century, Essays in Research, practice and organisation to be presented to Sir Daniel Hall*, Oxford 1939.

Alexander, W., *Notes and Sketches* = *Notes and Sketches, being Illustrations of Northern Rural Life in the Eighteenth Century*, Aberdeen 1876.

Anderson, James, *Essays* = *Essays relating to Agriculture and Rural Affairs*, 3rd edn. 2 vols. Dublin 1779.

Anderson, William, *The Scottish Nation*, 3 vols. Edinburgh 1865.

*A.P.S.* = *Acts of the Parliaments of Scotland*, 12 vols., VOLS. I, V, VI, ed. C. Innes, VOLS. II, III, IV, VII, VIII, IX, X, XI, ed. T. Thomson, London 1814-75, VOL. XII, ed. A. Anderson, Edinburgh 1875.

Argyll, George Douglas Campbell, Duke of, *Scotland* = *Scotland as it was and as it is*, 2nd edn. Edinburgh 1887.

Astor, Waldorf Viscount, and Rowntree, B. Seebohm, *British Agriculture*, London 1938.

*B.O.A.S.* = Board of Agriculture for Scotland.

Bradley, A. G., *Squires and Farmers* = *When Squires and Farmers Thrived*, London 1927.

Brown, P. Hume, *Scotland before 1700*, Edinburgh 1893.

Bryant, Arthur, *English Saga 1840-1940*, London 1940.

Burt or Birt, Edward, *Letters* = *Letters from a Gentleman in the North of Scotland to his Friend in London*, 2 vols. 3rd edn. London 1815.

Chambers, R., *Domestic Annals*, VOLS. I-II = *Domestic Annals of Scotland from the Reformation to the Revolution*, 2 vols. Edinburgh 1858.

——, *Domestic Annals*, VOL. III = *Domestic Annals of Scotland from the Revolution to the Rebellion of 1745*, Edinburgh 1861.

Childe, V. Gordon, *The Prehistory of Scotland*, London 1935.

Cobbett, William, *A Tour in Scotland and in the Four Northern Counties of England*, London 1833.

Cockburn, John, *Letters* = *Letters to his Gardener 1727-44*, ed. James Colville, Scottish History Society VOL. XLV, Edinburgh 1904.

Coulton, G. G., *Scottish Abbeys* = *Scottish Abbeys and Social Life*, Cambridge 1933.

*Coupar Abbey Rental Book* = *Rental Book of the Cistercian Abbey of Coupar-Angus*, ed. C. Rogers, 2 vols. Grampian Club, London 1879-80.

*Crofters Commission Report* = *Report of Her Majesty's Commissioners appointed to inquire into the Conditions of the Crofters and Cottars in the Highlands and Islands of Scotland*, Edinburgh 1884.

Curwen, E. C., *Plough and Pasture*, London 1946.

D.O.A.S. = Department of Agriculture for Scotland.

Donaldson, James, *Husbandry Anatomized, or an Enquiry into the Present Manner of Teiling and Manuring the Ground in Scotland for the most Part and several Rules and Measurements laid down for the better Improvement thereof, in so much that one third part more Increase may be had and yet more than a third part the Expence of the present way of Labouring thereof saved*, Edinburgh 1697.

Douglas, Charles, " Agric. during the war " = " Scottish agriculture during the war," in *T.H.A.S.*, 5th ser. XXXI (1919).

Douglas, R., *Agric. Roxburgh* = *General View of the Agriculture in the Counties of Roxburgh and Selkirk*, Edinburgh 1798.

Dunbar, E., *Social Life in Moray* = *Social Life in Former Days, chiefly in the Province of Moray*, 2nd series, Edinburgh 1866.

Ernle, R. E. Prothero, Lord, *English Farming* = *English Farming Past and Present*, 5th edn. ed. Sir A. D. Hall, London 1936.

*Farm Reports* = *Reports of Select Farms*, Library of Useful Knowledge, London 1831.

Findlay, W. M., *Oats* = *Oats, their cultivation and use from ancient times to the present day*, Aberdeen University Studies No. 137, Edinburgh 1956.

Franklin, T. Bedford, *Scottish Farming* = *A History of Scottish Farming*, London 1952.

*F.S.A.* = First *Statistical Account of Scotland*, ed. Sir John Sinclair, 21 vols. Edinburgh 1791-99.

Fussell, G. E., *Farmer's Tools* = *The Farmer's Tools 1500-1900*, London 1952.

Graham, H. G., *Social Life* = *The Social Life of Scotland in the Eighteenth Century*, 4th edn. London 1937.

Grant, Sir Arthur, " State of Monymusk " = " Description of the present state of Monymusk," in *Miscellany of the Spalding Club*, VOL. II, ed. J. Stuart, Aberdeen 1842.

Grant, I. F., *Highland Farm* = *Everyday Life on an old Highland Farm 1769-1782*, London 1924.

——, *Social Development* = *Social and Economic Development of Scotland before 1603*, Edinburgh 1930.

Henderson, John, *Agric. Caithness* = *General View of the Agriculture of the County of Caithness*, London 1812.

Henderson, T. G., " Co-operation in Scotland " = " Agricultural co-operation in Scotland ", in *T.H.A.S.*, 5th ser. XLI (1929).

Innes, Cosmo, *Legal Antiquities* = *Lectures on Scotch Legal Antiquities*, Edinburgh 1872.

Innes, Cosmo, *Middle Ages* = *Scotland in the Middle Ages*, Edinburgh 1860.

*J.R.A.S.E.* = *Journal of the Royal Agricultural Society of England.*

Kames, Henry Home, Lord, *Gentleman Farmer* = *The Gentleman Farmer ; being an attempt to improve Agriculture, by subjecting it to the test of Rational Principles*, Edinburgh 1766.

Keith, G. Skene, *Agric. Aberdeenshire* = *A General View of the Agriculture of Aberdeenshire*, Aberdeen 1811.

Lawson, Peter and Charles, *Agrostographia*, 5th edn. Edinburgh 1855.

Lees, J. Cameron, *County of Inverness* = *A History of the County of Inverness—mainland*, Edinburgh 1897.

*Liber de Calchou* = *Liber Sancte Marie de Calchou, Registrum cartorum abbacie Tironensis de Calchou*, ed. Cosmo Innes, Bannatyne Club, Edinburgh 1846.

Loudon, J. C., *Encyclopaedia* = *An Encyclopaedia of Agriculture*, London 1825 and 1831.

McCombie, W., *Cattle and Cattle-Breeders*, 4th edn. Edinburgh 1866.

Macdonald, James, *Agric. Hebrides* = *General View of the Agriculture of the Hebrides*, London 1811.

Macdonald, James, " Agriculture of Sutherland " = " On the agriculture of the county of Sutherland ", in *T.H.A.S.*, 4th ser. XII (1880).

Macdonald, W., " Agriculture of Inverness " = " On the agriculture of the county of Inverness ", in *T.H.A.S.*, 4th ser. IV (1872).

MacKay, William, *Urquhart and Glenmoriston*, 2nd edn. Inverness 1914.

MacKenzie, Osgood H., *Hundred Years* = *A Hundred Years in the Highlands*, London 1921.

Marshall, David, " Agric. during the war " = " Scottish agriculture during the war ", in *T.H.A.S.*, 5th ser. LVIII (1956).

Marshall, W., *Agric. Central Highlands* = *General View of the Agriculture of the Central Highlands of Scotland*, London 1794.

Martin, Martin, *Western Islands* = *A Description of the Western Islands of Scotland*, ed. Donald J. Macleod, Stirling 1934.

Middleton, T. H., *Food Production* = *Food Production in War*, Carnegie Endowment for International Peace ; Economic and Social History of the World War, British series, Oxford 1923.

*Monymusk Papers* = *Selections from the Monymusk Papers 1713-1755*, ed. H. Hamilton, Scottish History Society, 3rd ser. VOL. XXXIX, Edinburgh 1945.

Nicolson, A., *History of Skye*, Glasgow 1930.

*N.S.A.* = New *Statistical Account of Scotland*, 18 vols. Edinburgh 1845.

Orwin, C. S., *English Farming* = *A History of English Farming*, London 1940.

Pennant, T., *Tour* = *A Tour in Scotland and Voyage to the Hebrides 1772*, 1790 edn. London, 2 vols.

Pidgeon, D., " Evolution of implements " = " The evolution of agricultural implements ", in *J.R.A.S.E.*, 3rd ser. III (1892).

*P.S.A.S.* = *Proceedings of the Society of Antiquaries of Scotland.*

Ramsay, A., *History H.A.S.* = *History of the Highland and Agricultural Society of Scotland,* Edinburgh 1879.

Ramsay, John, *Scotland and Scotsmen* = *Scotland and Scotsmen in the Eighteenth Century,* ed. A. Allardyce, 2 vols. Edinburgh 1888.

Reid, J., *The Scots Gard'ner,* 1683 and 1776 edns. Edinburgh.

Robertson, G., *Agric. Kincardineshire* = *General View of the Agriculture of Kincardineshire or the Mearns,* London 1810.

——, *Agric. Midlothian* = *General View of the Agriculture of the County of Midlothian,* Edinburgh 1793.

Robertson, J., *Agric. Perth* = *General View of the Agriculture of the County of Perth,* Perth 1799.

*R.P.C.S.* = *Register of the Privy Council of Scotland,* 3 series, Edinburgh 1877-1933.

Salaman, R., *History of the Potato* = *The History and Social Influence of the Potato,* Cambridge 1949.

Scarlett, R. L., " Market gardening " = " Marketing gardening in the Lothians ", in *Scientific Horticulture,* x (1951).

*Scot. Agric.* = *Scottish Agriculture.*

Seebohm, M. E., *English Farm* = *The Evolution of the English Farm,* London 1927.

Sinclair, Sir John, *Agric. Northern Counties* = *General View of the Agriculture of the Northern Counties and Islands of Scotland,* London 1795.

——, *General Report* = *General Report of the Agricultural State and Political Circumstances of Scotland,* 5 vols. including Appendix, Edinburgh 1814.

Singer, W., *Agric. Dumfries* = *View of the Agriculture, State of the Property, and Improvements in the County of Dumfries,* Edinburgh 1812.

*S.J. Agric.* = *Scottish Journal of Agriculture.*

Small, J., *Treatise on Ploughs* = *Treatise on Ploughs and Wheel Carriages,* Edinburgh 1784.

Smith, S., *Agric. Galloway* = *View of the Agriculture of Galloway,* London 1810.

Somerville, Robert, *Agric. E. Lothian* = *General View of the Agriculture of East Lothian,* London 1805.

Souter, D., *Agric. Banff* = *General View of the Agriculture of the County of Banff,* London 1812.

*The Standard Cyclopædia of Modern Agriculture and Rural Economy,* ed. Sir R. P. Wright, 12 vols. London 1908-11.

*T.H.A.S.* = *Transactions of the Highland and Agricultural Society of Scotland.*

Thomson, J., *Agric. Fife* = *General View of the Agriculture of the County of Fife,* London 1800.

Trevelyan, G. M., *Social History* = *English Social History,* London 1944.

*Urie Court Book* = *The Court Book of the Barony of Urie*, ed. Douglas Barron, Scottish History Society VOL. XII, Edinburgh 1892.

Walker, John, *History Hebrides* = *An Economical History of the Hebrides*, 2 vols. Edinburgh 1808.

Watson, J. A. S., and Amery, G. D., " Early writers " = " Early Scottish agricultural writers 1697-1790 ", in *T.H.A.S.*, 5th ser. XLIII (1931).

Watson, J. A. S., and Hobbs, M. E., *Great Farmers*, 2nd edn. London 1951.

Whetham, E. H., *British Farming* = *British Farming 1939-49*, London 1952.

Whitehead, T., McIntosh, T., *et al.*, *Potato* = *The Potato in Health and Disease*, Edinburgh 1945.

Wight, A., *State of Husbandry* = *Present State of Husbandry in Scotland*, 4 vols. Edinburgh 1778-84.

Wilson, James, " Farming in Aberdeenshire " = " Farming in Aberdeenshire, ancient and modern ", in *T.H.A.S.*, 5th ser. XIV (1902).

Wilson, J., " Border farmer " = " Half a century as a Border farmer ", in *T.H.A.S.*, 5th ser. XIV (1902).

# APPENDIX I

Chronological list of books relating to Scottish
Agriculture published down to 1850

It is probably impossible to make a list of books on Scottish agriculture
absolutely complete, and there may be a debatable border-line between
agriculture and other related subjects. This list contains all specifically
Scottish books known to the author, and a number of more general application to British agriculture.

Only one location is given for each book, although the majority may be
found in several libraries. In the first instance the National Library of
Scotland, Edinburgh, is given; then other libraries in Edinburgh; and
failing these the British Museum or, in a few cases, other libraries in England.
Locations are abbreviated as follows:

B.M. = British Museum
E.U.L. = Edinburgh University Library
N.L.S. = National Library of Scotland
R.A.S.E. = Royal Agricultural Society of England, London
S.L. = Signet Library, Edinburgh

Brackets round an author's name indicate that the work was originally
published anonymously.

1596  NAPIER, SIR ARCHIBALD, *The new order of gooding and manuring all
      sorts of field land with common salt, whereby the same may bring
      forth in more abundance both of grass and corn of all sorts, and
      far cheeper than the common way of dunging used heretofore in
      Scotland.* Edinburgh.                          No copy found.
1624  HUNTAR, ALEXANDER, *A Treatise of weights, mets, and measures of
      Scotland, with their quantities, and true foundation, and sundrie
      profitable observations arising upon every one of them, together
      with the art of metting, measuring, & compting all sorts of
      land, with diverse tables.* Edinburgh.                    N.L.S.
1683  REID, JOHN, *The Scots Gard'ner, whereunto is added the gard'ner's
      Kalendar.* Edinburgh.                                     N.L.S.
      New edn. Edinburgh 1756.                                  N.L.S.
1684  *Whole Yearly Faires and Weekly Mercats of this Ancient Kingdom
      of Scotland, plainly set down, according to their several Shyres,
      Cities, Touns, etc.* Aberdeen.                            S.L.
1697  DONALDSON, JAMES, *Husbandry Anatomized; or an enquiry into the
      present Manner of Teiling and Manuring the Ground in Scotland
      for the most Part ; and several Rules and Measures laid down for
      the better Improvement thereof, in so much that one third part
      more Increase may be had and yet more than a third part the
      Expence of the present way of Labouring thereof saved.* Edinburgh.
                                                                N.L.S.

1699 [HAMILTON, JOHN, 2ND BARON BELHAVEN], *The Countrey-Man's Rudiments; or, an Advice to the Farmers in East-Lothian how to Labour and Improve their Ground,* Edinburgh.
1713 edn. N.L.S.

1703 MARTIN, MARTIN, *A Description of the Western Isles of Scotland, to which is added a brief description of the isles of Orkney and Shetland.* London. N.L.S.
Also ed. Donald J. Macleod, Stirling 1934. N.L.S.

1717 *A Report from the Commissioners appointed to Enquire of the Estates of certain Traitors, etc. in that Part of Great Britain called Scotland.* London. N.L.S.

1719 *To the Honourable the House of Commons, a Further Report, Humbly Offered by the Commissioners and Trustees who acted in Scotland* . . . London. N.L.S.

1724 SOCIETY OF IMPROVERS, *A Treatise concerning the Manner of Fallowing of Ground, Raising of Grass-Seeds and Training of Lint and Hemp for the increase and improvement of the linnen-manufactories in Scotland.* Edinburgh. N.L.S.

1724 *The farther Report of the Commissioners and Trustees Appointed to Enquire into the Forfeited Estates in Scotland* . . . London. N.L.S.

1724-7 DEFOE, DANIEL, *A Tour thro' the whole Island of Great Britain.* London. B.M.
7th edn. London 1769. N.L.S.

1725 *The final Report of the Commissioners and Trustees of the Forfeited Estates in Scotland* . . . London. N.L.S.

1729 [MACKINTOSH, WILLIAM], *An essay on Ways and Means of Inclosing, Fallowing, Planting, &c. Scotland; and that in Sixteen Years at farthest.* Edinburgh. N.L.S.

1729 *Short Rules and Observations for Sowing of Lint-Seed and Hemp-Seed and for pulling and dressing the flax and hemp.* Edinburgh. N.L.S.

1731 *A short enquiry into the cause of the general non-improvement of land in Scotland and the best method to remove it.* Edinburgh. N.L.S.

1732 GRANT, SIR ARCHIBALD, *A true Particular and Inventory of* . . . *the lands, tenements, and hereditaments etc., which I, Sir A. G., was possessed of in 1730.* London. B.M.

1732 [MACKINTOSH, WILLIAM], *An essay on the Husbandry of Scotland, with a proposal for the further Improvement thereof.* Edinburgh. N.L.S.

1733 [LINDESAY, PATRICK], *The interest of Scotland considered, with regard to its Police in imploying of the poor; its Agriculture; its Trade; its Manufactures and Fisheries.* Edinburgh. N.L.S.

1734 *A Letter to the author of the Interest of Scotland considered.* Edinburgh. N.L.S.

1735 BUCHAN FARMERS' SOCIETY, *A true method of treating light hazely ground* . . . *in Buchan.* Edinburgh.
Reprinted in D. SOUTER, *General View of the Agriculture of the County of Banff.* London 1812. N.L.S.

1739-1817 *The Scots Magazine.* Edinburgh. N.L.S.

1742 HAMILTON, JAMES, *Virgil's Pastorals translated into English Prose, and also his Georgicks . . . with an Appendix shewing Scotland's chief . . . interest.* Edinburgh. N.L.S.

1743 MAXWELL, ROBERT, *Select Transactions of the Society of Improvers in Knowledge in Agriculture in Scotland.* Edinburgh. N.L.S.

1744 *Some Considerations on the present state of Scotland: in a letter to the Commissioners for improving fisheries and manufactures.* Edinburgh. N.L.S.

1745 *The Present State of Scotland considered, and its sinking condition charged upon the conduct of the landed Gentlemen &c. Shewing . . . that the only mean of relieving their Estates . . . is by their joining together to promote home manufacture.* Edinburgh. N.L.S.

1747 MAXWELL, ROBERT, *The Practical Bee-master.* Edinburgh. B.M.
2nd edn. included in JOHN REID, *The Scots Gard'ner,* 1756 edn. Edinburgh. N.L.S.

1747 *Conditions upon which the premium of 15s. per acre for raising flax is to be allowed, and rules and directions for raising flax.* Edinburgh. B.M.

1747 *Essay upon feudal holdings, superiorities, and heritable jurisdictions in Scotland.* London. N.L.S.

1750 *The Laird and the Farmer, a dialogue upon farming, trade, cookery, and their method of living in Scotland balanc'd with that of England.* London. B.M.

? 1750 *Rules and directions for flax and hemp in Scotland, after the Flanders and other approved methods.* Edinburgh. B.M.

1754 [BURT OR BIRT, CAPTAIN], *Letters from a Gentleman in the North of Scotland to his Friend in London, containing a description of a capital town in that northern country; with an account of some uncommon customs of the inhabitants; likewise an account of the Highlands, with the customs and manners of the Highlanders.* 2 vols. London. N.L.S.

1754 GRAEME OF ARDGOMRY, THOMAS, *Report of the Committee appointed for visiting and examining the mosses in Stirling and Perth Shires.* Reprinted in R. MAXWELL, *The Practical Husbandman,* Edinburgh 1757. N.L.S.

1756 HOME, FRANCIS, *The Principles of Agriculture and Vegetation.* Edinburgh. N.L.S.

1756 [MAXWELL, SIR GEORGE CLERK], *Observations on the method of growing wool in Scotland, and proposals for improving the quality of our wool.* Edinburgh. N.L.S.

1756 *The Flax-husbandman and Flax-dresser instructed; or, the best methods of flax-husbandry and flax-dressing explained.* Glasgow.
Rothamsted Experimental Station.

1756 *Political Observations, occasioned by the State of Agriculture in the North of Scotland.* N.p. N.L.S.

1757 [GRANT, SIR ARCHIBALD], *The Farmer's New Year's Gift to his Countreymen, . . . Heritors, and Farmers for the year 1757.* Aberdeen. B.M.

1757 MAXWELL, ROBERT, *The Practical Husbandman, being a collection of miscellaneous papers on husbandry.* Edinburgh. N.L.S.

1759 *A friendly Address to the farmers of Scotland.* N.p. N.L.S.

1760 *A Dissertation on the Chief Obstacles to the Improvement of Land, and introducing better methods of agriculture throughout Scotland.* Aberdeen. N.L.S.

1762 DICKSON, REV. ADAM, *A Treatise of Agriculture.* 2 vols. Edinburgh. N.L.S.

1765 FORDYCE, GEORGE, *Elements of Agriculture.* Edinburgh. N.L.S.
2nd edn. with appendix, London 1771. N.L.S.

1766 [HOME, HENRY, LORD KAMES], *The Progress of Flax-Husbandry in Scotland.* Edinburgh. N.L.S.

1767 *Select Essays on Husbandry; extracted from the Museum rusticum, and foreign essays on agriculture, containing a variety of experiments, all of which have been found to succeed in Scotland.* Edinburgh. N.L.S.

1768 *The Modern Farmer's Guide.* 2 vols. Glasgow. B.M.

1770 [THOM, REV. WILLIAM], *Seasonable advice to the land-holders and farmers in Scotland.* Edinburgh. N.L.S.

1771 PENNANT, THOMAS, *A Tour in Scotland 1769.* Chester. B.M.
3rd edn. Warrington 1774. N.L.S.

1771 THOM, REV. WILLIAM, *A Letter of advice to the farmers, land labourers, and country tradesmen in Scotland concerning roups of growing corn, and of tacks.* Glasgow. N.L.S.

1771 *A Candid Enquiry into the Causes of the Late and the Intended Migration from Scotland. In a letter to J ... R ...* Glasgow. N.L.S.

1772 *Directions for raising flax.* Edinburgh. N.L.S.

1773 *A Letter to the west country farmers concerning the difficulties and management of a bad harvest.* Paisley.
Rothamsted Experimental Station.

1773-4 *The Scots Farmer; or select essays on agriculture, adapted to the soil and climate of Scotland.* 2 vols. Edinburgh. N.L.S.

1774 PENNANT, THOMAS, *Tour in Scotland and voyage to the Hebrides 1772.* Chester. N.L.S.

1774 *Rules and Articles by the Commissioners of the Annexed Estates in Scotland, for the improvement of Highland Farms, and for the Encouragement of Tenants upon the said Estates.* Edinburgh. N.L.S.

1775 ANDERSON, JAMES, *Essays relating to Agriculture and Rural Affairs.* Edinburgh. B.M.
2nd edn. Edinburgh 1777. N.L.S.

1775 JOHNSON, SAMUEL, *A Journey to the Western Islands of Scotland.* London. N.L.S.

1775 [MURRAY, PATRICK, LORD ELIBANK], *Eight sets of queries ... upon the subject of wool, and of the woollen manufacture.* Edinburgh. N.L.S.

1776  HOME, HENRY, LORD KAMES, *The Gentleman Farmer; being an attempt to improve agriculture, by subjecting it to the test of rational principles.* Edinburgh.          N.L.S.

1776  WEDDERBURN, ALEXANDER, *Essay upon the Question What Proportion of the Produce of Arable Land ought to be paid as Rent to the Landlord?* Edinburgh.          N.L.S.

1776  *Transactions of the Society for the encouragement of Agriculture within the counties of Dumfries and Wigtown and the Stewartry of Kirkcudbright.* Nos. 1-2. Dumfries.          R.A.S.E.

1777  ANDERSON, JAMES, *Observations on the means of exciting a spirit of national industry, chiefly intended to promote the agriculture, commerce, manufactures, and fisheries of Scotland.* Edinburgh.          N.L.S.

1778-84  [WIGHT, ANDREW], *Present State of Husbandry in Scotland, extracted from the reports made to the Commissioners of the annexed estates.* 4 vols. Edinburgh.          N.L.S.

1779  ANDERSON, JAMES, *An Inquiry into the causes that have hitherto retarded the advancement of agriculture in Europe, with hints, for removing the circumstances that have chiefly obstructed its progress.* London.          B.M.

1780  BALD, ALEXANDER, *The farmer's and corn-dealer's assistant, or, the knowledge of weights and measures made easy, by a variety of tables.* Edinburgh.          N.L.S.

1782  DOUGLAS, FRANCIS, *A general description of the East Coast of Scotland, from Edinburgh to Cullen.* Paisley.          N.L.S.

1784  BARRON, WILLIAM, *An Essay on the mechanical principles of the Plough.* Edinburgh.          N.L.S.

1784  [KNOX, JOHN], *A view of the British Empire, more especially Scotland; with some proposals for the improvement of that country, the extension of its fisheries, and the relief of the people.* London.          N.L.S.

1784  SMALL, JAMES, *Treatise on Ploughs and Wheel Carriages.* Edinburgh.          N.L.S.

1784  *Observations on the management of flax, . . . also a plan of farming books.* Edinburgh.          R.A.S.E.

1785  ANDERSON, JAMES, *An account of the present state of the Hebrides and Western Coasts of Scotland, in which an attempt is made to explain the circumstances that have hitherto repressed the industry of the natives: and some hints are suggested for encouraging the fisheries, and promoting other improvements in those countries.* Edinburgh.          N.L.S.

1785  YOUNG, DAVID, *National Improvements upon Agriculture; in twenty-seven essays.* Edinburgh.          B.M.

1786  FRASER, HON. ARCHIBALD, *Certain arrangements in civil policy necessary for the further improvement of husbandry, mines, fisheries, and manufacture in this kingdom.* London.          E.U.L.

1786  GIFFORD, THOMAS, *Historical Description of the Zetland Islands in the year 1733.* Reprinted from original edn., ed. T. G. Stephenson, Edinburgh 1879.          N.L.S.

1788 EUNSON, G., *The ancient and present state of Orkney, particularly the capital borough of Kirkwall.* Newcastle upon Tyne.
N.L.S.

1788 *Regulations of the Banffshire Farming Society.* Aberdeen.
R.A.S.E.

1789 BONNER, JAMES, *The Bee-master's companion, and assistant.* Berwick upon Tweed.
B.M.

1789 DEMPSTER, GEORGE, *A Discourse, containing a summary of the Proceedings of the Directors of the Society for extending the Fisheries and improving the Sea Coasts of Great Britain since the 25th of March 1788, and Thoughts on the present Emigrations from the Highlands.* London.
N.L.S.

1789 *Essay on the General Oeconomy and Management of Black Cattle Farms in Scotland, under a breeding stock; Including the management of the dairy; with the most effectual methods of preventing and curing diseases, to which such cattle are subject.* Edinburgh.
N.L.S.

1790 *A Treatise on Pasturage.* Edinburgh.
Rothamsted Experimental Station.

1791 SINCLAIR, SIR JOHN, *Address to the Society for the Improvement of British Wool.* Edinburgh.
B.M.
2nd edn. London 1791.
N.L.S.

1791-9 *The Statistical Account of Scotland. Drawn up from the communications of the Ministers of the different parishes by Sir John Sinclair, Bart.* 21 vols. Edinburgh.
N.L.S.

1793-1816 BOARD OF AGRICULTURE, Surveys of the agriculture of Great Britain by counties. Volumes on Scotland usually bear the title *General View of the Agriculture of the County of . . .* etc.

| County | Author | Place and date | |
|---|---|---|---|
| ABERDEEN | Anderson, James | Edinburgh 1794 | N.L.S. |
| | Keith, Rev. George Skene | Aberdeen 1811 | N.L.S. |
| ANGUS | Roger, Rev. Mr | Edinburgh 1794 | N.L.S. |
| | Headrick, Rev. James | Edinburgh 1813 | N.L.S. |
| ARGYLL | Robson, James (and western part of Inverness-shire) | London 1794 | N.L.S. |
| | Smith, Rev. John | Edinburgh 1798 | N.L.S. |
| AYR | Fullarton, Col. William | Edinburgh 1793 | N.L.S. |
| | Aiton, W. | Glasgow 1811 | N.L.S. |
| BANFF | Donaldson, James | Edinburgh 1794 | N.L.S. |
| | Souter, David | Edinburgh 1812 | N.L.S. |
| BERWICK | Lowe, Alexander and Bruce, A. | London 1794 | N.L.S. |
| | Kerr, Robert | London 1809 | N.L.S. |
| BUTE | Headrick, Rev. James (deals with Arran) | Edinburgh 1807 | N.L.S. |
| | Aiton, W. | Glasgow 1816 | N.L.S. |

| County | Author | Place and date | |
|--------|--------|----------------|---|
| CAITHNESS | Sinclair, Sir John (Northern counties) | London 1795 | N.L.S. |
| | Henderson, John | London 1812 | N.L.S. |
| CLACKMANNAN | Erskine, John | Edinburgh 1795 | E.U.L. |
| | Graham, Rev. Patrick | Edinburgh 1814 | N.L.S. |
| DUMFRIES | Johnston, Rev. Bryce | London 1794 | N.L.S. |
| | Singer, Rev. William | Edinburgh 1812 | N.L.S. |
| DUNBARTON | Ure, Rev. David | London 1794 | N.L.S. |
| | Whyte, Andrew and Macfarlane, Duncan | Glasgow 1811 | N.L.S. |
| EAST LOTHIAN | Hepburn, G. B. | Edinburgh 1794 | N.L.S. |
| | Somerville, Robert | London 1805 | N.L.S. |
| FIFE | Beatson, Robert | Edinburgh 1794 | N.L.S. |
| | Thomson, Rev. John | Edinburgh 1800 | N.L.S. |
| HEBRIDES | Heron, Robert | Edinburgh 1794 | N.L.S. |
| | Macdonald, James | Edinburgh 1811 | N.L.S. |
| INVERNESS | Robson, James (western part) | London 1794 | N.L.S. |
| | Robertson, Rev. James | London 1808 | N.L.S. |
| KINCARDINE | Donaldson, James | London 1795 | B.M. |
| | Robertson, George | London 1810 | N.L.S. |
| KINROSS | Ure, Rev. David | London 1795 | E.U.L. |
| | Graham, Rev. Patrick | Edinburgh 1814 | N.L.S. |
| KIRKCUDBRIGHT | Webster, James | Edinburgh 1794 | N.L.S. |
| (Galloway) | Smith, Rev. Samuel | London 1810 | N.L.S. |
| LANARK | Naismith, John | Brentford 1794 | E.U.L. |
| (Clydesdale) | Naismith, John | Glasgow 1798, 1813 | N.L.S. |
| MIDLOTHIAN | Robertson, George | Edinburgh 1793, 1795 | N.L.S. |
| MORAY AND NAIRN | Donaldson, James (Moray) | London 1794 | N.L.S. |
| | Donaldson, James (Nairn) | London 1794 | N.L.S. |
| | Leslie, Rev. William and Grant, John (Moray) | London 1798 | N.L.S. |
| | Leslie, Rev. William | London 1813 | N.L.S. |
| ORKNEY | Sinclair, Sir John (northern counties) | London 1795 | N.L.S. |
| | Shireff, John | Edinburgh 1814 | N.L.S. |
| PEEBLES | Johnston, Thomas | London 1794 | N.L.S. |
| (Tweeddale) | Findlater, C. | Edinburgh 1802 | N.L.S. |
| PERTH | Donaldson, James (Carse of Gowrie) | London 1794 | N.L.S. |
| | Robertson, Rev. James (southern districts) | London 1794 | N.L.S. |
| | Robertson, Rev. James | Perth 1799 | N.L.S. |

| County | Author | Place and date | |
|---|---|---|---|
| RENFREW | Martin, Alexander | London 1794 | E.U.L. |
| | Wilson, John | Paisley 1812 | N.L.S. |
| Ross and CROMARTY | Sinclair, Sir John (northern counties) | London 1795 | N.L.S. |
| | Mackenzie, Sir George | London 1813 | N.L.S. |
| ROXBURGH | Ure, Rev. David | London 1794 | N.L.S. |
| | Douglas, Dr Robert | Edinburgh 1798 | S.L. |
| SELKIRK | Johnston, Thomas | London 1794 | N.L.S. |
| | Douglas, Dr Robert | Edinburgh 1798 | S.L. |
| STIRLING | Belsches, Robert | Edinburgh 1796 | S.L. |
| | Graham, Rev. Patrick | Edinburgh 1812 | N.L.S. |
| SUTHERLAND | Sinclair, Sir John (northern counties) | London 1795 | N.L.S. |
| | Henderson, John | London 1812, 1815 | N.L.S. |
| WEST LOTHIAN | Trotter, James | Edinburgh 1794 | N.L.S. |
| | Trotter, James | Edinburgh 1811 | N.L.S. |
| WIGTOWN (Galloway) | Webster, James | Edinburgh 1794 | N.L.S. |
| | Smith, Rev. Samuel | London 1810 | N.L.S. |
| ZETLAND | Sinclair, Sir John (northern counties) | London 1795 | N.L.S. |
| | Shireff, John | Edinburgh 1814 | E.U.L. |

## Other areas

| | Author | Place and date | |
|---|---|---|---|
| CARSE OF GOWRIE | Donaldson, James | London 1794 | N.L.S. |
| CENTRAL HIGHLANDS | Marshall, W. | London 1794 | N.L.S. |

1794 ANDERSON, JAMES, *A practical Treatise on Peat Moss, considered as in its natural state fitted for affording fuel, or as susceptible of being converted into mold capable of yielding abundant crops of useful produce.* Edinburgh. N.L.S.

1795 BONNER, JAMES, *A New Plan for speadily increasing the Number of Bee-hives in Scotland, and which may be extended . . . to any other part of the world capable of producing flowers.* London. N.L.S.

1795 NAISMITH, JOHN, *Observations on the different breeds of sheep, and the state of sheep farming, in the southern districts of Scotland.* Edinburgh. N.L.S.

1795-6 DONALDSON, JAMES, *Modern Agriculture, or the present state of husbandry in Great Britain.* 4 vols. Edinburgh. N.L.S.

1796 ANDERSON, JAMES, *Two letters to Sir John Sinclair, Baronet, President of the Board of Agriculture, on the subject of draining wet and boggy lands . . .* Edinburgh. N.L.S.

1797 ANDERSON, JAMES, *A practical treatise on draining bogs and swampy grounds.* London. N.L.S.

1797 JOHNSTONE, JOHN, *Account of the most approved mode of draining land, according to the system practised by Mr Joseph Elkington.* Edinburgh. N.S.L.

1799-1806 ANDERSON, JAMES, *Recreations in Agriculture, Natural History, Arts, and miscellaneous literature.* 6 vols. London. N.L.S.

1799-1843 *Prize Essays and Transactions of the Highland Society of Scotland* (continued as *Transactions* of the Highland Society, later the Highland and Agricultural Society, later the Royal Highland and Agricultural Society of Scotland). Edinburgh. N.L.S.

1801-25 *The Farmer's Magazine.* 26 vols. Edinburgh. N.L.S.

1802 BELL, BENJAMIN, *Essays on Agriculture, with a plan for the speedy and general improvement of land in Great Britain.* Edinburgh. N.L.S.

1802 IRVINE, ALEXANDER, *An Inquiry into the Causes and Effects of Emigration from the Highlands and Western Islands of Scotland, with observations on the means to be employed for preventing it.* Edinburgh. B.M.

1802 SINCLAIR, SIR JOHN, *Essays on miscellaneous subjects.* London. N.L.S.

1803 BRISTED, JOHN, *A pedestrian Tour through part of the Highlands of Scotland in 1801.* 2 vols. London. S.L.

1803 FRASER, ROBERT. *Letter to the Right Hon. Charles Abbot, Speaker of the House of Commons, containing an enquiry into the most effectual means of the improvement of the Coasts and Western Islands of Scotland, and the extension of the fisheries, with a letter from Dr Anderson to the author on the same subject.* London. N.L.S.

1804 FORSYTH, ROBERT, *The Principles and Practice of Agriculture.* 2 vols. Edinburgh. N.L.S.

1805 BARRY, GEORGE, *The History of the Orkney Islands; in which is comprehended an account of their present as well as their ancient state.* Edinburgh. N.L.S.

1805 DOUGLAS, THOMAS, 5TH EARL OF SELKIRK, *Observations on the present state of the Highlands of Scotland, with a view of the causes and probable consequences of emigration.* London. N.L.S.

1805 [HORNE, T. H.], *The Complete Grazier; or Farmer and Cattledealer's Assistant . . . together with a synoptical table of the different breeds of neat cattle, sheep, and swine.* London. B.M.
8th edn. revised by W. Youatt, London 1846. N.L.S.

1805-08 FORSYTH, ROBERT, *The Beauties of Scotland; containing a clear and full account of the agriculture, commerce, mines, and manufacturers; of the population, cities, touns, villages, &c., of each county.* 5 vols. Edinburgh. N.L.S.

1806 [BROWN, ROBERT], *Remarks on the Earl of Selkirk's Observations on the present state of the Highlands of Scotland, with a view of the causes and probable consequences of emigration.* Edinburgh. N.L.S.

1806 COVENTRY, ANDREW, *Remarks on Live Stock and Relative Subjects.* Edinburgh. N.L.S.

1806 NEILL, PATRICK. *Tour through some of the Islands of Orkney and Shetland.* Edinburgh. N.L.S.

1807 GRANT OF LAGGAN, MRS ANNE, *Letters from the Mountains,* 3 vols. 2nd edn. London. N.L.S.

1807 HALL, JAMES (AND THOMSON, WILLIAM), *Travels in Scotland by an unusual route; with a trip to the Orkneys and Hebrides, containing hints for improvements in agriculture and commerce, with characters and anecdotes.* 2 vols. London. N.L.S.

1807 HOGG, JAMES, *The Shepherd's Guide; being a practical treatise on the diseases of sheep, their causes, and the best means of preventing them; with observations on the most suitable farm stocking for the various climates of this country.* Edinburgh. N.L.S.

1807 NAISMITH, JOHN, *Elements of Agriculture.* London. N.L.S.

1807 RENNIE, REV. ROBERT, *Essays on the Natural History and Origin of Peat Moss.* Edinburgh. N.L.S.

1807 *The Complete Farmer; or general dictionary of agriculture and husbandry.* 2 vols. 5th edn. London. N.L.S.

1808 COVENTRY, ANDREW, *Discourses explanatory of the object and plan of the course of lectures on agriculture and rural economy.* Edinburgh. N.L.S.

1808 GRAY, ANDREW, *The Plough Wright's Assistant; or a practical treatise on various implements employed in agriculture.* Edinburgh. N.L.S.

1808 WALKER, JOHN, *Essays on natural history and rural economy.* Edinburgh. N.L.S.

1810 BOARD OF AGRICULTURE, *Particulars regarding the merino sheep imported by C. Downie of Paisley. In answer to certain queries transmitted by Sir J. Sinclair to the Spanish shepherds who have charge of them. From the communications to the Board of Agriculture.* London. B.M.

1811 BROWN, ROBERT, *Treatise on Rural Affairs; being the substance of the article Agriculture published in the Edinburgh Encyclopaedia; with improvements and additions.* 2 vols. Edinburgh. N.L.S.

1812 SINCLAIR, SIR JOHN, *Account of the systems of husbandry adopted in the more improved districts of Scotland.* Edinburgh. N.L.S.

1812 WALKER, JOHN, *Economical History of the Hebrides and Highlands of Scotland.* 2 vols. London. N.L.S.

1813 NEILL, PATRICK, *On Scottish gardens and orchards.* Edinburgh. N.L.S.

1814 GRAY, ANDREW, *Explanation of the engravings of the most important implements of husbandry.* Edinburgh. N.L.S.

1814 SINCLAIR, SIR JOHN, *General Report of the Agricultural State and Political Circumstances of Scotland.* 5 vols. Edinburgh. N.L.S.

1815 *An address to the Nation on the relative importance of agriculture and manufactures, and the means of advancing them both to the highest degree of improvement of which they are capable.* London. N.L.S.

1816 BOARD OF AGRICULTURE, *Agricultural State of the Kingdom in February, March, and April 1816; being the substance of replies to a circular letter, sent by the Board of Agriculture to every part of the Kingdom.* London. N.L.S.

1816 SINCLAIR, GEORGE, *Hortus Gramineus Woburnensis.* London. B.M. 3rd. edn. London 1826. N.L.S.

1817 SINCLAIR, SIR JOHN, *Code of Agriculture, including observations on Gardens, Orchards, Woods, and Plantations.* London. B.M. 2nd edn. London 1819. E.U.L.

1819 MACCULLOCH, JOHN, *Description of the Western Islands of Scotland, including the Isle of Man.* 3 vols. London. N.L.S.

1820 LOCH, JAMES, *An account of the improvements on the estates of the Marquess of Stafford, in the counties of Stafford and Salop, and on the estate of Sutherland.* London. N.L.S.

1821 *Brief Thoughts on the Agricultural Report. By a musing bee within the hive.* London. N.L.S.

1822 NAPIER, WILLIAM, LORD, *Treatise on Practical Store Farming, applicable to the mountainous region of Ettrick Forest, and pastoral part of Scotland in general.* Edinburgh. N.L.S.

1822 SINCLAIR, SIR JOHN, *Address . . . pointing out effectual means for remedying the agricultural distresses of the country.* Edinburgh. N.L.S.

1822 STEWART, DAVID, *Sketches of the character, manners, and present state of the Highlanders of Scotland.* 2 vols. Edinburgh. N.L.S.

1823 [FAIRBURN, JOHN], *A Treatise upon Breeding, Rearing, and Feeding Cheviot and Black-faced Sheep in High Districts. With some account of—and a complete cure for—the rot. Together with observations upon laying out and conducting a store farm.* Berwick upon Tweed. N.L.S.

1823 LOW, DAVID, *Observations on the present state of landed property, and on the prospects of the landholder and the farmer.* Edinburgh. N.L.S.

1825 LOUDON, J. C., *An Encyclopaedia of Agriculture.* London. N.L.S.

1825 SINCLAIR, SIR JOHN. *Analysis of the Statistical Account of Scotland, with a general view of the history of that country, and discussions on some important branches of political economy.* London. N.L.S.

1826 STEPHENS, GEORGE, *Essay on the utility, formation, and management of irrigated meadows.* Edinburgh. E.U.L.

1826-71 *The British Farmers' Magazine.* London. N.L.S.

1827 HENDERSON, ANDREW, *The Practical Grazier.* Edinburgh. N.L.S.

1827 TAYLOR, ALEXANDER, *The Farmer's Guide and Agriculturalist's Companion.* Edinburgh. S.L.

1828 MACKENZIE, SIR GEORGE S., *A Letter to the store farmers of the North on the wool question.* Inverness. E.U.L.

1828-9 KENNEDY, LEWIS, *The Present State of the Tenancy of Land in the Highland and Grazing Districts in Great Britain.* 2 vols. London. S.L.

1829 HARLEY, WILLIAM, *The Harleian Dairy System; and an account of the . . . methods of dairy husbandry pursued by the Dutch.* London. E.U.L.

1829 KENNEDY, LEWIS, *On the cultivation of Waste Lands in the United Kingdom, for the Employment of the able Poor.* London. S.L.

1829 ROBERTSON, GEORGE, *Rural recollections, or the progress of improvement in agriculture and rural affairs.* Irvine. N.L.S.

1831 YOUATT, WILLIAM, *The Horse . . . with a treatise on draught.* London. B.M.

New edn. London 1843. N.L.S.

1831 *Reports of Select Farms.* Library of Useful Knowledge. 7 parts. London. S.L.

1833 DRUMMOND, WILLIAM AND SONS, *Exhibition of Agricultural Productions at Stirling.* Stirling. E.U.L.

1834 [BURKE, J. F.], *British Husbandry, exhibiting the farming practice of the various parts of the United Kingdom.* 2 vols. London. N.L.S.

1834 LOW, DAVID, *Elements of practical agriculture.* Edinburgh. N.L.S.

1834 STEPHENS, GEORGE, *The Practical Irrigator and Drainer.* Edinburgh. E.U.L.

1834 YOUATT, WILLIAM, *Cattle, their breeds, management, and diseases.* London. N.L.S.

1836 LAWSON, PETER AND SON, *The Agriculturist's Manual.* Edinburgh. N.L.S.

1837 YOUATT, WILLIAM, *Sheep, their breeds, management, and diseases.* London. N.L.S.

1841 [BURKE, J. F.], *On land drainage, subsoil-ploughing, and irrigation.* London. N.L.S.

1842 LOW, DAVID, *The breeds of the domestic animals of the British Islands.* 2 vols. London. N.L.S.

1843 HUNTER, JAMES, *The improved Scotch swing plough: with practical illustrations on ploughmaking and ploughing.* Edinburgh. E.U.L.

1843 SMITH, JAMES, *Remarks on thorough draining and deep ploughing.* 6th edn. Stirling. N.L.S.

1844 DAVY, SIR HUMPHRY, *Elements of agricultural chemistry, with instructions for the analysis of soils, and copious notes* by John Shier. Glasgow. N.L.S.

1844 [GORDON, THOMAS], *The Farmer's Lawyer; being a Manual of the Law of Scotland in relation to Agricultural Subjects.* Edinburgh. S.L.

1844 JOHNSTON, JAMES F. W., *Lectures on Agricultural Chemistry and Geology.* Edinburgh. N.L.S.

1844 LOW, DAVID, *On landed Property and the economy of estates.* London. N.L.S.

1844 MACKENZIE, SIR GEORGE S., *Brief remarks . . . on subjects connected with the choice of wheat for seed, interesting to farmers, cornfactors, and bakers.* Edinburgh. E.U.L.

1844 STEPHENS, HENRY, *The Book of the Farm.* 3 vols. Edinburgh. N.L.S.

1845   LOW, DAVID, *On the Domesticated Animals of the British Isles.* London.
                                                                N.L.S.
1845   *The New Statistical Account of Scotland, by the Ministers of the respective Parishes, under the superintendence of a committee of the Society for the Benefit of the Sons and Daughters of the Clergy.* 15 vols. Edinburgh.                                   N.L.S.
1847   ALISON, WILLIAM P., *Observations on the famine of 1846-47, in the Highlands of Scotland and in Ireland, as illustrating the connection of the principle of population with the management of the poor.* Edinburgh.                                               N.L.S.
1847   YOUATT, WILLIAM, *The Pig; a treatise on the breeds, management, feeding, and medical treatment of Swine.* London.
                                                                N.L.S.
1847-50   CENTRAL BOARD FOR THE RELIEF OF DESTITUTION IN THE HIGH-LANDS AND ISLANDS OF SCOTLAND:
          1st-7th *Reports.* Edinburgh 1847.                   N.L.S.
          8th-13th *Reports* of the Glasgow Section. Glasgow 1848-50.
                                                                N.L.S.
          *Reports.* Edinburgh 1848-50.                        N.L.S.
          *Report on the Islands of Mull, Ulva, Iona, Tiree, and Coll, and on part of the Parish of Morven.* Glasgow 1849.   N.L.S.
          *Report on the Outer Hebrides, or Long Island.* Glasgow 1849.
                                                                N.L.S.
1849   CAIRD, JAMES, *High Farming vindicated and further illustrated.* Edinburgh.                                           N.S.L.
1849   JOHNSTON, JAMES F. W., *Experimental Agriculture.* Edinburgh.
                                                                N.L.S.
1849   JOHNSTON, JAMES F.W., *On the use of Lime in Agriculture.* Edinburgh.
                                                                N.L.S.
1849   [MACLAUGHLAN, THOMAS], *The depopulation system in the Highlands; its extent, causes, and evil consequences—with practical remedies.* Edinburgh.                                               N.L.S.
1850   ALISON, WILLIAM P., *Observations on the reclamation of waste lands, and their cultivation by croft husbandry considered, with a view to the productive employment of destitute labourers, paupers, and criminals.* Edinburgh.                                 N.L.S.
1850   LOW, DAVID, *Appeal to the common sense of the country regarding the present condition of the industrious classes, and exposition of the effects of what is called free trade on British agriculture and the classes dependent on it, as well as on the general prosperity of the Empire.* Edinburgh.                                     N.L.S.

# APPENDIX II

Principal Acts of Parliament affecting the growing, threshing, selling, importing and exporting of grain, trees, animals, etc. (Up to Union of Parliaments, Scotland ; G.B. thereafter.)

| Ruler | Year | Ref. Record Edition | Subject | References (*A.P.S.*) |
|---|---|---|---|---|
| David I | | | Fiscal policy introduced export customs grain to be levied | I, 667-72 |
| Alex. II | 1214 | c1 | Bondmen compelled to plough or dig land | I, 397 |
| David II | 1366 | | Damage to crops by riders forbidden | I, 499 |
| James I | 1424 | c9 | Taxes for king's ransom imposed on grain of various kinds | II, 4 |
| | 1424 | c10 | Destruction of trees forbidden | II, 7 |
| | 1424 | c20 | Destruction of rooks | II, 6 |
| | 1424 | c20 | Law of 1214 *re* ploughing and digging of land reaffirmed and strengthened in 1427 | II, 8 |
| | 1425 | c13, 15 & 22 | Measures—New size of boll | II, 10, 12 |
| | 1426 | c6 | Compulsory sowing of wheat, peas and beans | II, 13 |
| James II | 1449 | c6 | Protection of tenants | II, 35 |
| | 1449 | c11 | Forestalling forbidden. Threshing of grain | II, 36 |
| | 1452 | c3-5 | Threshing, storing and selling of grain—regulations | II, 41a |
| | 1454 | c2 | Imports of grain—regulations | II, 41 |
| | 1457 | c15 | Feuing of land—commended | II, 49 |
| | 1457 | c27 | Planting. Trees, sowing broom, also 1503, 1535, 1555, 1567, 1551 | II, 51 |
| | 1457 | c28 | Reaffirmation of 1426 Act *re* compulsory grain sowing | II, 51 |
| | | c31, 32 35 | Keeping and destruction of wild beasts and birds | II, 61 |
| | | c38 | Muirburn | II, 61 |
| | 1468 | c3 | Export of cattle forbidden | II, 92 |
| | 1469 | c10 | Regulations *re* Poinding and Eviction | II, 95 |
| | 1474 | c16 | Rabbits | II, 107 |
| James IV | 1491 | c7 | Removal of tenants | II, 225 |
| | 1503 | c36, 37 | Feuing | II, 253 |
| | 1503 | c50 | Plough oxen not to be taken for debt if other goods available | II, 246 |
| James V | 1525 | c10 | Fire-raising cornstacks capital offence | II, 298 |
| | 1535 | c25 | Exports grain, cattle and sheep forbidden | II, 346 |
| | 1535 | c26 | Forestalling forbidden | II, 347 |
| | 1540 | c22 | Damage to crops by riders (Riding forbidden except by great barons) | II, 362 |

| Ruler | Year | Ref. Record Edition | Subject | References (*A.P.S.*) |
|---|---|---|---|---|
| James V | 1540 | c32 | Forestalling forbidden | II, 376 |
| | 1540 | c38 | Burning of corn ricks capital offence | II, 377 |
| Mary | 1551 | c15 | Killing of young lambs forbidden | II, 486 |
| | 1551 | c24 | Forestalling forbidden | II, 488 |
| | 1555 | c14 | Exports of grain forbidden | II, 495 |
| | 1555 | c20 | Weights and Measures | II, 496 |
| | 1555 | c25 | Damage to crops | II, 497 |
| | 1555 | c30 | Sheep Act of 1551 reaffirmed | II, 498 |
| | 1555 | c32 | Chickens | II, 498 |
| | 1563 | c6 | Food. Threshing of grain | II, 538 |
| James VI | 1567 | c31 | Exports of grain and forestalling forbidden | III, 40 |
| | 1567 | c40 | Fire-raising a capital offence | III, 34 |
| | 1579 | c26 | Forestalling forbidden | III, 146 |
| | 1581 | c14 | Maiming plough oxen—a capital offence. Poinding of plough oxen forbidden | III, 217 |
| | 1581 | c29 | Horses forbidden hard grain in summer | III, 225 |
| | 1581 | c31 | Exports of cattle and sheep forbidden | III, 226 |
| | 1585 | c12 | Exports of grain | III, 379 |
| | 1587 | c38 & 39 | Exports and forestalling grain forbidden | III, 452 |
| | 1587 | c40 | Act of 1581 (c29) reaffirmed | III, 452 |
| | 1587 | c57 | Destroyers of corn to be treated as thieves | III, 460 |
| | 1587 | c136 | Weights and measures | III, 521 |
| | 1592 | c70 & 71 | Exports of cattle and sheep forbidden and Forestalling | III, 576, 577 |
| | 1594 | c76 | Forestalling forbidden | IV, 86 |
| | 1597 | c25 | Regulations *re* customs on exported grain | IV, 137 |
| | 1621 | c31 | Hunting and Hawking | IV, 629 |
| Charles I | 1641 | c128 | Destroyers of trees and enclosures | V, 420 |
| | 1647 | c152 | Exports of grain | V, 677 |
| | 1649 | c32 | Exports of grain forbidden | VI, 148 |
| Charles II | 1661 | — | Import duty Irish grain removed. (No Act Parliament.) | VI, p. 710 |
| | 1661 | c284 | Enclosing land regulations | VII, 263 |
| | 1663 | c18 | Customs applied imported grain | VII, 463 |
| | 1663 | c35 | Exports permissible under certain prices. To encourage growers | VII, 476 |
| | 1669 | c20 | Export duties nominal | VII, 568 |
| | 1669 | c38 | Fencing of arable land alongside roads required | VII, 576 |
| | 1672 | c3 | Irish grain imports prohibited | VIII, 61 |
| James VII | 1685 | c49 | Enclosing land | VIII, 488 |
| | 1686 | c21 | Winter Herding Act | VIII, 595 |
| | 1686 | c26 | Irish grain and cattle imports | VIII, 598 |

| Ruler | Year | Ref. Record Edition | Subject | Reference (*A.P.S.*) |
|---|---|---|---|---|
| William and Mary | 1695 | c36 | Run-rig enclosures | IX, 421 |
| | 1695 | c54 | Land, Sandhills, Pulling Bent | IX, 452 |
| | 1695 | c63 | Export bounties, grain | IX, 458 |
| | 1695 | c69 | Division of Commonties | IX, 462 |
| | 1696 | c6 | Meal to be sold by weight | X, 34 |
| | 1696 | c27 | Import of victuals encouraged | X, 64 |
| | 1696 | — | Pow of Inchaffray | X, 67*b* |
| Anne | 1703 | c8 | Butchers forbidden to be graziers | XI, 109 |
| | 1703 | c10 | Irish imports of grain forbidden | XI, 109 |

*Union of Parliaments. Acts of Parliament (Scotland) cease.*

| | Ruler | Year | Ref. | Subject |
|---|---|---|---|---|
| 5 | Anne | 1707 | c29 | Export bounty regulations |
| 13 | George III | 1774 | c43 | Scale of duties, import and export correlated with price levels. Export duty 2s. per quarter when oats under 14s. per quarter |
| 31 | | 1791 | c30 | Above scales modified. Colonial preference given |
| 36 | | 1796 | c21 | Bounties became payable on imports 1795-96, years of scarcity |
| 44 | | 1804 | c109 | Procedure *re* determination of average prices |
| 45 | | 1805 | c86 | New procedure adopted. |
| 54 | | 1814 | c69 | Exports of grain permitted, but no bounties |
| 55 | | 1815 | c26 | New scales determining import duties Colonial preference continued |
| 3 | George IV | 1822 | c60 | Revised scale of import duties grain |
| 6 | | 1825 | c64 | Revised scale of import duties grain |
| 9 | | 1828 | c60 | Revised scale of import duties grain |
| 5 and 6 Victoria | | 1842 | c14 | Revised scale of import duties grain, and new procedure for determining average prices |
| 6 and 7 | | 1843 | c29 | Reduced import duty Canadian wheat |
| 9 and 10 | | 1846 | c22 | Nominal grain import duties as from 1st February 1849 |
| 32 and 33 | | 1869 | c14 | Import duties abolished |
| 7 and 8 George V | | 1917 | c46 | Corn Production Acts. Guarantees wheat and oats |
| 10 and 11 | | 1920 | c76 | Corn Production Acts. Extended |
| 11 and 12 | | 1921 | c48 | Corn Production Acts. Repealed |
| 11 and 12 | | 1921 | c35 | Uniform Sales Act |
| 22 and 23 | | 1932 | c24 | Wheat Act. Aid to be applied |
| 1 Edward VIII 1 George VI | | 1937 | c70 | Aid for oat and barley growers |
| 2 and 3 George VI | | 1939 | c48 | Agricultural Development Act |
| 10 and 11 | | 1939 | c55 | Emergency Powers Defence Act |
| 10 and 11 | | 1947 | c48 | Agriculture Act (guaranteed prices and markets) |

# APPENDIX III

Fiars Price of Oats per Imperial Quarter 1647-1770 for Haddington.
Thereafter British Prices until 1944 ; 1944-56 England and Wales.

*Note.*—The Haddington Fiars prices for various reasons, including the
superior quality of the grain, were above those of the other Scottish
counties.

| Year | £ | s. | d. | Year | £ | s. | d. |
|---|---|---|---|---|---|---|---|
| 1647 | 0 | 13 | 0¼ | 1692 | 0 | 8 | 4 |
| 1648 | 0 | 15 | 6¾ | 1693 | 0 | 9 | 7¼ |
| 1649 | 0 | 15 | 9½ | 1694 | 0 | 10 | 3¾ |
| 1650 | 1 | 4 | 0½ | 1695 | 0 | 15 | 2½ |
| 1651 | 1 | 2 | 1 | 1696 | 0 | 19 | 5½ |
| 1652 | 0 | 17 | 2 | 1697 | 0 | 13 | 6¾ |
| 1653 | 0 | 7 | 6½ | 1698 | 1 | 2 | 1 |
| 1654 | 0 | 5 | 3 | 1699 | 0 | 19 | 9½ |
| 1655 | 0 | 5 | 8¾ | 1700 | 0 | 12 | 2¼ |
| 1656 | 0 | 7 | 6½ | 1701 | 0 | 9 | 1¾ |
| 1657 | 0 | 8 | 4 | 1702 | 0 | 9 | 10 |
| 1658 | 0 | 12 | 7 | 1703 | 0 | 10 | 3¼ |
| 1659 | 0 | 13 | 8¾ | 1704 | 0 | 10 | 3¼ |
| 1660 | 0 | 12 | 2¼ | 1705 | 0 | 9 | 1¾ |
| 1661 | 0 | 11 | 5¼ | 1706 | 0 | 5 | 8¾ |
| 1662 | 0 | 9 | 1¾ | 1707 | 0 | 8 | 4 |
| 1663 | 0 | 8 | 4 | 1708 | 0 | 11 | 5¼ |
| 1664 | 0 | 5 | 8¾ | 1709 | 0 | 15 | 2½ |
| 1665 | 0 | 6 | 0¾ | 1710 | 0 | 12 | 11 |
| 1666 | 0 | 8 | 1 | 1711 | 0 | 10 | 3¼ |
| 1667 | 0 | 6 | 10½ | 1712 | 0 | 9 | 10 |
| 1668 | 0 | 6 | 8½ | 1713 | 0 | 10 | 7½ |
| 1669 | 0 | 7 | 6½ | 1714 | 0 | 11 | 5¼ |
| 1670 | 0 | 9 | 1¾ | 1715 | 0 | 11 | 5¼ |
| 1671 | 0 | 12 | 4¼ | 1716 | 0 | 9 | 6½ |
| 1672 | 0 | 8 | 4 | 1717 | 0 | 10 | 11¾ |
| 1673 | 0 | 9 | 1¼ | 1718 | 0 | 10 | 11 |
| 1674 | 0 | 17 | 8¾ | 1719 | 0 | 12 | 7 |
| 1675 | 0 | 16 | 0¼ | 1720 | 0 | 10 | 9¾ |
| 1676 | 0 | 6 | 5 | 1721 | 0 | 0 | 0 |
| 1677 | 0 | 7 | 5¼ | 1722 | 0 | 12 | 2¼ |
| 1678 | 0 | 6 | 5 | 1723 | 0 | 12 | 9¾ |
| 1679 | 0 | 7 | 6½ | 1724 | 0 | 10 | 11¾ |
| 1680 | 0 | 8 | 1 | 1725 | 0 | 11 | 7¾ |
| 1681 | 0 | 10 | 11¾ | 1726 | 0 | 10 | 11¾ |
| 1682 | 0 | 12 | 2¼ | 1727 | 0 | 11 | 5¼ |
| 1683 | 0 | 7 | 6½ | 1728 | 0 | 14 | 5 |
| 1684 | 0 | 8 | 4 | 1729 | 0 | 12 | 9¾ |
| 1685 | 0 | 7 | 6½ | 1730 | 0 | 10 | 6¼ |
| 1686 | 0 | 7 | 6½ | 1731 | 0 | 9 | 11¼ |
| 1687 | 0 | 7 | 6½ | 1732 | 0 | 8 | 10¾ |
| 1688 | 0 | 9 | 1¾ | 1733 | 0 | 10 | 11¾ |
| 1689 | 0 | 10 | 9¾ | 1734 | 0 | 10 | 6¼ |
| 1690 | 0 | 12 | 9¾ | 1735 | 0 | 12 | 7 |
| 1691 | 0 | 8 | 1 | 1736 | 0 | 12 | 2¼ |

| Year | £ | s. | d. | Year | £ | s. | d. |
|------|---|----|----|------|---|----|----|
| 1737 | 0 | 10 | 6¼ | 1797 | 0 | 17 | 10½ |
| 1738 | 0 | 8 | 5¼ | 1798 | 0 | 19 | 2¼ |
| 1739 | 0 | 12 | 7 | 1799 | 1 | 19 | 3 |
| 1740 | 0 | 18 | 3½ | 1800 | 2 | 8 | 11¾ |
| 1741 | 0 | 12 | 7 | 1801 | 1 | 3 | 9½ |
| 1742 | 0 | 9 | 1¾ | 1802 | 1 | 1 | 0½ |
| 1743 | 0 | 8 | 1 | 1803 | 1 | 3 | 2¾ |
| 1744 | 0 | 12 | 4¼ | 1804 | 1 | 7 | 0 |
| 1745 | 0 | 13 | 3¼ | 1805 | 1 | 6 | 10½ |
| 1746 | 0 | 11 | 5¼ | 1806 | 1 | 10 | 8 |
| 1747 | 0 | 9 | 10 | 1807 | 1 | 16 | 11 |
| 1748 | 0 | 10 | 11¾ | 1808 | 1 | 14 | 9½ |
| 1749 | 0 | 11 | 5¼ | 1809 | 1 | 11 | 9¾ |
| 1750 | 0 | 11 | 10½ | 1810 | 1 | 8 | 10 |
| 1751 | 0 | 15 | 1¼ | 1811 | 1 | 13 | 5 |
| 1752 | 0 | 16 | 0¼ | 1812 | 2 | 10 | 9¾ |
| 1753 | 0 | 14 | 7¾ | 1813 | 1 | 10 | 2½ |
| 1754 | 0 | 11 | 2½ | 1814 | 1 | 7 | 4¼ |
| 1755 | 0 | 14 | 5 | 1815 | 1 | 2 | 5 |
| 1756 | 0 | 18 | 3½ | 1816 | 2 | 0 | 3¼ |
| 1757 | 0 | 17 | 2 | 1817 | 1 | 16 | 0½ |
| 1758 | 0 | 9 | 11½ | 1818 | 1 | 15 | 3 |
| 1759 | 0 | 9 | 11¼ | 1819 | 1 | 4 | 5¼ |
| 1760 | 0 | 9 | 10 | 1820 | 1 | 3 | 0 |
| 1761 | 0 | 10 | 11¾ | 1821 | 1 | 3 | 7 |
| 1762 | 1 | 0 | 7¼ | 1822 | 0 | 19 | 11 |
| 1763 | 0 | 13 | 11½ | 1823 | 1 | 7 | 2¼ |
| 1764 | 0 | 16 | 8½ | 1824 | 1 | 5 | 9 |
| 1765 | 0 | 19 | 8 | 1825 | 1 | 8 | 6 |
| 1766 | 0 | 19 | 5½ | 1826 | 1 | 17 | 1½ |
| 1767 | 0 | 18 | 9¼ | 1827 | 1 | 4 | 4¼ |
| 1768 | 0 | 13 | 3¼ | 1828 | 1 | 6 | 4 |
| 1769 | 0 | 15 | 1¼ | 1829 | 1 | 3 | 0 |
| 1770 | 0 | 15 | 6¾ | 1830 | 1 | 6 | 11 |
| 1771 | 0 | 18 | 6½ | 1831 | 1 | 4 | 4 |
| 1772 | 0 | 19 | 5½ | 1832 | 0 | 19 | 10 |
| 1773 | 0 | 18 | 10½ | 1833 | 0 | 19 | 1 |
| 1774 | 0 | 18 | 4½ | 1834 | 1 | 0 | 11 |
| 1775 | 0 | 13 | 11½ | 1835 | 1 | 1 | 1 |
| 1776 | 0 | 13 | 10 | 1836 | 1 | 3 | 0 |
| 1777 | 0 | 15 | 9½ | 1837 | 1 | 3 | 0 |
| 1778 | 0 | 15 | 6¾ | 1838 | 1 | 2 | 4 |
| 1779 | 0 | 12 | 7 | 1839 | 1 | 5 | 10 |
| 1780 | 0 | 15 | 9½ | 1840 | 1 | 5 | 8 |
| 1781 | 0 | 13 | 8¾ | 1841 | 1 | 2 | 4 |
| 1782 | 1 | 4 | 4½ | 1842 | 0 | 19 | 2 |
| 1783 | 0 | 18 | 9¼ | 1843 | 0 | 18 | 4 |
| 1784 | 0 | 19 | 4 | 1844 | 1 | 0 | 6 |
| 1785 | 0 | 15 | 2½ | 1845 | 1 | 2 | 6 |
| 1786 | 0 | 18 | 9¼ | 1846 | 1 | 3 | 8 |
| 1787 | 0 | 18 | 3½ | 1847 | 1 | 8 | 8 |
| 1788 | 0 | 13 | 10 | 1848 | 1 | 0 | 6 |
| 1789 | 0 | 18 | 1 | 1849 | 0 | 17 | 6 |
| 1790 | 0 | 19 | 6¾ | 1850 | 0 | 16 | 4 |
| 1791 | 0 | 17 | 10¼ | 1851 | 0 | 18 | 6 |
| 1792 | 0 | 19 | 1¼ | 1852 | 0 | 19 | 0 |
| 1793 | 1 | 0 | 8½ | 1853 | 1 | 1 | 0 |
| 1794 | 1 | 0 | 4¼ | 1854 | 1 | 7 | 10 |
| 1795 | 1 | 6 | 8 | 1855 | 1 | 7 | 4 |
| 1796 | 1 | 0 | 5¾ | 1856 | 1 | 5 | 2 |

| Year | | | | £ | s. | d. | Year | | | | £ | s. | d. |
|---|---|---|---|---|---|---|---|---|---|---|---|---|---|
| 1857 | . | . | . | 1 | 5 | 0 | 1907 | . | . | . | 0 | 18 | 10 |
| 1858 | . | . | . | 1 | 4 | 6 | 1908 | . | . | . | 0 | 17 | 10 |
| 1859 | . | . | . | 1 | 3 | 2 | 1909 | . | . | . | 0 | 18 | 11 |
| 1860 | . | . | . | 1 | 4 | 4 | 1910 | . | . | . | 0 | 17 | 4 |
| 1861 | . | . | . | 1 | 3 | 8 | 1911 | . | . | . | 0 | 18 | 10 |
| 1862 | . | . | . | 1 | 2 | 6 | 1912 | . | . | . | 1 | 1 | 6 |
| 1863 | . | . | . | 1 | 1 | 2 | 1913 | . | . | . | 0 | 19 | 1 |
| 1864 | . | . | . | 1 | 0 | 0 | 1914 | . | . | . | 1 | 0 | 11 |
| 1865 | . | . | . | 1 | 1 | 10 | 1915 | . | . | . | 1 | 10 | 2 |
| 1866 | . | . | . | 1 | 4 | 6 | 1916 | . | . | . | 1 | 13 | 5 |
| 1867 | . | . | . | 1 | 6 | 0 | 1917 | . | . | . | 2 | 9 | 10 |
| 1868 | . | . | . | 1 | 8 | 0 | 1918 | . | . | . | 2 | 9 | 4 |
| 1869 | . | . | . | 1 | 6 | 0 | 1919 | . | . | . | 2 | 12 | 5 |
| 1870 | . | . | . | 1 | 2 | 10 | 1920 | . | . | . | 2 | 16 | 10 |
| 1871 | . | . | . | 1 | 5 | 2 | 1921 | . | . | . | 1 | 14 | 2 |
| 1872 | . | . | . | 1 | 3 | 2 | 1922 | . | . | . | 1 | 9 | 1 |
| 1873 | . | . | . | 1 | 5 | 5 | 1923 | . | . | . | 1 | 6 | 8 |
| 1874 | . | . | . | 1 | 8 | 10 | 1924 | . | . | . | 1 | 7 | 2 |
| 1875 | . | . | . | 1 | 8 | 8 | 1925 | . | . | . | 1 | 7 | 2 |
| 1876 | . | . | . | 1 | 6 | 3 | 1926 | . | . | . | 1 | 5 | 1 |
| 1877 | . | . | . | 1 | 5 | 11 | 1927 | . | . | . | 1 | 5 | 4 |
| 1878 | . | . | . | 1 | 4 | 4 | 1928 | . | . | . | 1 | 9 | 0 |
| 1879 | . | . | . | 1 | 1 | 9 | 1929 | . | . | . | 1 | 4 | 7 |
| 1880 | . | . | . | 1 | 3 | 1 | 1930 | . | . | . | 0 | 17 | 2 |
| 1881 | . | . | . | 1 | 1 | 9 | 1931 | . | . | . | 0 | 17 | 5 |
| 1882 | . | . | . | 1 | 1 | 10 | 1932 | . | . | . | 0 | 19 | 6 |
| 1883 | . | . | . | 1 | 1 | 5 | 1933 | . | . | . | 0 | 15 | 7 |
| 1884 | . | . | . | 1 | 0 | 3 | 1934 | . | . | . | 0 | 17 | 5 |
| 1885 | . | . | . | 1 | 0 | 7 | 1935 | . | . | . | 0 | 18 | 7 |
| 1886 | . | . | . | 0 | 19 | 0 | 1936 | . | . | . | 0 | 17 | 8 |
| 1887 | . | . | . | 0 | 16 | 3 | 1937 | . | . | . | 1 | 3 | 11 |
| 1888 | . | . | . | 0 | 16 | 9 | 1938 | . | . | . | 1 | 1 | 1 |
| 1889 | . | . | . | 0 | 17 | 9 | 1939 | . | . | . | 0 | 19 | 3 |
| 1890 | . | . | . | 0 | 18 | 7 | 1940 | . | . | . | 1 | 17 | 1 |
| 1891 | . | . | . | 1 | 0 | 0 | 1941 | . | . | . | 2 | 0 | 10 |
| 1892 | . | . | . | 0 | 19 | 10 | 1942 | . | . | . | 2 | 1 | 6 |
| 1893 | . | . | . | 0 | 18 | 9 | 1943 | . | . | . | 2 | 3 | 7 |
| 1894 | . | . | . | 0 | 17 | 1 | 1944 | . | . | . | 2 | 5 | 3 |
| 1895 | . | . | . | 0 | 14 | 6 | 1945 | . | . | . | 2 | 8 | 9 |
| 1896 | . | . | . | 0 | 14 | 9 | 1946 | . | . | . | 2 | 9 | 0 |
| 1897 | . | . | . | 0 | 16 | 11 | 1947 | . | . | . | 2 | 14 | 9 |
| 1898 | . | . | . | 0 | 18 | 5 | 1948 | . | . | . | 3 | 3 | 3 |
| 1899 | . | . | . | 0 | 17 | 0 | 1949 | . | . | . | 3 | 3 | 3 |
| 1900 | . | . | . | 0 | 17 | 7 | 1950 | . | . | . | 3 | 5 | 0 |
| 1901 | . | . | . | 0 | 18 | 5 | 1951 | . | . | . | 3 | 17 | 6 |
| 1902 | . | . | . | 1 | 0 | 2 | 1952 | . | . | . | 4 | 0 | 0 |
| 1903 | . | . | . | 0 | 17 | 2 | 1953 | . | . | . | 3 | 12 | 9 |
| 1904 | . | . | . | 0 | 16 | 4 | 1954 | . | . | . | 3 | 5 | 0 |
| 1905 | . | . | . | 0 | 17 | 4 | 1955 | . | . | . | 3 | 15 | 0 |
| 1906 | . | . | . | 0 | 18 | 4 | 1956 | . | . | . | 3 | 13 | 9 |

# APPENDIX IV

## AGRICULTURAL STATISTICS

TABLE I.—*Total acreage of crops—Scotland. Collected at significant dates.*

| | Estimated 1814 | Collected Board of Trade 1856 | End of prosperity 1879 | End of Peace 1914 | Depression peak 1933 | War peak 1943 | Post-war 1953 |
|---|---|---|---|---|---|---|---|
| Total area acres | 18,944,000 | ... | 19,496,132 | 19,068,728 | 19,068,728 | 19,068,728 | 19,068,728 |
| Acreage crops grass | 5,043,450 | ... | 4,713,159 | 4,786,181 | 4,613,708 | 4,427,000 | 4,387,525 |
| Wheat | not given | 263,328 | 76,613 | 60,521 | 78,386 | 170,623 | 72,953 |
| Barley | separately | 165,739 | 278,584 | 194,109 | 59,808 | 213,619 | 194,562 |
| Oats | ... | 918,644 | 1,004,535 | 919,580 | 855,857 | 1,010,895 | 887,930 |
| Turnips | ... | 460,131 | 491,904 | 430,608 | 351,653 | 326,043 | 278,910 |
| Potatoes | ... | 149,351 | 174,743 | 152,318 | 152,513 | 236,271 | 174,245 |
| Sugar Beet | ... | ... | ... | ... | 1,706 | 13,421 | 10,697 |
| Rotation grass | ... | 1,475,775 | 1,459,951 | 1,481,909 | 1,477,507 | 1,250,102 | 1,485,752 |
| Permanent grass | ... | ... | 1,159,387 | 1,490,694 | 1,583,628 | 1,056,661 | 1,165,320 |
| Grain and root crops | ... | 2,053,952 | 2,081,414 | 1,813,578 | 1,552,573 | 2,120,059 | 1,736,443 |
| Fruit and small | ... | ... | ... | 7,271 | 8,582 | 6,911 | 10,697 |

TABLE II.—*Stock Numbers.*

| | Estimated 1814 | Collected Board of Trade 1855 | End of prosperity 1879 | End of peace 1914 | Depression peak 1933 | War peak 1943 | Post-war 1953 |
|---|---|---|---|---|---|---|---|
| Horses | 243,489 | 185,407 | 195,747 | 209,360 | 149,483 | 126,764 | 51,186 |
| Cattle | 1,047,142 | 967,047 | 1,083,601 | 1,214,974 | 1,293,637 | 1,377,474 | 1,646,536 |
| Sheep | 2,851,867 | 5,816,560 | 6,838,098 | 7,025,820 | 7,811,144 | 6,766,415 | 7,465,866 |
| Pigs | ... | 126,924 | 127,721 | 152,768 | 167,028 | 190,249 | 470,876 |
| Poultry | ... | ... | ... | ... | 8,094,000 | 6,177,932 | 9,885,551 |

459

TABLE III.—*Labour in Scotland. Number of persons employed in Agriculture.*

|  | 1921 | 1931 | 1941 | 1951 |
|---|---|---|---|---|
| Regular workers (males) . | 82,099 | 79,370 | 74,222 | 74,415 |
| Regular workers (females) . | 21,772 | 18,060 | 19,758 | 13,295 |
| Casual workers (males) . | 11,544 | 8,203 | 7,527 | 10,516 |
| Casual workers (females) . | 11,483 | 6,833 | 8,145 | 5,874 |
| Total . . . | 126,898 | 112,466 | 109,652 | 104,100 |

TABLE IV.—*Produce of crops in Scotland. Estimated yields per acre of Principal Crops 1894-1954. Ten years' average.*

|  | 1894-1903 | 1904-1913 | 1914-1923 | 1924-1933 | 1934-1943 | 1944-1953 | 1954 |
|---|---|---|---|---|---|---|---|
| Wheat . . . . | cwt. 21·1 | cwt. 22·6 | cwt. 22·0 | cwt. 22·0 | cwt. 22·4 | cwt. 22·6 | cwt. 25·1 |
| Barley . . . . | 17·9 | 17·9 | 17·6 | 18·9 | 19·7 | 21·0 | 25·1 |
| Oats . . . . | 13·7 | 14·1 | 14·7 | 15·9 | 16·3 | 16·7 | 18·6 |
| Hay rotation . . | 31·88 tons | 32·2 tons | 30·7 | 33·0 tons | 32·2 tons | 31·5 tons | 33·5 tons |
| Potatoes . . . | 5·67 | 6·27 | 6·6 tons | 6·7 | 7·2 | 7·4 | 7·6 |
| Turnips . . . | 14·69 | 16·81 | 16·5 | 16·4 | 16·8 | 17·2 | 18·7 |
| Sugar Beet . . . | ... | ... | ... | 7·7 | 7·7 | 8·8 | 8·8 |

TABLE V.—*Estimated total production in thousands of tons.*

|  | 1900 | Average 1936-38 | 1940 | 1941 | 1942 | 1943 | 1954 |
|---|---|---|---|---|---|---|---|
| Wheat . . . | 50 | 104 | 115 | 118 | 136 | 188 | 98 |
| Barley . . . | 199 | 81 | 104 | 114 | 159 | 215 | 231 |
| Oats . . . . | 637 | 647 | 761 | 889 | 967 | 845 | 793 |
| Hay rotation . . | 683 | 638 | 615 | 603 | 549 | 607 | 592 |
| Potatoes . . . | 596 | 943 | 1220 | 1369 | 1511 | 1762 | 1266 |
| Turnips . . . | 7139 | 5625 | 5611 | 5660 | 5995 | 5879 | 5174 |
| Sugar Beet . . | ... | 55 | 57 | 58 | 83 | 104 | 119 |

TABLE VI.—*Value of agricultural output in Scotland.*

|  | Average of Years 1936-37 and 1937-38 | 1943-44 | Provisional 1952-53 | Preliminary 1953-54 |
|---|---|---|---|---|
|  | £000 | £000 | £000 | £000 |
| Gross output . | 37,952 | 76,909 | 145,309 | 151,109 |
| Total crops . . | 7,671 | 29,508 | 31,092 | 28,795 |
| Oats . . . | 1,856 | 6,321 | 5,229 | 4,986 |
| Wheat . . . | 589 | 2,792 | 1,711 | 1,726 |
| Barley . . . | 502 | 4,093 | 3,951 | 3,476 |
| Sugar Beet . . | 106 | 439 | 594 | 713 |
| Potatoes . . | 2,818 | 10,442 | 12,587 | 11,529 |
| Fruit and Vegetables | 1,174 | 3,671 | 5,176 | 3,992 |
| Total Livestock . | 30,281 | 47,401 | 114,217 | 122,314 |
| Fat Cattle . . | 8,821 | 11,739 | 23,047 | 24,595 |
| Fat Sheep . . | 3,713 | 5,453 | 12,792 | 12,950 |
| Fat Pigs . . | 1,623 | 2,120 | 13,783 | 14,816 |
| Poultry . . | 537 | 1,037 | 2,453 | 2,257 |
| Store Cattle . | 1,094 | 1,173 | 621 | 3,933 |
| Store Sheep . | 669 | 849 | 1,624 | 2,643 |
| Store Pigs . | 15 | 35 | 33 | 33 |
| Poultry . . | 72 | 227 | 349 | 319 |
| Milk . . . | 9,111 | 17,806 | 39,320 | 41,018 |
| Eggs . . . | 3,344 | 5,334 | 15,005 | 14,234 |
| Wool . . . | 882 | 1,369 | 4,633 | 4,843 |

TABLE VII.—*Agricultural price index.* 1927-29 = 100.

| | | | | | |
|---|---|---|---|---|---|
| 1939 . | . | . | . | . | 91 |
| 1944 . | . | . | . | . | 157 |
| 1945 . | . | . | . | . | 162 |
| 1946 . | . | . | . | . | 170 |
| 1947 . | . | . | . | . | 188$\frac{1}{2}$ |
| 1948 . | . | . | . | . | 211$\frac{1}{2}$ |
| 1949 . | . | . | . | . | 222 |
| 1950 . | . | . | . | . | 230 |
| 1951 . | . | . | . | . | 236 |
| 1952 . | . | . | . | . | 244 |
| 1953 . | . | . | . | . | 273 |
| 1955 . | . | . | . | . | 288 |
| 1957 . | . | . | . | . | 280$\frac{1}{2}$ |

TABLE VIII.—*Agricultural Units*—1947.

| | Number of Holdings | Number of Agricultural Units | Percentage | | | |
|---|---|---|---|---|---|---|
| | | | Full-time | Part-time | Spare-time | Others |
| Scotland . . | 77,557 | 63,853 | 51 | 23 | 17 | 9 |
| North-East . | 21,764 | 17,832 | 64 | 20 | 10 | 6 |
| East . . . | 9,131 | 7,130 | 71 | 12 | 8 | 9 |
| South-East . | 5,232 | 4,292 | 70 | 11 | 10 | 9 |
| South-West . | 16,236 | 13,257 | 70 | 11 | 10 | 9 |
| Highlands . . | 25,194 | 21,342 | 17 | 39 | 32 | 12 |

TABLE IX.—*Distribution of full-time Farms.*

| | Scotland | North-East | East | South-East | South-West | Highlands |
|---|---|---|---|---|---|---|
| Full-time . . | 32,208 | 11,307 | 5033 | 2987 | 9234 | 3647 |
| Hill sheep . | 2,025 | 77 | 305 | 233 | 614 | 796 |
| Stock-raising . . | 6,697 | 3,090 | 632 | 321 | 1015 | 1639 |
| Stock-raising and feeding | 6,943 | 4,687 | 677 | 642 | 675 | 262 |
| Cropping . . | 6,141 | 2,307 | 2,286 | 896 | 400 | 252 |
| Dairy . . . | 8,306 | 914 | 691 | 564 | 5585 | 552 |
| Dairy, Hill sheep . | 361 | 3 | 12 | 29 | 216 | 101 |
| Horticultural . . | 757 | 59 | 221 | 138 | 328 | 11 |
| Intensive livestock . | 699 | 84 | 156 | 136 | 314 | 9 |
| Unclassified . . | 279 | 86 | 53 | 28 | 87 | 25 |

TABLE X.—*Net income by type of Farming.*

| | 1943-44 | 1953-54 |
|---|---|---|
| Hill sheep . . . | £760 | £1059 |
| Stock-raising . . | £956 | £458 |
| Stock-rearing and feeding | £1290 | £805 |
| Arable plus livestock . | £1743 | £1097 |
| Dairy . . . | £1546 | £1253 |

# INDEX

Aberdeen-Angus cattle; 174, 178, 327-9.

Aberdeen Egg Producers, Ltd. : 427.

Aberdeenshire : "twal-owsen" plough in, 14, 385 ; extent of husbandland in, 18 ; infield and outfield cultivation in, 21-2 ; famine in, 103 ; effects of "seven ill years" in, 104 ; improvers in, 111-13, 139-40, 140-1 ; survival of thirlage in, 151-2 ; labourers, wages of, 160, housing of, 161 ; cattle-farming in, 183, 196-7, 322, 325-7, 328 ; grain acreage constant 1877-1914, 197 ; example of fall in population from, 293 ; bee-keeping in, 346 ; growing of whins for cattle food in, 397 ; fruit-growing in, 411-12, 415 ; co-operative movement in, 425, 426, 427.

Alexander II : legislation concerning agriculture by, 32, 39, 50, 59, 453 ; donation of Ettrick Forest to Melrose Abbey, 59 ; abundance of grain in reign of, 66.

Alexander III : valuation of land by, 32 ; interest in gardening, 59, 413 ; abundance of grain in reign of, 66.

allotments, 258, 420-1.

Anderson, of Monkshill, Dr James : on millers, 46 ; as scientific farmer, 139 ; on land near Aberdeen, 140 ; *Essays relating to Agriculture and Rural Affairs*, 139, 305, 351 ; on sowing of clover and grass-seed, 349, 351 ; on drainage, 401, 402.

Anglo-Saxons : invasions of, 13 ; agriculture of, 13 ; cattle of, 321.

Angus : broom parks in, 25 ; improvements by Earl of Strathmore in, 147 ; sugar-beet growing in,

232 ; cattle-breeding in, 327-8 ; horticulture in, 419.

animal rationing scheme : 251-2.

Anne : legislation concerning agriculture in reign of, 455.

Archibald, of Overshiels, Adam, James, and John : sheep-breeding by, 333.

Argyll : condition of agriculture in, *c.* 1700, 92 ; resettlement of Kintyre, 129 ; improvements in, 147, 407 ; sheep-farming in, 276 ; potato-growing in, 371, 373. *See also* IONA ; TIREE.

Ayrshire : dairy-farming in, 147, 172, 312 ; improving breed of cattle in, 174, 329-31 ; potato-growing in, 205, 378; growing of rye-grass seed in, 354.

Ayrshire cattle : 329-31.

Badenoch : extent of davoch in, 31 ; Mackintosh of Balnespick, 91-2, 126-7, 401.

Bakewell, Robert : cattle-breeding by, 324-5.

Balnespick : *see* MACKINTOSH, WILLIAM.

Banffshire : improvements by Earl of Findlater in, 145-6, 290 ; founding of Tomintoul, 290 ; description of agriculture in, 1683, 300.

Barclay of Ury, David : use of Baron's Court by, 93-6 ; revival of tenants' services by, 93 ; treatment of tenants by, 93-4; improvements by, 94-5.

Barclay of Ury, Robert (3rd) : 94-5.

Barclay of Ury, Robert (5th) : improvements by, 137-8 ; temperament and methods of, 138-9, 144 ; drainage by, 400.

NOTTINGHAM
UNIVERSITY
SCHOOL OF
AGRICULTURE
LIBRARY

PRINTED IN GREAT BRITAIN BY
OLIVER AND BOYD LTD.
EDINBURGH